$995.

ELEMENTARY SCHOOL SCIENCE

AND HOW TO TEACH IT

GLENN O. BLOUGH

University of Maryland

JULIUS SCHWARTZ

Bureau of Curriculum Research,
New York City Board of Education

NEW YORK · CHICAGO · SAN FRANCISCO · TORONTO · LONDON

ELEMENTARY SCHOOL
SCIENCE AND HOW TO TEACH IT

THIRD EDITION

HOLT, RINEHART AND WINSTON

A NOTE ON THE AUTHORS

Glenn O. Blough, former president of the National Science Teachers Association (1957–1958), is also a former member of the staff of the United States Office of Education and in that capacity consulted with state departments of education. He has taught in the elementary schools for many years and is now Professor of Education at the University of Maryland.

Julius Schwartz is Consultant in Science to the Bureau of Curriculum Research of the New York City Board of Education. Much of the material contained in this textbook has been tested in his classes for teachers in training and in service at the Bank Street College of Education, New York City.

PREFACE

Each year brings a more dramatic expansion of scientific knowledge. And each year brings the development of new and better ways of teaching science in the schools. In this, the third edition of *Elementary School Science and How To Teach It,* the authors have attempted to reflect both changes in science content and new and more effective methods of teaching that content.

What is happening in elementary school science teaching? Many things. Almost all elementary schools have now made science an integral part of their curriculum. New courses of study that include solid science content throughout the grades are gaining in acceptance. School science programs are placing greater emphasis on science as a *method of discovery*. Children are increasingly being encouraged to find problems for themselves, to propose their own methods of investigation, to make their own observations, and to draw their own conclusions. Mathematics is playing a greater role in contributing precision to elementary school science investigations.

The surging front of science in this space age is having a great influence on what is happening in classrooms. Man-made satellites, space travel, atomic science, and astronomy are contributing new content and interest to the curriculum. Researchers and teachers are discovering that many children can think more abstractly; can learn more advanced science in a more advanced way than was thought possible before. New conceptions of content and methods of teaching are influencing the design of a great variety of new materials aimed at helping today's teacher to work effectively with science and children.

Elementary School Science and How To Teach It has been revised to reflect these new conceptions and to present both the content and the methods of developing that content in terms that the teacher can grasp and use in her own teaching. The book retains its familiar organization. Part I presents a general statement on teaching elementary science that will bring the teacher up to date on methods of instruction. It discusses the objectives of teaching science and the practices through which these can be achieved as teacher works with children. Case studies of classroom experiments and procedures illustrate these practices. Part I also offers help to the teacher in making lesson plans and to both teacher and administrator in organizing a science curriculum from kindergarten through the grades. It presents useful criteria for selecting materials—textbooks, supplementary materials, and apparatus. New information on testing and evaluation has been added, as has an expanded discussion of the use of television, science fairs, and community resources. Particularly, Part I stresses the methods of instruction that will help pupils to discover for themselves.

Parts II, III, and IV again are divided into A and B chapters. Each A chapter presents a specific body of science content; the accompanying B chapter describes how to teach it. The A chapters include science information that is important to the teacher both as a citizen in our scientific world and as a leader of children's science learning in the classroom. Out-dated information has been supplanted in both text and illustration by the latest discoveries. Examine the chapter on space science and that on weather as examples. While the material remains nontechnical in the sense that it is not loaded with unnecessary science vocabulary and formulas, it is nevertheless solid science based on the most significant concepts.

The B chapters present up-to-date methods for helping children learn how to learn. Experiments are suggested that challenge children to explore on their own. These experiments present a variety of approaches and possible solutions; they show methods of encouraging children to use their capacities to investigate. The B chapters also describe field trips, observations, constructions, and many other purposeful activities that will stimulate problem-solving discovery. Mathematics plays an important role in many of the experiments and activities. Specific assistance is given in selecting, obtaining, and using both class-made and commercially purchased apparatus.

The teacher who herself is thinking and acting as an investigator can best help pupils to plan and carry out their investigations. Several features of the text are designed to assist her in this effort. Each A chapter concludes with a feature called "Resources to Investigate." Each B chapter contains a section called "Discovering for Yourself." Both of these sections suggest investigations and discoveries that teachers may make to equip themselves as leaders of children who are inquiring into the mysteries of science around them.

In addition to the foregoing features, this new edition has more drawings to help teachers see how to do experiments and many new photographs taken in classrooms and elsewhere to illustrate methods of teaching or illuminating the science subject matter. There are many suggestions for making and using materials and apparatus to implement the science program.

The book has been designed as a permanent guide and reference work for the teacher-in-training as well as for the teacher-in-service. It is a textbook to be kept on the teacher's desk for ready reference. Teachers in colleges and universities will find the many suggestions for discovery and investigation useful as assignments, the results of which may be shared in class to the mutual benefit of all concerned. Teachers will find the subject matter inclusive and appropriate.

A companion volume to this book is *Making and Using Classroom Science Materials in the Elementary School* by Glenn O. Blough and Marjorie H. Campbell (New York: Holt, Rinehart and Winston, 1954). It contains further suggestions for teaching science in the elementary school as well as detailed descriptions of how to make and use a wide variety of teaching aids.

G. O. B.
J. S.

Washington, D. C.
New York City
March 1964

ACKNOWLEDGMENTS

Many minds have worked together on the preparation of this book. Administrators, supervisors, teachers, and pupils from many parts of the United States have helped in many ways. To all of them the authors are sincerely grateful. To the following they wish to express specific appreciation:

To the late Albert J. Huggett, for his contribution as co-author of the first edition of this book.

To Paul E. Blackwood, of the U.S. Office of Education, for reading parts of the manuscript. To Scott, Foresman and Company for permission to quote material and use illustrations from *Discovering Our World*. To Samuel N. Namowitz, principal of Charles Evans Hughes High School, New York City, for his review of the chapter on the earth and its surface. To Sarah Lee Lippincott, Sproul Observatory, Swarthmore, for her review of the chapters on astronomy. To Frank Forrester, U.S. Geological Survey, for his review of the chapter on weather. To James M. Beall, U.S. Weather Bureau, for his assistance in supplying information and materials on meteorology. To Otto P. Burgdorf, Bryant High School, New York City, for his review of the chapters on living things. To Jerry Schur, Hofstra College, for his assistance with the chapters on living things. To Martha Munzer, of the Conservation Foundation, for her review of the chapter on conservation. To Charles H. Callison, of the National Audubon Society, for his review of the chapter on conservation. To Norman D. Newell and Sidney Horenstein, The American Museum of Natural History, for their review of the chapter on ancient animals and plants. To Barnet Simon, Stuyvesant High School, New York City, for his review of the chapters on matter and energy.

To Kenneth Hobbs, National Aeronautics and Space Administration, for his assistance in supplying photographs on aviation and space. To Muriel Green, Bureau of Curriculum Research, New York City Board of Education, for providing leads to many picture sources. To Wallace W. Sawyer, of the Elementary Science Study of Educational Services, Inc., for his assistance in providing photographs of children in the process of experimenting. To Shirley Miller and Elizabeth Guthrie, of the National Audubon Society, for helpful suggestions and materials. To Irvil P. Shultz, United States Geological Survey, for his help in obtaining photographs in earth science. To Richard V. Herre, Union Pacific Railroad Company, for his assistance in selecting photographs for this book. To the New York City Board of Education for permission to quote material and use illustrations from the publication, *Science K–6*.

Allen Creek School (Rochester, New York), 63

American Cancer Society, 316

American Machine and Foundry Company, 482

American Museum of Natural History, 81, 84, 214, 217, 330, 331, 332, 337, 338, 339, 341, 343, 344, 345, 346, 347, 350, 372

Baltimore (Md.) Public Schools, 246

Board of Education, City of New York, 383

Brookhaven National Laboratory, 471

Bureau of Plant Industry, U.S. Department of Agriculture, 243

Lynwood M. Chace from National Audubon Society, 227, 260, 275

Chicago (Ill.) Public Schools, 325, 501, 529

Cleveland (Ohio) Public Schools, 9, 14, 32, 46, 408

Commonwealth Edison Company, 457

George Daffin Cope for Educational Services, Incorporated, 296

Corning Glass Works, 609

Courier-Journal and Louisville Times, 156

David H. Curl, Columbus, Ohio, 54

Dearborn (Mich.) Public Schools, 291

Decatur (Ill.) Public Schools, 20

Detroit (Mich.) Public Schools, 11

Douglas Photographers, 353

Dowd, Redfield & Johnstone, Inc., for Alitalia, the national airline of Italy, 395

Duluth (Minn.) Board of Education, 298

Edward L. Dupuy from Monkmeyer Press Photo Service, 542

Educational Services, Incorporated, 1, 7, 29, 52

Elementary School Science Bulletin, 203

Federal Aviation Agency, 613

Free Lance Photographers Guild, Inc., 562, 570

General News Bureau, General Electric Company, 514

Bernard L. Gluck from National Audubon Society, 256

Grand Rapids (Mich.) Public Schools, 38

Hal H. Harrison from National Audubon Society, 209, 230, 264

Robert C. Hermes from National Audubon Society, 258

Indianapolis (Ind.) Public Schools, 65, 271

Kitchen-Kinne from National Audubon Society, 219

Leviton, Atlanta (Ga.) Public Schools, 615

Life (photograph by Frances Miller, © Time, Inc.), 374

Los Angeles County (Calif.) Schools, 16, 27, 42, 76, 495, 504, 556

Miami Daily News Photo from the American Red Cross, 185

Mt. Wilson Observatory (and American Museum of Natural History), 108, 141

Mt. Wilson and Palomar Observatories, 122, 148, 150

National Aeronautics and Space Administration, 113, 123, 154, 174, 175, 431, 594, 596, 603, 605, 606

National Board of Fire Underwriters, 412

National College of Education (Evanston, Ill.), 22

National Foundation, 397

National Radio Astronomy Observatory, 153

National Science Teachers Association, 322

New York Times, 319

Oklahoma City, (Okla.) Public Schools, 527

Chas. Pfizer & Company, 317, 319

San Diego (Calif.) City Schools, 3

Science Service, 444

Scientific American, 286, 315

Dr. Benjamin Martin Shaub, Associate Professor Emeritus of Geology and Geography, Smith College, 87

Smithsonian Institution, 584

Soil Conservation Service, U.S. Department of Agriculture, 95, 98, 364, 366, 367, 382, 390

J. Warren Southwick, Grand Rapids, Michigan, 267

Sparta (N.J.) Public Schools, 423

Hugh Spencer from National Audubon Society, 282

Standard Oil Company, 177, 486

Taylor Instrument Company, 172

Tennessee Valley Authority, 377, 506, 521

Toronto *Globe and Mail*, 121

Transcontinental Gas Pipe Line Corporation, 417

Union Pacific Railroad Company, 79, 90, 93, 94, 95, 99, 211, 215, 333, 359, 492

U.S. Department of Commerce, Weather Bureau, 160, 186

U.S. Forest Service, 274, 279, 281, 362, 369, 418

U.S. Geological Survey, 97

U.S. Navy, 110

U.S. Weather Bureau, 169, 173, 173 (L. E. Johnson), 177, 177 (H. T. Floreen)

F. E. Westlake from National Audubon Society, 278

Carl E. Wilson and Walter E. Loomis, *Botany*, Third Edition, New York, Holt, Rinehart and Winston, Inc., 1962, 226, 262

Winnetka (Ill.) Public Schools, 49

WPIX-11, 37

Yerkes Observatory (and American Museum of Natural History), 116, 118, 119

CONTENTS

PART ONE
TEACHING ELEMENTARY SCIENCE

PART TWO
THE EARTH AND THE UNIVERSE

PART THREE
LIVING THINGS

PART FOUR
ENERGY AND MATTER

Teaching Elementary Science

PART ONE

CHAPTER 1

Science in the Elementary School

Since this book was first presented in 1951, science in the elementary school has gone far in its growing up. There is hardly a school system that is not consciously attempting to bring its science program up to a level with the other school subjects, and teachers are working diligently to improve their teaching. Science in our good schools is no longer "done when we have time," or based on a few questions children ask and on the stuff they lug to school, or considered a tail to the social studies kite. Science is as definitely a part of the program as arithmetic and reading, and this situation compels the teacher to be as well equipped to teach science as she is to teach any other subject.

Even with this increase in the stature of science, the elementary school teacher is still not expected to be able to answer all of the questions children ask. No one can do this. No good teacher would do it even if she could; instead, she directs the learning so that pupils learn how to solve problems at the same time as they are learning the subject matter. (More of this later when we discuss teaching objectives.) But the elementary school teacher may as well face the fact that she cannot teach science if she does not know any, any more than she can teach arithmetic if she cannot add, subtract, multiply, and divide. Some basic knowledge of what is to be taught and what direction should be taken are essential to good science teaching. If the teacher knows neither the subject matter nor the direction of proceeding and the children do not know it either—so that there is no one in the room to exercise leadership —the possibility of arriving at a worthwhile goal is practically impossible.

This book is designed to help the wide audience of teachers who want to improve in their ability to teach elementary school science.

The authors have avoided unnecessarily technical vocabulary but included the essential words for the basic concepts. The book does not treat exhaustively any one specific phase of science. Instead, it attempts to supply enough information in various areas of science subject matter so that the teacher can help children to explore the world about them in a truly scientific manner. Since the earlier editions, we have moved ahead in what we expect from children and teachers; consequently, in this edition we have delved more deeply into science—but still without unnecessary technicality. A small boy once asked his fourth-grade teacher to explain how a rocket engine works. The quick-witted teacher replied, "George, ask your father. You know that's his specialty." "But Miss Stevens," George objected, "I don't want to know *that* much about a rocket engine." And indeed he did not. This book intends to stay within the boundaries of the subject matter that the teacher as a layman needs in order to interpret the world he lives in, as well as what he needs as a background to teach today's scientifically curious children. The book also intends to illustrate the importance of relating both a philosophy of teaching and a knowledge of the objectives of education to what happens to children in the classroom.

Part one (chapters 1 through 5) provides in a practical way some general and specific suggestions for teaching science. They are based largely upon the experience of the authors and their many teacher colleagues in helping children learn science. These chapters and the methods chapters that follow describe and explain these tried-and-found-useful practices and procedures. The remaining chapters, constituting parts two through four, deal with the subject matter of various fields of science and with experiences and activities in each of these fields; the A chapters present the subject matter, the B chapters give suggestions for teaching it.

In this second revised edition, the authors have added new subject-matter material appropriate for elementary school teachers that has come into being since the earlier editions were issued. They have also brought the book up to date in its description of teaching methods. This edition also places more emphasis on science for primary grades, and provides additional material on the use of the environment in teaching.

This book has been written for college students preparing to teach who have had little or no experience working with children in classrooms but want to learn something about how to teach science to children. It is also for the use of experienced teachers who say, "I think my pupils should have more experience with science, but I don't feel that I have the background to help them. Some of them even seem to know more science than I do."

THE TEACHER'S BACKGROUND

To the teacher: science teaching is not nearly so difficult as you think. Even though you need to know some science in order to teach it, you do not have to be an Einstein. In your own science experiences, you may even have had some trouble with physics problems or chemical formulae. Perhaps all you saw through the microscope in your college biology laboratory was your eyelashes. Do not let that concern you. There are plenty of things in your favor. Here are just a few:

1. Almost all girls and boys like science.
2. They do not expect you to know all the answers to their questions.
3. Science in the elementary school is based on concepts that are essentially easy to understand.
4. You can learn with the children.
5. It is no harder to teach science than it is to teach social studies or any other subject. If you are a good teacher in the elementary school, you can learn to be a good teacher of elementary science.
6. Science experiences and learning often combine naturally with the general learning going on in your room.
7. The first time over the ground is the hardest; a little practice in teaching science will bolster your confidence.
8. There is more help available to you in teaching science than you may realize. (See the pointers following.)

It is hoped that these eight points in your favor will become increasingly apparent as you progress in studying these pages and as you teach more science.

Many teachers already teach more science than they realize. For example, they keep an aquarium or a pet animal in the classroom, help children keep a weather chart, raise house plants of various kinds, help children plant gardens, and so on. These are really science activities. It is also true, however, that many teachers need to use a more scientific approach in order to help children get more out of these activities. Consider the aquarium, for example. Often we assemble materials and put them together to build an aquarium, but pay little attention to it after the aquarium is stocked. Water evaporates from it, snails lay eggs on the glass, plants reproduce, tadpoles grow legs, and all sorts of other things go on unnoticed. With some planning, potentialities such as these could be realized for the enrichment of children's experience.

Here are some pointers on how you can equip yourself to handle science more adequately. They are not arranged in order of importance, because we have no way of knowing what that order would be for you.

1. Read science material both on the children's level and on your own—such as this book. Keep this material on your desk for ready reference. (See bibliography at the end of this book for specially selected list of books.) Do not be ashamed to make your initial contact with a new area of science through a book written for children. If it helps you, use it.
2. Do some of the "Discovering for Yourself" and pay some attention to the "Resources to Investigate" that this book and others offer. After you get started, you may be surprised at your own enthusiasm. Each of the B chapters in this book contains some of these specific suggestions.
3. Do by yourself some of the experiments suggested for pupils' use. They are interesting and there is no substitute for firsthand experiences—for teachers as well as pupils. Doing the experiments yourself will increase your confidence and probably your interest.
4. Find a junior high school science teacher and ask for his help and suggestions. It will do each of you good to know what the other is doing. You can exchange ideas and make use of each other's background.

5. Find out whether your state, county, or city has a course of study or bulletin on the teaching of science. It may be published under separate cover or as part of a bulletin on the total elementary school curriculum. In either case, it is bound to be full of teaching ideas. (See bibliography for state courses of study.)

6. Be sure to order the teacher's manuals that go with the textbooks used in your school. They are good sources of help that are often overlooked.

7. Watch current periodicals and other publications for articles about science teaching. (See bibliography for list of magazines.)

8. Try to arrange to watch an experienced teacher working with children and science. You may get many good ideas in this way.

9. Avail yourself of any opportunity provided in your school to attend workshops, extension courses, or other projects that can better equip you to teach science. Some of the summer workshops are offered on a scholarship basis; they are well worth applying for.

10. Be open-minded in your approach to the teaching of science! Methods of teaching science, like science itself, are subject to change.

11. Note that many teachers have hobbies that help to supply scientific background, and they have used the confidence of such knowledge to start their science work in the elementary school. Typical of such hobbies are: gardening, indoor plant raising, tropical fish raising, bird watching and feeding, star gazing, and camping.

12. Remember that in many classes there are children with more than usual talent and interest in science. They can help you in dozens of ways and help themselves at the same time.

13. Join some science association—national, state, or local—where you can learn, by attending meetings and reading their publications, more about current practices in the teaching of science.

WHAT IS SCIENCE IN THE ELEMENTARY SCHOOL?

The term *science* means the same at any level. In one sense, it is a body of information and principles that help us understand the world around us—from atoms to stars, from microscopic water life to man. In another sense, science may be regarded as methods (and there are many) of discovery, the methods by which new information is uncovered, new principles arrived at, old principles modified or discarded. It is characteristic of science that it starts with a perplexing problem, proceeds with the trying of different methods of solution, and results in a new discovery. It is also characteristic that new discoveries in science lead to new perplexing problems.

Science is everywhere in the lives of today's children *and in the lives of their teachers too*. It is not only children who live in a scientific age; teachers do also! One difference, alas, is that some teachers are not as curious as children and are sometimes harder to motivate. But from the atom to the universe itself, science presents an unending number of questions to children: What is the moon made of? What makes it rain? What makes things rust? Where does the sun go at night? Etc., etc. Any adult who lives with children knows that they are full of questions, many of a scientific nature.

How can children find the answers to their science problems? They can do so through the methods of problem-solving—sensing the problem, hypothesizing, gathering data, drawing conclusions and testing them. This is science.

Children who use their senses to discover are beginning to experience the satisfaction of learning. An aquarium or other environment for living things provides such firsthand opportunities.

How can children be sure that the answers are reliable? They must be careful and accurate in judgment, must not jump to conclusions, must base conclusions on reliable sources. These are but a few of the safeguards that must be used in the process of scientific thinking. Gradually, this way of thinking becomes a part of children. This, too, is science.

It is often repeated that we live in an age of science; even a brief survey of our environment bears this out. In the study of science, we learn ways of exploring in order to learn about the world. For children, the study of science consists of their exploring the world about them in order to learn about it and so answer their questions about it, the better to enjoy and appreciate their surroundings. It seems a natural thing to wonder what makes a rainbow, how magnets can pick up iron nails, how far away the stars are, how a compass can point north, and how an airplane can stay in the air. It appears natural, too, to try out things to see how they work, to experiment, to manipulate, to be curious, to ask questions, to seek answers. These tendencies, with which children seem to be naturally equipped, make science a natural part of their education and a reasonable subject to include in their school experiences.

While we all live in a world surrounded by products of science, this world is not necessarily populated by people who *think* scientifically. Throughout this book, you will find emphasis on scientific thinking. To learn to think scientifically is to learn those concepts and principles which will enable one to make wise choices in deciding how to live with one's environment. This is indeed science for the citizen.

But let us say at the outset that the study of science is not a thing apart from the rest of the interests and activities in the school life of children. Indeed, science is closely interwoven with the other interests, and its method of study is much like that used in exploring any interest. The study of science does, however, have special contributions to make to children as we shall see in the discussion of objectives in the next chapter.

SOME TRENDS IN ELEMENTARY SCHOOL SCIENCE

In order to get a full view of science in the elementary school, it is important that we try to see the direction in which our school science programs seem to be moving. Since this is a book primarily for teachers rather than administrators, we shall cite the trends that are of primary importance in teaching science.

CONTENT AND METHODS OF TEACHING

1. As stated before, science is becoming as definitely a part of the elementary school curriculum as reading and mathematics.
2. Research dealing with how much and what kind of science young children are capable of learning, indicates that more science content can be included in the curriculum. Many of these research projects are important to watch. Many of the discoveries such as those of the *Elementary Science Study*[1] will be cited in various places in this book.
3. A greater correlation between science and mathematics is tending to make the teaching of science more quantitative and thus more scientific, and the teaching of mathematics more meaningful.
4. Science programs are being built around the setting up and solving of problems, rather than on the absorption and recall of information.
5. More emphasis is being placed on the use of firsthand experiences whenever possible to make the learning in science more meaningful. There is more *doing* with definite purpose on the part of children. These experiences include experimenting and discovering as well as observing applications of scientific principles in everyday life.
6. A *discovery* approach is being experimented with, in which children are confronted with selected phenomena and situations, and in which they suggest the problems to be solved and propose methods of solution.
7. An open-end approach is emphasized, in which the solution of problems leads to new problems, or in which there are a number of correct but different solutions to the same problem.
8. An increasing stress has been placed on the *methods* of science; children learn these methods by involvement in situations which demand the use of these methods rather than by being told about "the scientific method."
9. There is increasing interest in and support of *experimentation by teachers*— trying different approaches in the teaching of science so that science education can make its own discoveries in classroom laboratories.

---

[1] A project sponsored by Educational Services, Inc., Watertown, Mass.

Caring for an animal pet provides these Cleveland, Ohio, pupils with an opportunity to observe, discover, and learn. Even very young children can engage in this method of discovery.

MEETING NEEDS OF CHILDREN

10. Attempts are being made in many cases to recognize children who have special science aptitudes and interests and to insure that proper attention is given to them, while at the same time providing a challenging and interesting program for all children. (See pages 76–77 for further discussion.)

11. Persistent efforts are being made to fit the science offerings and the learning methods to the needs, interests, and abilities of the learners. These, of course, vary from individual to individual and from place to place.

12. Increasing effort is being made to determine how science can make a unique contribution to the development of children and also fit into the total learning situation.

DEVELOPMENT OF SCIENCE CURRICULUM

13. Science in the best elementary school systems is now being thought of as a part of a kindergarten through twelfth grade (and in some instances kindergarten through college) program of continuous development. Interest and activity of local school systems, science associations, the National Science Foundation, and other groups on a national basis, in improving science at all levels has helped to bring about this trend and others listed here.

14. Many state, city, and county units are developing or have completed more or less definite courses of study or curriculum guides to enrich the study of science in schools. Such course outlines help to ensure a sequence of subject matter from grade to grade through the elementary school and into the high school.

15. Supervisors, administrators, teachers, and pupils are working together to an increasing extent to plan and carry out an effective program of science study. These efforts have resulted in much local in-service activity designed to meet the specific needs of teachers and others. There is considerable urgency to make use of persons with special competency (scientists, college and university professors, and others) when there are not qualified persons on the local staff.

USE OF RESOURCES

16. Considerable stress is laid on using community resources in order to bring science to life. (See "Resources to Investigate" in subsequent chapters.)

17. More scientific apparatus and equipment is being made available for use in elementary schools. (See pages 55–59 for discussion.)

18. The use of television as a teaching aid is increasing both in amount and effectiveness as teachers learn to use it when it serves sound educational purposes, in the same way as they use audio-visual aids, texts, and other learning aids. (See page 36 for discussion.)

19. Wider use is being made of school and classroom libraries containing science trade (supplementary) books to augment the ever-increasing number of basic texts.

The foregoing are some indications of how our science program in the elementary school is changing and growing. These points may be used by teachers to evaluate some of the things they do in their classrooms with science and children, and they may be used by supervisors and administrators in evaluating their programs. Careful consideration of these points will be helpful regardless of the extent of the teacher's experience. They will help new teachers to see the direction in which the science phase of their elementary curriculum may move. They will help experienced teachers to take stock in order to improve their science work with children.

An analysis of these trends is helpful in planning for the teaching of science, for the trends seem to indicate that science must be an integral part of the elementary school curriculum, that it must serve the needs and interests of the pupils, that it must be broad in its scope, and that it must deal with the problems that exist in the communities in which the children live. The courses of study and bulletins listed in the bibliography will serve to expand the teacher's knowledge of trends beyond this brief treatment.

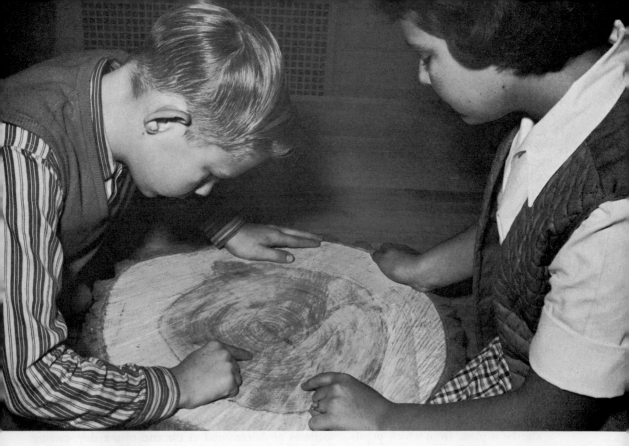

CHAPTER 2

The Objectives
in Elementary Science

What exactly do we have in mind for children as they progress through our elementary schools? The objectives of the elementary school have been stated in various places in a variety of ways. Without going into unnecessary technicalities here, we can sum up these objectives in this important general purpose: to help children gain the ideals, understandings, and skills essential to their developing into good citizens.

What is involved in this broad general purpose? Certainly it means spending a considerable amount of time on the skills of reading, writing, and arithmetic, as essential equipment for enjoyment, for gaining information, and for communication. The importance of these aims is generally understood, although we still have much to learn about the best ways to accomplish them for each pupil. Then there are other skills. There is the ability to use one's hands to make them do what one wants them to. There is the skill of seeing things around you and seeing them accurately. We miss a great deal because our senses are not trained to help us observe. Too, there is the skill of listening intelligently and the skill of speaking effectively so that we can express our ideas coherently and accurately. Added to this is the skill of sensing problems and solving them in a scientific way, so that the results are dependable. These skills are essential for the full development of the thinking process—

development of a thinker who is open-minded, fair, careful in arriving at conclusions, accurate, free of prejudice and superstition, and intensely curious about his environment.

Participating in the elementary school curriculum for six or eight years, from nine o'clock to three, is supposed to accomplish still other things in girls and boys, as our over-all statement of objectives indicates. The classroom experience should provide many occasions to identify and understand social procedures and problems. Each day children should have opportunities to identify problems and to solve them. They need chances to use their minds to suggest ways of solving problems and to carry out these suggestions through working together. They need an opportunity to check the results, to say to each other, "How well did we do this?" "Was our plan good?" "What would have made it better?" While they are working together, they should be developing social sensitivity to the needs of one another and of the group. They should be learning coöperation, democratic procedure, and group planning; they can learn these things only through practicing them every day and seeing how they operate.

The school environment should be a place conducive to physical and mental health of children in order to achieve the general objectives we have suggested. Among other things, this means that the schoolroom should be a cheerful place, alive with purposeful industry. It should be a place of real achievement, where children learn to work diligently and to take pride in accomplishment. It should be a place where children are not afraid to say, "I don't understand," or "I think so and so," or "I want to ask a question." It should be a place where children feel secure and at home, where they belong, where they can live happily. It should also be a place from which pupils sometimes go home tired at the end of the day, having engaged in hard work that has real purpose. It should be a place where pupils stretch their minds through challenging mental activities just as they stretch their muscles at recess. The prevalent saying, "I often wonder if we are not underestimating the capacity of many of our elementary pupils," is not just idle musing.

Furthermore, the elementary school, if it is to achieve our purposes, ought also to be a place where children learn to develop wholesome interests for their leisure time. Because of school, there ought to be less of "Mother, there's nothing to do!" on rainy Saturdays and summer days. There ought to be numerous interesting things children want to do because they experienced pleasure and satisfaction in doing them at school.

Perhaps it "goes without saying" that the elementary school must be a place where children *learn something*. But we do not mind running the risk of repetition by saying, "Let's stop being slightly apologetic when we say we expect children to know some facts." Knowledge is important. *What* we learn *is* important, just as *how* we learn it is important. We must become increasingly skillful at selecting *what* is to be studied and then concentrate on seeing that it is well taught and that those able to do so learn it. It is on the basis of *facts* that generalizations are made. Children cannot do much problem solving without data—these often consist of facts gathered through scientific investigation. Whether or not children will remember them all or whether or not we expect them to do so is a horse of a different color. We do expect to help children understand "big meanings," but without facts not even "small meanings" can be built.

Perhaps you are saying, "I thought this book was going to show me how to teach science in the elementary school." So it will. But science, or any other subject in school, exists only because it can contribute something to what we intend girls and boys to gain from their entire school experience. We need, therefore, to establish some general goals for this total experience and to see how science can be geared into them.

OUR INTENTIONS FOR ELEMENTARY SCIENCE

Science teaching is good only if it is based on sound objectives and if it keeps to the methods intending to accomplish them. One of our troubles lies in our failure to make our aims on paper become our real intentions in the classroom. Unless everyone in the science class knows what the objectives are and is heading in their direction, the learning situation has a low degree of efficiency.

There is no question that the subject matter of science *is* important. We do need persons in our society who are well informed about the world in which they live. An informed person is likely to be an interesting one, we should probably agree. But let us not consider a person educated scientifically just because he can tell us how many legs a cricket has, or that a certain pair of pliers is an example of a first-class lever, or what a tufted titmouse looks like, or the definition of chemical change. The facts of science are important, as we have stated earlier, but how these facts are put together into meaningful ideas is also very important. This leads us to one of the major objectives for teaching science: *to help girls and boys come to understand some generalizations or "big meanings" or scientific principles that they can use in solving problems in their environment.* Perhaps an example will help us see what this statement means.

Sixth-grade children are about to study soil. The teacher in this case, alas, is somewhat uninspiring, for she begins by saying, "We can scarcely learn much about soil unless we know what soil actually is. Take out paper and pencil and write your definition of soil. Then we shall open our books to page 140 and see if we are right." The result of this "far-from-flying" start is that pupils finally read a factual definition of soil which has little meaning for them, and as the study proceeds they add to this other unrelated facts about soil.

In contrast to this, suppose, in preparation for their study, pupils were asked to bring samples of soil to school for examination. They bring garden soil, soil from a woods, soil from "down under" where a house basement is being dug, and the teacher furnishes some sand that was left over from making an aquarium. A small amount of each sample is spread out on a piece of white paper, and the pupils examine each with a magnifying glass to discover answers to the questions: What do you think these different kinds of soil are made of? How are they alike? How different? Which one do you think will grow the best vegetables?

In order to solve these problems and others that arise as they observe and proceed with the study, the pupils continue to observe; they read; they consult the County Agriculture Agent; they experiment with growing things and gradually gather information about what composes soil, how soils differ from each other, what plants take from the soil, how this can be replenished, etc. No doubt the students would otherwise learn what soil is, and they would learn other facts about it, but this specific approach to the problem emphasizes the important big ideas or generalizations instead of just the accumulation of unrelated facts. Through these experiences, they learn such generalizations as: soil is composed of many different materials both living and non-living; different kinds of plants need different food materials; plants cannot grow in soil that does not supply the needed food materials.

An understanding of such important generalizations in science is not acquired automatically by exposure—as one catches the mumps. Such generalizations come to be part of the children's mental equipment if the teacher *intends* that they shall and if he helps the children to arrange the learning experience accordingly. These generalizations come to be real as the result of many experiences; they are put together gradually as the children

Examine, compare, observe, experiment, and you will begin to see what soils are made of, why they are important, and how they can be improved. These concepts are as important to city children as they are to those in rural areas.

proceed; they *are not memorized* from some printed material but are built from many experiences.

Now how do these concepts, as they are comprehended by children, fit into our large pattern for children in the elementary school? If we look back over what was said about the objectives of elementary education, we can see that these generalizations cannot result without using the fundamental skills of learning. Here is a place to use reading to find out, writing to record findings, possibly arithmetic to co-ordinate observations. Understanding these large concepts involves intelligent, accurate observation, skill in identifying and solving problems, planning together, and evaluating—that is, if the teacher *intends* to see that this sort of understanding results. It means, however, that the teacher must stop *telling* children the answers. It means that the teacher must help to make the problems real and challenging. She must let the pupils do some of their own planning to solve the problems. She may let them make some mistakes in plans and judgments so that they can see the results of such errors and have a better understanding of how errors come about. But at the same time she must exercise leadership to see that the learning process is not aimless and inefficient. She must be aware of the possible procedures. Uninformed and unprepared teachers cannot direct effective learning; someone in the room must know the direction to take, or the possible directions, or no one can arrive.

Another major objective for the study of science is: *to help pupils to grow in ability to solve problems effectively.*

A science class should be a place to ask questions as well as to answer them. It is probably true, unfortunately, that teachers are in the habit of giving greater recognition to the pupils who know the answers than to those who ask thoughtful questions. The thinking child says, "If that is true, *why* . . . ?" or "I understand that, but *why* . . . ?" Science is problem-seeking as well as problem-solving. No one ever became a good problem-solver by filling in blanks in a workbook, by listening to someone tell the answer, by looking up the definition for something, or by just living in the same room with a rack full of test tubes and a set of science books. How, then? By going further and solving some real problems that have meaning to the learner and are important to him. By being conscious of the essential processes involved in problem-solving, by using these processes over and over and thus becoming convinced that there are ways to solve problems that are good because they produce reliable results.

Now this does not mean that at the elementary level we drag out the ladder of problem-solving every five minutes and make pupils climb the steps: stating the problem, making several hypotheses, gathering data, verifying these data, and drawing and checking conclusions. What, then? It means, first of all, that we stop *telling* children so much and that we stop thinking that our responsibility is over when we say, "Look it up for yourself; you'll remember it longer." It means that we begin to give more and more attention to helping children formulate and find solutions to problems. These problems may arise because of children's experiences: "Miss Brown, last night I saw the moon come up. It was big and the color of oranges. How come?" Problems may result from children's reading: "Miss Brown, it says here that sunlight is made of all different colors. How can that be?" Problems may come from a book, from experiences, from excursions, and from many other places. Later we shall discuss more fully the selection of problems. Learning to solve them in a truly scientific spirit is as much the goal with elementary school children as the learning of subject matter itself.

Let us illustrate one way to accomplish this goal, by relating an actual experience from a sixth-grade class. New classrooms are being added to the schoolhouse, and construction is going on just outside the window. Children watch at recess with their noses pressed to the windows. They see men with pulleys lift wheelbarrows full of bricks; they see steam shovels at work, construction elevators being built, and all sorts of machines cutting, digging, pulling, and pushing. It is the chief topic of conversation. The teacher watches too. The children raise questions: "How can a man lift a big hunk of the cement sidewalk with an iron bar?" "How can a man lift a hundred bricks by pulling down on a pulley rope with one hand?" These and other problems are raised, stated carefully, and recorded. The teacher, a sincere, curious person, says, "I'd like to know how these machines work, too." And she adds some of her own problems to the list. As the study proceeds other questions are added.

Then, because she has an eye on the objective of improving ability to solve problems, she says, "Now these are good problems. How shall we find the answers?" And the pupils, after some discussion, say, "We can experiment. We can look in science books and library books. We can ask the workmen. We can ask other people who know. We might watch the machines more closely. We might find a motion picture that will help us." After these possibilities are considered, the pupils select a problem to begin with and their work begins.

To help start the work of problem-solving and to help pupils see how experiments may help solve problems, the teacher comes into the classroom one day with a brick and a six-foot board from the scene of construction. She says to her class, "Can anyone in this class lift me?" After a quick survey everyone gives up without trying, and she says, "Can anyone in our class use this brick and this board to lift me?" Some of the pupils volunteer. They place the brick on the floor, place the board on it with more of it on one side of the brick than on the other, and say to their teacher, "Miss Wright, stand there," pointing to the short side of the board. Miss Wright does as directed. The pupils push down on the other end of the board and up comes Miss Wright. A lever has been used to lift a weight. Other children try to lift her. The smallest girl in the class lifts Miss Wright without difficulty. "How come?" "How does it work?" The pupils begin to observe what has happened. They observe that this is similar to the iron bar and the hunk of cement sidewalk which they have seen outside the classroom window. They see that the push goes down and the weight goes up. They see that the push goes farther down than the weight moves up. They move the brick closer to and farther away from Miss Wright. They go out to the seesaw and try lifting each other by sitting at various distances from the teetering point. These are some of their problem-solving activities by *doing*. They are *seeing* and *feeling* how the levers work. They have used a lever to do real work, work that they could not do otherwise.

As the study proceeds, they gather reading materials to find out more about levers and how they work and are used. In so doing, they practice the language-arts skill of locating materials by the use of index, table of contents, and card catalogue. They plan an interview with the construction foreman to ask him questions about machines and how they work. This calls for making an outline of their findings and for presenting a well-organized, clear, oral report to the class. They locate pictures that can be arranged in sequence to show some of the ways in which machines are helpful. They find a motion picture that will help to clear up ideas about how machines work. They devise other ways to gather information, test it, and apply it to their problems about machines.

These pupils are discovering more about how to state their problems carefully, they are learning how to collect appropriate materials to solve them. They test their findings, they record them in brief sentences. Later, in discussing her work with the pupils on machines, Miss Wright says, "The study of machines seemed very successful because the children wanted to know the answers and were interested in setting up ways to find out. They learned something about problem-solving and so did I. I learned, too, that simple material was most useful, that near-at-hand problems raised by the class were important, and I came to know that the pupils liked solving problems that were their own."

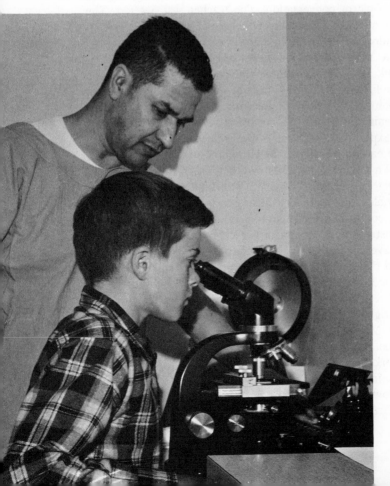

Interest and appreciation grow and develop when children have contact with real-life situations. Here a pathologist in Los Angeles County shows red blood cells to a child when he visits a laboratory.

Learning to solve problems is one of our important objectives. How does this fit into our general elementary school plan for children? Certainly our success in living with one another is increased if we are skillful in solving our daily problems—knowing what is pertinent, reliable information, learning how to apply it, knowing how to check the validity of results. Problem-solving, if it is truly scientific, provides ample opportunity for real cooperation and for giving and taking advice and criticism, and it produces a satisfying experience from a job successfully done. But make no mistake about it, these things do not automatically result from a study of machines; the teacher must plan to teach in a way that will bring them about. Above all, the teacher and the learners must be aware of the objective.

The field of science provides children with countless problems that are of real concern because they are near at hand and possess a fascination because of their nature. Then, too, the same method used in solving problems in science is used successfully in social studies, arithmetic, or, indeed, in living together at school and at home. This is true insofar as we pay attention to the problems children find, let them have some voice in how the problems are to be solved, and act as a guide to make the learning effective. More is learned about problem-solving in half an hour when pupils are working on something that really concerns them than is learned in hundreds of hours when children are forced to work on something that is too difficult for them or is presented in a deadly routine manner. As will be pointed out later in a discussion of the curriculum, this is not intended to imply that *all* questions and problems must come from pupils. Other sources may be equally effective if the teaching is good.

It is also important to note that pupils need help in seeing how this method of problem-solving in science is like problem-solving in other areas. They may never make this connection unless it is pointed out to them. The teacher may frequently say, "You remember how we found the answers when we worked on the problems about machines? How can we use what we learned there to help us find the answers in this new problem in our social studies?" Or the new problem may be, "How can we organize a good safety patrol for our school?" Such problems as this help pupils to transfer the lessons in problem-solving to their everyday living.

The study of science should develop in children a scientific attitude. We have been *saying* this for years, but we need to *do* more about it. The development of a scientific attitude, like the development of better problem-solvers, comes about only through conscious efforts. First, to achieve this important objective, we must understand what it means. Then we must teach so that children cannot get along without using a scientific way of thinking. What, then, does having a scientific attitude mean? Here are some of the characteristics that a scientifically minded person possesses:

He is open-minded—willing to change his mind in the face of reliable evidence—and he respects another's point of view.

He looks at a matter from many sides before he draws a conclusion. He does not jump to conclusions or decide on the basis of one observation; he deliberates and examines until he is sure.

He goes to reliable sources for his evidence. He challenges sources to make sure that they are reliable.

He is not superstitious; he realizes that nothing happens without some cause.

He is curious. He is careful and accurate in his observations. He plans his investigations carefully.

It is these characteristics that we are trying to develop in children through their science experiences. But it is possible to work with science apparatus, read source books, recite in science classes, set up exhibits for science clubs, and do a lot of other things without making a gram of use of the scientific attitude. This happens every day in some of our science classes, because teachers do not actually *try to see that a scientific attitude is emphasized.* We do not teach with this objective always in mind. Every time an experiment is performed, whenever children read, take a field trip, see a motion picture, report their findings to the class, set up a problem to solve, or do anything else in science classes, their scientific attitude ought to be showing! It should become a real part of their thinking equipment. There should be much of "Hey, wait a minute!" "Let's try that again." "How do you know that's true?" "I've changed my mind since I read what scientists say." "Where did you find that answer?" "You may be right but tell me more about where you found your information." These remarks and similar ones should be heard often in our science classes—and not only there, but also in social studies classes, arithmetic classes, and anywhere else where children are working together at solving problems.

Now let us be specific. In a fourth-grade class the pupils have been studying plants and how they grow. They have experimented, and see that plants need water to grow. Someone asks, "Where does the water go?" To answer this question the pupils take a stalk of celery, cut off the bottom of the stem with a sharp knife, and set the stem in a jar of water colored with red ink. Later they examine the stalk, cut it open to observe the channels, and note the colored veins in the leaves which show where the water went. Someone then remarks, "The book says that some of the water goes off from the leaf into the air." The teacher asks, "Could you suggest a way to find out whether this is true?" Someone suggests that they put something over a plant to catch any water that might come from the leaf. Pupils suggest that they invert a quart jar over a small geranium plant. They do this and the next day notice that there are tiny droplets of water collected on the inside of the jar. "How many of you think this shows us that the geranium leaves give off water?" the teacher asks. The class members agree that it does—*but they should not.* The water might have come from the soil in which the plant was growing or from the air around the leaf; the pupils have not investigated all possibilities.

The teacher cautions them to reconsider, because she believes in the importance of helping pupils to think more scientifically. As a result, someone suggests, "Maybe some of the water is coming from the soil. We ought to cover the soil with a piece of cardboard." "That's a good suggestion," the teacher says encouragingly, and the experiment is reassembled in its improved form. Again the water condenses on the inside of the jar and the pupils are about to be satisfied with the results when somebody says, "Maybe the moisture is coming from the air. It could be, you know." And indeed it could. The teacher comments favorably on this kind of thinking and says, "How can we set up our experiment to make it more reliable?" Someone suggests using two sets of equipment exactly alike except that only one jar contains a growing plant. "Then if that jar with the plant has water on it and the other one doesn't, we'll know that the water really came from the plant."

The group performs other, similar experiments and does further "research" reading before pupils finally decide that plants give off water into the air. The teacher *intends* to see that the scientific attitude is kept in action.

Does it take more time to experiment in this way? Yes, it does. But how better can you spend time than in helping boys and girls be more careful and accurate in their judgments? Frequently in the performance of experiments the subject matter learned may be of less importance than the method used and the attitude acquired. This is often said, but we frequently forget to emphasize the method and attitude. This method of questioning, checking details, expressing opinion, and withholding judgment should be used whenever experiments are performed, whether they come from a basic textbook, a supplementary science book, or are originated by the children.

Experiments that do not "work" as they are supposed to "work" the first time they are performed often produce the best learning situations imaginable. To figure out *why* an experiment did not "work" often brings into play the best thinking possible.

Whenever children read, there is plenty of opportunity for the application of scientific thinking. When young children ask, "Is that a really true story?" there is opportunity for them to get acquainted with the differences between factual material and fiction and to learn that one is read for the purpose of finding the answer and the other more usually for entertainment and enjoyment.

The pupils' discovery of mistakes in books may be a landmark in the development of their scientific attitude. To realize that a statement's appearance in print is no guarantee for its accuracy may be an eye opener to a child who is being introduced to reliability as a criterion for selecting material to read for answering questions. One book, for example, may state, "There are eight planets"; another may say, "There are nine known planets." Here is an opportunity for discussion to show that scientists are continually revising and adding to our knowledge. Children come to appreciate the importance of using up-to-date material for reference work. They come to know that such words as "known," as it is used in the sentence about the number of planets, are extremely important, as are such phrases as "scientists think," "it is generally believed," "it may be true that," "some people say," and "evidence seems to indicate that." Again, it is this same attitude that should permeate our activities in social studies and other areas of learning in the elementary school.

The following quoted letter written by an eight-year-old to an author of a book is an illustration of challenging the accuracy of information:

Dear ———
     You wrote a book called the *Pet Show* didn't you? One of the stories in it is called the "Guinea Pigs at the Show." One sentence says, "They can run about when they are only a few days old."
     This is not true.
     They can run about the day they are born.

                                        Yours truly,
                                        MARY LOU ———

P. S. I raise them.

Here, obviously, is a pupil who is learning to evaluate some of her reading and to relate it to her own experience. Some adult, either at home or at school, urged her to write to the author to find out why her experience and the book did not seem to agree. Through such an experience the child learns something about how books are written, how limited experience may sometimes be misleading, and how different statements of fact may only *seem* to be in disagreement.

Spectacular stories from newspapers on such subjects as "Men from Mars," "Death Ray Bombs," or "The Future of Our Earth" provide materials for use in developing the

Who says toads will give you warts? In Decatur, Illinois, these pupils are checking on this superstition—an example of the exercising of scientific attitudes. Do horsehairs turn into snakes? Does the moon influence plant growth? Can we investigate to find out?

scientific way of looking at things. Who has written the articles? What do the words actually say? Are the articles setting forth theories or facts? These questions and similar ones are important to discuss.

Children's reports of horsehairs turning to snakes, and other superstitions, should be subjected to investigation and checking to develop scientific attitudes. Statements such as these are often made by children: "You can't believe the weatherman!" "Animals can tell if the winter is to be very cold." "Fortunetellers can help you tell what is the best thing to do." These remarks offer excellent opportunities for the use of scientific investigation and checking. They involve finding the answers to such questions as, "Who says so?" "How can we find out the facts?" "Why do some people say these things?"

We have given but a few examples of situations that can help transplant a "scientific attitude" from the printed page into the minds of children. We shall present other ideas for accomplishing this important purpose as we go on. Watch for them in the B chapters in parts two through four.

If you reread the paragraphs describing the objectives for the total school program, you will easily see how our objectives for helping children to gain a scientific attitude fit into our general intention for the elementary schools. Compare them, for example, to the objectives in the field of social studies and the relationship becomes obvious.

Science is, furthermore, supposed *to create in children an interest in and an appreciation for the world in which they live.* Just now, as this is being written, the evening sky is flaming with a hundred hues. The clouds five miles away, made of countless droplets of water, are reflecting some of this light through the window. The window glass itself was made by heating sand to which chemicals have been added, and the result offers protection from the weather. Growing almost into the window, leaves of a vine glisten green in the light of late afternoon. In leaves such as these, the food for the world is being made. The leaf is a wonderful manufacturing plant where water, lately fallen from the sky as rain, comes up from the roots in the ground and meets with carbon dioxide from the air. There in the green leaf, in the presence of sunlight, food is manufactured from this water and carbon dioxide. On this the whole world depends for its existence. In the world about us there are, indeed, great things to wonder about: How can sunlight be changed to brilliant colors at sunset? how are clouds formed? how is glass made? how do plants manufacture food? indeed, how did the world itself come to be, and how has it changed through the ages of time? Some wise person has said, "He who can no longer pause to wonder is as good as dead."

Young children deserve to find in schools a nurturing influence for their natural curiosity about the world. They deserve, too, to have this curiosity expanded to new fields, about which they have never wondered because they did not know that such fields exist. They deserve the opportunity to come to appreciate, through understanding, the wonders of the world. About how this appreciation is to be developed, we still have much to learn. Experience seems to show that children do not gain it through listening to the sentimental gushing of some adult. Perhaps it comes about through adults providing opportunities for children to discover for themselves. We can perhaps provide opportunities to observe at firsthand, to feel, to see, to use the senses so that satisfying experience will result. Perhaps through knowledge thus gained—through satisfying experiences—each child may develop for himself an appreciation that fits his person. Certainly there can be great thrills in discovery, great satisfaction through contact with natural objects and phenomena.

As these paragraphs were being written, the colors disappeared from the west. Twilight is here, and soon night will come. The earth is turning from the sun, darkness comes. Elsewhere the earth is turning toward the sun and day is coming. In a few weeks the leaves will drop from the vine outside the window, the days will grow colder, autumn will be here, then winter, then spring, and again summer. Here is the cycle of the seasons. Then there is the cycle that water follows as it disappears from the surface of the earth and appears again, falling from the sky as rain; the cycle of seed from tiny germ to adult plant and the production of seeds again. These are some of the phenomena to which we want to introduce young children through experiences that they will remember with pleasure. This is what we have in mind when we talk of increasing their interest and developing their appreciation. As in the case of the other objectives discussed, this one is realized only if we intend it to be, and teach accordingly.

Perhaps we have talked too emphatically and too long about objectives. But they are important, for they guide our science teaching in every detail. We shall refer to them again and again and try to make them even more concrete throughout this text. Every day we teach, we should challenge the things we do with children by asking ourselves, "What exactly is this supposed to do for children?" If the answer is questionable, then let us try hard to find a better way of teaching. If the answer is satisfactory, let us strive to increase the effectiveness of what we are doing. Above all, let us keep in mind that science deserves to be included in the elementary curriculum only to the extent that it contributes toward the goals of the total program. This point of view largely determines what subject matter is selected, how the teaching proceeds, and how the results are evaluated. Indeed, science has certain unique things to contribute to the growth and development of children, but these are realized only if we *intend* that they shall be and are willing to see that science learning fits into the total experience of children.

What we have said about keeping in mind the objectives of science holds equally true for the teaching of every other subject in the elementary school. We point this out to emphasize our contention that science teaching is very similar to the teaching of other subjects. Great strides could be made in our educational program if we applied to the curriculum the following criterion: does the study of this problem, the use of this activity, this plan of work actually contribute to the attainment of our over-all objectives? If problems, activities, and plans that did not meet this standard were discarded and replaced, our school program would be immeasurably revitalized.

CHAPTER 3

Helping Children Learn Science

What happens in the classroom is what counts. Neither cupboards of equipment and shelves of books, nor the best course of study will in themselves accomplish our objectives. They are accomplished where the teaching and learning go on. The teacher who can put into practice the suggestions in this chapter is well on the road toward realizing her intentions.

Whatever is done by children to learn science should be *purposeful*, because it is planned to move pupils along toward the accomplishment of the aims of science teaching. It should be *challenging*, because it is on the intellectual and interest level of the learner. It should be *appropriate*, because it seems, insofar as it is possible to tell, to be the best way to solve the problems at hand. If we keep these things in mind, we do not perform experiments just because we need activity, we do not make murals because we need something for the bulletin board, and we do not take field trips because our school is near the zoo. Our activities are designed to accomplish our aims.

With our aims in mind, then, how shall we help children achieve them? Many of the aims are achieved through solving problems, for, as we have stated earlier, science is a method of discovery. And how do children make discoveries and solve problems? By experimenting, observing, reading, taking field trips, talking with someone who knows, looking at pictures, and in many other ways. In short, children solve problems by doing a purposeful thing—something that will bring a realness to what they are trying to learn. Through this process, appropriate attitudes, appreciations, skills, and knowledge will result if the teacher so intends.

EXPERIMENTING TO FIND OUT

There is something fascinating to children about experiments. "Oh, good, we're going to have an experiment today!" the children chorus when there is to be some demonstration. This interest in "trying out" is an important one to capitalize on. We ought to try not to take away any of the fun of experimenting but at the same time we should help children to realize that an experiment is an important way of discovering the answer. Merely performing an experiment according to printed directions and recording the results in blank spaces in a book is not enough. Following the recipe is generally quite sufficient in cake-baking, but our objective in performing experiments is quite different. Let us look at a third-grade class that is performing a simple experiment to learn which things a magnet will attract. One child reads from the text the directions for performing the experiment; another child performs the experiment accordingly; and a third child reads from the book the results of the experiment. This illustrates perfectly how *not* to experiment, but it happens to be an account of a real observation.

Pupils have planned procedures, assembled materials, experimented, read, discussed, asked, and finally summarized their findings in this study of magnets. Bulletin boards and a work space have been essentials in their work.

Let us consider now an illustration that comes closer to our ideals. Pupils have brought magnets to school, have used them informally, and have shown each other the things they discovered. One child contends that magnets will pick up metals. Some pupils agree with him; some do not. The question is raised: "What will a magnet pick up?" "How can we be sure what it picks up?" the teacher asks. "Try it," children say. "Good idea!" the teacher says. The pupils, through discussion, decide to:

1. Write the purpose of the experiment on the board—namely, "to find out what things a magnet will pick up." Someone suggests, "Let's find out if it is correct to say that it will pick up metals, too," and the teacher adds to the purpose: "to find out whether a magnet will pick up metals."
2. Work out some directions for doing the experiment. The following simple directions are worked out:
   a. Gather metals and other things that we want to test (paper, cork, glass, an iron thumbtack, a steel needle, an iron nail, a steel pen point, cloth, a nickel, a penny, etc.).
   b. Use a strong magnet carefully to see whether it will pick these up.
   c. Make a pile of things the magnet will pick up and one of the things it will not pick up.
   d. See if the experiment really answers our questions.

The directions are followed carefully, and pupils finally decide, "Our experiment seems to show that this magnet will pick up things made of iron and steel." They decide, too, that they need to do some reading to be sure of their answers, since they themselves cannot try out all materials. This they do, and their reading seems to confirm their original conclusion, except that nickel was listed as a metal that would be attracted by a magnet. This leads to further reading and investigating (see chapter 21A). Then someone raises the question about the statement made that magnets would attract metals. This question is settled by looking up a definition of metals: "substances such as iron, gold, silver, copper, lead, tin, aluminum, steel, bronze, and brass." This definition and the results of their experiment help them to determine the truth of the statement made by one of the pupils that magnets will pick up metals.

What is good about this procedure: the experiment was done in response to a perplexing problem; experimenting seemed the logical way to find the answer; the design for the experiment and the plan for its use was made by the pupils with some help from the teacher; the pupils did not generalize from too little evidence; the experience contributed something toward accomplishing the over-all objectives for science teaching.

It is not always essential to write the problem or the procedure on the board. It is, however, always important to allow the pupils to state the problem exactly as they wish to solve it and to plan the procedure just as they wish to follow it. It may be, and frequently is, necessary to make changes in the plans as the experiments go on. The teacher will help where needed in order that the most effective results may be achieved.

By some standards, this experiment might be described as "quite cut and dried," that is, there are not many opportunities for creative thinking on the part of individuals, and the activity probably ends with the discovery of the answer, leaving not many offshoots of other ideas to pursue. What can be done to make such an experience more "open-ended," i.e., more "on-going" and thought-provoking? Here are suggestions: Let pupils try more materials before they read. Suggest that magnets of different strengths, shapes, and sizes be used to observe any differences in results. Suggest that different shapes and sizes of materials to be attracted be used. Suggest that different parts of the magnet be used and the results noted. Such suggestions as these and others that pupils make will help to introduce children to the methods used by research scientists who "leave no stone unturned," as they search for answers to problems and related information. This is but one example of such experimental procedure. More "open-endedness" may be encouraged by questions beginning: "What would happen if _____?" "Where could you find _____?" "What other ways are there of _____?" "How could you prove that _____?" "How could you make a _____?" Other illustrations will be found in the B chapters that follow.

A further improvement in the experimenting process is, whenever possible, to make the results more scientific by making them more definite through the use of mathematics. Too little attention has been paid to this possibility, for both science and mathematics are made more meaningful when they are thus related. This use of quantitative skill runs all the way from counting the number of thumbtacks that different magnets can hold, to measuring the lengths of shadows made by a stick at various times of the day, to working out the relationships of the amount of effort needed to lift a weight, to determining the length of the part of the lever where the effort is being applied, to determining the amount of air pressure on a rectangular tin can. The quantitative aspect of various experiments and experiences will be pointed out in subsequent B chapters.

The following are specific suggestions to help make experimenting an effective experience in elementary school science:

1. Keep the experiment simple. Whenever possible use simple, homemade equipment. (See discussion of apparatus.)
2. Perform experiments in such a manner as to cause children to think. If you plan to *tell* children the answer or let them *read* the answer, why bother with an experiment? An experiment done to find the answer to a genuine problem raised by children is sure to be more thought-provoking than one done to "prove" something that is already known by many of the pupils.
3. Let pupils do as much of the planning as they can. Then follow the plan. If it goes wrong, pupils have some basis for deciding why it did not work, since they themselves helped make the plan.
4. Challenge pupils when they make sweeping generalizations from one experiment. "Magnets will pick up all nails." After a limited experience with a box of nails the teacher may say, "Do all of you believe that we can say this?" The discussion may well result in further experimentation. If pupils are permitted to make false generalization, they defeat one of the purposes of experimenting.
5. Experiments ought to be simple enough and safe enough for pupils themselves to do. If classes are large and there is sufficient material available, pupils may work in groups to give many of them opportunity to experiment. If this is not possible, the material may be left available for use before school, at recess, or during the noon-period. The teacher should remember that it is one thing to manipulate apparatus yourself and quite another to watch at a distance while somebody else does it.

6. In teaching science, we should often say, "Can anyone think of something we can try or an experiment we can do to help us solve this problem?" Such a procedure gives a chance for real thought, careful planning, and organization.

7. The understandings gained through performing an experiment should help answer questions about things children see in the world about them. It is this application to "real-life" situations that is often missed.

8. Aimless experimenting is likely to be useless. An experiment should have a specific purpose, and it should be known and understood by all. It is often advisable to have on the chalkboard a simple statement of purpose to guide the thinking as the experiment goes on and as the conclusions are drawn.

9. Making a complete record of all experiments performed in the elementary school is not always necessary or desirable. The old idea of recording in a notebook for each experiment the object, materials used, drawing, procedure, and results and conclusions is deadly and is certain to take away the natural interest in experimenting which children seem to possess. Sometimes it seems sensible to record in a sentence or two the important outcomes of an experiment, either for future reference or to be sure that the ideas are clearly understood. If the experiment is one that takes several days to complete, it may be helpful to record each day's observations by making drawings or by writing a short paragraph. The guiding idea may well be, "Is there any good reason for writing anything about this experiment?"

So much, then, for experimenting as a way of working in science. It is an important way to learn. We can realize its potentialities, however, only when we use it in accordance with the broad objectives given in chapter 2. Then experimenting makes work in science more interesting and meaningful and provides plenty of opportunity for thinking, reasoning, and problem-solving, for planning and carrying out the plans, and for checking the effectiveness of these plans.

This book cannot possibly provide an exhaustive list of experiments to do in the chapters that follow. Many are included, and suggestions are made for helping pupils devise others. The nine points just given are illustrated in the examples you will find throughout the B chapters of parts two through four. Elementary science books are rich sources of experiments, and the books listed in the bibliography may be used profitably by pupils and teachers to supplement the experiments given in this text.

READING TO FIND THE ANSWERS

Children cannot learn everything by experimenting or by firsthand experiences. Neither can anyone else. We learn much from reading in textbooks, supplementary books, bulletins, magazines, and newspapers. Reading is sometimes condemned as a way to learn science, because it is often used so much that the science course degenerates into a course of reading about science. This criticism is leveled not against reading as a way to learn but against the *way* in which we use reading. We often hear school supervisors say, "Don't use your science books as readers!" How then? Let us see how to use a science book in a way that avoids this criticism.

Reading is an important tool for gaining new ideas, deepening concepts, and acquiring insights. Pictures help make the ideas real; comparing sources of information is valuable experience.

Assume that the area of study has been decided upon. The class in grade four is going to study sound. The big problem is: "How are sounds made?" Suppose we begin by suggesting to the class that each pupil bring something to science class that will make a sound. To add to the interest we may say: "Don't tell anyone else what you are going to bring; try to bring something that no one else will think of."

As preparation for solving this problem, you, as the teacher, have read carefully the section in the pupils' textbook about sound, have read chapters 22A and 22B in this book, have explored to see what other reading materials are available, have located in the school building and in the neighborhood examples of the principles of sound, and have assembled a few of the things you will need that the children probably cannot themselves find.

The next day, pupils come in with their sound-makers. You suggest that, as each child demonstrates his sound-maker, pupils observe carefully to see: (1) "what makes the sound," and (2) "how the sounds are different from each other."

The sound-making begins. Ned has brought his violin, Charlie his trumpet, and they make sounds with them. Mary and Alice use rubber bands, plucking them when they are stretched; Paul stands up in front of everybody and shouts, "Hey!" There are several other examples of sound. After these demonstrations, you suggest that everybody listen quietly to hear any sounds around them. They hear the clock tick. A car starts up outside and the sound changes as the car gains speed. Across the street, someone is driving a nail into a board. A bell rings somewhere in the schoolhouse.

After each sound is made, the pupils tell what they think may be the answer to the two questions. They are not at all sure what it is that makes the sounds, but they have noted that some of the sounds are loud, some soft, some high, and some low. There is discussion about how Paul made the sound when he said, "Hey!" "Let's feel our throats when we talk," the teacher suggests. "Something in there quivers," somebody volunteers. "That's what my violin string does when I draw the bow across it. It vibrates," Ned says. But what is it that makes the sound? The teacher suggests that pupils observe closely to see if something is vibrating in each case where sound is made. They see, and feel, and listen. The children agree that when something is making sound it is vibrating. But a question still remains. "What has this to do with the sound I hear in my ears, and how does the sound get there?"

This is a good time to use reading, since pupils are now faced with a problem they cannot solve through use of an experiment alone. Pupils find the section on sound in the book; a picture on the first page shows pupils making sounds. Pupils read, then, to see whether they can discover an answer to their question. They read about vibrations and discover an experiment which they can do with a tuning fork. "Let's do the experiment on page 11." The teacher produces the necessary tuning fork. The simple directions are read. The experiment is performed. Pupils feel the vibrations in the tuning fork. Mary and Alice are asked to demonstrate their rubber bands again, since the book mentions vibration in connection with rubber bands of various sizes. After this experiment, pupils return to their books and finish reading about vibrations, how they make sounds, and how sounds travel in waves from place to place.

As the study proceeds, the pupils read, study pictures in their books, search for supplementary books on the subject of sound, perform experiments described in books, perform some of their own experiments, and do other things to find answers. An important skill for a teacher to develop is that of getting into the book when necessary and getting out of it when not. It is getting stuck in the book that is bad. The bibliography at the end of this book provides an extensive list of books of a so-called supplementary nature. They often supply the exact material needed and should be relied on heavily for their contribution to the science program.

Contrast the foregoing procedure with: "Today we are going to study sound. Open your books to page 18. Read the first six pages and then tell me what you have read." It is this kind of procedure that makes people say, "Do not use your science books as readers. Do not do so much reading *about* science." It is also the kind of procedure that makes children dislike science or say that it is not very interesting.

There is much to be said in favor of building a library of trade (supplementary) books in addition to the basic text or texts: (1) They meet the needs of *individual* children. (2) They permit the pursuit of a topic in depth. (3) They develop the habit of using many sources. (4) They permit pupils to work independently. (5) They may serve with special effectiveness the pupils who have reading difficulty. Large numbers of excellent supplementary curriculum-enriching books are available. (See bibliography at end of book.)

Reading, then, is one of the important tools to use in learning science. We can step up reading efficiency if we keep in mind the following things:

1. Read with specific purposes—to check conclusions, to answer a question or solve a problem, to find additional information, to learn how to do an experiment, or for some other definite reason.
2. Reading is often more effective if it is done from several supplementary sources that provide more information and different points of view.

3. In science, pupils may come to a clearer realization that there is a real difference between materials that are read for fun and those read for information. (See the discussion on scientific attitude, pages 17–18.)

4. Selecting the material to be read may be done by both the pupils and the teacher. The use of table of contents, index, and other reference tools is necessary. Pupils may take notes on the reading they do. This may be an essential part of the "research reading" done in science. Selecting material on varying levels of difficulty is essential if reading is to function as a tool for learning. In any grade, it is not usual for all pupils to be ready to read the science book written for that grade.

It has been said often that if science is to be learned, enjoyed, and made functional in the lives of girls and boys, it must leave the pages of a book and get into their daily experiences in a meaningful way. Textbooks and other books are essential as guides; reading supplies much of the needed information. We must not, however, overwork this channel of information to the exclusion of other more important or equally important ways to learn. Again, this point of view does not differ from our view on any other elementary school subject. Our use of reading as a tool in science study does not differ from the way we use it in social studies, for example.

The magnifying glass brings new information into focus, uncovering wonders otherwise unknown. Careful observation is the initial step in identifying, gathering information, and finding answers. Children, given opportunity and assistance, grow in ability to observe—an essential skill in learning.

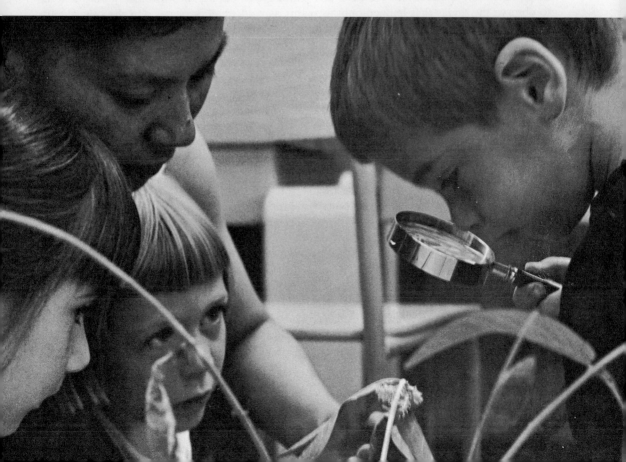

OBSERVING

When children bring unfamiliar science "things" to school, the wise teacher may say, "Let's examine it carefully to see what we can observe." The senses are used to discover. The observations are assembled. Questions are raised. There is now some information to use as pupils "look it up" or use some other means of gaining more information. Good lessons begin with thoughtful observation.

We hope through a study of science to make girls and boys more skillful in observing, more scientific in reporting and interpreting what they see, and more interested in looking about them. Observing is not, of course, a skill divorced from experimenting, reading, and the other ways to learn. Careful, accurate observation is an essential part of all activities that pupils engage in.

We often characterize a good observer as one who has learned to use his senses—to feel, see, hear, smell, and touch—intelligently. In a study of sound, children *feel* vibrations of a piano, *see* the vibrating strings, and *hear* the sound. Their careful use of the senses makes learning more vivid. Pupils observe to see changes in seeds as they sprout, to see changes in frog eggs as they hatch, to see what happens in an experiment. If opportunities are provided, pupils can learn to become more and more accurate observers as they progress in their study of science.

In climates where there are distinct changes in the seasons, teachers often take pupils for walks to observe. There is great variety in what is accomplished on these walks: some of them produce little of value; others are truly eye openers. It is well to keep in mind that young children cannot observe as many different things at one time as older pupils can. Trips for young children should be short. Third-grade pupils, therefore, may take a walk to observe the things that happen only to plants as cold weather comes. On the other hand, sixth-grade pupils on a similar trip may make observations about both plants and animals and solve problems of a more complex nature than younger children can.

The effectiveness of a walk may be greatly enhanced if pupils go to solve a problem. Thus a third grade may take a walk to find out: "How do plants change as the seasons change?" In order to note *change* pupils will need, of course, to take more than one trip. They must plan to make several, and to observe carefully and record their observations for future reference. Suppose the first trip is taken in early autumn. In many parts of the United States pupils may observe that: some plants are dying; some are making seeds; some are losing their leaves; some are keeping their leaves, but the leaves are turning brown; some plants, such as the evergreens, do not seem to change very much.

Pupils may bring the following things from their walk into their classroom to observe more closely: several kinds of seed pods (to examine them, to count the seeds, and to try to grow them); some specimens to show the different ways in which plants spread their seeds; some twigs from trees (to find out how the buds are formed and how they are protected in winter); some grass plants (to see which part dies and which stays alive—some of the grass is planted indoors to see whether it will grow if it is watered and kept at room temperature); some twigs from trees that still have their leaves (to see how the leaves join the twig); some evergreen twigs (to see if some of the needles are new and green and others are old). Children may use magnifying glasses to see buds and seeds closely. Many of these observations may well be considered "open-ended" experiences, for they and others like them will provide opportunity for the development of individual interests, creative thinking, and continuing exploration.

After careful observing, pupils may together prepare a record, commonly called an "experience chart," to record their observations. This chart, together with the materials observed, will be kept for future reference.

A month or so later the same trip is taken to observe the same plants in order to gather more data on how plants are changing as the seasons change. A second record is made and kept with the collected materials.

During the school year five or six trips are taken, each for the same purpose. Records are made. In May the final chart is prepared and pupils examine all of their previous records. Now they are prepared to give a more complete answer to their original problem. They are beginning to see the importance of observing over a sufficiently long period of time before drawing conclusions. They are learning to look carefully in order to be certain that their report will be accurate. They also see the sense of keeping carefully made records.

Contrast this with the common practice of mounting leaves on a chart labeled "Our Leaves" or collecting seed dispersal samples and calling them "World Travelers."

It is through careful observation that pupils become more aware of the things that are happening about them. To look through a magnifying glass at snail eggs hatching on the aquarium glass, or to see a snail's tongue as it scrapes the aquarium glass for food, is a most interesting experience. Observing is a part of the method of discovery. Much can be learned from our surroundings if we become skillful observers.

FIELD TRIPS

The previous description of a field trip embodies the essentials for making a good trip. Trips to the zoo, the museum, a greenhouse, the water-purification plant, a new building under construction, the park, and similar places are important in making science more meaningful. But taking a field trip with a bunch of fourth-graders may be a headache to the teacher and useless boondoggling for the children unless some of the following points are observed:

1. There should be a real reason for making the trip. If pupils need to find the answers to questions or problems, make sure that everyone has them in mind and knows what he is to look for. Whatever the reason for making the trip, it should be obvious to all.
2. There should be planning for safety, transportation, a suitable guide, time schedule, note-taking, and other details before the trip.
3. The teacher, with a committee of pupils, might well make a preliminary trip to to determine the suitability of the place, brief the guide about the desires of the group, and make other necessary arrangements. Certainly the teacher should make such a preliminary trip.
4. There should be group discussion about conduct and courtesy on the trip. Public relations are at stake every time children leave the schoolhouse to make a visit. A pack of junior warriors will certainly give adults a bad impression of the effectiveness of the school. The adults who are to help the children on the visit are quite reasonable in expecting interested attention from them. Groups not accustomed to making such visits will need to set up some standards to ensure a

A field trip to the zoo in Cleveland, Ohio, provides these pupils with an opportunity to observe animals' structural adaptations to environment, food-getting, and protection. Field trips are most effective when pupils go with specific questions that they have planned.

profitable trip. This does not mean that the discipline has to be so rigid as to spoil the fun. It means reasonable conduct, often determined by the pupils themselves.

5. Individuals and small groups may be designated to watch or listen for certain things and report them to the class. Specific responsibility of this kind often produces very good results.

6. Do not hurry children too much or plan for them to see more than they are able to take in at one exposure. Sometimes in our zeal to keep the group together, we forget that children are individuals and cannot all react with the same speed or be interested at the same time in the same things. A hurried trip to see too many things may be as unsatisfactory as not going at all.

7. The follow-up conversations and the recording of information is important. Accurate reporting of what was seen and observed is essential but the child who said to his field-tripping friend, "Don't look or you'll have to write!" had a point. Do not overdo the writing. Application of the information to the specific problems and questions is best done in the classroom on return.

Potentially, "going to see" is one of the most enjoyable and instructive ways to learn. When teachers, pupils, and the adults in the place to be visited work together in planning and carrying out the excursion, the results are most likely to be those we hope for. Specific suggestions for field trips for special purposes are described in the B chapters of parts two, three, and four of this book. (See also "Resources to Investigate" in these chapters for suggestions.)

VISUAL AIDS

"One picture is worth a thousand words, but it takes words to say so." Visual aids—that is, motion pictures and slide films, still pictures, models, etc.—are among our most useful tools, but they do not teach by themselves without intelligent planning and use by the teacher. Much thoroughly bad teaching is done in the name of "showing 'em a movie."

Before we go further into a discussion of visual aids and their use, let us establish an understanding about them. A fifth-grade classroom we visited contained the following materials that were currently being used in one way or another: a daily weather map; some pupils' drawings to show how heat travels; a sketch of some science apparatus; a collection of apparatus made by a group of children studying electricity—some dry cells, wire, an electric bell, a worn-out electric toaster, and some transparent light bulbs; science books; several kinds of plants and an aquarium. Are all these things visual aids? There are some people who would not only say yes but would probably go still further and include the schoolhouse itself. Persons with the opposite point of view contend that visual aids are restricted chiefly to motion pictures and slide films.

Be that as it may, we will all agree that our success in teaching is greatly enhanced if we are able to make ideas concrete. We have all had the experience of asking someone to explain something to us and having him make a drawing that supplements his explanation so well that when he is finished we understand him perfectly. We have also had the experience of reading a book and finding ourselves lost in a wordy explanation, only to come upon a sketch or drawing or map that illuminates the idea so that we understand completely.

If you think of visual material as it functions in these two situations, perhaps it will help you understand this section. Whenever we, as teachers, use the chalkboard so that children may *see* more clearly what we mean, or help children perform experiments to find out, or help them study a picture to answer their questions, we are using visual materials. Whether or not we label them as such is unimportant. It *is* important, however, that we become increasingly aware of visual aids' potentialities and more skillful in their use.

The *chalkboard* is an aid to learning, and its use is available to every teacher. But, as is the case with so many obvious, close-at-hand possibilities, we sometimes overlook a chalkboard's potentialities. A large drawing that illustrates an idea—for example, how the parts of a seed are located in relation to each other—is a very effective teaching aid. Colored chalk helps to show the ideas more clearly. Large chalkboard drawings make it possible for all children in a group to center attention on the same place while they discuss a problem. The use of the board is not limited to teachers. Pupils should be encouraged to make more extensive use of the chalkboard to explain their ideas. When they do this, they often find that their ideas are not quite clear or are perhaps inaccurate, and consequently they discover the importance of accurate observation and reading.

Observation of current practice in the use of chalkboards would indicate that they are needed, although the following suggestions may seem obvious to some readers:

1. Make all diagrams and other illustrative material large enough to be seen by all pupils, and make the labels and other writing neat and legible.
2. Seat pupils where they can all see the board; do not clutter the board with too much material.
3. Organize the presentation so that it can be followed easily.
4. Use colored chalk when it seems desirable to add to the ease of comprehension.
5. Start with a clean board.
6. Use rulers and other helps to produce a clear, easily understood drawing or table.
7. Sit down in the back of the room sometimes and look at your chalkboard work from the pupils' view.

Motion pictures and filmstrips are widely used but not always as effective as they might be. Following these points will help:

1. Select the film as carefully as you would a book. Children cannot comprehend a film that is too difficult for them any better than they can a book. Any film indicated as appropriate for both high school and elementary school is almost certain to be useless at one level or the other unless it is on some relatively non-technical subject, such as life in a beaver colony.
2. The film selected should bear directly on the problem or problems under consideration.
3. Films should be previewed before they are used. This is done by the teacher, sometimes with the assistance of a committee of pupils in order to plan for its wise use. Film guides often provide very excellent suggestions for the use of the film. If there is no time to preview a film, its effectiveness may be limited.
4. Pupils should be prepared for seeing the film. The preparation may consist in arranging the problems and questions in sequence as they are dealt with in the film, indicating any unfamiliar vocabulary used, calling attention to difficult spots that may need advance discussion, suggesting new things in the film that the class has never considered, and in other ways paving the way for good listening and seeing.
5. There should always be a real reason for using a film. Just because there is a film in the school building about the Great Wall of China, the teacher is not justified in calling off work on "How we can make our community a better place to live in." Films are shown in science because they are often the most effective way to move in the direction of attaining our objectives. They can show things in action, show sequence in an event, illustrate a difficult idea, or in some other way help to promote learning. They are often shown so that children can find the solution of a problem or problems. It may be a problem about how something works (machines), how a process takes place (erosion), how to do something (make a feeding station), how a living thing grows (seed germination).
6. A film may be worth showing more than once. If it is especially long, it may be shown in parts, with discussion at the stopping places. The attention span of children may be our clue to how much of a film may be shown at one time.
7. The follow-up discussion of a motion picture, like the follow-up of a field trip, is often the most important part of the film's use. It will be based on the "things to look for" that were set up before the showing.

We have touched on only the most obvious points to be observed in the use of motion pictures and filmstrips. An extensive treatment of the use of these audio-visual aids as well as others is to be found in Edgar Dale's *Audio-Visual Methods in Teaching*.[1]

A *filmstrip* is a series of pictures on a length of film. The pictures are usually so related to each other as to make a continuous sequence. A filmstrip's use has certain advantages over those of a motion picture as well as certain disadvantages. A filmstrip projector is easy to operate. Filmstrips are inexpensive; it is possible to make them yourself. Since the film-

---

[1] Edgar Dale, *Audio-Visual Methods in Teaching*. Rev. ed. (New York, Holt, Rinehart and Winston, 1954).

strip presents the pictures in a fixed sequence, this may become a disadvantage if that sequence is not suitable. Filmstrips are discussed at length by Dale[2] and in many other sources.

Pictures that tell a story in science are being used to good advantage by many teachers. These may come from magazines and newspapers and may be filed for ready use. The back copies, for example, of the *National Geographic Magazine* and *Life* are excellent for use in identification of insects, birds, other animals, and rocks and minerals. Pictures are especially useful when science classes are considering such questions as: How do plants and animals change as they grow? How and where do animals build their homes? What happens when a river floods its banks? How are plants and animals classified? How do animals and plants help and harm one another? What kinds of machines are used to build a skyscraper? How does chemical change affect our lives? This list could be lengthened, but it illustrates that pictures are most useful if they are organized so that they will help to answer specific problems. A vertical filing system, with all pictures filed upright, is indispensable if pictures are to be easily accessible to teacher and pupil. Many schools keep a central file of pictures which have been assembled cooperatively by many teachers.

Since there are so many still pictures available, it is well to decide which pictures are worth saving for future reference. Dale[3] gives the following standards for judging a still picture:

Will it help achieve my teaching purposes?
Does the picture convey a generally true impression?
Does the picture give an accurate impression of relative size?
Will the picture add to the students' fund of knowledge?
Will the picture stimulate the imagination?
Is this a good picture technically and artistically?
Does the picture focus attention upon one main idea?
Does the picture have the proper amount of detail?

Charts that may be purchased for use in the elementary science classes are frequently expensive and usually not worth the price. Charts that children themselves make are often much more appropriate. For example, charts that children prepare to show which animals are mammals, birds, amphibians, reptiles, and fish may be very interesting. Another example of a chart is one made to show changes in temperature by weeks as fall changes to winter. The chart can play an important part in a current project, and when completed serve as a summary and lead to further learning. Similar ideas lend themselves to purposeful chart-making by children.

The same things may be said of expensive *models*. For example, in the elementary school we are not usually concerned with the detailed study of parts of a flower or of the human ear. Therefore, an expensive model of these is not needed. Pupil-made models may often serve a sensible purpose. For example, a model of the solar system constructed to show relative sizes and distances may involve careful reading, accurate measuring, and considerable meaningful discussion before it can be satisfactorily finished. The making of the visual aid in this case is a purposeful activity, as long as it does not take an undue amount of time.

---

[2] *Ibid.*
[3] *Ibid.*

The finished product is useful, but so is the method of production. There are many other examples of model-making and construction that constitute worthwhile activity in the elementary school science classes.

TELEVISION AND RADIO

There is no doubt that the curve of educational television is upward. There are many good offerings and some poor ones. There is not space here for long discussion but from the point of view of the classroom teacher, television presentations are useful if they are:

1. Designed to supplement and enrich the course of study that the school is following.
2. Concentrating on doing and showing things that cannot be done as well or better in the confines of a classroom.
3. Presented on the level of comprehension and interest of the children.
4. Demonstrating awareness of the objectives for science teaching.
5. Using good teaching techniques.
6. Providing manuals that describe the programs in advance and give educationally sound suggestions for their use.

Classroom reception must be good, the time of the telecast must fit into the school day, and the physical setup for classroom reception must be satisfactory. If these conditions exist, the key to satisfactory results is in the hands of the classroom teacher. She must approach the use of television with an open mind, and share the responsibility for improving the programs by giving helpful and constructive criticism. Lines of communication between the television producers and teachers and the classroom users must always be open.

There is no doubt that television is a valuable teaching tool for use in the classroom. It does not intend to replace the classroom teacher any more than does any other teaching aid. If the programs are good they can do much toward furthering the objectives for science teaching. Teachers and children both learn from good programs.

In addition to the programs beamed for specific classroom use, a considerable number of after-school science programs, both from local stations and on national hookups, may be used to advantage in schools by alert teachers. At the beginning of the school year teacher and pupils may make special efforts to obtain from local sources the time and date and subject matter of series of interesting programs. Suggestions for watching the programs and reporting on them may be devised by pupils and teachers.

A number of school systems have for some time been using radio as an integral part of the elementary science program. Lessons are broadcast for specific classroom use. The foregoing discussion of telecasts applies also to the use of radio programs. If the radio programs meet the above six criteria for evaluation, if the classroom conditions meet the standards described, the rest is up to the teacher.

As in the case of television, radio broadcasts designed for the general public often include programs of scientific interest that may be used in elementary schools. Advance notice of these broadcasts is usually available and is indeed necessary if full use is to be made of them in the science program. Pupils may be urged to listen for ideas that will help them to solve some of the science problems they have been considering.

Youngsters at one of New York's public schools get set for the morning's science lesson with "Miss Barbara," the Regents Educational Television Project's Barbara Yanowski who teaches "The Science Corner" on WPIX-11.

Inaccuracies sometimes creep into radio and television programs, especially when an attempt is made to dramatize a scientist's life or to "dress up" science facts in a narrative form. Discussions of these inaccuracies may become a very important part of listening. This brings us to a closely related idea. We all know that many advertisers broadcast nonscientific claims about their products, sometimes to the point of being ridiculous. Even young children may come to recognize the use of extravagant words and phrases to describe products as being able to accomplish miracles. This we believe is important, especially today, when children are hearing and seeing great quantities of advertising material.

Our present treatment of visual and other aids to teaching in science is admittedly too brief. It is intended to focus attention on the basic principle that intelligent use of any teaching aid in science requires careful preparation and thorough integration with the ongoing science program.

In this chapter we have attempted to indicate some of the ways in which children learn science and to give some advice on how best to use these ways. Good science teaching in the elementary school uses all these ways to whatever degree and in whatever order the situation demands. It is difficult to imagine a good science program that does not use experimentation, reading, and observation. Field trips to see the real thing are important, and so are other aids. But they all fall flat if they are not based on the objectives we are trying to accomplish. In subsequent B chapters we shall say more about the specific use of some of these ways to learn science.

CHAPTER 4

Organizing the Science Program

An examination of the science subject matter in parts two through four of this book gives an idea of the material that is available to choose from in formulating a curriculum in the elementary school. As someone has said, we have the "universe and other things" to select from—living things, forces, the earth, astronomy, and so on. What guides shall we use in our selection? The *Fifty-Ninth Yearbook* of the National Society for the Study of Education[1] suggests that we consider four factors in making our choices: (1) the child with his emotional, intellectual, and physical needs, (2) the sciences, especially biology, chemistry, physics, and astronomy, (3) the environment, both natural and man-made, in which the child lives, and (4) the total school program.

It certainly makes sense to consider needs and interests of children if we are planning a curriculum for them. If science subject matter is interesting and challenging to children, they will want to learn it, and if they want to learn it, they will tackle the problems relating to it and thus develop problem-solving skills. Children need to have their curiosities and intellectual needs satisfied as they pursue their interests.

---

[1] National Society for the Study of Education, "Rethinking Science Education," *Fifty-Ninth Yearbook*, Part I. (Chicago, University of Chicago Press, 1960), pp. 119–124.

Let us set forth some views on interest. For, if it is to be used as a criterion for selecting content, we should be well acquainted with its many facets.

1. Interest is a tremendous motivating factor.
2. Interest changes frequently—may be long or short lived in the elementary school.
3. Interest of young children manifests itself in many ways. One very obvious one is that it prompts them to ask questions and set up problems. Some of these are vital; some nonsense. Some are asked because children like to please their teachers, like to hear themselves talk, like to show off to their neighbors, and because of other similar reasons. Some are motivated by real desire to know. These are the questions and problems that we need to pay attention to and to be more skillful at recognizing.
4. Interest is likely to be one-track unless it is broadened through the guidance of skillful teachers. There are classes that would spend their entire fifth-grade year studying dinosaurs and in so doing miss much other important science if their interests were not directed to other equally interesting channels.
5. Interest is often caught from situations, from other individuals including the teacher, from books and elsewhere. This fact puts responsibility on the teacher to provide "interest-catchers" by the dozen.
6. Interest of children in any specific class is bound to vary in kind, quality, intensity, and longevity. This means that children's interests can be but one criterion for subject matter selection, that teachers must be alert to channel, organize, and broaden sparks of interests that seem persistent and important enough to demand attention.

Observing an animal is fun and it is a way to learn. It is an example of children's interest that seems universal. Good science programs take advantage of this interest by including problems about animal life.

These things about interest tell us: by all means pay attention to it, develop it, use it intelligently but do not depend on it to the exclusion of other criteria for selecting subject matter.

The various fields of science (biology, chemistry, physics, astronomy, etc.) offer the subject matter—the questions and problems—that springs from the natural and physical world in which children live. As we shall see later in the discussion of the problems of organization (see pages 41–46), each year of the science sequential development may include problems from the various aspects of science.

The environment of children supplies us with more information on which to base content selection. The local environment is to some extent to be taken into account. How, for example, do the children's parents make their living: through agricultural pursuits, through dairying, by working in chemical plants? What are the local problems that must be solved in making the home, school, and community safe, healthful places in which to live? Are there problems of soil erosion, weather forecasting, animal and plant conservation? Are there special scientific activities going on in the community? Are there things going on in the school building that have important scientific aspects: soundproofing the auditorium, building an addition to the school, installing new equipment in the cafeteria or new fire-extinguishing equipment? These are a few examples of how the local community might influence, temporarily at least, the selection of material to be studied.

Then, too, there is the world environment of children which must be taken into account. The air age, the atomic age, the space age—the modern scientific world in general—demand to be understood if men and women are to become intelligent citizens in this world.

The selection of material in the elementary school should—in fact, must—be decided partly on the basis of a twelve-year program. Changes in the junior and senior high school program must be taken into consideration in formulating the program in the earlier years. We must keep in mind that school does not stop at the end of grade six, even though we in the elementary school sometimes act as though it did. It does not start at grade seven either, as some junior high school teachers seem to suppose. If there is a science program in grades seven, eight, and nine, the planning in the elementary grades must indeed consider this. Otherwise, pupils in grade seven are sure to say (and there is reason for it), "Aw, we *had* weather in the sixth grade." We shall touch on this problem again.

Subject matter content of the other elementary school subjects, notably social studies, may also influence the content of science. While these two areas are distinctly different disciplines, they do have relationships. In some instances they relate closely. In others they should exist independently. Further discussion of the relationship of these areas will be found in the next section.

In summary, let us say that selection of subject material should certainly be made on the basis of the objectives we wish to attain, on what we know about the children, on world and local conditions and trends, on the content of the various sciences, and on the total twelve-year school sequence.

ORGANIZING THE MATERIAL OF INSTRUCTION

We have considered some of the criteria for selecting subject matter in learning science. How shall this great body of subject matter be organized for study? Again there are several factors to be considered, and again we ought first to examine the objectives. If we are to bring about the comprehension of broad concepts in science, help pupils grow in ability to use the process of inquiry, and accomplish our other objectives, we must make definite provision in the program to include sufficiently challenging and appropriate material. If we are to satisfy children's curiosity and broaden their interests, they themselves should have some voice in how, when, and where the science experiences shall come.

Can the material be built and organized entirely around the questions children ask, the things they bring in, or other incidental happenings? Experience would cause us to answer "no" to this question. Incidental science is likely to be inadequate and disorganized.

Scarcely anyone believes that an adequate social studies program can be built around incidental experiences. We do not, for example, wait until fire breaks out in the neighborhood to decide to study "community helpers," i.e., the fire department, the postman, etc. Nor do we usually decide on a study of pioneer life because someone happens to bring in a candle mold. These topics are considered by many educators important enough to include in an elementary school social studies program, and consequently we include them. An *organized* program is considered essential for elementary school social studies. The same reasons make an *organized science program* likewise essential.

Experience indicates, certainly, that some of our best teaching sometimes results when incidental problems are raised because of some local happening, some current reading, or by way of science material that children bring in. However, a well-rounded program in line with our objectives cannot be achieved *only* through incidental teaching. Nor can a good program be built if we *ignore* these incidental learning situations. How, then, can we allow for them and still have an organized program?

Many schools have solved this problem of organization, in part at least, through including two types of experiences in their programs and through operating within a general framework that is flexible. Each grade and each grouping of grades (i.e., kindergarten and grades one, two, and three; grades four, five, and six; and grades seven and eight—depending on the general school organization) includes time for incidental learning as well as for planned experiences.

Incidental learning may, for example, include short discussions on sea shells brought to class by a pupil who has just returned from a beach trip, or it may center around a new type of airplane illustrated and discussed in a current newspaper, or around a recent or anticipated eclipse. Sometimes, after the short initial discussion, an "investigation committee" studies the problem further and brings a report to the class, finds reading material for interested pupils, or arranges an exhibit of pictures on the bulletin board. If the incidental experience turns out to be of much more than passing interest, the schedule must be flexible enough to permit a shift in plans. In many instances, with careful planning by teachers and pupils, this experience may result in attaining many of the same objectives as the planned experience might have; frequently the incidental experience can be geared into the planned experience.

The so-called "incidental" interests of children cannot be ignored, for if they are we may miss some excellent learning opportunities. Neither can they form the chief basis for our courses. If they do, we leave out valuable material and have a hodgepodge curriculum. The sample problems for primary and intermediate grades included in the outline that follows illustrate the necessity for organizing learning into a sequence of planned experiences.

According to the *Forty-Sixth Yearbook*,[2] an important work that, even though issued some time ago, still gives us excellent guidance, indicates that children should at the

---

[2] National Society for the Study of Education, "Science Education in American Schools," *Forty-Sixth Yearbook*, Part I. (Chicago, University of Chicago Press, 1947), pp. 75–76.

A committee of sixth-grade pupils from the Los Angeles County schools pooled theories that they learned about Mars and developed this display. The project involved reading from many sources as well as evaluation and organization.

end of each school year "have experienced growth in the broader areas of the physical and biological environment, such as the following":

> *The Universe:* Study of the stars, the sun, the moon, the planets and their interrelationships; the causes of day and night, seasonal changes, tides, eclipses; and (less completely) the vastness of the Milky Way and of galactic systems beyond our own.
>
> SAMPLE PROBLEMS
> | | |
> |---|---|
> | Primary | How does the sun help us? |
> | | What can we see in the sky at night? |
> | Intermediate | What is the solar system like? |
> | | How do the movements of the earth affect us? |

> *The Earth:* Origin, formation of mountains, weathering of rock into soil, erosion, volcanism, prehistoric life, and the forces that are changing and have changed the earth.
>
> SAMPLE PROBLEMS
> | | |
> |---|---|
> | Primary | What was life like long ago? |
> | | What is the outside of the earth like? |
> | Intermediate | How does the earth's surface change? |
> | | How has life on the earth changed through the ages? |

> *Conditions Necessary to Life:* What living things need in order to exist, how they are affected by changes in the environment and the struggle for existence.
>
> SAMPLE PROBLEMS
> | | |
> |---|---|
> | Primary | What do plants need so that they can grow? |
> | | What do animals need so that they can grow? |

Intermediate   How do living things change as the seasons change?

What are living things like on different parts of the earth?

Living Things: Variety, social life, adaptations for protection, life cycles of plants and animals, how they obtain food, their economic importance, and man's influence upon nature.

SAMPLE PROBLEMS

Primary   How are plants and animals useful to us?

How do animals and plants change as they grow?

Intermediate   How are plants and animals fitted to live in different places?

How does man take care of plants and animals?

Physical and Chemical Phenomena: Common chemical and physical phenomena such as light, sound, gravity, magnetism, and electricity; changes in matter; and phenomena associated with radiant energy and atmospheric changes.

SAMPLE PROBLEMS

Primary   What can magnets do?

How do we use electricity?

Intermediate   How do chemical changes help us?

What makes weather change?

Man's Attempt to Control His Environment: In gardens, on farms, in orchards; inventions and discoveries; use of power and of minerals; his control over living things; his study of places he cannot reach directly; and other such topics.

SAMPLE PROBLEMS

Primary   How can we make a good garden?

What things do we use from the earth?

Intermediate   How are inventions and discoveries made?

How do we use different kinds of energy?

An outline of this kind points the way to both the selection and organization of content material. An analysis of some of the better-known courses of study (see the bibliography) or the more recent widely used textbooks will indicate how experiences in these six groups have been organized. Investigation shows that there is no great uniformity as yet in the selection of material in courses of study and basic textbooks for specific grades. Although they may disagree in specifics, they generally agree in total content to be covered by the end of the elementary school.

Now to be more specific let us select "the universe," our first broad area, to see how subject matter may be assigned to grades in order to give continuity to our planned program. Each of the problems suggested in our outline may be the basis for organizing a unit of work. Remember, however, that our program will leave room for "incidental experiences" also.

In the primary grades (kindergarten and grades one, two, and three), pupils will have many and varied experiences with measuring lengths of shadows, watching the changes of seasons and their effect on living things, observing the moon or the Big Dipper and reporting what they have seen, and noticing the varying lengths of days and nights. An especially appropriate problem for this level might be: "How is the sun important to us?" Pupils may, in this connection, come to know that: The sun is very hot. The sun is very large. It looks small because it is so far away. The sun keeps us warm. It helps plants to grow. It helps to make us healthy. The earth travels around the sun.[3]

In the intermediate grades (four, five, and six) pupils may spend some time studying details about the sun's family—the solar system. They will add to their knowledge about the sun and the other members of the solar system. Their experiences will build on those of the earlier grades. If, for example, they study the solar system, they will learn details about the planets, gravity, comets, meteors, meteorites, and the moon.[4] They will discuss causes of day and night and observe the seasons change, and learn about the eclipses.

In the upper grades (seven and eight) the picture enlarges, and pupils study the relationship between the solar system and the universe; learn cause of seasons and tides; study stars, their distances, size, composition; study the Milky Way and other galaxies; learn about novae, nebulae, and whether or not there are other solar systems.[5] Here again these experiences enlarge on those developed in earlier grades and expand to include new material.

It is apparent that each time an area of science (in this case the universe) is encountered, the new work should build on that previously experienced, add to it, and increase in difficulty. That is, the generalizations become somewhat more complex as the pupils progress. There is only enough repetition to make a connection; not enough to cause pupils to lose interest. The same over-all objectives hold for all levels. On each level pupils should be left with the idea that there is still more interesting material to learn—indeed, that there are still things that scientists themselves have not discovered. And we who teach hope that we teach so well that pupils will *want* to learn more.

We have indicated briefly a possible organization of subject matter to bring about understanding of principles and generalizations. We have said little about organization to achieve the other objectives of science teaching. But we assume that if the program is effective, no matter what organization of subject matter is followed, there will be continuous emphasis on growth in problem-solving, in development of scientific attitude, and in interest and appreciation. We assume this, however, only if the program that we develop is effective—that is to say again, if we *intend* to provide experience that will produce development in these objectives.

How we find time for science depends, of course, on our philosophy regarding it and its potentialities. An increasing number of schools consider it as a separate subject. They include science periods in the week's schedule. Some schools with differing ideas fuse it with social studies and plan a large block of time to include it along with social studies, language arts, and other learning experiences. Some schools still teach science only incidentally; these schools generally have inadequate programs. The length of class hours and the number of hours per week vary in schools.

There is general agreement that science is an essential part of any effective elementary program and time must be allocated for it. Science often seems to fuse naturally with other learnings; yet often it stands more or less by itself. Let us examine briefly the implications involved.

If you review our original statement of objectives, you will recall that we discussed the relationship of science to the total school program and indicated that it contributed in

---

[3] G. O. Blough and I. De Pencier, *How the Sun Helps Us* (New York, Harper & Row, 1958), 36 pp.

[4] B. M. Parker, *The Sun and Its Family* (New York, Harper & Row, 1958), 36 pp.

[5] B. M. Parker, *Beyond the Solar System* (New York, Harper & Row, 1960), 36 pp.

many ways to the achievement of our over-all goals. For this reason it is often considered to relate to the other curriculum subjects, especially social studies.[6]

As we have indicated earlier, sometimes these subject matter areas need each other. Sometimes they do not. How can we tell? One clue comes when we examine our over-all objectives for teaching a unit of work or pursuing an area of study. If, in order to achieve our objectives, we need subject matter from both social studies and science, we put them together. If we do not, we do not. To do otherwise may well distort the aims, pull in inappropriate subject matter from both areas and result in mishmash.

An example of sensible fusion occurs when pupils work on such a problem as: "What are the important conservation problems in our state and how can they be solved?" This over-all problem may break down into others such as: "Why did the rains last spring do so much damage in our community?" "Why must we conserve our water supply and how can we do it?" In solving this problem and the related ones, we consider soil, water, wild life, mineral resources, and human resources. Here we need a considerable amount of science information in order to understand: the formation and composition of soils, the action of wind and water on soil and other materials, the interdependence of animal and plant life, and many other science topics. But these cannot be fully comprehended without a study of modern man's relation to them and his responsibility toward them. Each learner must see his own relationship to the problem and must see how his actions relate to those of other persons. The scientific and social aspects of the problem of conservation are closely related. If we are to achieve the goals for a study of conservation we need the information, skills, and attitudes offered by both subject matter areas. It makes sense to combine them. There are other such situations.

There are also many situations in which these two subjects areas do not fuse easily. In these cases we cannot accomplish the objectives of either if we insist on considering both areas together. For example, in a study of the westward expansion in social studies, the fact that the progress of peoples to the west in our early history was hampered by bad weather conditions is hardly a legitimate reason for dabbling in a study of weather when this study is under consideration. To do so gets off the track of the west, and the small study of weather pulled in will be inadequate to answer children's real concerns about this interesting part of their surroundings. Weather is a great influence in the lives of girls and boys. They are interested in how it is caused, how it changes and how these changes can be forecast. The westward movement is an important part of the history of our country. But the two do not need each other in order to achieve the objectives set up for the study of either one. Forcing them together damages them both.

An astronomy unit is an example of a science unit that needs no or very little social studies to achieve its objectives. The outline of problems as presented on this subject in the previous section stands on its own.

One important aspect of the fusion of science and social studies lies in the consideration of the total objectives for both of them. In both areas we are concerned with the development of problem-solving and the fostering of social and scientific attitudes. Here there is a real relationship. Our problem-solving methods in both areas are similar; they reinforce each other. The development of scientific attitude is of concern to both areas.

Health education and science may both sometimes profit by being fused. In health education, when we are studying problems of diet and foods, for example, the "horse sense"

---

[6] National Council for the Social Studies Twenty-Seventh Yearbook, *Science and The Social Studies*, 1956–1957, "Science and Social Studies in Today's Elementary School," pp. 186–199.

of eating certain foods in proper amounts will be more obvious if we treat some of the aspects of diet as more or less pure science. When pupils learn that their growing bones have the chemical elements of calcium and phosphorus in them, they understand more readily the importance of drinking milk which contains both of these elements. It is in such places as this that science and other areas, if they are considered together, benefit one another and increase their contributions to children's learning.

In solving problems in science, it is often essential that pupils use the skills of the language arts. Here again is an opportunity for fusion. If it seems necessary and desirable to read, we read. If writing and speaking are useful, we use them. If it becomes necessary to use art skills, we do so readily, but we must be careful not to drag in art or any other area merely for the sake of saying that we have "integration."

One very easy way to kill interest in science is to require pupils to do unnecessary writing as a result of their study. The idea of writing up in detail each experiment performed, as we have said previously, is guaranteed to dampen enthusiasm for science. So too is adding technical science vocabulary to the spelling list. Some science words commonly used may be learned through use and reading context but at age eight or ten it is hardly important to demand that children learn to spell such a word as photosynthesis. Some of the activities described in the B chapters in the later sections of this book give specific examples of integrating some other study areas with the study of science problems.

BEGINNING TO TEACH

The teacher who says, "I'm *just* a member of my group, I never know quite what's going to happen in my room," should split up her pay check with her children. Any teacher worth being called one is more than a member of her group. She is a leader. This does not

Three Cleveland, Ohio, pupils are testing their homemade airplanes in a fan-made air stream. As a result of building these models and then adjusting them, they will understand better how the control surfaces of an airplane affect its flight. A trip to an airport to see real planes will now be more meaningful.

mean that she makes all of the decisions. But she guides. She plans beforehand. She outlines general directions. She knows the possibilities. In this picture there are still opportunities for children to make decisions—of the kind they are capable of making—to plan within the frame.

There are certain first steps which the teacher will make in planning. Let us suppose that we want to teach, in third or fourth grade, some concepts about evaporation and condensation. There are several things the teacher should do in order to prepare herself adequately. If she needs it she should, first of all, read subject matter material on the grade level as well as material on a more advanced level. If she is inexperienced, she may well perform a few of the simple experiments suggested and investigate some of the local resources available (for example, the weather bureau). In short, she should do some of the things suggested in chapter 9B. She may also investigate possible other sources of information—books, audio-visual aids, maps, bulletins. Then she may set down quite carefully, but simply, the specific aims that this experience with the phenomena of evaporation and condensation might achieve. In so doing, the teacher will keep in mind the general and specific objectives of her total elementary school program as well as the general objectives for teaching science in the elementary school. The aims for this unit might be something like these:

1. To provide experiences that will help pupils formulate simple science principles and generalizations about evaporation and condensation of water.
2. To help pupils apply these principles and generalizations in interpreting events that happen around them.
3. To provide opportunity for using a scientific attitude and for using skills in problem-solving.
4. To broaden children's interests in the everyday phenomena in their environment.
5. To give opportunity for growth in social adjustment.

Now the teacher has committed herself. She has pledged herself to use these aims as a guide in determining everything that is to be done from now on. Unless she takes her aims seriously she is wasting time.

Remembering that one of our objectives is to emphasize science principles rather than to accumulate isolated, unimportant facts, let us think through what this subject matter might include. The reading the teacher has done, the course of study if there is one, and the textbooks will be a general guide to the possible scope of the unit. She may make this list of important ideas as she reads to gain the necessary subject matter background, or she may find such a basic list in teachers' guides to textbooks. In the study of evaporation and condensation, the following are examples of the subject matter concepts that might be used as an outline:

When water evaporates, it changes to water vapor.
Water evaporates into the air from many places.
When water vapor changes back into water, we say it condenses.
Water vapor often condenses on cold things.
Water vapor may condense to make dew.
Dew evaporates.
Water vapor may come out of the air as frost on freezing cold surfaces.
Frost melts into water when warmed.

Rain comes from clouds.

Some clouds are made of many tiny drops of water; some are made of tiny crystals of ice.

Some of the rain water evaporates; some of it goes into the ground.

There are many kinds of clouds.

Snowflakes are made of ice crystals.

Snow melts into water when warmed.

Wind makes water evaporate more rapidly.

Until now the teacher is building her own background so that she will have more confidence—so that she will have a clearer direction of how the study might proceed. *This does not mean that she herself does all of the planning in advance.* She is getting ready so that she can do a more intelligent job of guiding the pupils when they begin to work.

Having become somewhat familiar with the possibilities, the teacher is now ready to begin working and planning with the pupils. Open-mindedness is a prerequisite to successful planning with children. Unless the teacher sincerely wants suggestions to come from the pupils and is prepared to work with pupils in evaluating their suggestions and then proceeding with them, she should not ask for them. Pupils, when they are convinced of the sincerity of the teacher, are full of suggestions. But they seldom become convinced when the teacher asks for their ideas and then ignores them.

For purposes of illustration, our subject matter has already been selected, and the teacher needs to think of ideas for launching it—for making it interesting, real, concrete, vital, and enjoyable—of raising some perplexities that will result in problems and questions. Where can we begin? Well, the water level in the schoolroom aquarium keeps getting lower so that every week the water needs to be replenished. Pupils have been curious about this. Water colors in the paint boxes dry up as they are being used and more water must be added. Why? Wet clothes are hung near heat to help them dry. It rains, the sun comes out, the grass gets dry, and pupils can then go out to play. These are everyday happenings involving evaporation. Children see them and are curious about them. If they have not noticed them, the teacher draws their attention to some of them and suggests that they observe others; they are all possible starting places.

Suppose we use the aquarium as a starting point. Since pupils have noticed that the water is disappearing, the question arises: "Where do you suppose the water goes?" Pupils offer their explanations: "The aquarium leaks," or "The water goes into the air," or "The fish drink it." These are some of their theories. "Have you seen other places where water disappears like this?" the teacher asks. Pupils list a number of places. "Where do you think the water is going?" she asks. Pupils suggest places. "Sometimes water disappears quickly, sometimes slowly. Why do you suppose this happens?" Pupils offer explanations. Through such a preliminary discussion as this, pupils raise problems, and interest is aroused; a readiness for the study is coming about. This preliminary experience is essential if we are to establish problems of any consequence that represent concerns of children and are worth answering. The questions that arise are listed for answering. Some of them may be: "What happens to the water when it disappears?" "Why can't we see it then?" "Why does it disappear?" "Could we keep it from disappearing?" "Can we get it back again?" "How can we make it disappear faster?" The teacher may add some of her own questions if she finds that the children's questions omit some of the important ideas. This, as has been previously pointed out, is important. Other questions and problems will be added as the study goes on.

Experiments help to solve problems. Here, Winnetka, Illinois, public school pupils are using a simple vacuum-pressure stirrup-type hand pump to inflate a balloon which they will use in learning the properties of a gas.

"Now, how do you suppose we can find the answers?" the teacher asks. Suggestions from the pupils are important here. We want them to learn ways to solve their own problems and then to use these ways so that they will arrive at reliable conclusions. The pupils suggest reading, experimenting, asking questions, watching things, and other methods.

"What shall we do first?" Pupils make suggestions. The questions may be arranged by the teacher and children in some order that seems logical for answering. Then they begin with question one and decide which of their ways to find the answer will be appropriate. The whole group may work on the same problem, or, if it seems appropriate (depending on the age of the children, their experience at group work, etc.), pupils may work in groups, each group working on a different problem. Everyone assumes some responsibility for finding printed material, experiments, apparatus, and other learning materials. A special library committee, working with the teacher, may search for books. These sources will suggest various experiments and activities. Suggestions have already been made for use of reading material, for experimenting, and for observing. These suggestions are kept in mind as the study proceeds.

In performing experiments, as in all other activities, it is essential to keep them geared to the purposes for teaching the unit. For example, we want to help pupils grow in the use of a scientific attitude. We say, "Don't let pupils jump to conclusions, and be sure to use a control whenever possible in performing experiments." Let us illustrate. In this unit, one of the problems may be: "Why do clothes on the line dry faster on a windy day?" To solve this problem, pupils may perform the experiment of putting a wet spot on the chalkboard and fanning it vigorously with a piece of cardboard. The spot will, of course, soon disappear.

Pupils will conclude immediately that the wind made by fanning caused the water to evaporate faster. But they should not conclude that. As a small, alert boy once said under such circumstances, "I can't remember how big that spot was to begin with." So the question arises, "How can we arrange our experiment so that we can be sure that wind is helping the water evaporate faster?" "Put two spots on the chalkboard, fan one, and don't fan the other," someone suggests. Now you are getting on the track. So two spots are made near each other and one fanned. Someone says, "Some of the fanning is getting on both spots." "What shall we do?" someone asks. "Put the spots farther apart," another pupil suggests. This is done, but one of the spots is small, the other large. "There's still something wrong with the experiment," someone says. "What is it?" "The spots must be just alike or we can't decide that the wind is helping." The experiment is tried again—this time with two spots as nearly alike as possible and sufficiently far apart. This time the pupils are willing to decide that the experiment helps them to see that wind aids in evaporation of water. But they must be sure to have more experiences and make further observations before they decide definitely.

When we work with high school and college students, we urge them to use a *control* in performing an experiment to make the results more valid. In the case of the wet spots on the chalkboard, the spot that was not fanned was the control. In the elementary school we usually do not use the word control; instead we urge pupils to "Do your experiment so carefully that you can be sure about what happens." Children will be urged to repeat experiments. Children themselves will caution each other about nonscientific procedures in experimenting if they get in the habit of experimenting cautiously.

Through this method of keeping careful check on how their conclusions are drawn, children gradually come to be more accurate in their observations and reporting—an objective to be highly desired.

But, as we have said earlier, experiments help us to solve problems, and their further application helps us to interpret situations in our environment. Consequently, after this experience with the wind on the wet spots the teacher may say, "Now, have you ever seen other situations where wind helps evaporation?" The teacher has in mind blowing on ink to make it dry when she has no blotter; hair driers; and the like. The pupils suggest situations such as these, and they are compared with what happened in the experiment.

Teachers frequently express concern over their ability to plan individual science lessons. While there are many different ways to plan science lessons, all acceptable plans have the same general structure. A good plan for science lessons is clear in its statement of objectives to be realized and problems to be solved; indicates an approach designed to create interest and arouse curiosity; lists the materials to be used (printed, visual, and physical material to be used for observation and experimenting); allows for planning by pupils and teachers but indicates the general direction of procedure; provides for continuity to the next lesson and may indicate some outside observation or "research"; indicates possibilities to compensate for individual differences; and is flexible enough to take into account the unexpected. A rereading of the description of the lesson on evaporation will illustrate some of these points.

As the study proceeds, textbook and other informational sources will be used as they are needed. If a trip seems necessary, the pupils may visit the local weather station. They may see a motion picture that explains the cause of evaporation and condensation.

It is essential that the teacher keep referring to the generalizations originally assembled by her if the children's experiences are to lead toward an understanding of them. The pupils will not immediately connect the disappearance and reappearance of water with the concept of what causes rain, snow, and other weather forms. This connection will come to them as their study progresses. Since the teacher has previously assembled these core ideas, she can help to direct the activities so as to include the broader aspects of the problem.

If there is sufficient interest in the study, the pupils may want to plan a culminating activity. This may be done in many ways. Again it is important for pupils to plan—with the guidance of the teacher. They may wish to show the results of their work to another grade, to their parents, or at a school assembly. For this purpose they may plan, perform, and explain a series of easy experiments; plan and draw a series of large pictures that show the important ideas they have learned; or write stories to illustrate the generalizations they have discovered. Here is an example of writing, speaking and listening as necessary activities in science. Here also is a great opportunity to waste time by getting bogged down with aimless activity of constructing things that are of no use to anyone. Keep both eyes on the objectives, and do not get carried away with yards of brown paper, papier-mâché, and cardboard boxes. Much of this has nothing to do with purposeful review.

The foregoing is an illustration of long-range planning. It may take several weeks to complete the study depending on the number and length of class meetings. Day-by-day lesson planning is also essential. See page 66 for discussion of such planning.

In the foregoing discussion and elsewhere in this book, a problem approach in science teaching has been used—children plan and do things in order to find the answers to problems that have arisen. So-called units of study in science are perhaps most effective if they follow—in a general way, at least—the procedure of letting pupils raise problems, organize the problems, suggest ways of answering them, and then carry out their plans. As this procedure and the illustration given here show, the process of teaching science is in many ways similar to the methods used in teaching any other subject. As this point becomes increasingly apparent as teachers work with children in science, the teaching of science will become increasingly effective. Even though science has unique contributions to make to the development of children, the methods of teaching the subject have much in common with those of other subjects.

The best science teaching is not necessarily done by persons who can answer all the questions that children ask, or, to speak more realistically, by teachers who have extensive backgrounds in science subject matter. The best teaching of science is often done by classroom teachers who understand children, know how to work with them, and are willing to increase their science backgrounds through study and activity. These teachers will still need sometimes to say, "I don't know the answer to that but I can help you find out." They know enough science to point the way, to lead into worthwhile areas of study, and to organize for learning.

STUDYING CHILDREN

An unsuccessful farmer was once encouraged by his well-meaning neighbors to see the County Agriculture Agent for more "know-how" about farming. After a bit of reflection the farmer said, "I don't farm as well as I know how now." It is so with teaching. There is much that we know about children and learning that we do not use to best advantage. Some things we know from experience with children; research has indicated some of them; and some seem obvious when we use our common sense. The following are taken from a discussion by Dr. Ralph Preston in Part I of the *Forty-Sixth Yearbook* of the National Society for the Study of Education. Some of them we have already briefly touched on.

Children are making daily observations to note changes, recording these changes, and using the results to solve a problem. In so doing, they are using the methods of scientists. They are learning how to learn.

THE CHILD IS AN INVESTIGATOR

If the child is naturally an investigator, then certainly we should let him investigate. His tendency to manipulate, to try out, to see what-will-happen-if, to take apart and put back together again should be encouraged and directed into profitable channels of achievement. By all means let us try to keep this tendency alive by providing opportunity for it to grow and develop instead of holding it down so that it has completely disappeared by the time the child has passed through our elementary school. Many of our schools are so academic in their approach to science learning that children with this natural tendency to manipulate have to wait until Saturday before they can express it. We must first of all realize that this tendency of pupils is a valuable one, that we must have more purposeful *doing* in our science teaching. This means that we must provide the equipment, time, and space

A CHILD REACTS TO ALL ASPECTS OF HIS ENVIRONMENT

Interest studies seem to show, and everyone who has worked thoughtfully with children realizes, that children's questions concern all kinds of environmental objects and phenomena. Listening to and watching a good "show, share, and tell" time in an elementary school tells us that children are excited about astronomy, electricity, airplanes, space ships, and animals. Today's science must be broader than the former study of ducks and dandelions if it is to take into account what we know about children's interests.

A CHILD'S IMAGINATIVE ACTIVITIES CONTRIBUTE TO HIS GROWTH

Although science is exact and is indeed factual by nature, its discoveries are made through intelligent use of the imagination. Without the active imagination, great inventions and discoveries would scarcely have come about. There must be ample opportunity in our science experiences for the use of imagination as well as for the opportunity to see the differences between fact and fiction.

A CHILD SEEKS TO PARTICIPATE IN PLANNING AND IN CARRYING OUT HIS ACTIVITIES

In all our illustrations of concepts in this book, we try to show how children may help to plan ways of solving their problems and to continue planning as they proceed in their experimenting, reading, observing, and other activities. If we pay some attention to children's desire for participation—the importance of which is difficult to overestimate—we, as teachers, must make fewer of the planning decisions ourselves and place more and more responsibility on the children. This does not mean that the teacher is unimportant in the plans. Because she knows many things that should be considered in planning, she should not hesitate to use her knowledge when it is advisable.

A CHILD FOLLOWS HIS INDIVIDUAL PATTERN IN DEVELOPING CONCEPTS

Previously we have suggested that there is no reason to expect *all* children to arrive at an understanding of a science concept at the same time. We must evaluate, insofar as possible, on an individual basis. The fact that many different types of activities (experimenting, observing, reading, etc.) are involved in problem-solving in science makes it possible for pupils of different interests and aptitudes to participate. Nearly every pupil can find opportunity to contribute something to the solution of the problem.

THE CHILD LEARNS THROUGH DOING

If we believe that the child learns through doing, the implications for our science experiences are indeed great. Again, throughout this book we stress the importance of purposeful doing on the part of children and minimize the importance of passive listening to someone *telling* the answers.

THE CHILD LEARNS THROUGH SEEKING TO ACHIEVE HIS PURPOSES

It seems reasonable to assume that children who have a purpose to accomplish will work more profitably than those who do not. The more sense the purpose makes to children, the better. Repeatedly we have indicated the importance of studying problems the answers to which seem to make a difference to the learners.

CHAPTER 5

Problems and Questions about Teaching

In this chapter we have gathered together certain bothersome problems and questions that must be solved in order to facilitate the teaching process. These questions and problems are about the same for teachers in Newton, Massachusetts, as they are for teachers in Long Beach, California, and for first-grade teachers as for sixth-grade teachers.

Although every chapter in this book is intended to help solve some aspect of science-teaching problems, we have gathered in this chapter some of the more persistent ones, which can best be considered all at one time. Some of the problems deal with obtaining materials with which to work. Some involve the use of resources available within the community. Some concern the identification of the various specimens that children are constantly bringing to school. Others center about the organization of the science program—the planning of lessons, the selection of textbooks, and the motivation of pupils. These problems have been raised again and again by students and by in-service teachers.

WHERE CAN I GET SCIENCE MATERIALS?

As the science program has become better organized and more firmly established in our schools, the problem of selecting appropriate apparatus and material becomes more pressing. The special emphasis on science in the elementary school has resulted in the purchase of much scientific apparatus. In the zeal to provide materials, apparatus has been made available that the average classroom teacher scarcely knows which end to look into, or which is the bottom. Here are some criteria for selection and use of science apparatus for elementary schools: (1) it is purchased on the basis of what is necessary to teach the course of study; we do not order materials and then decide how we can use them; (2) it should be appropriate to the age and abilities of the children for whom it is intended; (3) some of it can be homemade, provided the making teaches children some science, as time spent making apparatus that can be easily purchased may be a waste of time; (4) children should become acquainted with scientific instruments as well as with homemade apparatus; (5) much science equipment is available from homes and elsewhere in the community. The elementary school teacher should keep all of these criteria in mind when choosing equipment to use in her science teaching.

Anything unsafe to handle should never be included as part of the equipment for use in the elementary school. Most people can do an excellent job of teaching science in the first six grades without acids, Bunsen burners, and similar things that cause many elementary teachers concern because they feel there is a safety hazard. The equipment listed below is easily obtained and quite adequate for elementary school teaching of science.

Ordering materials from scientific supply houses is hardly a job for the amateur because of the technical way in which sizes and descriptions are commonly given in scientific catalogues. Because only small quantities are required, it may be necessary for the teacher to have the order for elementary school supplies accompany the order for the high school. In this way the trained high school teacher can help with the ordering. Kits of material are available that contain the essential materials already selected and boxed ready for use.[1] Many teachers find these kits most convenient. The care and storage of these materials is discussed later in this section.

The following list of material useful in teaching science in the elementary school is organized into two parts and is divided according to science subject matter areas in which it is to be used. This list is rather comprehensive, and it is quite possible to teach well without all the items listed. How much of the material is needed depends in part upon the curriculum, the class, and other specific factors. Subsequent chapters show how the material is used in science classes.

It is important to note that many persons may assume responsibility for assembling appropriate materials for science teaching. Some is purchased, some borrowed, some gathered; the school administration, the teacher, parents, and pupils may all assist.

---

[1] Science Kit. A collection of simple equipment for performing experiments with young children. Order from Science Kit, 204 Dexter St., Tonawanda, N. Y. (There is also a Junior Science Kit available.)

Stansi Science Kit. Materials and apparatus for use in elementary school. Order from Standard Science Supply Company, Chicago, Illinois.

Curriculum Materials Center. 5128 Venice Boulevard, Los Angeles 19, California. Write for catalogue.

Science Materials Center. 59 Fourth Avenue, New York 3, New York. Write for catalogue.

Science Education Products Co. 2796 Middlefield Road, Redwood City, California. Write for catalogue.

Central Scientific Company. 1700 Irving Park Road, Chicago 13, Illinois. Special elementary science apparatus catalogue.

Available from Supply Houses[2]

I.   Electricity and Magnetism

Piece of lodestone

Pair of bar magnets

Large horseshoe magnet

U magnet (Alnico if possible)

Knitting needles

Shaker of iron filings

Magnetic compass

Magnetic needle

Glass friction rod

Hard-rubber friction rod

Friction tape

Fur for rubbing friction rods

Colored pith balls for static-electricity experiments

Telephone receiver or earphone

Telephone transmitter

Dry cells 1½ volts

Insulated copper wire (No. 22 or 18)

Electric push buttons

Electric bell and buzzer

Electric lamps and sockets (small)

Knife switch

Electric motor (St. Louis type)

II.   Air and Weather

Aneroid Barometer

Glass barometer tube with well, and funnel for filling it with mercury

Mercury (3 lbs.)

Anemometer (small demonstration)

Convection apparatus

Hygrometer, Wet and Dry Bulb

Rain Gauge

III.   Sound and Light

Tuning forks of different pitch

Concave and convex mirrors

Prism

Magnifying glass, 4-in. diameter or larger

Color rotator to show the results of mixing colors

Mirrors of different sizes

Old box camera

Concave and convex lenses

Megaphone

Microscope (elementary)

Radiometer

IV.   Fire and Heat

Ball and ring apparatus to show that metals expand when heated

Compound bar to show that some metals expand more than others when heated

Apparatus to show that heat travels faster in some metals than in others

Apparatus to show that some substances conduct heat better than others

---

[2] Not all of this material is strictly essential. How important various items are depends on the curriculum, the maturity level and interest of pupils, and other factors.

For further information about apparatus, see Albert Piltz, *Science Equipment and Material for Elementary Schools*, Office of Education Bulletin 1961, No. 28. U. S. Government Printing Office, 1961, 66 pp.

V. MACHINES
Pulleys (single and double)
Spring balance—capacity 25 lbs.

VI. GENERAL SUPPLIES AND APPARATUS
Canned heat (as a source for heat if hot plate or alcohol lamp is not used)
Iron ring stand, large size
Clamp for ring stand
Iron ring with clamp for fastening on ring stand
Wire gauze with asbestos center for placing over rings or tripod
Iron tripod
Forceps for handling heated objects and chemicals
Tongs for lifting heated objects
Iron spoon for heat and chemical work
Alcohol burner or Bunsen burner (Bunsen burners usable only with gas)
Alcohol for burner
Rubber tubing for Bunsen burner, ¼-in. inside diameter (needed only if you have gas), 4 feet
Rubber stoppers, solid, 1- and 2-hole, assorted sizes, Nos. 2–6
Cork, bag of assorted sizes, Nos. 12–26
Corks, bag of assorted sizes, Nos. 0–11
Test tubes, 6″ X ¾″
Test-tube holders
Test-tube brush
Test-tube rack; holds 12 tubes
Glass tubing, 6-mm. outside diameter (5 lbs.)
Rubber or plastic tubing to fit glass tubing, ³⁄₁₆-in. inside diameter
Thistle tube
Triangle file (to cut glass tubing)
Pyrex flask, 1-pint size
Battery jars, small and large
Glass funnel, 100-mm. top diameter
Glass graduate, 100-cc. capacity
Thermometer, Centigrade –10° to 110° and Fahrenheit 0° to 220° (indoor-outdoor)
Pyrex beakers—assorted sizes
Powdered iron
Petri dishes (for growth of bacteria)
Litmus paper
Asbestos mats
Plaster of Paris
Iodine
Rubber plunger
Tweezers

The following list of materials is composed of items available from local sources (home, ten-cent store, drug store, etc.). Some items, such as the kitchen tools and musical instruments, will, of course, be used for only a short period of time and returned; others will become a part of the permanent equipment of the science room.

OBTAINABLE FROM LOCAL SOURCES

I. LIVING THINGS

An aquarium (stocked with fish, snails, water plants, etc.)
A terrarium (stocked with growing plants, etc.)—a suitable place to keep a
    small turtle, a frog, a salamander, or a small snake
Larvae of different kinds
Cocoons and chrysalises
Seeds (bean, corn, etc.)
Growing plants (geranium, ivy, begonia, bulbs, cactus, etc.)
An ant observation house

II. GLASSWARE

Fruit jars

Milk bottles

Glass tumblers and jars

Lamp chimneys

Cups and saucers

Pieces of window glass which may be cut
    into small pieces

III. MISCELLANEOUS

Safety matches

Scissors

Teaspoons and tablespoons

Rubber bands

Ball of string

Iron bolt or large nail for making
    electro-magnet

Scraps of different kinds of metal
    (zinc, aluminum, copper, etc.)

Worn-out dry cell

Electric appliances out of repair
    —i.e., extension cord, hot pad,
    etc. (for examination)

Bags, paper, and cellophane

Boxes, wooden and cardboard,
    assorted sizes, for storage and
    other uses

Flower pots (various sizes)

Small mirrors

Mechanical toys illustrating ma-
    chine principles

Pans of various shapes and sizes

Paring knife and table knife

Colored chalk

Blotters

Balls

Wire—steel and copper

Flashlight

Thread

Scraps of different kinds of cloth
    (silk, wool, cotton, etc.)

Burned-out light fuses of various kinds

Burned-out light bulbs (not fluores-
    cent lights)

Worn-out electric motors

Candles of various lengths

Sand, clay, loam, humus

Globe and map of the world

Medicine dropper

Hot plate

Needles for making a compass

Tack puller

Tongs or forceps for holding heated
    objects

Egg beater

Rubber balloons

Cellophane (clear and colored)

Pet cages

Yardstick

Chalk boxes

Nutcracker

Wedges

Broken thermometer (to be examined)

Musical instruments of various kinds

Gummed labels

Dowels, assorted diameters

Plates, assorted sizes

Steel wool

Cement, building and rubber

IV. CONSTRUCTION MATERIALS

    Nails, tacks, screws
    Paints and varnishes
    Hammer, pliers, file, screwdriver, and other common tools
    Glue and paste
    Tin shears
    Paints, oil, water color, show card
    Sandpaper, assorted

V. CHEMICALS

Soda	Limewater	Table salt	Iodine (mark poison)
Starch	(drugstore)	Paraffin	Dyes
Sugar	Red ink	Ammonia	Powdered sulfur
	Vinegar	(household)	
		(mark poison)	

VI. COLLECTIONS

Seeds and fruits   Birds' nests (collected in autumn)
Leaves   Local rocks, minerals, fossils
Shells and other sea life   Science pictures of various kinds
                            Insects

There is a place for everything and a record to tell where it is when it's out of place. Under the guidance of a teacher, children take charge of this central storage room where science materials are checked in and out.

HOW CAN I TAKE CARE OF THE MATERIALS?

Organizing and taking care of science material is a problem that involves both teachers who use the materials and principals who must keep track of the inventory. To be useful, material must be near at hand and organized so that it is easy to locate. Materials that are used frequently should be in the classroom if there is space available for it. Material that is used only infrequently and materials that are shared by the whole school should be kept in central storage with a convenient check-out system so that materials can always be located. An elementary teacher with some interest and background in science may assume responsibility along with the school principal for the initial organizing and assembling of the material, and then under the teacher's supervision a committee of pupils may be of considerable assistance in dispensing and checking in material.

In some instances, specially designed cabinets have been built and placed on casters for use in rooms where no experimenting space is available. Some schools have made tables from old kitchen cabinets and covered the top surface with varnished linoleum. Acidproofing is not necessary, since acid is not commonly used in the elementary school. The drawer space of the cabinets is used for storing equipment.[3]

WHAT COMMUNITY RESOURCES ARE AVAILABLE?

Especially in science there is much material in the immediate surroundings that is very useful. But where is it? How do we get it to school? What are some of the kinds of materials that are appropriate? It is amazing how many magnets, magnifying glasses, garden seeds, insect specimens, musical instruments, and similar materials girls and boys can contribute if they are urged to do so.

These are only a few of the resources that are available in the community for use in science instruction. There are countless places to visit, people to enlist, and other resources to use if we begin to look for them and if we challenge pupils to suggest them and help provide them.

We sometimes give the impression in all our school work that what we are studying happens only in faraway places. A great many of the things children study in science can be observed within a mile or two of where they are studying. To carry this a step farther, almost everything described in the activity or B chapters of this book can be seen if you look around the room where you are sitting, go outside and walk a mile or so and keep watching, look into a modern house or a store, or observe a farm. In addition to the suggestions given here, there are many others given in the section called "Discovering for Yourself" at the end of each A chapter and in the section called "Resources to Investigate" at the end of each B chapter.

THE SCHOOL

It is important for pupils to discover that there is a wealth of scientific material in the school, not only because it is useful in making ideas clearer to the pupils but also because

---

[3] For further discussion of materials and equipment, see G. O. Blough and M. H. Campbell, *Making and Using Classroom Science Materials in the Elementary School* (New York, Holt, Rinehart and Winston, 1954), 229 pp.

seeing science at work in their own environment helps pupils to realize how *real* science is. Note the following examples.

Pupils are learning how heat travels and how heating systems function (chapter 18B). The book diagrams are helpful. Experiments are important. Reading is necessary too. But heat is traveling into their schoolroom from somewhere—from a furnace in another building, from one in the basement of the building where the pupils are studying, or from a stove in the classroom itself. Why not investigate? The school custodian will help. Take a trip to the furnace room, look into the furnace, trace the pipes to the room, discover how the air currents travel in the room. These and similar activities bring reality to the project.

Pupils are studying electricity (chapter 21B). They learn about fuses, lights, conductors, insulators, switches, and meters. If the school uses electricity, all these things are easily observed. Again, the school custodian knows where the fuse box is, can change a fuse, and knows where the meter is, how the switches operate, and many other things. Actually seeing these things helps to get the phenomena of electricity out of the book and into the realm of the child's understanding and seeing.

Pupils are studying chemical changes (chapter 16B). They observe the process of rusting and of burning (furnace), note the various products of chemical change (window glass, paper, etc.) in the schoolroom, examine the fire extinguisher to see how it operates by means of a chemical change, and observe how undesirable chemical changes are controlled and desirable ones encouraged.

Examples of other science material abound. Do not overlook thermostats, electric bells, pulleys and other simple machines, light fixtures, pianos and other musical instruments, plants, pressure cookers in the school cafeteria, school radios, telephones, aquariums. The list of materials is nearly endless.

AROUND THE SCHOOL

Do not forget to look out of the schoolroom window. The schoolyard, too, is teeming with science material, and much of it will be very useful in your classes.

For example, the class is studying the effects of erosion on land forms. A heavy rain falls. A trip to the edge of the schoolyard reveals a temporary stream, brown as coffee, carrying away the top soil of the playground. A tumbler full of the water held to the light reveals the cause of the color. Letting the glass stand for an hour will settle the soil at the bottom of the glass. The sidewalk next to the yard is covered with soil washed from the playground. Here is a real example of erosion. A small gully is beginning to form, and the experience of having observed it and of trying to stop erosion by using appropriate means is a real beginning to understanding conservation practices.

Another example: The class is studying animals and how they live together. In the ground just outside the window, ants are busy taking care of their young, guarding the queen, feeding her, getting food, and doing the many other things the pupils have read about. Seeing ants under a magnifying glass, watching them carry food, seeing them make a tunnel, are all activities that make the study real.

Many other things wait to be discovered in the schoolyard: trees and other plants going through the annual cycle of growth and dormancy; birds, insects, and other animals; swings and seesaws, which illustrate gravity and leverage; plants with special adaptations; flowers, rocks, seed pods; dew and other forms of precipitation; fungus growths; nodules on clover roots; and examples of different kinds of soils. Exploration of these helps to bring science ideas to life and to create appreciation of them.

AT HOME

The homes of children contain many examples of the science objects and phenomena about which they study in school. Science in the home takes on new meaning when pupils can relate it to their school study. For example, the children are studying machines and how they help to do work. Modern homes contain many of the things commonly used to illustrate the principles of doing work. In the kitchen: egg beaters, can openers, knives, corkscrews, and many other tools. In the shop: hammers, saws, and chisels. In the garage: jackscrews and levers. In the basement: washing machine and lawn mower. Perhaps there are pumps, farm machinery, a windmill, pulleys for loading hay, inclined planes for loading livestock, balances for weighing, pulleys for hanging out clothes or storing hay. They are all illustrations of the science principles which children are studying.

Suppose children are learning how we use plants in our daily living. They keep an account of the different kinds of plants that are growing in their home gardens or farms. They search the kitchen cupboard for examples of spices and herbs. While learning how plants are adapted to the environment, they dig up dandelions to examine the long root system; bring various kinds of leaves to school for examination; and bring plants to school that show special adaptations.

Other science resources of the home include heating and lighting systems, refrigerators, pets, farm animals, methods of insect control, and fuels.

IN THE COMMUNITY

Every community is rich in resources that are indispensable to good science teaching. They include not only places to visit but persons to consult. The use of an individual as a resource person carries with it certain responsibilities for both pupils and teachers. Extending an invitation, planning for active audience participation, introducing the visitor to the group, and conducting questioning periods must all be planned for by the teacher and pupils. Careful planning is essential, too, if pupils are to receive maximum benefits from these resource persons. A list of questions may be prepared in advance to help give proper focus to the meeting. There is no reason to assume that Mr. Jones, who built his own telescope and knows more about Mars than anybody in town, can talk helpfully to a fifth grade. He may not have seen, since his own school days, so many girls and boys in one room and he may have little idea of their interests and capacities. The list of questions prepared by the class and teacher and a talk with the teacher prior to this appearance will be very helpful to him and advantageous to the pupils.

If you begin to think about it, you can make a long list of places to visit in your community that would be fruitful in terms of science experience. Your list would probably include the water purification plant, the airport, industrial plants, museums, weather bureaus, parks, radio stations, city departments, greenhouses, bird sanctuaries, and markets. Again, the value of such visits will be greatly enhanced by careful pupil-teacher planning in answering such questions as: What arrangements must be made before taking the trip? How can we make best use of our time? What things do we want to find out? How can we best organize this information? What use shall we make of the findings after the trip?

The examples we have noted of places to visit in the community are more likely to be accessible to schools in towns and cities. There are, however, many other places to visit in rural areas or in villages. Some of them are: a gravel pit or stone quarry, where rocks and fossils may be gathered and where different layers of soil may be observed; a woods, where plants and their relationship to their environment may be observed, and where conservation study may become a very real experience; a burned-over area, where the destructive effects of fire may be observed; a field, where plants may be examined, insects collected, and erosion effects noted; a new building under construction, where machines are at work, and insulation, heating equipment, electrical equipment, and similar things may be observed; a sawmill, where tools and trees may be studied, and conservation practices or the lack of them may be observed; a farm, where there are problems of raising animals and plants and where many other scientific processes go on; a garden, where scientific principles of plant growth and insect control may be observed; and an apiary, where the social life of insects may be observed.

Many teachers who are inexperienced at teaching science say, "These suggestions sound very easy to follow when they are described but I can't think of them by myself." This is to be expected, but through the use of the suggestions given in this book a habit of more careful observation of possibilities may be established. The following suggestions will also be helpful: Begin with an area of science with which you are already somewhat familiar. Make a list of the big ideas that you wish to develop (see lists at the ends of the A chapters). Use this list as a basis for exploring. Enlist the assistance of the children in your class, parents, high school students and science teachers, and others.

HOW CAN I IDENTIFY THINGS?

We continually urge children to bring things to school to use in science learning, and one of the first things children are likely to ask about a stone or an insect or some other "nature lore" is, "What is it?" Answering this question is difficult for many teachers. If you have taught in the elementary school, you can recognize yourself in the next paragraph. If you have not and are going to, you will soon come to realize what Miss Brown is up against.

What is it? There is no doubt that this insect is a praying mantis. This pupil at the Allen Creek School in Rochester, N.Y., has discovered that it looks like the picture, behaves as the description says it does, and was found where the book says they are likely to live. He is learning how to find out for himself.

"Miss Brown, this morning I saw a strange bird sitting in a tree in our back yard. It was black and white and made the funniest sound. What was it?" "Miss Brown, my brother says this rock is fool's gold. Is it?" In spring wilted specimens of flowers are brought in for identification. The children ask her what they are, and Miss Brown does not know.

It is not possible for *any* teacher of elementary school children to know the name of *every* insect, flower, plant, or rock that comes to school. There are several hundred species of birds that are likely to be seen in almost any locality of the United States. The number of kinds of insects that can be found in any specific neighborhood is stupendous. Varieties of plants in each locality number in the thousands. In fact, scientists have identified and described more than 225,000 different kinds. No wonder, then, that when children ask, "What is this?" we often honestly say, "I don't know." But let us add, "Perhaps we can find out what it is." Then we can help children learn how to find out. Now let us go back to naming an animal that Billy brings to school.

In the first place, as we said earlier, naming the thing is not an end in itself. We need to have its name because we are going to learn more about it. So perhaps we might begin by finding out, if possible, what kind (mammal, reptile, etc.—see chapters 10A and 10B) of animal it is, and in order to do this we need to look carefully at it to note its characteristics. This starts us on the road to careful observation, and as soon as we begin to observe we begin also to learn something besides merely the name. Through this careful observation pupils can usually decide whether the animal is a vertebrate or an invertebrate and, if it is a vertebrate, to which of the five groups it belongs.

But children want to know more than the group to which an animal belongs; they want to know its name. To find that out, more observing needs to be done—and it cannot be just a helter-skelter look. It is part of being "scientific" for Billy to look carefully, so that he will not say, "Miss Brown, I saw a strange bird that made a funny sound. What was it?" Here, for example, are some of the things pupils should learn to observe about a bird if they want to identify it: *its general appearance*—its size, shape, and color markings; *its head*—color, crest, and shape of beak; *its feet*—webbing and size; *its habitat*—swamp, field, buildings, or forest; *its food*—seeds, berries, worms, or insects. They are some of the things we look for with children if we take trips to observe birds; what begins as simple identification can develop into better understanding of a living animal or plant in its natural environment.

Perhaps you feel that you still could not identify many of the common birds even if you knew all of these things. That is quite understandable, since there are so many. In the bibliography, we have listed a number of inexpensive books that will help you in identification of birds and other animals. Some of them are for sale in local stores. The color in these books is not always accurate (neither is it in some of the very expensive books), but the descriptions are clear. By carefully matching your observations with these descriptions, you ought to have fair success. Again, it is good scientific practice to say, "I think" or, "From what we are able to tell" when you try to identify and you are not sure. Do not forget that often there are persons in the community—a parent, a teacher, or someone else in the neighborhood—who make a hobby of knowing the names of everything in sight. These people are very useful. So, by the way, is your local museum.

Those mustard jars with holes punched in the lids that children bring to school with an insect or two inside—katydids, moths, butterflies, crickets, fireflies, and all the rest— also present problems in identification. Again, it is more than the name that we hope will be discovered, although that may well be the starting point. As in the case of anything else you want to name, look first for identifying characteristics of the insect. Examine the legs, wings, and head. Try to learn where it was found and anything else about its habits. Here

Indianapolis, Ind., pupils have used pictures from magazines to help identify the shells in their collection. Then they have learned how these water animals are adapted to their environment: how they grow, reproduce, get food, and move. They are learning to check their information and organize their knowledge.

is opportunity to observe in order to find likenesses and differences. How are all insects alike? How do insects differ from birds? Why is a spider not an insect? Naming the insect is only a beginning. Keeping it alive, furnishing it with a home and food, observing its activities makes the insect a "teacher" who answers questions put to it by inquisitive pupils.

Specimens brought to school may provide all kinds of worthwhile experiences that lead toward achieving the objectives discussed in chapter 2. Several good books for the identification of insects are listed in the bibliography.

Plants, too, are classified according to certain characteristics.[4] Classifying them as precisely as possible helps to identify them. Finding the name of a specimen hinges on observing carefully and then seeking a book or person for further help if necessary.

Flowering plants are identified in much the same way as animals. Do not jump to conclusions. The fact that the color and general appearance of the specimen and the picture seem to match is often not sufficient evidence to decide on its name. Look carefully at the structural characteristics: *the leaves*—shape, size, how they grow from the stem; *the flower* —color, size, shape, number of parts, arrangement; *the habitat*—high or marshy, kind of soil, shady or sunny; and other distinguishing facts and characteristics.

Rocks that children bring to school are often difficult to identify. By examining their structural characteristics you may be able to determine whether rocks are igneous, sedimentary, or metamorphic (see chapter 6A). Sometimes it helps to break a rock into pieces with a hammer to see the inside and thus discover something more about its appearance and composition. A sample set of specimen rocks and minerals is very helpful for identification. Shells are also somewhat difficult to identify, but labeled collections and reference books can help.

---

[4] W. L. Beauchamp and G. O. Blough, "How Are Living Things Put in Groups?" *Science Is Experimenting* (Chicago, Scott, Foresman, 1962).

One more thing about identifying things: let us not ask everybody in the class to be able to identify twenty trees, fifteen birds, ten insects, and twenty flowers in order to pass science. This, you may recall, is one of the reasons why you may have found science a little on the dull or annoying side. It is fun to know the names of things when you are studying about them. As you use the names, they gradually begin to stick in your mind because you have used them again and again. But it is dull to sit down and learn the names of fifteen birds from pictures when you have no need to know them. If somebody likes to learn to identify things—some people do—he should not be discouraged from so doing, but let us not require everybody to do it just because it is suggested as an activity at the end of a chapter.

HOW DO I MAKE A LESSON PLAN FOR TEACHING ELEMENTARY SCIENCE?

In the previous chapter we discussed long-range planning. Another problem that bothers many teachers is how to plan individual lessons so that they will be an integral part of this long-range plan. There are many ways to make lesson plans, just as there are many ways to teach. There are many forms for recording plans. Some are formal and include details; some are very sketchy. Why do we make lesson plans? For many reasons. Some teachers make them chiefly to satisfy administrative requirements; others feel that they need some sort of outline guide to follow. Certainly, we are not likely to do good teaching without some preliminary planning. We need to think out possible ways to teach, to make some provision for materials that may be needed, and to formulate quite carefully what we hope the pupils will accomplish. But remember: *making a lesson plan does not mean that the teacher will do all of the planning and leave none for the children.* The teacher's plan will allow plenty of opportunity for children to plan together. Remember too: *when you begin to work with pupils, your plan may change entirely; it is almost certain to be somewhat modified.*

For the sake of illustrating one way to make a lesson plan, let us suppose that we are studying magnets in grade four. Pupils have thus far learned: what things magnets will attract, what things magnetism will travel through, how to make a magnet by rubbing a needle on a magnet, and the law of magnets. They have demonstrated these things by simple experiments and have read about them in their books.

At the end of the last lesson someone brought up the subject of compasses. You encouraged this, because you know that a compass is actually a free-swinging magnet; you told them about this connection. The pupils decided to make a compass. You suggested that before the next lesson pupils try to find out for themselves how to make a compass. This is not a formal assignment. It provides an opportunity for those who are interested to do some "research."

In thinking about your plan, you may proceed something like this: "I want to build on what they already know from our previous lessons, use any investigating that my pupils may have done outside of class, help them to organize their knowledge in order to solve the problem of how to make a compass, help them make a compass, and raise some new problems about compasses and their uses. My purposes are: to see that the children derive some satisfaction from their interest and curiosity, to give them an opportunity to engage in experimentation and problem-solving, to let them see that it is important to work carefully, to help them to learn about compasses, and to give them opportunity to see that they can find out for themselves."

You will probably plan to begin your lesson by letting pupils tell or show what they discovered outside of class about a compass. Naturally, you will not know in advance what ideas pupils will have. You, yourself, are prepared to produce materials (needles, dishes of water, magnets, and flat corks).

In all probability, some one will bring a small compass from home. If so, he will want to show it to the class and tell whatever he thinks he knows about it. Some of this information will be correct; some wrong. You plan to make a chalkboard record of some of the important things that are said. In all probability, pupils will challenge the accuracy of some of these statements, and part of your plan will be to help the pupils find out whether these statements are true or not. You plan to let the pupils who bring in the information tell why they think it is true. You plan to ask the pupils how they propose to check the accuracy of the statements. They will probably suggest experimenting, reading, or asking someone. Some of these things will be done during the class, some must be planned for at a later time, some will be done by committees of pupils working independently during their free time.

You can approach the making of a compass by letting a child show how he thinks one may be made with the material he has brought in, and then checking to see that it is done correctly (if the needle points north and south). If the compass does not work, pupils should be asked to give their theories about why it does not work and what should be done to correct the fault. The theories should be tested. If this does not work, pupils may go to their books to check on the method to see why. If no one has brought materials, you plan to produce the materials you have assembled, and say something like this: "Can any one use these materials to make a compass for us?" You plan to let the pupil who volunteers *tell* his plan first. In order to make sure that everyone understands the plan, you may want to write a brief outline of it on the board as he tells it. The class may add suggestions to the plan. It may then be carried out and checked.

Several compasses may be made at the same time in order to compare them and to give more pupils opportunity to learn by doing. When the compass is made (the needle is magnetized by rubbing it—one way only—on the magnet and is floated on the cork in the dish of water), you expect someone to ask "What makes the needle point north and south?" This is the problem that will undoubtedly be left for your next lesson, along with checking the accuracy of the statements on the board that have not been checked.

This, in general, is some of the thinking that may go into your plan. Look back at your intentions. Read them over. Is this plan pointed toward achieving them? Have you allowed for children to plan? Have you provided opportunity for them to think? Have they used ways of finding out for themselves? Will this kind of plan keep their interest alive? Is it a flexible plan? This, then, is an example of one way to plan one kind of science lesson. Adaptations of it will, of course, be necessary in different situations. How much of this material you write down depends on you and your situation. In all probability, you need only a brief outline of how you hope to go ahead, but you do need to sit down and think out ways to proceed—especially if you have not done much science teaching.

Several descriptions of teaching procedure in this section of the book are really examples of lesson planning procedures. Many of the B chapters contain such material for plans.

WHAT IS THE RELATIONSHIP OF ELEMENTARY SCHOOL SCIENCE TO JUNIOR AND SENIOR HIGH SCHOOL SCIENCE?

The best science programs today are being planned jointly by teachers, supervisors, and administrators who represent all grade levels. Unfortunately, we cannot say that this represents the general rule. Each year more school systems attempt K–12 planning. As junior and senior high schools revise their curricula, the elementary program must also change. When primary, intermediate, and secondary school teachers work together in deciding content and methods of working, in selecting books, and in determining ways to work, a program such as we have described in chapter 4 can result. In courses that evolve in this way, there is less likely to be disturbing overlapping or duplication of subject matter. The attitude of all teachers concerned is almost sure to be better. As teachers at different levels learn more about the work of teachers at other levels, they grow in understanding of the problems of other teachers and in ability to fit their own work into the total sequence.

We have said repeatedly that teaching the subject matter of science is but one of our aims. We also intend to help pupils become more scientific in their attitudes, more active in raising problems, more skillful at solving problems, and more interested in and appreciative of their environment. With respect to attaining these objectives, there seems little likelihood that there will be too much overlapping from grade to grade. The skills of problem-solving and the attitudes and appreciations we seek to develop come to be a part of pupils' thinking only after long exposure and many repetitions.

If we consider our total objectives and if we are willing to plan cooperatively for a continuous program, the problem of who will teach what and whether or not there is repetition largely disappears. If you are an elementary school teacher, ask yourself: "How much do I know about what is required of my pupils when they leave my grade for the next one?" "Do I know enough about the experiences my pupils have had in the years before they came to my grade?" "Do I take these things into consideration when I plan for and work with my pupils?"

HOW CAN I INTEREST EVERY CHILD IN SCIENCE?

You cannot *all* of the time. If you believe that children are individuals, and consequently differ in ability, background, interests, and many other characteristics, you do not expect *all* of them to be equally interested in any *one* topic or subject. The best a teacher can do is to make it possible for children to explore their present interests, discover new ones, and derive satisfaction from pursuing them. Above all, let us try to keep interest alive and not kill it by forcing children to go farther than their interests and abilities will carry them. It is just as important to know where and when to stop the study of a problem in science as when to start it. Remember that children will, in their later school experience, have other opportunities to study science; consequently, it is not necessary for them to exhaust the subject in the elementary school. Even if it is their last school contact with the specific material, there is still nothing to be gained by running it into the ground.

Some children in the elementary school will have a burning desire to learn, learn, and learn science. They may become our future scientists. And it is here that we have a

What materials do birds use for nest building?

How can we find out?

Interest grows through exploration. A challenging problem, a plan of work, some material to work with, and the excitement of discovery results. Birds' nests are being examined here.

special responsibility in the elementary school. While it is true that we are not trying primarily to make scientists of elementary pupils, we *are* trying to identify pupils with special interests and aptitudes and to encourage them in their talents. Many famous scientists have made their beginnings at the elementary school level. Unfortunately, too many of them have been successful in their careers in *spite* of their early teaching and not *because* of it. The most successful elementary school teachers provide opportunities for especially talented students by evidencing interest in their accomplishments, providing resources (people, places, printed material, etc.) for them, using them as special science assistants, and encouraging them in other ways.

The vast majority of our pupils will find satisfaction in science as they do in their other school subjects, with interest spurts and interest lags, depending on the specific problems being considered. Some—we hope relatively few—will have but passive interest in science, and during science work their minds will be elsewhere. It is when the minds of *most* of the pupils are elsewhere during science study that we should show real concern. It is then that we have a real problem on our hands. It is then that we should examine critically the content and the teaching techniques.

HOW CAN I SELECT BOOKS
TO USE IN SCIENCE TEACHING?

No matter how much use we make of firsthand experiences in learning science, children must still learn a great deal from textbooks, supplementary books, and other printed material, for it is not possible to learn everything by experimenting and observing. We have discussed reading as a way of learning science, but upon what bases shall we select our basic and supplementary science books? The problem of book selection in science is very much like the problem of book selection in any other field. Probably it needs more attention than it now receives. Obviously, some books serve our purpose better than others because they fulfill certain requirements. Whether the books are for use as basic science texts or as supplementary reading materials, here are some of the considerations to keep in mind in selecting them.

PHYSICAL MAKE-UP

The book should be attractive, of suitable size, and durable. The type and page format should make for readability and be pleasing to the eye. The paper should be of a good quality.

ILLUSTRATIONS

Pictures should help to teach as well as to make the book more attractive. They should, by all means, be interesting and scientifically accurate. They should be clearly produced and well placed on the page, and should be placed near the text that they illustrate. Drawings, charts, and other visual aids should be appropriate as to grade, helpful in interpreting the text, and clear in meaning.

TEXT

The text must be accurate. Even though a full explanation of a given scientific phenomenon cannot be presented, the part that is given should be correct and not misleading. "But how can I check the accuracy of a book?" you ask. "I don't know enough science." One criterion is the authorship of the book. It is usually possible to find out something about the reputation of the authors and publishers of the book. It is also possible to compare statements in a book with those of a known authority to see whether they are accurate. Remember that having checked a few facts does not permit you to conclude that the entire book or series is accurate. Remember, too, that there are almost always science teachers and others with science background who are available to lend a hand in making decisions about the accuracy of material.

Some of the books children find in their libraries are full of talking, reasoning animals. These books are used primarily for enjoyment and *not* as sources of information. This distinction, as we have indicated elsewhere, must be made very early in the child's school life and is an important one. The fact that these books are not "scientific" in their approach does not mean that we cannot use them; it merely means that we keep in mind the purpose for which they are to be used.

The writing should be appropriate to the subject matter. This means, for example, that the book should be written in accordance with its purpose. If the purpose is primarily to give interesting and appropriate information, the device of long, involved story content and conversation usually gets in the way of the child who is using the book to answer questions or solve a problem. The style should be understandable and interesting.

The organization and development of the text should, furthermore, be in accordance with a philosophy of science education. If, for example, you believe that pupils should become acquainted with certain concepts or generalizations, you will choose reading material that emphasizes them rather than presents a collection of relatively unimportant and unrelated experiences and facts. If you believe in the problem-solving approach to science teaching, then the text should be written from the problem-solving point of view, i.e., problems should be stated and the text should be developed accordingly.

The text should also fit into the general plan of the course of study, if one is being followed. The texts, supplementary books, and course of study should be geared to one another with respect to content, philosophy, and organization.

The text may well be accompanied by thought-provoking problems and activities that will stimulate further study by the reader. A usable index and table of contents is important, and there should be a glossary of science terms with clearly stated explanations of meanings and, where necessary, pronunciation helps.

The text material should be judged on the basis of its effectiveness in helping pupils reach the objectives set up for the study of science—*provided it is well used.* No matter how carefully books are prepared and chosen, if they are poorly used in the classroom, they cannot serve their intended purpose. Earlier, we discussed the use of books in science teaching; it is well to remember that the general principles we follow in using any other book with pupils also apply in using science texts and supplementary material.

WHAT SHALL I DO IF AN EXPERIMENT DOES NOT "WORK"?

Teachers are naturally concerned over the success of their experiments because they do not want to appear inadequate before their pupils. This concern is understandable but perhaps a little exaggerated, because no teachers, even those with many years of experience, can always guarantee that an experiment will always "work" just as it is supposed to. The problem becomes less acute if the experiment is set up as a let-us-try-to-find-out activity rather than on a let-us-prove-this basis. Under such circumstances every experiment works to the extent that it provides students with results which they can record and consider.

We would almost say, "Be glad of it!" when an experiment does not "work" just as expected. Many times it is only then that pupils really begin to think. Especially is this true if the teacher herself is not sure why the experiment did not quite occur as expected. Then the experiment really becomes a problem and everybody pitches in to help find out why; there is real reason for each pupil to think at his best, for he may be the one to solve the problem. Pupils, in answer to the question, "Why didn't it 'work'?" begin to give their theories. The one that seems to be the most reasonable is tried out. If it does not help, another idea is tried out. This goes on until the experiment does "work." In this way the purpose of the experiment may become much more real to many of the pupils; they may have begun to think about it carefully for the first time.

We have placed the term "work" in quotes, for in one sense every experiment is successful. Experimenting is a method of discovery. If an experiment is done to try to answer a question or solve a problem, no matter how it progresses it is still a method of discovery. In a true experiment the child (like a scientist) does not always have a preconceived notion of what is going to happen. He ponders, evaluates, and concludes on the basis of his observations. He repeats his process, controls his procedure and assembles his data. He substantiates this by other methods of discovery. In this sense every experiment "works." In the laboratory of scientists, experiments that did not "work" as expected have led to many great discoveries. To paraphrase what one scientist has said, "cherish and guard your exceptions, and look at them constantly."

HOW CAN WE TELL HOW WELL
WE ARE ACCOMPLISHING OUR INTENTIONS?

For some teachers the problem of evaluation is relatively simple, because they base the total evaluation on whether or not a pupil makes a satisfactory grade on a test that covers the subject matter studied. But our objectives for science teaching in the elementary school are much broader. The importance of testing recall of facts is somewhat questionable. As a matter of fact, these facts in themselves may be of no great concern. As we have previously said, we are really concerned with how these facts are put together into broad, meaningful concepts, with the methods by which the problems are solved, and with the attitudes, interests, and appreciations that have developed. It is these things that we want to measure when we evaluate. This makes evaluation difficult.

Most of the examinations we give children are designed to test their retention of facts. But suppose that the child can name ten trees in his neighborhood. What of it, if he goes out on Saturday and breaks the branches from a young sapling that someone has planted along the street? A child gets a "hundred" on his subject matter examination but refuses to change his mind in the face of evidence, jumps to conclusions, is prejudiced, and in general is unscientific. Has he "passed"? Have you as his teacher passed or failed? It is this part of the picture that makes evaluation in science difficult, for as yet we have very few instruments adequate to measure growth in attitudes, appreciations, ability to think and to solve problems, and similar intellectual equipment. Much research and experimentation must be done in the field of evaluation and some of this can best be done with the help of classroom teachers who will contribute their daily classroom experience.

OBSERVING CHILDREN

One way to evaluate the effectiveness of science teaching in our elementary school is to observe children—especially if we record these observations and accumulate them for the time when we are to formulate an opinion. Since these observations are made in terms of our objectives, they include incidents that show growth in ability to solve problems —i.e., contributions made by individuals during class discussion of a problem, originality and resourcefulness in doing "research" to find the answer through reading, suggestions made in setting up an experiment to solve a problem. Our observations would also include evidence of growth in scientific attitude—i.e., willingness to withhold judgment until sufficient evidence is available, questioning sources of information, willingness to change an opinion in the face of conclusive evidence, a "wait a minute" attitude toward hastily reached conclusions. There are many situations in which such attitudes are observable as children work together in science. The recording of specific incidents helps us greatly in evaluating our efforts.

Acquiring these anecdotes of behavior takes time, but the information they yield is important. Some teachers jot them down systematically and use this information in the general evaluation of the child's growth and development—another illustration of how science fits into the general program of the elementary school. Here are a few anecdotes which one teacher recorded:

J. D. Brought his chemistry set to school to demonstrate. Questions were raised which he could not answer. He acted as chairman of a group to find the answers. Exercised initiative and good leadership.

C. L. Refused to believe that a statement in reference book he was using was correct because it disagreed with something an adult friend of his had said. Class suggested way to investigate. Book was right. C. L. had good attitude about changing his mind.

F. B. Took leadership in planning trip to Museum of Science and Industry.

C. F. Has made progress in being able to get along with small groups as they work on experiments.

F. A. Has made a bird feeding station at home and frequently reports his observations to the group. Has invited the class to come to see it.

G. B. Has improved in general interest in science.

L. T. Is keeping account of weather reports for the class to test their accuracy. Voluntary.

Such records as these help teachers to prepare a meaningful survey of accomplishments on which to base an evaluation of changes in behavior of children. To be valid, records must be made over a comparatively long period of time. We must remember that in science, as elsewhere, we are trying to evaluate on an individual basis. What represents great accomplishment for one child because of his potentialities may be much less important for another.

CHILDREN CAN HELP IN EVALUATING

Children themselves should whenever possible help to evaluate the work of their group as well as their own work. There are many situations in which this is possible and many reasons why it is desirable. Such evaluation may begin by letting children themselves help to set up the standards of accomplishment for later use as criteria for evaluation. For example, some fifth-grade pupils were studying electricity. Many problems were raised, and pupils planned ways to solve them. These plans were carried out. At the end of the unit, pupils decided to show and describe some experiments to the fourth grade. This involved making a summary of the broad concepts they had learned, planning experiments to illustrate them, obtaining the materials, and planning how to perform and explain the experiments so that younger children could understand them. It also involved planning the details of the program and making arrangements about the time and place for it.

From time to time as the activity progressed, the teacher and pupils sat down together to answer the question: "How are we doing?" The first time this happened the pupils raised this question: "How can we measure how well we are doing?" Together the group set up some ways to judge. Some of them were: Is everyone getting an opportunity to help in the planning and working? Are our science facts correct? Do our experiments show what we want them to show? Is everyone getting his job done on time and in the best way he can? These examples show some of the things the children thought were important.

Some of the comments made at the final evaluation period, after their program had been presented, were interesting and revealing: "Some of us didn't speak loudly enough to be heard." "Some of us forgot to ask the fourth-graders if they had any questions to ask us." "Our experiments all worked the way they were supposed to." "Our explanations seemed to be clear to the fourth-graders." "Our program was too long; some of the children got tired." These examples illustrate how children may evaluate the group activity and use their findings to improve their future work. Through conversations with the teacher, individuals helped to evaluate their own accomplishments. It is important to help children learn to give and take constructive criticism from one another when such evaluating periods are held. Here is an opportunity to exercise scientific attitude: basing conclusions on reliable evidence and being open-minded and not prejudiced.

The activity described provides opportunity for the teacher to observe individuals to see how they are showing evidences of growth, or lack of it, with respect to the objectives. There is opportunity to see which children seem to have a satisfactory grasp of the essential subject matter, which have shown progress in ability to solve problems, which are improving in scientific attitude, and which appear to have developed an increasing interest and appreciation.

EVALUATION INSTRUMENTS

As long as we give grades for accomplishment in science, we shall need some kinds of measuring tests. As we have said previously, tests have their limitations but their effectiveness is improved if we observe the following suggestions:

> The test must be designed to measure, insofar as possible, the attainment of all the objectives and not merely the children's mastery of subject matter.
>
> The test scores should be *only one* of the criteria for evaluating the progress of the pupil.
>
> The test should be used as a teaching device as well as an evaluation instrument.
>
> The test should evaluate the success of the teacher as well as the learner.
>
> The test should be so constructed that pupils will have to do the following kinds of things: recall information and apply it to new situations, see relationships between facts, analyze data and draw appropriate conclusions from them, and make decisions on the basis of material read.
>
> The test should be simple, clear, and short and should contain a variety of types of questions.

A good test may require a child to attempt to design a new experiment to solve some specific problem. It may present him with a faulty setup of an experiment and ask him to react to it. It may present a paragraph, a picture, a chart or some other material and ask him to draw conclusions from it. Such material may be selected to emphasize scientific attitude or method of investigation or some other elements of our science objectives. The pupil may be asked to identify relationships to show that he sees how facts may be added together to make generalizations. The pupil may be asked to identify objects in order to discuss them or to show what he knows about them. It is not always essential that tests be in written form. Oral response to a situation may be more effective for some children. These suggestions are made in the interest of better test designing to measure our total objectives, and to insure greater variety and interest in testing.

Above all, remember that all pupils cannot be expected to progress at the same rate toward any specific goals you have set up. Try to consider growth as an individual matter; it is, you know.

EVALUATING A LESSON

The experience of evaluating a lesson makes us realize the importance of the science instruction itself. We wrap ourselves up in curriculum construction, theories of teaching, selecting and judging materials, and other similar educational matters and forget that *everything depends on what happens when we work with the children.* After all, no matter how well all the preliminary planning is done, science dies on the vine unless our classroom lessons are good.

There are many ways of setting up criteria for judging a science lesson, as there are many kinds of lessons and many purposes underlying them. Here are some general criteria that may be used as a nucleus to which the individual teacher may add her own. The teacher may ask such questions as this about her science lessons:

To what extent were the objectives I had in mind realized? This is a most important question to answer. If you are unable to answer it satisfactorily, the probability is that you have wasted your time.

Was there pupil interest? Did it grow? If many children are bored, the fault may lie with the presentation or with the subject matter selection, or it may be due to some other cause that can be determined only by careful evaluation.

Was there sufficient pupil participation? Participation may be of many different kinds —asking or answering questions, making thoughtful suggestions, giving careful attention, helping with experiments, etc.

Did I give attention to the individual needs of the pupils? Those who need special opportunities, those who have special talents and interests, those who need encouragement, and those who for many other reasons need individual attention should receive it when conditions make this possible.

Did pupils think, and did I give them time to think? If pupils can get along without thinking for themselves, the lesson is not likely to be a success; if the procedure is so hurried that no one gets an opportunity to think, one of the main purposes of the lesson is lost.

Was the lesson situation an enjoyable one for all concerned? Unless the lesson is satisfying to pupils and teacher, there is not likely to be much learning.

Was there opportunity for pupil planning? There are many opportunities for planning, and pupils cannot grow in ability to plan effectively unless they have many opportunities to do so.

Was there good pupil-teacher relationship? This hardly has anything to do with always letting pupils do what they want to do. When decisions are made cooperatively pupils contribute according to their varying ability and experience, and there is mutual respect.

Was the material adapted to the ability of the group? Material that is too difficult is discouraging; material that does not challenge causes pupils to lose interest.

This is obviously not an exhaustive set of criteria. It serves to illustrate the kinds of questions useful in evaluating the results of day-to-day teaching. Again we say that the same set of standards used in judging any other lesson is appropriate for judging the results of science teaching.

WHAT SHALL I DO ABOUT THE ESPECIALLY GIFTED CHILDREN IN MY SCIENCE CLASSES?

First of all, find them and let us not confuse glibness or superficial talk with talent. Literature on gifted pupils contains many sets of criteria for identifying especially talented children. These criteria include such items as: the gifted child shows continued interest in science problems, is able to do abstract reasoning, has a good scientific vocabulary, persists in attempting to solve problems, is skillful in manipulating apparatus and materials, chooses to read scientific material generally above the level of his fellow students.

These ten-year-old twins in Los Angeles County schools have developed an interest in gasoline engines and have been requested by older children to make a display of parts and explain how such engines operate.

Having spotted pupils who appear to be gifted in science, it is important to remember that they have many of the same needs as all other children have, and these should be provided for. Although their talent should be encouraged, it should not be exploited to the point where their over-all development suffers.

A good science program is designed so that children with science aptitudes will naturally make themselves known because opportunities for individual expression are provided. Science talent expresses itself in different ways—one student may be gifted in designing apparatus, another in dealing with the mathematical aspects of science, a third in raising especially thoughtful problems. A teacher may encourage creativity and talent by having available books, science kits, science magazines, and other aids which will permit individual students to work on their own.

In dealing with especially gifted children, if you as the teacher cannot provide stimulus, guidance, and other assistance, you must look elsewhere for it. Sometimes the best contribution a teacher can make to a child is to put him next to a scientist or a science teacher who is willing to provide the necessary help. Science clubs for gifted children have been very successful if there is good leadership for them. The solution may be conferences with parents who, together with the school, will provide the proper help. Giving the pupil opportunity to use his talent as an assistant to the teacher and to other teachers in the building may be helpful, but when this is done the pupil should be urged to be accurate with his information and check his sources. It is sometimes easy for children under such circumstances to get false ideas of their talents.

In the elementary school we are attempting to help *all* children attain the objectives. Good science teaching will do this for all those who are able. Good teaching will also discover the more able and interested, and more such children will appear when the teaching is good. Having discovered them, we attempt to tailor a program to fit their needs insofar as we are able, realizing that such children place on us an added responsibility to be gifted ourselves in our ability to respond to them.

SHALL WE HAVE A SCIENCE FAIR?

In the past few years science fairs have blossomed like dandelions in spring. Some are good. Some not. It is important to note that science fairs on the secondary level serve quite a different purpose from those in the elementary school. Before a school decides to have a science fair, the principal and faculty and perhaps some interested parents would do well to answer the question: "What can be accomplished through this activity?" Having thus set up the objectives, the procedure can be determined and the results evaluated. At the elementary school level there should be little or no emphasis on competition and great opportunity for children to:

1. Exercise creativeness in showing what they have learned in science.
2. See what other groups have done
3. Broaden their interests in science.
4. Show their talents in science.
5. Gain experience in reviewing, organizing, and presenting science ideas.

By all means the work should be done by the children themselves. If parents wish to have a science fair of their own, this might be a most interesting and rewarding experience. The fair should not be just a collection of commercially prepared materials and projects; it should be an opportunity for children to grow as indicated in the five points above. If the science fair seems to be a very good way to accomplish these things, the school may decide to have one.

HOW CAN TEACHERS PREPARE TO HELP CHILDREN LEARN TO USE METHODS OF INQUIRY?

At the end of each of the content (A) chapters, there is a section called *Discovering for Yourself*. Some of the suggested investigations require only brief observation and some recording. Some involve reading from several sources. Some provide opportunity for organized inquiry of the type that teachers are hoping to inspire on the part of their pupils. It is generally agreed that teachers who themselves have engaged in systematic inquiry are most successful in helping others to do the same. With this end in view, we suggest that teachers and prospective teachers engage in some investigations that will help them to:

1. Become better acquainted with the methods of inquiry.
2. Be better equipped to pass along to their pupils this skill of learning how to learn.
3. Become aware of the many unsolved problems that abound in the environment.
4. See the importance of stating a problem carefully and accurately.
5. Apply the use of scientific attitudes as they attempt to draw conclusions.
6. Come to realize that problems sometimes remain unsolved even after the most carefully planned efforts are carried out, and that new problems arise as the inquiry proceeds.
7. Exercise creativity and originality in the pursuit of inquiry.
8. Develop a greater appreciation for the nature of science and its processes.

Here are some specific suggestions:

Select a problem that interests you and to which you do not actually know a solution. State it carefully and delimit it in scope to make it reasonable. The problem may come from your immediate environment—growth or lack of growth of plants, behavior of an animal, a superstitious saying, a statement you have read which you wish to challenge, an account in a newspaper that causes you to wonder. A problem may come as the result of some discussion in which various points of view are expressed. A problem may arise through some experience in and about your home, i.e., cooking, gardening, repairing, or some other activity.

Make your hypotheses carefully, record them, keep them in mind.

Plan your procedure step by step as carefully as you can, realizing that you will make many changes as your investigation proceeds.

Exercise caution in drawing conclusions—see page 17 for a discussion of the use of scientific attitudes.

The Earth and the Universe

PART TWO

CHAPTER 6A

The Earth and Its Surface

ON FEBRUARY 20, 1943, Dionisio Palido, a farmer of Parícutin, Mexico, went to his fields to plow for the coming sowing of corn. He noticed with surprise that a small familiar hole in the ground had opened a little wider to become a crevice. At four o'clock he heard thunder and saw nearby trees trembling. In the hole, the ground swelled and then raised itself six or seven feet high. A fine ashy dust began to issue from part of the crack. Smoke arose with a loud continuous hissing and there was a smell of sulphur. Dionisio fled back to the village.

Later, red-hot stones, ashes, and sparks were seen thrown into the air from the opening. By midnight, incandescent rocks were being hurled high into the sky from this roaring hole in the earth.

Thus was a volcano born in a Mexican cornfield in our own lifetime. In all written human history we have records of the beginnings of no more than ten volcanoes, and information about all of the previous ones is meager. Parícutin provided scientists with a "case study" that they could investigate at firsthand. From the third day of its birth, skilled observers with many instruments at their disposal set down all the significant events in the birth and growth of this volcano.

And grow it did: On February 21, the second day of its life, it grew from 30 to 150 feet in height. Lava—molten rock—

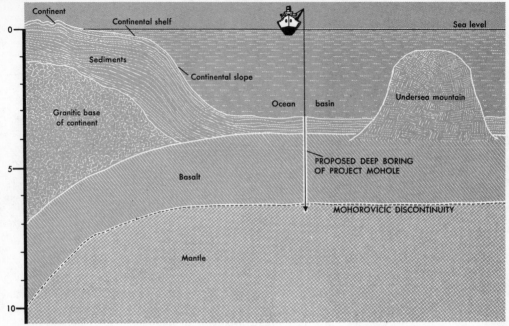

Project Mohole is one of the most imaginative geological ventures in history: the effort to drill a hole through the earth's crust and to the next layer, the mantle. Since the crust is thinnest under the oceans, Project Mohole calls for several miles of drilling at the bottom of the ocean, under three miles of water.

began to pour out, advancing slowly over the cornfield at the rate of 15 feet an hour.

Seven weeks after its birth, this lusty infant was almost 500 feet high. Heavy ash flying out of the volcano covered the country-side for miles, raining on the fields and eventually destroying the village of Parícutin.

At the age of 7 months, the Parícutin volcano had become a mountain 1,500 feet high and about a mile in diameter. By 1952, at the age of 9 years, the volcano had become relatively quiescent.

Parícutin is a dramatic reminder that the earth and its surface are changing today, and that these changes are a part of a process that began in the past and will extend into the future.

TO THE CENTER OF THE EARTH

A journey to the center of the earth, fancifully described by the novelist, Jules Verne, would not be practicable for many reasons. One of these reasons is the rising temperatures encountered with descent. At a depth of only three miles, the temperature is literally high enough to make the blood boil.

Actually, man has seen very little of the interior of the earth. Even the deepest oil wells are but pinpricks in the earth, penetrating a mere five miles into a sphere whose center is four *thousand* miles from its surface. We have had to rely mainly on indirect evidence, such as the outpouring of volcanoes and seismograph records of earthquakes, for our knowledge of the earth's interior.

Studies by scientists have revealed that the earth is composed of a series of concentric shells, each made of different materials. The outermost shell is the *crust*, a relatively rigid zone which varies in thickness from three to forty miles. Most familiar to us is the loose material on the surface of this shell: soil, sand, gravel, rock fragments, and boulders. We know that this loose material is only "skin" deep. If we dig a few feet, or at most a few hundred feet, we strike the solid bedrock in the earth's crust. In mountainous areas, much of the bedrock lies exposed to man's view. In other areas, as in the plains, the bedrock is almost completely covered by soil. Here it is exposed only occasionally by the cutting action of rivers or the digging of man, or because an isolated mass of hard rock has not yet been leveled and broken down. The exposed bedrock is called an *outcrop*.

The covering of soil and other loose materials is discontinuous, varying in depth from zero to a few hundred feet, but the bedrock forms a continuous layer, underlying the continents and extending under the beds of the oceans.

Before descending to the interior of the earth, let us spend a few moments more examining its face. Looking at the planet Earth from the moon, one would be impressed by the fact that most of it is covered with water. The Pacific Ocean alone covers about half of the globe; all of the seas together cover about 70 percent of the area of the earth. The floors that underlie the oceans are not flat; soundings have shown that they are as rugged in profile as the continents. The greatest depths of 25,000 to 35,000 feet are found in a number of *troughs* and *trenches* which may exceed 100 miles in width and 1,000 miles in length. The world record for depth, 35,948 feet, is in the Marianas Trench of the Pacific Ocean. In comparison, the recently scaled Everest, highest of all our continental mountains, extends 29,000 feet above sea level.

These mountain heights and ocean depths of the earth's crust, enormous as they may appear to man, are insignificant in relation to the size of the earth. On the average classroom globe, a true scale representation of these irregularities in the earth's surface would scarcely be visible to the eye.

Continents and oceans lie on the crust of the earth. The crust is not uniform in thickness, as is evident in the illustration of the earth's crust. It is twenty to forty miles thick under the continents but only three to ten miles thick under the oceans. Because of the relative thinness of the crust at the bottoms of oceans, this portion has been selected as the site of a probe known as Project Mohole, which has as its goal the piercing of the crust. Using new techniques for drilling holes in the ocean floor, scientists began operations in 1951 under 12,000 feet of water off the coast of Mexico. If the project is successful, it may throw light on such problems as the origin of continents, ocean basins, and mountains, the causes of earthquakes and volcanoes, and the history of life on earth.

The crust is made largely of two kinds of rocks: basalt and granite. Basalt is found under continents and oceans. Granite lies over the basalt on the continents. The crust is solid except for deep pockets of hot, liquid rock, called *magma*. These pockets are the reservoirs for the volcanoes that occasionally burst through the upper crust.

Beneath the crust lies the *mantle*, a zone about 1,800 miles thick, composed of rock at red- to white-hot temperatures. The rock of the mantle, which probably contains much iron, is believed to be heavier than the crustal rock but lighter than the material in

The inside of the earth, according to present-day knowledge.

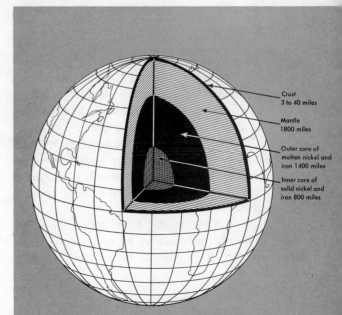

Crust
3 to 40 miles

Mantle
1800 miles

Outer core of molten nickel and iron 1400 miles

Inner core of solid nickel and iron 800 miles

Above left: *Granite, an igneous rock.*
Above right: *Sandstone, a sedimentary rock.*
Left: *Black slate, a metamorphic rock.*

the innermost zone, the *core*. The central core is a sphere about 2,200 miles in radius, just about the size of the planet Mars. The outer core is 1,400 miles thick, and is made of nickel and iron in a hot, plastic condition. The inner core is also made of nickel and iron, but appears to behave more like a true solid than does the outer core. It is estimated that the temperature of the inner core is about 5500° F.

Thus, in this 4,000 mile trip to the center of the earth we have encountered an average of 30 miles of bedrock in the crust,

about 1,800 miles of hot rock in the mantle, about 1,400 miles of molten metal in the outer core, and 800 miles of solid metal in the inner core.

KINDS OF ROCK

SEE PAGE 103

The large variety of rock that nature displays is impressive and at the same time somewhat mystifying. In one place we see rocks arranged in banded layers, sometimes straight, sometimes arched. In other places we see massive blocks of unbanded rock forming cliffs. Close inspection reveals diversities of color, texture, hardness, weight, luster, and many other qualities.

Order is brought into the bewildering array of rocks if we group them according to their *method of origin*. Some rocks have been formed from the cooling and hardening of hot molten material from within the earth's crust. These are called *igneous* rocks. An example is basalt, a characteristic rock in the lava that flows from volcanoes.

Some rocks are formed by the cementing together of materials like sand, clay, mud, and pebbles. These are the *sedimentary* rocks. An example is sandstone, formed by the joining together of sand particles.

Some rocks are formed by the changing of existing rocks into new kinds. These are the *metamorphic* rocks. An example is marble, which is derived from limestone.

All rocks, then, may be classified as igneous, sedimentary, or metamorphic, depending on their method of formation. Let us consider each of these groups more carefully.

IGNEOUS ROCK. The millions of tons of molten rock that poured out of the volcano Parícutin illustrate the method of origin of igneous rock. Pockets of hot liquid rock—*magma*—found deep in the earth sometimes erupt to the surface through fissures in the crust. (When magma reaches the surface, it is called lava.) Rocks like obsidian, pumice, and basalt are formed in this way.

Obsidian, sometimes called volcanic glass, results from the rapid cooling of surface lava; it is a dark, glassy rock that can transmit light wherever the rock is thin enough. A mass of this rock makes up Obsidian Cliff in Yellowstone National Park.

Pumice is so full of holes formed by escaping gas at the time of its origin that it is often light enough to float in water. Basalt is the dark-colored, heavy, dull rock common in lava flows such as the series making up

the Columbia Plateau in the northwestern United States. This plateau—with its 150,000 square miles of hardened lava, in places one mile thick—is one of the earth's greatest volcanic constructions.

Sometimes the liquid magma does not reach the surface of the crust in its upward movement. Instead it forces its way into or between masses of rock. Here it solidifies into rocks like granite, which is the most common of all igneous rocks in the continental crust of the earth. Although granite is formed under the crust, it is often found exposed in some areas because the overlying rocks have been gradually worn away. Granite is a popular building stone in many parts of the world. In America, however, its greatest use is for monuments.

Granite is easily recognized because of its speckled appearance. Close examination reveals that the speckling is caused by the different kinds of materials in its make-up. Among these materials, called *minerals*, are quartz, a glass-like substance, and feldspar, which may be red, white, gray, or green. Mica, a sparkling mineral, is also often present in granite.

Masses of granite rock can be seen in the Rockies, the Adirondacks, the Black Hills of South Dakota, and the White Mountains of New Hampshire.

SEDIMENTARY ROCKS. Sedimentary rocks are interesting because their method of formation permits them to preserve plant and animal remains in a chronological sequence, as we will see in chapter 14A. These rocks are built up under water by the depositing there of materials like sand, clay, mud, pebbles, or gravel. These materials, called *sediments,* are brought to the shallow waters of lakes and oceans by the streams or rivers that flow into them. Wind and moving glaciers of ice are also transporting agents. Other sedimentary rocks are made from plant and animal remains such as shells or ferns. Still others are derived from minerals such as rock salt or gypsum that were once dissolved in the water. The pressure of accumulating materials slowly forces the lower layers of sediment to stick together and to harden into rock. In this process, some natural cementing materials such as lime and quartz found in ocean and lake waters may help cement together coarser sediments such as sand or gravel. The kind of rock produced depends on the kind of materials deposited. Cemented sands become sandstone; hardened clay and mud form shale; cemented pebbles form conglomerate; clay and lime produce marl; seashells provide the material for limestone; plants provide materials for coal.

Sedimentary rocks are very common. Many are easy to identify. Sandstone is obviously made of grains of sand. Sometimes the grains are very loosely joined, and if two pieces are rubbed, grains of sand are dislodged. Shale when wet smells like mud, from which it was actually formed.

Most sedimentary rocks have a banded, "layer-cake" appearance, due to the different kinds of materials that are deposited, one on top of another, where the rock is forming. For example, if yellow clay is deposited over white clay, different layers of shale will form. Or if sand is deposited over clay, a layer of sandstone will form over a layer of shale. The kind of "layer-cake" rock that is made depends on the size, color, and texture of the particles that go into it.

METAMORPHIC ROCK. Soft coal is found in western Pennsylvania; hard coal in eastern Pennsylvania. All the coal in this state was formed in the same geological period. Why, then, are these two coals so different? A study of the coal beds reveals that those in the hard coal region are buckled into tight folds, while those in the soft coal area are nearly horizontal. We infer from this, and from many other evidences in other lands, that high pressure and high temperatures associated with the crushing and folding of the beds changed the soft coal, which is classified as sedimentary rock, into hard coal, which is classified as metamorphic rock.

Hard coal is not only harder than soft, it is more lustrous; it breaks into smooth-surfaced, irregular fragments instead of rectangular blocks; it has a higher percentage of carbon in it; and it is harder to start burning —as our colonial forefathers discovered.

The change involved in the transformation of soft or bituminous coal into hard or anthracite coal is one example of *metamorphism*. In general, it may be said that when bedrock is subjected to greatly increased pressures or very high temperatures or both, it may be changed in its chemical and physical properties to become metamorphic rock. The pressure may result from large movements of the earth's crust that crumple and fold the bedrock. The heat may come from the friction of moving layers or from the proximity of hot magma.

We have listed here some of the important metamorphic rocks and the rocks from which they are derived:

Metamorphic Rock	*Derived from*
Anthracite Coal	Bituminous Coal
Gneiss	Granite or Shale
Marble	Limestone
Quartzite	Sandstone
Schist	Shale
Slate	Shale

THE MINERALS IN ROCKS

If a rock is thought of as a kind of fruit cake, the minerals in it may be compared to the cake's nuts, raisins, cherries, citron, and other ingredients. Minerals are natural substances of definite chemical composition. More than 2,000 different minerals have been identified in the rocks of the earth's crust. Some, like gold, diamond, and ruby are found in relatively few rocks. Ten minerals, including familiar quartz and mica, make up about 90 percent of the rocks.

Rocks, like cakes, vary in their ingredients. Limestone, for example, is commonly made only of the mineral calcite. Granite, as we have seen, always has feldspar, quartz, and at least one other mineral in it. It owes its speckled appearance to the separate crystals of these minerals.

THE AGE OF ROCKS

Evidence gathered by scientists shows that the earth is very old. Let us see how scientists determine the age of the earth's rocks.

The two methods we are going to describe have one feature in common. To appreciate this feature, think of a piggy bank, in which a thrifty child regularly deposits a dime every Saturday night. When the bank is full, it is broken open and is found to contain one hundred dimes. A little arithmetic will show that it took about two years to save that much money.

Sedimentary rock represents a kind of piggy bank, in which sand, mud, and pebbles are deposited instead of money. From a study of sedimentation going on in some places on the earth, geologists estimate that it takes four to ten thousand years to form a layer of sedimentary rock one foot deep. Let us apply this rough standard to only a *part* of the wall of the Grand Canyon, where we will study a layer of limestone fifteen hundred feet thick. Arithmetic shows that it took from six to fifteen million years for this layer of rock to form.

When we assemble and add up information about sedimentary rocks in various parts of the earth, we get clues not only to the age of individual rock masses, but to the age of the earth itself.

The second method of determining the age of rocks involves a unique kind of banking, in which the piggy bank starts off full of quarters that are gradually replaced by pennies. This method is based on the natural breakdown of the element uranium (the quarters) into a special kind of lead (pennies).

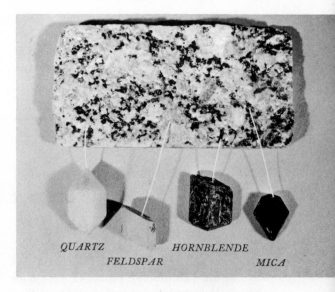

QUARTZ   HORNBLENDE

FELDSPAR   MICA

Granite rock is speckled with the crystals of the different minerals of which it is composed. Four typical minerals found in granite are shown here.

Uranium is widely distributed in rocks. Its atoms are radioactive, splitting without man's aid into lead. With the passage of time, the amount of uranium in a rock decreases and the amount of lead increases. We know two things about uranium in rocks which enable us to use it as a "time clock":

1. Measurement shows that each year one ounce of uranium will yield $\frac{1}{7,600,000,000}$ of an ounce of lead.
2. The rate of change of uranium to lead is constant under all conditions of temperature, pressure, and chemical surroundings.

Most of this radioactive uranium is found in igneous rock. We infer that it was incorporated as a mineral at the time the rock solidified. From that point on, the radioactive "clock" began ticking, with uranium breaking down into lead at the rate just given.

This method has provided a more exact measure of the age of rock than any other thus far. The oldest rock measured in this way in the United States is about two billion years old.

The study of sedimentary rocks and the use of the radioactive "clock" indicate that the earth is four or five billion years old.

FORCES THAT CHANGE THE EARTH

SEE PAGE 104

Men once thought the mountains, plains, plateaus, and other large features of the earth had always existed. The science of geology reveals that two processes work continuously in sculpturing and altering the face of the earth: the forces of construction and the forces of destruction.

The constructive forces, as the geologist defines them, are those that lift up land masses to produce forms like mountains. Earthquakes and volcanoes reflect the working of these constructive forces. The destructive forces are those which tend to level down the mountains and hills. The cutting action of running streams and the scouring of glaciers of ice are among the forces that erase the high places of the earth.

Both these processes of construction and destruction are at work today. Let us consider the first of them to see how the mountains of the earth were built.

KINDS OF MOUNTAINS

SEE PAGE 105

The origin of a mountain in our own time from a volcanic eruption has been described in the opening paragraphs of this chapter. Parícutin is one of a kind of *volcanic mountains* which have arisen as individual peaks. Mount Popocatepetl, also in Mexico, and Mount Etna, in Italy, are of this type. Some volcanic mountains form chains, possibly because they have burst out of weak points in a line in the earth's crust, like those in the Hawaiian and Aleutian Islands.

Volcanic activity may force magma under previously existing layers of rock, as we have seen in our study of igneous rock. This may lift the overlying rocks sufficiently to form *domed mountains*, which are usually oval or circular in shape. The Black Hills of South Dakota, the Henry Mountains of Utah, and the Adirondack Mountains of New York are examples of domed mountains.

Folded mountains arise in a different way. Their origin can be understood easily

Hot liquid rock under pressure from the earth's interior is pushed up to the surface and gradually builds a volcanic mountain.

 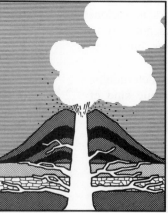 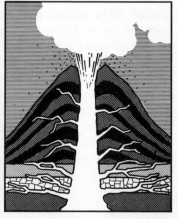

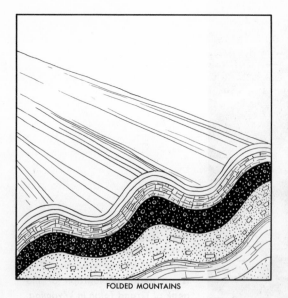

FOLDED MOUNTAINS

BLOCK MOUNTAINS

Left: *When the crust of the earth is subjected to pressure it may buckle up to great heights to form folded mountains.*

Right: *Block mountains are formed when large blocks of the earth's crust are raised and tilted. Block mountains are usually rectangular in shape.*

if you experiment with a pad of paper. Push the opposite edges toward each other to throw the pad into a series of folds with elevations and depressions. In a similar way the crust of the earth has been subject to forces that have crumpled it into long parallel ridges whose length may be as great as a thousand miles. Folding of the crust accounts, at least in part, for great mountain ranges like the Alps, Andes, Appalachians, and Rockies.

It is difficult to believe that anything as hard as rock can be folded into waves. Rocks, contrary to popular belief, are quite elastic. Just as a long bar of something as hard as steel can be bent, so too can long sections of the rocky crust of the earth.

Sometimes, however, when the pressuring forces are sufficiently great, the crust may break. The fracturing of the rock may be accompanied by a slippage along the break—*i.e.*, the rocks on one side are pushed up higher than the rocks on the other side of the break, resulting in the elevation of the rock on one side. This sudden slipping, fol-

lowed sometimes by the tilting of the raised rock, results in the formation of *block mountains*. The largest of the block mountains in the United States are the Sierra Nevadas, which are over four hundred miles long, with the elevated side of the broken rock facing eastward to form one side of the Great Basin.

The classic explanation for the origin of crust-folding and crust-cracking pressures emphasizes the shrinkage of the crust into wrinkles because of the cooling of the earth. Although this "contracting earth" theory has not been completely discarded, geologists have recently proposed new theories, which we will not discuss here, to account for crustal activities.

LIFE HISTORY OF MOUNTAINS

Mountains have their own kind of life history, passing from youth to maturity and then to old age. The life span of mountains covers hundreds of millions of years,

High jagged peaks, narrow valleys, and steep slopes are characteristic of young mountains. This is an aerial photograph of the peak of Grand Teton in Wyoming.

but we are familiar with all stages of their development because there are mountains of different ages in existence today. The Laurentians, for example, are older than the Appalachians, which in turn are older than the Rockies.

In their early youth mountains are still growing, evidencing this by volcanic eruptions, by earthquakes, by the slow rising of rock layers, or by all of these. Young mountains are high and rugged, with sharp peaks, narrow valleys, and steep slopes. The Himalayas, Andes, Sierra Nevadas, and the Rockies are young mountains.

When mountains have stopped growing, they are said to be mature. Weathering and erosion breaks rocks into fragments and carries them away. Peaks are lowered, slopes become gentler, valleys become wider. The Appalachians, the White Mountains, the Adirondacks, and the Green Mountains of Vermont are mature mountains.

Continued erosion, principally by running water, brings mountains into their old age. This wearing down eventually erases the peaks and may produce a flattened area called a *peneplane*, whose level aspect is occasionally relieved by some rolling hills or by solitary rock masses, known as *monadnocks*, that have withstood the forces of destruction. Manhattan and the Bronx in New York City are located on a peneplane. Stone Mountain in Georgia is a monadnock on the Piedmont Upland, which is a raised peneplane.

EARTHQUAKES

The nearest thing to an earthquake that most of us ever experience occurs when a heavy truck rolls down the street, starting a tremor that passes through the ground to the foundation of our home and thence to walls and floors, setting window panes rattling and teacups dancing. Magnify this several million times and you have an earthquake.

The earth scientist, with a cheerful, long-range point of view, regards earthquakes as constructive forces because they are part of the process that pushes up and builds rock structures above the surface of the earth. To the common man, however, earthquakes are fearful things, resulting in widespread destruction of life and property in the areas where they occur. In 1923, an earthquake in Japan took a toll of 140,000 people killed or missing. The highest loss of life due to earthquakes on record is estimated at 830,000—the result of an earthquake in China in 1556.

Ninety-five percent of all earthquakes occur in two geographic belts, one ringing both sides of the Pacific and the other crossing the Mediterranean area as shown in the the map. These belts also include most of the world's active volcanoes and young mountains. Indeed, earthquakes, volcanoes, and mountain building are all associated with turbulence in the earth, with great crustal pressures and tensions. We have seen, in our study of mountain formation, how the pressures within the crust may cause it to buckle up and fracture. An abrupt movement of large blocks of the earth's crust on each side of the fracture is essentially what happens during an earthquake.

Earthquakes often occur along lines, called *fault lines*, that represent an old wound in the earth's crust produced by a previous fracturing of the rock. The San Francisco earthquake of 1906 took place along such a line, called the San Andreas fault, that ex-

tends for several hundred miles from northern to southern California. This line was known to geologists for many years prior to the quake. On both sides of this line, pressures and tensions were built up in the adjoining rocks. The 1906 break released the tensions as the rocks snapped, like the springing of a steel trap. Map studies of the location of roads and rivers before and after the break show that this earthquake resulted in a *horizontal* movement along the San Andreas fault. Roads and fences that crossed the fault were offset as much as twenty-one feet, moving northward on the west side of the fault and southward on the east side.

Some earthquakes result in a *vertical* movement of rock. In Yakutat Bay, Alaska, a section of seacoast was lifted as much as forty-seven feet during an earthquake in 1899.

The abrupt release of energy in the snapping and shifting of rocks starts strong destructive waves that can be detected thousands of miles away by delicate instruments called seismographs. The seismograph record, as interpreted by the seismologists, gives the duration, the intensity, and the distance of the earthquake center from the seismograph station. The exact location of the center can be determined by the records of

The principal earthquake belts of the world.

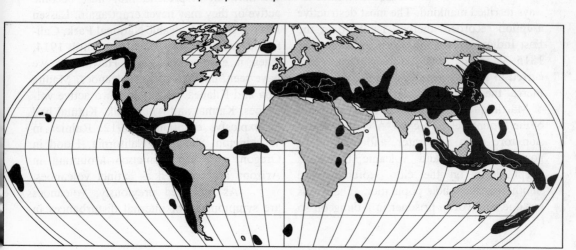

these widely separated stations within a few hours after the earthquake has occurred.

Incidentally, the study of seismograph records (called seismograms) has revealed a great deal about the internal structure of the earth, described earlier in the chapter. Earthquakes act like x-rays, enabling us, with the help of seismographs, to "see" through the earth.

Many strong earthquakes originate in the crust under the Pacific Ocean. Here they may start ocean waves that travel as fast as 500 miles an hour and may break over coastal areas in waves as high as 60 feet. These are mistakenly called tidal waves, although they have nothing to do with tides. The scientific name is tsunamis (tsŏo-nä'mēz), a word of Japanese origin. In 1946, an earthquake originating off the Alaskan peninsula started great waves that traveled two thousand miles to the Hawaiian Islands, causing widespread damage.

A series of devastating earthquakes rocked Chile in 1960. Some 6,000 people were killed, and the property damage was estimated at $400,000,000. A major factor in destruction was a great tsunami, which did great damage, not only in Chile but in Japan and in the Hawaiian Islands as well.

VOLCANOES

Volcanoes, like earthquakes, have always terrified mankind. The most destructive eruption recorded, that of Tamboro in the East Indies, killed 56,000 people in the year 1815. A more recent volcanic disaster occurred in 1902, when 30,000 residents of St. Pierre, the capital city of the French island of Martinique, were all killed by an eruption of the Mount Pelée volcano. A violent explosion tore open the crater, and a cloud of poisonous gases and volcanic fragments swept down on the city, scorching and smothering the whole population. There was but one survivor, a prisoner in a dungeon so badly ventilated that the poisonous fumes could not reach him.

The greatest natural explosion in historic time occurred when the volcano that makes up the island of Krakatoa erupted in 1883. Half of the island either blew away or collapsed into an underlying cavity. Ash rose to a height of 17 miles and was carried all around the world, causing beautiful sunrises and sunsets on all continents for many months. The noise of the explosion was heard 2,000 miles away. The shock produced great sea waves that rose 50 to 80 feet high as they smashed over nearby coasts, drowning about 35,000 people. One large vessel was carried a mile and a half inland and left stranded there 30 feet above sea level.

Not all volcanoes are explosive; some pour lava out of craters or from breaks in their sides. Mauna Loa and Kilauea on the island of Hawaii are famous volcanoes of this type.

Volcanoes differ in size and shape too. Some volcanic mountains are shaped like inverted saucers; some rise gracefully from a wide base to a tall slender peak.

Some volcanoes grow rapidly—Parícutin, as we have seen, was 1,500 feet high at the end of 7 months; Monte Nuovo, born in 1538 at the edge of the Bay of Naples, rose to a height of 440 feet in *one day*.

Some volcanoes continue to erupt for centuries; others cease very quickly. Many are dormant at present; they may become active or they may never erupt again. Lassen Peak in Lassen Volcanic National Park, California, was considered extinct until 1914, when it erupted suddenly. Hawaii, as we have seen, has two active volcanoes, Mauna Loa and Kilauea. Alaska has two active volcanoes, Katmai and Aniakchak. Katmai had an explosive eruption in 1912. Rainier in Washington, Shasta in California, Hood in Oregon, and San Francisco Mountain in Arizona are regarded as extinct volcanoes.

As indicated previously, volcanoes are symptomatic of internal disturbances in the earth. They are concentrated in regions of the world where earthquakes and young mountain belts are located.

Recent evidence strengthens the belief that the molten rock erupted from volcanoes comes from relatively shallow sources in the outermost part of the earth's mantle or in the crustal zone. Ordinarily, this underlying rock is solid because of the pressure on it from above. If the pressure is lessened by breaks or faults in the crust, or if, as scientists have recently suggested, the temperature is increased by radioactive heating within the earth, the solid material becomes liquefied into magma. The expanded magma, now lighter than the surrounding rock, tends to rise wherever it can find an opening, as it did recently in Parícutin.

Recently we have developed techniques for forecasting eruptions. Seismograph records are helpful, since volcanic activity is accompanied by earth vibrations. For twenty days before the birth of the Parícutin volcano, numerous earth tremors were felt in the nearby countryside. Other clues include the tilting of the ground around volcanoes and local changes in the earth's electrical currents and magnetism.

Old Faithful Geyser in Yellowstone National Park spouts regularly. Underground hot water explodes into steam and blows the water above it up through the opening in the rocks into the air.

HOT SPRINGS AND GEYSERS

Since the earth's temperature increases 1° F. for every 50 to 75 feet of descent into the earth, water rising from deep wells or springs may be warm enough to form warm or hot springs. Hot springs also occur in areas of comparatively recent volcanic activity. Here the rock just a short distance below the surface is hot enough to boil water, part of which comes to the surface as a hot spring, at boiling or near boiling temperature.

A geyser is a hot spring equipped with a natural "plumbing" system that causes water and steam to be shot up. Old Faithful in Yellowstone is noted for its height and

relative regularity, propelling a million gallons of water over 150 feet in a few minutes. It puts on this performance about once an hour.

The essential "plumbing" structure in a geyser is a natural tube extending from the surface down to very hot rock. Inflowing underground water is heated above the boiling point, but does not boil because the weight of the column of water above it exerts enough pressure to prevent this. (At this point it is something like a home pressure cooker, in which water is heated above the boiling point of 212° F. without boiling into steam.) However, the rise of steam bubbles throws some water out of the top. Viewers see this as a preliminary spurt that

The Grand Canyon and the Colorado River which carved it are shown in this view from Toroweap Point.

announces the coming of the big show. The loss of this water reduces the pressure enough so that the superheated water below explodes into steam, blowing out the water above it as a geyser. Then the cycle starts all over again.

SEE PAGES 105 TO 106

WEARING DOWN
OF THE LAND

We have seen how forces working from the interior of the earth have thrust up the large features of our planet. Let us turn our attention now to the work of water, ice, wind, frost, chemicals, and living things, to see how they have altered these features to form the present face of the earth.

WATER. The Grand Canyon of the Colorado River is the work of running water. Long ago the Colorado River flowed on high level land, over the layers of sedimentary rock that had been laid down in previous eras. As time went on, the running water, aided by fragments of rock that it carried, cut deeper and deeper into the rock. Weathering, discussed on pages 98–99, gravity, and rain helped the river attack the walls of the valley and widen the narrow cut into its present V-shape.

A river, then, carves a valley as it flows downhill on its way to the sea. At first the valley is narrow and V-shaped. The young river rushes rapidly through the valley, filing, scraping, and sanding out a deeper and deeper bed. As the river's bed deepens, its banks cave in and the valley is widened. The river begins to slow down. Its ability to rush over large boulders and other obstructions is lost. The river is more easily deflected sideways into a meandering course.

Running water is the most important tool of nature in wearing down the surface of the earth. Not only does it cut and dislodge, it transports the material that it and other forces have pried loose. The rivers of the United States carry about a billion tons of materials to the oceans each year. This represents an average leveling down of the entire surface at the rate of one foot in eight thousand years. What is most significant to us now is that much of this transported material is the valuable topsoil that is essential to our existence. This is a conservation problem created largely by man, and one that can and must be solved by man. (We will discuss this more fully in chapter 15A.)

Running water is responsible, at least in part, for many land forms that we do not have space to discuss here: gullies, badlands,

The spring runoff caused by warm rains on frozen ground removed a sheet of valuable topsoil from this wheat farm in the state of Washington.

potholes, rapids, waterfalls, flood plains, oxbow lakes, and deltas.

Ocean waters also affect the surface of the earth. Ocean waves, rolling with a force that may rise to thousands of pounds in each square foot, smash our rocky seacoasts, splitting and moving rocks and scouring bedrock with the aid of sand and pebbles. Breakers can also build up barrier beaches of sand, like those of Long Beach, Jones Beach, and Fire Island off the southern coast of Long Island. Shore currents, running parallel to the coast line, may carry sand and pebbles to form new beaches and sand bars.

ICE. Glaciers have left their mark in many areas of the United States. In the last million years, great ice sheets have moved down from the Arctic regions, covering Canada, northern United States, and northern Europe. The ice sheets advanced and retreated many times, the last retreat ending as recently as 9,000 years ago. At one time 30 percent of the land areas of the earth was covered with glaciers; today only 10 percent is under glacial ice. Four-fifths of this is on the Antarctic Continent.

What is now New York City was once under a solid mass of ice half a mile

The pounding of waves smashes the rocks at Cypress Point on the Monterey Peninsula.

The heavy black line indicates the southernmost advance of the glaciers in the last ice age. There are evidences of the glacier's action on the earth's surface—rock deposits, lakes, rock scratches, moraines, and other effects—in the states shown.

high. A trip to Central Park in Manhattan Island will reveal many evidences of this glacial visit. The outcrop, or exposed bedrock, in this city oasis is scratched, grooved, and polished in a way that is characteristic of land over which a glacier of ice has passed. With a compass, it is easy to find that the scratches are all parallel, running roughly from the northwest to the southeast, indicating the direction of movement of the glacier. The western slope of each outcrop of bedrock rises gently toward the east, and shows evidence of smoothing and scratching by the advancing glacier. The eastern slope drops abruptly and irregularly because the rocks on this side were plucked out as the glacier moved away from the mass. Here and there, perched on the outcrop, are large round boulders, made of entirely different rock from the underlying bedrock, which in Central Park is mica schist. Evidently these boulders were plucked out of some mass of rock by the glacier some miles to the north of New York City, and then dropped to their present position when the ice melted.

New York City and Long Island mark the southernmost advance of the Atlantic end of the last glacier. This front is revealed to us by a mass of loose earth, including sand, gravel, and boulders, that was deposited when the tip of the glacier melted. This material, forming what is known as a *terminal moraine*, extends 140 miles from Brooklyn across northern Long Island to its eastern tip.

We are able to study glaciers at firsthand because some exist today. Glaciers begin as great snow fields that are slowly compacted into ice by the accumulation of more snow on top. Glaciers form in those regions where snow accumulates more rapidly than it melts. This happens in two places: near the tops of high mountains and in the frigid zones of the earth.

Valley glaciers originate in mountains and, as they grow, fill the valleys leading down, as a river might. The western United States has valley glaciers in the Sierra Nevadas, the Rockies, and the Cascade Mountains. The glaciers in Glacier National Park in Montana and Mount Rainier National Park in Washington attract thousands of tourists every year.

Continental glaciers originate over large cold land masses in the frigid zones, where they cover the land with ice sheets thousands of feet thick. When the ice becomes thick enough, it moves out in all directions toward the seacoasts. Greenland and Antarctica are almost entirely covered by glaciers of this type.

Glaciers, like rivers, move downhill from the upper snow fields where they form. Glaciers in the Alps move at average speeds of 1 to 3 feet a day; those in Alaska and Greenland may move as much as 40 feet or more a day. These masses of ice always move forward, but their *fronts* may advance, remain stationary, or retreat. The front advances over the land as long as the ice moves faster than it melts. When the rates of moving and melting are equal, the front is stationary. In Greenland the glaciers advance faster than they melt, even at sea level. In Greenland and other places, when glaciers reach the seacoast they break off to become *icebergs*.

Valley glaciers are great movers of materials on the earth's surface. They gouge out huge depressions and carry the material along to be deposited elsewhere as the glaciers melt. Passing through V-shaped valleys, these glaciers change them into U-shaped ones. Continental glaciers also carry along huge boulders and soil and deposit them elsewhere. The soil of much of the northern part of the United States has been materially changed by continental glaciers that visited this area during the last million years.

Lakes and ponds are often the result of glaciation. Valleys become blocked with the soil and rocks of moraine deposits, which act as dams to hold back water. In some cases glaciers have gouged out or deepened basins that now hold water. The Great Lakes

A valley glacier, such as this one in Alaska, is a river of ice. Its origin is in high mountain snow fields, where snow is compressed into ice. As it moves slowly down the valley, it grinds away the valley walls, changing the original V-shape into a U-shape.

occupy ancient river valleys that were deepened and dammed by glaciers.

The glacial periods, or ice ages, of the past were presumably caused by fluctuation in the earth's temperature, when a drop of several degrees allowed a vast accumulation of ice to occur. It is thought that in the glacial periods the sea level may have been as much as 300 feet lower than it is now since much of the oceans' water was locked up in glaciers.

It is conjectured by scientists that we are now in a warm or *interglacial period*. Measurements taken in recent years suggest that the sea is now rising at the rate of two and one-half inches per one hundred years. Perhaps this rise is due to the rapid melting of the world's glaciers. It is variously estimated that if the existing glaciers melted completely, the sea level would rise from 60 to 200 feet.

WIND. We have seen how running water and moving glaciers carry soil and other materials across the earth's surface. Wind also is a carrier of soil. This has been dramatically and tragically demonstrated in the dust storms that have plagued some areas

These dunes in Tremont County, Idaho, are caused by strong constant winds. Notice the sand ripples in the foreground, and the contrast between the windward side (on the left here) and the leeward side of the dunes.

of our country. We shall have more to say about the cause and effect of dust storms in chapter 15A.

There are other results of wind erosion that we see occasionally when wind piles up sand into dunes. Pictured here are some of the beautiful sand dunes found in Idaho. There are similar huge hills of sand in many other parts of the United States. They are alike in appearance, and they are all created in essentially the same way.

We all know that a strong wind can carry sand. Some of the sand carried by the wind is dropped when the wind slows down because of an obstacle or for some other reason. The pile of sand thus deposited gradually forms a hill called a dune. The windward slope of a dune is gentle; the lee side drops more sharply. The transfer of sand from the windward to the lee side results in the slow movement of the entire dune in the direction of the wind. Dunes may march as much as 100 feet in one year.

The formation of sand dunes requires a great deal of dry sand to be moved and stretches of flat surfaces over which the wind can sweep. The migration of dunes sometimes buries towns, farms, and forests. On the eastern shores of Lake Michigan westerly winds have built dunes that are migrating inland over Indiana, slowly burying a forest area there known as Dune Park. The migration of dunes can be halted by the planting of grasses and shrubs in the sand.

Running water, moving ice, and winds are regarded by the geologist as forces of *erosion*, that is, as forces that not only break rock but also carry away the fragments. On the other hand those forces that break rock but do not carry the pieces away are grouped under the title *weathering*. Included under weathering are the work of frost, chemicals, and living things. Let us consider these briefly.

FROST. Large piles of rock are often deposited at the base of steep mountains by the cracking off and tumbling of fragments from above.

The action of frost helps in the splitting of rock. When water freezes it expands its volume about 9 percent. (The bulge on the upper surface of the ice cubes in your refrigerator is due to this expansion.) If the water that seeps into small cracks in rocks or into porous rocks freezes, it exerts tremendous pressure on the rock, splitting off chunks from it.

SEE PA 10

CHEMICAL ACTION. The chemicals found in nature act on rocks, changing them into new materials and breaking them down. The oxygen of the atmosphere unites with the iron that is present in many rocks, making it rust and decay. Water combines with some of the substances in rocks, mica for example, to form new materials that eventually crumble. The carbon dioxide of the air dissolves in rain water to form a weak acid known as carbonic acid. This acid works on various minerals. Feldspar, a mineral found in granite, is decomposed by carbonic acid into clay.

LIVING THINGS. Plants affect rocks mechanically and chemically. As their roots grow into the crevices of rocks, they exert enough pressure to split them apart. The roots of lichens, plants that live on rocks, produce chemicals that attack and dissolve the surface of the rock, making it possible for these plants to absorb necessary minerals.

When plants and animals die and decay, acids are formed that react chemically with rock and help to weather it away.

SOIL

SEE PAGES 103 AND 106

Pour a handful of ordinary garden soil into a jar of water and shake vigorously. When it settles, skim off some of the material floating on top. Much of this will be bits of leaves, stems, and roots of plants, partly decomposed. Examine carefully the material that has settled to the bottom to find grains of sand and small pebbles, both of which are broken rock.

Soil has its origin in the decay of plants and animals and the weathering of rock. Soil is a final product in the destruction of rock. It is our greatest natural resource.

THE INTERNATIONAL GEOPHYSICAL YEAR

The International Geophysical Year (popularly known as the IGY), in 1957–1958, was one of the most significant enterprises in science in our history. From 4,000 major outposts girdling the globe, scientists from 66 countries made simultaneous obser-

Buttes in Monument Valley, Utah, making a last stand against wind, water, and other forces that tend to level the high places on the earth.

vations of the earth's interior, crust, and oceans, of the atmosphere, and of the sun. Almost every major land and sea area was studied. Scientists probed the earth's interior by setting off explosions which sent sound waves through it. Electronic devices in balloons, rockets, satellites, and in undersea capsules aided in the vast search. The IGY, which lasted for eighteen months, beginning July 1, 1957, yielded a great amount of new information about the earth. It was discovered, for example, that the earth is not simply a sphere with flattened poles—it is slightly pear-shaped. One of the ocean studies revealed a steep-sided submarine mountain range rising 10,000 feet from the floor of the ocean, about 1,000 miles long and 200 miles across at its greatest width. It is hard to believe that a mountain range of such a size was first discovered in 1958!

Twenty-five hundred years ago, the Greek philosopher Heraclitis said, "There is nothing permanent in the world except change." The earth itself is always changing; so too are the theories which men have held about the cause and the nature of these changes. The IGY and subsequent cooperative activities are uncovering a new portrait of the planet Earth.

In this brief picture of the earth and its changing surface, we have emphasized certain ideas; the chief ones follow:*

The earth is very old and has undergone great changes in its lifetime.

Scientists study rocks to learn about the history of the earth.

The earth is believed to be composed of concentric parts of different materials: the outermost is a hard rocky crust; next is a zone of heavier red-hot rock; the outer core is composed of molten metal, the inner core is of solid metal.

Seventy percent of the surface of the earth is covered by seas.

Rocks originate in three ways: from the cooling of molten materials, the cementing of small fragments, and the changing of existing rocks into new forms.

The co-architects of the earth's surface are the forces of construction and destruction—the forces that build mountains and the forces that level them down.

Mountains are formed from volcanic activities or from the buckling of the earth's crust.

The large forces responsible for the leveling down of the land are running water, moving glaciers, and wind.

Frost, chemical action, and living things are important in the splitting and breaking down of rock.

Soil, our greatest natural resource, is a final product of the destruction of rock.

DISCOVERING FOR YOURSELF†

1. Find out as much as you can about Project Mohole. Why is this project important?
2. Write to the State Department of Geology of your state for information about the land forms of your state and ask for a contour map of your locality. Learn to read the map and use this information in doing the project below.
3. Make a rough map of the county in which you live. Then from observation, reading, and other sources describe how you think the surface of the area may have changed during (a) the last 5000 years and (b) the last 50,000 years.

---

* Generalizations such as these will be found at the end of each of the A chapters; their purpose is to emphasize the essential meanings of the subject matter of the chapter.

† Here and in each of the subsequent chapters will be found a list of people, places, things, and special kinds of resources helpful in teaching the material of the chapter and in developing attitudes and appreciations. How many of them will be useful for a specific locality depends, of course, on local conditions. They have all been found helpful in many situations.

4. Make a tour of your surrounding counties to observe erosion effects, land changes made by rivers, and any other landscape changes.
5. Follow a stream to see (a) how the stream has changed the earth around it (b) load being carried (c) swiftness of the stream (d) deposits of the stream.
6. Observe a local area after a heavy rainstorm to determine (a) where erosion is taking place (b) why it is taking place (c) materials that are being carried away (d) where materials are being deposited (e) effects of deposits.
7. Make a rock collection, using as many different sources as you can for identification, and write an informative label for each specimen, telling its origin, its use, and its composition.

How does water change our earth?

Be ready to prove your answers by
1. experiments
2. demonstrations
3. pictures you have taken
4. drawings you have made of changes that you have seen
5. reports of qualified authorities

CHAPTER 6B

Teaching "The Earth and Its Surface"

Children are interested in rocks and often bring specimens and collections to school. They want to know the names of the rocks and what they are made of. In helping children to find out about the earth on which they live and to observe its changes more intelligently, it is important to direct their observations to the things that happen around them every day. It is easy for them to observe some of the changes in the earth's surface. Earth changes may be observed in any environment, city or country. The hills, valleys, rocks, and soil in the neighborhood are sources to observe. The school yard, "empty" lot, and park, exposed as they are to sun, wind, and rain are excellent places to observe the forces of nature at work. The school building with its natural and man-made stone shows how man uses some of nature's resources. The activities described in this chapter will appeal to children's curiosity and help answer their questions and explain their observations.

Some unit problems that grow out of this material are:

How does the surface of the earth change? or
How do we know that the earth is changing?

Or, if it seems advisable to consider problems of a more limited scope:

What is soil and how is it made?
How do water and wind change the earth's surface?
What are rocks made of and how were they formed?
How do we use rocks?
What happens when a volcano erupts?

Some of the activities described in this chapter are appropriate for both primary and intermediate grades. The following, although they may be used at any level, are especially appropriate for primary grades:

1. Examine soil. Sift soil through a coarse strainer to separate coarse particles and pebbles from finer soil. Spread soil samples (obtained from garden, field and forest) on a piece of paper to find out what they are made of: small pebbles, bits of plant material, grains of sand, seeds, animal materials. Use a magnifying glass.
2. Collect rocks. Look at them and feel them to see how they are alike and how different. Scratch them with a nail to see how they differ in hardness. Describe them, telling the color, shape, size, and other characteristics.
3. Walk in the schoolyard after a rain. See that water runs downhill, that it carries soil with it, that it uncovers rocks and pebbles and has other effects.
4. Look at pictures of different places on the earth—seashore, mountains, deserts, farm land, etc. Tell what can be seen in each picture and how the places are different from each other, i.e., rough, smooth, high, rocky, wet, etc. Children who have taken trips may help to extend the concept of the nature of the earth's surface by telling what they saw from the car, train, or plane window.
5. Make "man-made" rocks, by preparing concrete. Mix one-half cup of cement powder and one and one-half cups of clean dry sand in a large can. Add enough water to make a thick creamy mixture. Pour into milk cartons and allow to harden for several days. Take off the cardboard and examine the results.

MAKING A ROCK COLLECTION

There are many things to learn about rocks besides their names, but naming them seems to be one of the first interests. Here are some hints on how to help with the naming: use the local museum's rock collection; use a small rock collection purchased from a supply house; use pictures from books (see bibliography); ask a local high school science teacher if there is one who can help. Encourage pupils to devise their own methods of organizing their collections using titles such as: "Rocks used in our community," "Hardest rocks," "Unusual rocks," "Rocks Formed Under Water," "Rocks from Volcanoes." Pupils may then discuss how the rocks were formed and how they came to be in the shape in which they were found. A rounded granite pebble, for example, looks different on the inside from the way it looks on the outside. Break rocks apart with a hammer to look at the inside; note the sharp edges and discuss how these edges would become worn down if the stone were put into a creek bottom. A written account of the pupils' findings placed with the collection in the school corridor will create interest.

OBSERVING THE USE OF ROCKS

Rocks are used in construction of many of our public buildings. The school building itself may contain some granite, marble, or sandstone in its construction. Urge pupils to observe churches, banks, libraries, and other public buildings to see examples of different kinds of rocks. Suggest that they find out where these rocks came from. If some of them came from a quarry in the community, perhaps a group might visit the quarry to observe the layers of rocks and to learn how rock is cut and transported. If there is a monument works nearby, pupils may be able to obtain samples of granite and marble for examination.

An interesting rock hunting trip[1] may be organized to help children observe uses of rocks in their immediate environment. Pupils and teacher, as a result of study and observation, may prepare a guide with "stops" in sequential order. The first trip may be in and around the school itself. A later trip may include places and buildings in the neighborhood. Examples of the "stops": (1) The classroom: blackboards (slate); (2) The corridor: wall behind drinking fountain (marble); (3) The corridor: stairs (bluestone steps); (4) Basement: drinking fountain (soapstone); (5) Main lobby: steps (marble, terrazzo); (6) Entrance (limestone); (7) Front steps (granite). In writing the guide, pupils tell origin, color, use, and other special information about each of the rocks.

STUDYING PICTURES OF THE EARTH'S SURFACE

Travel folders, geography books, *Life Magazine,* the *National Geographic Magazine,* and other sources have pictures of mountains and many other features of the earth's surface. Children may study these pictures to see how the surfaces differ from one another, to see layers of different kinds of rocks, to see how the layers are tipped and twisted, and to see where the snow and vegetation are.

Pupils may summarize the important ideas they have learned through picture study and firsthand experiences by applying their findings to the area in which they live. They may assemble the magazine illustrations and prepare talks that tell important ideas they have learned about: "How the earth's surface has changed in our area through the ages." Depending upon the area involved, they may discuss lakes and rivers, sand dunes, mountains and rock formations, shore lines, desert areas, and other topographical features. Camera enthusiasts in upper elementary grades may wish to take photographs to illustrate their talks.

EXAMINING SAND

A look at some sand from the beach or elsewhere through a magnifying glass may be a very enlightening experience. Get two pieces of sandstone and grind them together. Examine the resulting grains of sand through the magnifying glass. From this experience pupils can see that sand has been formed by the grinding up of rocks. It may also help them to realize that rock is formed if grains become pressed together and cemented. A magnifying glass is very important in the study of rocks since the minute structure of rocks is significant in learning about their origin.

---

[1] Adapted from *Earth and Its Resources,* Board of Education of the City of New York, Publication Sales Office, 110 Livingston St., Brooklyn 1, N. Y. (50¢)

SHOWING MOUNTAIN FORMATION

A model to illustrate how mountains are formed and how the layers in the earth become curved and tilted is easily made by pupils. Place layers of different kinds of clay, sand, plasticine, and gravel in a cardboard box. These layers of material should be moist (about "mud pie" consistency). After the layers are packed together, cut out the ends of the cardboard box, but leave them in place, and slowly push the ends toward the middle. This forces the layers into a position resembling folded mountains. Now with a sharp knife cut down through the middle of the layers and lift the two parts away from each other. A baking pan may be used to hold the model. When pupils engage in an activity such as this, they should remember why it is being done and relate what they see in the demonstration to what they have learned.

Another way to get an idea of how mountains are formed is as follows: take several sheets of paper of different colors and textures and lay them flat on the desk. Place your hands on the papers near the ends and push them toward the middle of the paper. The paper forms a "hump" in the middle somewhat as a mountain may be formed by forces pushing on rock layers. If the paper could break, part of it would push past other parts and form a fault. The different colors and textures on the paper help to show how the layers would arrange themselves.

LOOKING FOR CHANGES IN THE EARTH

It is often possible for children to see many examples of erosion on their school ground or even on a short field trip. If possible, pupils should be taken to see where these changes are taking place. They might observe a river or creek to see how it is wearing away a bed, pick up stones from the creek bed to see how round they are, and explain why the

Soil erosion becomes more meaningful as these pupils plan and carry out a field trip to observe its effects. The equipment is listed here. Pupils' notebooks contain a list of problems to solve.

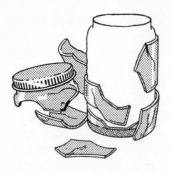

Freezing water has broken the jar in the refrigerator, much as water breaks rocks when it seeps into cracks and expands as it freezes.

creek bed is covered with stones (the lighter material has been carried away by the water). They may be able to observe trees and other plants growing out of rock formations and see how the rocks have split. They may examine tiny plants growing in rocky surfaces. If they try to lift one of the plants from its growing place, they will see how the tiny roots are growing into crevices in the rock itself.

A so-called "empty" lot may help pupils to see the results of forces that change the earth. They may try to answer, through careful observation, such questions as: (1) How have people changed the surface of the lot? (For example, people make short-cut paths across the lot, producing a bare area. What effect does this have on the surface?) (2) What signs of erosion can be seen? (Soil that has been moved, gullies, exposed rocks, róots of trees and other plants, effects of wind.) (3) What are the rocks like? How do you think they have changed through the years? How do you think they got there?

An excavation near your school is a natural place to visit to see what the earth is like under the surface. Pupils will note the darker top soil and the subsoil grading down to small and large rocks. They may also note different rock and soil layers.

A trip to look for different land and rock forms will help to give meaning to the material. Observe land forms: hills, bluffs, plains, beaches, and rock forms: outcrops, igneous, sedimentary, and metamorphic rocks, effects of glaciers, terminal moraines, etc. What pupils are able to observe depends, of course, on the location.

EXPERIMENTING WITH WATER

Fill a small glass jar with water to the top and screw the cover on. Set it in the refrigerator freezing compartment and let it freeze. It should be placed in a paper bag so that the results may more easily be examined. The jar will be cracked by the expansion of the water as it changes into ice. Plumbers or garage mechanics sometimes can supply metal pipes or parts that have been cracked by freezing water. Seeing these will help pupils realize as water freezes, it exerts a great force that can easily break up rocks. If there are rock formations nearby, pouring water on them may help pupils to see how it sinks down into the cracks.

Pouring several pails of water on a sloping part of the school playground will help pupils to see how water carries soil away with it. Dipping a drinking glass of water from a muddy stream after a heavy rain and examining it helps pupils to see that it is soil that makes the water brown and consequently that water is carrying off the soil.

RESOURCES TO INVESTIGATE†

1. Local public buildings to see the uses of rocks and minerals.
2. Local landscape to observe land forms and changes in them—rivers, stream beds, banks, pits, shores of bodies of water, valleys, etc.
3. A well-driller to furnish samples of different soils and rock formations from under-ground and for information about local conditions under the earth's surface.
4. Samples of different kinds of soil to discover how they are alike and how they are different, what they are made of, etc.
5. State Roads Commission for information about land formations where roads are being constructed.
6. Soil Conservation Department for information on erosion problems of local area and on conservation practices in action.
7. Pictures from books and magazines that show the earth's surface at many different places on the earth, to compare and contrast and to discover what changes may have occurred in these places.
8. National Park Service, Washington 25, D. C., for information about national parks.[2] Examine text and pictures for information about the park geology.

---

† Here and in each of the subsequent chapters will be found a list of people, places, things, and special kinds of resources helpful in teaching the material of the chapter and in developing attitudes and appreciations. How many of them will be useful for a specific locality depends, of course, on local conditions. They have all been found helpful in many situations.

[2] National Park Service, *Lassen Volcanic National Park*, Washington, D. C., U. S. Government Printing Office. For sale by the Superintendent of Documents, Washington 25, D. C. (5¢).

National Park Service, *Hot Springs National Park, Yellowstone National Park, and Glacier National Park*, Washington, D. C., U. S. Government Printing Office. For sale by the Superintendent of Documents, Washington 25, D. C. (5¢).

CHAPTER 7A

The Sun and the Planets

The 1958 edition of *Elementary School Science and How To Teach It* contained the following passage:

Perhaps school children in the twenty-first century will study astronomy from space ships. This would be most fortunate because they would then get a much clearer perspective of the universe than we earth-bound beings get now. No models, diagrams, or explanations would be necessary for them to learn that the earth is round, that the earth turns on its axis as it moves around the sun, that the moon tags along with the earth. From space ships children could see the half of the earth that is in daylight and the half that is in darkness. As they moved farther away from the earth, they could see that it is but one of nine planets that are part of the sun's family. They could experience the vast distances of space and come to understand that the earth is really a very small part of the universe.

We call attention to this passage to underscore the swift progression of events in the Space Age. We are no longer "earth-bound beings." We are able to share with astronauts, at least vicariously, the thrill of looking at the earth from space, of circling it in an hour and a half, of seeing in that time its light and dark halves. We look foward confidently to the deep penetration of space by men to whom the earth will appear but a tiny speck in a vast universe.

SEE PAG 140

THE SUN'S FAMILY

The sun is the center of a family of heavenly bodies known as the *solar system.* The head of the family, of course, is the sun, and the principal members are the nine planets that revolve around it, each in its own more or less circular orbit. In order of increasing distance from the sun, the planets are Mercury, Venus, Earth, Mars, Jupiter, Saturn, Uranus, Neptune, and Pluto. Somewhat less known are the more than two thousand small asteroids that revolve around the sun in the space between the orbits of Mars and Jupiter.

Many of the planets have their close "relations"—the satellites that revolve around them. Thirty-one satellites in all have been observed: one for Earth (which we call "Moon"), two for Mars, twelve for Jupiter, nine for Saturn, five for Uranus, and two for Neptune.

Also included in the family are the numerous comets, with eccentric orbits that bring them close to the sun and then far out into the solar system. Billions of meteors, varying in size from a grain of sand to a huge boulder, also move around the sun and are counted as members of its family.

The solar system is a vast race track with planets and their attendant satellites, comets, and meteors streaking around their celestial center—the sun.

GRAVITY AND THE SOLAR SYSTEM

Why do members of the solar system not fly away from the sun as they hurtle through space at thousands of miles an hour? What keeps them in their orbits? Sir Isaac Newton provided an answer in the seventeenth century with his law of gravitation. In its simplest form, the law states:

All bodies, from the largest star in the universe to the smallest particle of matter, attract each other with what is called a gravitational pull.

The strength of the gravitational pull between two bodies depends on their masses (roughly, the amount or weight of material in them).

The closer two bodies are to each other, the greater the mutual attraction. (Specifically, the attraction varies inversely as the square of the distance between the two bodies. If the distance between two bodies is doubled, the gravitational attraction is only one quarter as great. If the distance is halved the attraction is four times as great.)

The planets and the other bodies in the solar system do not streak off into space because of mutual gravitational attraction between these bodies and the sun.

THE SUN

Space travelers journeying to the outer edges of the solar system, to Pluto and beyond, would find the sun appearing smaller and smaller in the sky until it looked just like a star—which is exactly what it is. Our sun is but one of the billions of stars in the universe, and only a moderate-sized one at that. It looks larger than the other stars because it is so much closer to us. The sun is about 93 million miles from the earth. This figure means more if we translate it into other terms. Assume that a space ship travels at an average rate of 25,000 miles an hour, a speed which would enable it to circle the earth once in an hour. At this speed, it would require about five months to reach the sun.

THE FACE OF THE SUN. The familiar bright disk of the sun has a diameter of 864,000 miles, about 109 times that of the earth. The visible surface of the sun is known as the *photosphere,* or "light sphere." Photographs of the sun indicate that the photosphere has a mottled appearance (which you can observe around the edges of the photograph on page 110).

The sun, like the earth, has an atmosphere of gases around it. Extending outward from the bright photosphere is a layer that is known as the *chromosphere* (color sphere), a transparent gaseous layer thousands of miles thick, colored red with glowing hydrogen. From time to time eruptions hundreds of thousands of miles high stream out from the chromosphere to form colorful *prominences*. These are seen best during solar eclipses. Pictured on the first page of this chapter is the transparent *corona*, or "crown," forming the much larger layer of the sun's atmosphere, which reaches as far as ten million miles in some directions. This vast pearly halo, ordinarily invisible, can be seen during a solar eclipse.

Photographs taken through a telescope show that the sun's disk is not uniform: here and there are darker areas called sunspots. *(Note: Extreme care must be taken when looking at the sun. The sun should never be viewed through a telescope or any other optical device. To protect the eyes, the sun should be viewed briefly—a second for a look—through two layers of black photographic film negatives. To prepare the negatives, remove unexposed verichrome film, expose in daylight and develop fully. The film should now have what the photographer calls a film factor of 6.0.)* Sunspots have

been studied carefully by scientists. They are believed to be associated with magnetic disturbances in the sun. Sunspots grow large and then disappear, but it may take several weeks or months for this to happen. Sunspots appear dark because the temperature in these areas is somewhat less than elsewhere on the surface of the sun.

Sunspots range from 500 miles in diameter, barely detectable through a telescope, to 50,000 miles. If a particular sunspot is watched day after day, it appears to move from west to east. This movement is due to the turning of the sun on its axis. As the sun rotates, it carries the sunspots around with it. However, all parts of the sun do not move together: its equator takes 25 days and the region near its poles about 34 days for a complete rotation.

When magnetic storms rage on the sun, we are aware of it on earth. Magnetic needles tremble; radio reception and telegraph and telephone communication are disrupted. Scientists suspect that sunspot activity causes the sun to hurl a stream of electrified particles into space. These are believed to strike the earth's ionosphere, an electrically charged layer of the earth's upper atmosphere. The excessive charging of the ionosphere makes it act like an electrical blotter: it soaks up radio waves instead of reflecting

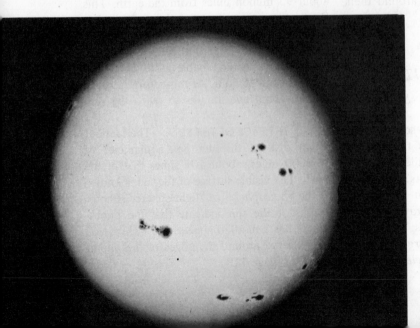

This large group of sunspots was photographed in 1957. Observe also the granular surface of the sun, shown more distinctly near the edges.

them back to earth, and thus weakens and distorts reception.

Another effect of this barrage from the sun on our atmosphere is to produce the beautiful display called the Northern Lights, or the Aurora Borealis.

THE SUN'S ENERGY.   For billions of years the sun has been radiating light into the vast reaches of space. What is the source of this energy? Recent findings of scientists indicate that the energy of the sun is *atomic energy* (see chapter 19A), produced in very much the same way as in a hydrogen bomb.

By means of instruments that measure the temperature of distant objects through an analysis of their light, scientists have calculated that the temperature on the *surface* of the sun is about 10,000° F. This fiercely hot temperature, however, would not be sufficient to sustain the hydrogen-bomb kind of activity going on inside the sun. Scientists estimate that the temperature there is somewhere near 40,000,000° F.

The sun shines in all directions all the time and the earth is not the only object to receive its rays. The small part of the sun's radiant energy that does reach the earth heats its surface comfortably, supplies green plants with the light essential for the manufacture of food (see chapter 10A), and thereby makes plant and animal life possible.

THE PLANETS

Planet means "wandering star," a word devised by the ancients to describe those heavenly bodies that changed their position in relation to the "fixed stars" of the constellations. They found, for example, that the individual stars making up the Big Dipper were always in the same spot in this constellation, whereas the planets Venus and Mars were seen in different places at different times, appearing to wander among the stars.

Today we know that the planets are not stars. Planets shine by light reflected from the sun, whereas stars (like our sun) shine by virtue of their own internal atomic activities. The nine planets are much smaller than most of the stars we see in the sky. Their apparent brilliance and size is indicative of their closeness to the earth.

The "wandering" of planets is due to their movement in a solar race track in which the earth is also moving. If we think for a moment of a real race track with nine horses galloping around it at different speeds, a jockey on a horse named Earth would see the other horses and their riders in different *relationships* as lap after lap was completed, both with respect to each other and when viewed against fixed objects in the distant landscape, like buildings and trees.

Let us look at the planets from another vantage point, that of an observer on the North Star (which is directly "above" the earth's North Pole). He would see that all of the planets move in the same counter-clockwise direction, and that their paths, or orbits, except for that of Pluto, are almost circular. If he used Earth time as his standard, he would find that Mercury on the inside track completed its circuit in 88 days, Earth in 365¼ days, outermost Pluto in almost 250 *years*.

A space observer would note that while the planets were moving around the sun they were also spinning like tops. The word *revolution* is used to designate the circuit around the sun; the word *rotation* designates the spinning. Revolution relates to a planet's orbit, to its "year." Rotation relates to its spinning, to its night and day.

It is difficult to visualize the vast distances, the empty voids in the solar system, without recourse to man-sized models. Picture the sun reduced to the size of a fifty-foot ball, perched on top of a large building. On this scale Mercury would be a handball, 2¼ inches in diameter, about 2,000 feet away. Venus would be a small melon, 5½ inches

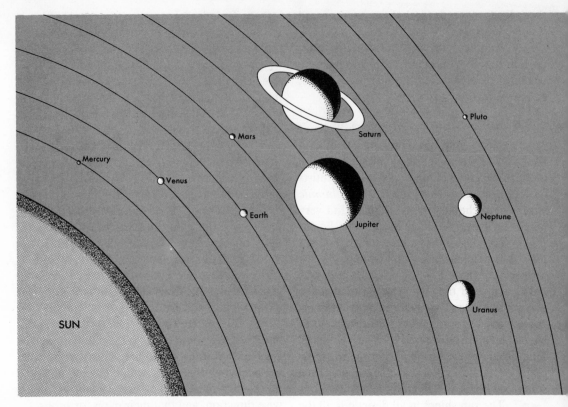

The planets are drawn to scale in this diagram, but not the distances between their orbits. The table on page 119 gives additional data on the planets.

in diameter, about ¾ of a mile from the sun. Earth, slightly larger than Venus, would be located 1 mile from the sun. Mars, the size of a ball 3 inches in diameter, would take its place 1½ miles from the sun.

Now we come to the "big four" in the planet world. In our scale they have the following sizes and distances from the sun: Jupiter, 5 feet, 5¼ miles; Saturn, 4 feet and 2 inches, 9½ miles; Uranus, 22 inches, 19 miles; Neptune, 21 inches, 30 miles.

Pluto, a small planet, would be a ball about 5 inches in diameter, 41 miles from the sun.

MERCURY. Mercury is so close to the sun and is so enveloped by its brightness that most city dwellers rarely get a chance to see it. We must look for this planet on the western horizon just after sunset, or on the eastern horizon just before sunrise. Added to our difficulty is the fact that Mercury is quite small; if it fell into the middle of the Atlantic Ocean it would not touch either shore.

Mercury completes its trip around the sun in 88 days, keeping the same side facing the sun at all times. This face, scorched by the strong rays of the close sun, must be very hot. Measurements taken by a device called a thermocouple through Mount Wilson's hundred-inch reflecting telescope show that the surface temperature on the sunny side is about 770° F., hot enough to melt lead. Its perpetually dark side, however, probably approaches *absolute zero*, 459° below zero F.

The sharp outline of the silhouette of Mercury when it passes in front of the bright face of the sun (this is called a *transit*) indicates that it is devoid of an atmosphere.

VENUS.   Venus has been called the mysterious planet, because even with our best telescopes we have not been able to penetrate the thick clouds that blanket her surface at all times. Sky telescopes and satellites are giving us a clearer and closer look at Venus. Telescopes have been hoisted on balloons to an altitude of 80,000 feet, above almost all of the earth's air. Clearer views are possible at high altitudes because the telescope is above the turbulence, dust, and water vapor that blurs celestial objects when viewed from the surface of the earth.

On December 14, 1962, the Mariner II spacecraft flew within 21,000 miles of Venus after a 109 day voyage of more than 180 million miles. Mariner's instruments radioed 65 million separate bits of information back to Earth. Interpretation of this data thus far has revealed the following information about Venus. The surface temperature of Venus is about 800° F., far above the melting point of lead—thus ruling out the possibility of life as we know it. Venus's atmosphere contains carbon dioxide but probably has little free oxygen or water vapor.

Venus is covered by a cold dense cloud layer which starts at a height of 45 miles above Venus's surface and extends about 15 miles up. The clouds are composed of condensed hydrocarbons (compounds of hydrogen and carbon).

Venus moves in an orbit between that of Mercury and the Earth, taking 224.7 days for a trip around the sun. Venus is almost the same size as the Earth, being only 300 miles less in diameter. Named for the Greek goddess of love, Venus is, with the exception of the sun and the moon, the brightest object in the sky.

We do not know whether Venus has continents or oceans. The problem of how long a day is on Venus has also been a mystery to scientists. The thick clouds around this planet have made it impossible to see definite, recognizable surface markings that could enable us to determine its period of rotation. However, in 1955 Dr. Audouin Dollfus of Meudon Observatory reported on a ten-year study he had made of this problem. Using special techniques, he was able to fix on certain surface features

An artist's conception of Mariner II as it flew by Venus in 1962. Data radioed back to Earth indicated that Venus has a surface temperature of 800° F.

that he detected through gaps in the high cloud layer. He believes that the period of rotation is 224.7 days, which is also the same time that it takes this planet to make one revolution around the sun. Data from the Mariner II flight of 1962 confirmed this finding. This means that Venus, like Mercury, always keeps the same face turned toward the sun. In this, it resembles the moon, which always presents the same face to the earth.

EARTH. It is interesting to compare the answers that children of different generations give to the question "How do we know the earth is round?" A half century ago the stock answer would have been based on the story of Columbus watching ships sail over the horizon, with the mast disappearing from view last. In the last few decades, a typical and more spontaneous answer has been, "Because we can fly around it." Today's children can say with accuracy, "Because we have taken pictures of the earth from rocket ships that show its roundness," or "Because astronauts orbited around it and saw that it was round." Perhaps for tomorrow's space-traveling children, the question will be an academic one; they will be able to see the earth as a planet in space.

If we measure the planet Earth, we find that it is not quite a perfect sphere: its diameter of 7,900 miles from pole to pole is 27 miles less than its equatorial diameter. During the International Geophysical Year (see chapter 6A), careful measurements revealed that the earth was slightly pear-shaped.

Earth, the third planet from the sun, hurtles along in its orbit at the rate of about 66,000 miles an hour to complete its yearly tour of approximately 600 million miles. This path is not a perfect circle; it is slightly elliptical, with the sun not quite in the center. As a result, the earth is closest to the sun on January 1, when it is 91½ million miles away, and furthest away on July 1,

when it is 94½ million miles away. On April 1 and October 1, the distance is between these extremes, about 93 million miles. These statistics may be surprising to those who have assumed that the seasons are determined by the distance of the earth from the sun. We will consider the cause of seasons presently.

While the earth is executing its yearly orbit or revolution around the sun, it is spinning on its axis, performing this rotation 365¼ times in this period. Places at the equator turn with the spinning planet at the rate of about 1,000 miles an hour; Salt Lake City, which is about halfway between the equator and the North Pole, turns at the rate of about 800 miles an hour.

DAY AND NIGHT. Since the earth is an opaque ball and receives light from one principal source, only one side of it can be lighted at one time. The half receiving light is in daylight while the other half is having night. Since the earth rotates on its axis, day and night alternate in regular fashion.

The apparent daily motion of the sun across the sky from east to west is of course due to the actual turning of the earth from west to east.

THE SEASONS. Put in simplest terms, the different seasons in the place where you live are determined by the differences in the amount of heat received from the sun at different times of the year. Consider for a moment just one square foot of any open field in your locality. Disregarding local conditions, the amount of heat received daily by this designated square will depend on two factors:

1. The number of hours of sunlight.
2. The strength of the sunlight.

Point 1 refers to the fact that in summer the days are longer, which means that there are more hours of sunlight to heat soil, rocks, and water.

SEE PAG 134 TO 135

SEE PAC 135 TO 137

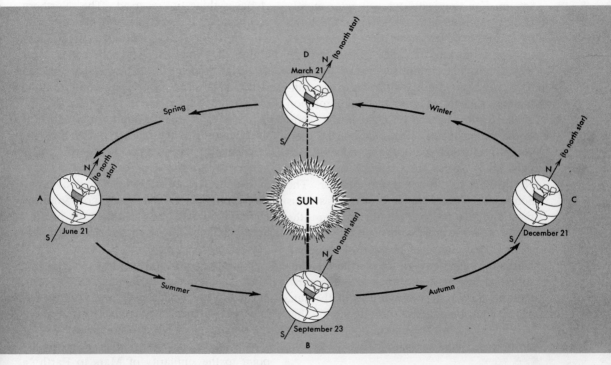

The causes of the seasons. For a detailed description, see pages 114–116.

Point 2 refers to the fact that in summer, when the sun rides high in the sky, the strength of the sunlight received is greater because its rays strike our part of the earth almost vertically. In winter, when the sun is lower in the sky, the rays of sunlight come to us at more of a slant. These slanting rays are spread over more of the earth's surface than rays that strike vertically; they therefore give less heat (see experiment and drawing, pages 135–136). Furthermore, slanting rays travel a greater distance through our atmosphere than those that strike vertically. The more air they go through, the more of their energy is absorbed along the way and the less is left to heat the surface of the earth.

But we have not yet explained why days vary in length, or why the sun's rays are more nearly vertical at some times than others. To understand this we must leave our little square foot in the field and adjust our vision for a space view of the earth in relation to the sun. The diagram on this page will be a helpful guide in showing the position of the earth in the various seasons.

Let us be guided by three important space facts:

1. *The earth moves, as we have found, in an orbit around the sun.*
2. *The earth's axis is not upright with reference to the plane of this orbit; it leans over, like the Tower of Pisa.*
3. *The earth's axis always points in the same direction in space—toward the North Star.*

Because of these three factors, the northern and southern hemispheres are alternately slanted toward the sun and away from it.

The seasons designated in the diagrams refer to those in the Northern Hemisphere. For simplicity, we will refer mainly to this hemisphere in discussing the following sequence of seasons.

At position A (June 21) the Northern Hemisphere is tipped toward the sun. The part around the North Pole has continuous daylight, despite the daily rotation of the earth. There is no night in the "land of the midnight sun" at this time of the year. As we go further south, the number of daylight hours varies from twenty-four at the North Pole to twelve at the equator. The Southern Hemisphere is in winter at this time and the South Pole region is in the midst of its six months of night.

Thus the tilted position of the earth makes for longer days in the Northern Hemisphere at this time. It also exposes the earth there to the strong, vertical rays of the sun, which contribute to the heating up of that part of the earth. To sum up, long days and strong rays make summer.

The polar cap on Mars shown here grows during the Martian winter and recedes during the summer. It is probable that the cap is more like ground frost than like the massive ice sheets of Earth's arctic regions.

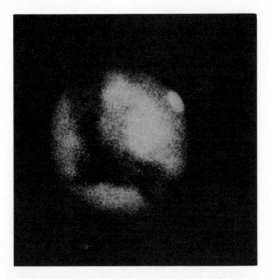

Let us bypass position B for a moment and go to C (Dec. 21). Compared to A, everything is reversed. The Northern Hemisphere is tilted away from the sun. The North Pole is in continuous night. Generally, the Northern Hemisphere has short days and long nights. The rays of the sun strike at a slant. Short days and slanting rays make winter.

At B (Sept. 23) and D (March 21), the beginning of the fall and spring seasons, respectively, the axis of the earth points neither toward nor away from the sun. Days and nights are equal in length all over the earth. Neither the Northern nor Southern Hemisphere receives stronger rays of sunlight.

MARS.   More than any other planet, Mars has excited the imagination of man. Novelists and philosophers as well as scientists have speculated and theorized about the possibility of life on this planet.

Those defending such a possibility point to the similarity of Mars to Earth: a Martian day is almost identical with ours, 24 hours and 37 minutes; Mars has an atmosphere with clouds in it; its axis is tilted at about the same angle as that of the earth, thus producing similar seasonal changes. The white polar caps have recently been shown to be made of ice, thus indicating a possible source of water for the planet. Temperatures, while not as high as those on earth, reach 70 to 80° F. near its equator. The changing colors observed during the different seasons might be attributed to changes in plant life. The canal-like lines described by some astronomers might be the work of intelligent beings. The best indication thus far of life on Mars was the discovery by W. Sinton with the 200-inch Mt. Palomar telescope of the presence there of organic molecules, the kind associated on earth only with living things.

Those who argue against the possibility of life on Mars point to the fact that the only common gases definitely identified in its atmosphere are carbon dioxide and nitrogen, there being no detectable trace of oxygen and practically no water vapor; that the average temperature for the planet is 20 to 30° *below* zero F. (the earth's average is 60° *above*). They point to the evidence indicating that the white caps that spread from the poles in winter are at best thin layers of frost; that most of the planet is a dry, barren desert, swept by thick dust storms.

Mars is nevertheless a fascinating planet for telescopic study. Its white polar caps advance and retreat with the seasons. The surface of its desert areas, which appear to range from light yellow to brick red, give Mars its ruddy color, and help the observer identify it in the sky without the use of a telescope. Other darker areas on the planet are gray, bluish, or greenish in winter, changing to brown or even violet or crimson in the summer. Two tiny moons circle the planet. Phobos, the nearer one, is ten miles in diameter and races around Mars in eight hours. Deimos, farther away, is only five miles in diameter and takes about thirty hours for its circuit.

At intervals of about fifteen years, the paths of Mars and Earth bring them relatively close to each other, so that only 35 million miles separate the two planets. At these times astronomers direct their instruments toward the ruddy planet to see if they can find answers to many unsolved problems about Mars. September 1956 provided such an opportunity; so, too, will August 1971.

We no longer have to wait for these close approaches of the two planets. Sky balloons and satellites sent into orbit around Mars carry instruments which serve as eyes in space for us. Perhaps while the current edition of this book is still in print, we will have placed men and equipment on Mars, and will know the full story of the red planet.

THE ASTEROIDS.   In a broad zone between the orbits of Mars and Jupiter are a swarm of thousands of smaller bodies, the asteroids. Fifteen hundred of these, ranging in size from a mile to five hundred miles, have been registered and named by astronomers. The largest and the first to be discovered was Ceres. Asteroids apparently lack water, air, and warmth. It is thought that they may have arisen from the breaking up of a planet.

JUPITER.   The next four planets we will consider are the giants of the solar system. They differ from the inner planets not only in size but in the speed of their rotation, taking only ten to fifteen hours to complete their daily spin. All have such deep atmospheres that we do not know where the solid part of the planet begins. Except for Neptune, they have numerous moons.

The leader among the giants, with a diameter eleven times that of the earth, is Jupiter, named after the most powerful of the Greek gods. To the naked eye, Jupiter is often the brightest object in the sky and may be confused with Venus. However, Venus sets soon after the sun, whereas Jupiter stays up late, so that it is not difficult to distinguish them. Through the telescope, we can see that Jupiter is encircled by yellow, brown, and orange bands, alternating with darker stripes, all more or less parallel to the equator. Close inspection by astronomers has shown that these banded markings are not on the solid part of Jupiter; they seem to be floating in the deep atmospheric ocean that surrounds the planet. Outside this atmospheric ocean, there are twelve moons revolving around Jupiter.

The chemical materials which make up this banded planet have attracted a good deal of attention from scientists. It is thought that Jupiter probably has a small solid core of rock and metal, covered by a thick layer of ice and frozen ammonia. Over this is a huge sea of liquefied methane (marsh gas). Over all is an enveloping atmosphere of hydrogen, helium, and gaseous ammonia and

A drawing of Saturn as seen through a 40-inch refracting telescope. Saturn's rings were first seen by Galileo in 1610.

methane. These materials, which make one think of a fuming chemical laboratory, plus the recorded surface temperature of minus 210° F., hardly make Jupiter an inviting place for a stopover by space tourists.

SATURN. Seen through a telescope, Saturn is an unforgettable sight. This showpiece of the solar system has three broad, thin rings that wheel around its equator. The rings were thought to be made of fragments of rock, possibly originating from the shattering of a moon that came too close to the planet. However, in August 1957, Gerard P. Kuiper, astronomer at the University of Chicago, stated that his observations of the rings led him to believe that they were made of snow crystals.

Saturn, one of the giant planets, has nine moons. One of them, Titan, is larger than our moon and is notable for the fact that it is the only one of the thirty-one satellites in the solar system on which we have detected an atmosphere.

URANUS. All of the planets described thus far were known to the ancients. The next three, Uranus, Neptune, and Pluto, revolving in the bleak outer regions of the solar system, were discovered by later astronomers equipped with telescopes. Uranus is twenty times as far from the sun as the earth is, Neptune thirty times, and Pluto forty times. From these planets the sun appears so small that it is hard to distinguish it from other stars.

Uranus was discovered in 1781 by the astronomer William Hershel, who, while making a systematic survey of stars, noticed one that refused to stay in place. Barely visible to the unaided eye, Uranus under powerful telescopes appears as a tiny green object with faint parallel bands. Unlike all the other planets, which spin like tops on the imaginary platforms of their orbits, Uranus spins like a top that has fallen over and is rolling along on its orbit.

NEPTUNE. If the discovery of Uranus might be termed an "accident," that of Neptune certainly could not. This planet was discovered when astronomers noticed that Uranus was not following the orbit expected by astronomers; instead it seemed to waver slightly in its path as if it were being attracted by another planet. In 1846 two astronomers, Adams and Leverrier, working independently, determined the exact position where that unknown planet should be. When telescopes were focused upon that position at the time indicated, the planet Neptune was discovered.

Neptune has two moons. The larger one, Triton, is about the size of the planet Mercury.

PLUTO. Pluto was discovered in much the same way as Neptune. Its existence was predicted because of Neptune's departure from the path calculated for it by astronomers. Pluto, the outermost of the planets yet discovered, takes 248 years to make its journey around the sun. Since its discovery in 1930 by Clyde Tombaugh, we have been able to observe only a small part of Pluto's orbit.

Beyond Pluto, are there other planets in our solar system? Some scientists think so. They feel that a larger body than Pluto must be responsible for attracting Neptune from its calculated course. Other planets in the outer bounds of the solar system may be detected by astronomers who are now scanning the skies with improved telescopes.

Are there planets outside of our solar system? Scientists speculate that, since stars are suns, it is possible that they too may have families of planets around them. Our present instruments would be inadequate, however, to detect planets as large as Jupiter, even on the nearest star.

SUMMARY OF FACTS ON THE SOLAR SYSTEM

Name of planet	Approximate diameter in thousands of miles	Average distance from sun in millions of miles	Length of year (revolution around sun)		Length of day (time for one rotation)	Number of moons
Mercury	3	36	88	days	88 days	0
Venus	8	67	225	days	225 days(?)	0
Earth	8	93	365¼	days	1 day	1
Mars	4	140	687	days	1 day	2
Jupiter	87	480	11.9	years	10 hours	12
Saturn	71	890	29.5	years	10 hours	9
Uranus	29	1,800	84	years	11 hours	5
Neptune	28	2,800	164.8	years	16 hours	2
Pluto	6(?)	3,700	248.7	years	6 days(?)	0

COMETS. In 1910, when Halley's comet appeared in the sky, it was regarded by thousands of people as an omen of disaster. These credulous individuals were perpetuating a fear that goes back to antiquity. An end-of-the-world panic gripped many, who thought that the comet's tail would sweep over the earth with poisonous gases and thereby execute all of mankind in a gargantuan lethal chamber.

When people found themselves alive the day after the predicted disaster, they were glad to forget the whole thing. A few curious ones, however, bothered to find out that the poisonous substance in the comet's tail was so diluted by space that the finest instruments could not detect it in the earth's atmosphere after the passing of the comet.

Halley's comet, named after the English astronomer Edmund Halley, is the most famous of all the comets. Halley was the first to understand that comets are true members of the solar system, not interlopers from outer space. Most comets revolve in orbits around the sun at regular intervals; some swing around once and may never return.

Comets differ from planets in a number of important respects. Comets generally have extremely elongated elliptical orbits, which may bring them close to the sun at one end of their swing in space and then way out beyond the known planets at the other end. It is when comets come near the sun that we can observe them. Unlike planets, comets circle the sun in every direction and in every plane.

This photograph of Halley's Comet was taken through a telescope. Astronomers can forecast the reappearance of comets with great accuracy. (The white streaks are the tracks of stars produced by the turning of the earth in this time-exposure photograph.)

The comets that attract most attention are those consisting of a head and a long tail. Although the head is the more permanent part, it has little substance, being made of small fragments of rock, of dust, and of some gases. The head of a comet is less dense than the earth's atmosphere. It shines, like planets, by reflecting sunlight.

The tail of the comet develops as the comet comes near the sun. This is thought to happen in a curious way. The intense rays of sunlight exert pressure on the minute particles in the head and push out the long spectacular tail, which may extend for millions of miles across the sky. The tail almost always points away from the sun; as the comet approaches the sun, the tail is behind the head; as it speeds away from the sun, the tail precedes it. The tail glows chiefly because of a light given off by the gases in it, acting like a fluorescent neon tube.

Comets travel at high speed, particularly when they are near the sun. Nevertheless they do not streak across the sky like a rocket, as some people think. They may be watched for days, weeks, or even months in their path around the sun. Most comets are small objects in the sky and require a telescope to distinguish them from the stars.

Some comets, like Encke's comet, return frequently. This particular comet has a nearly circular path and returns every three and one-third years. On the other hand, Halley's comet pursues an elongated course that brings it back on an average of once every 76 years. It has a date with you in 1986!

METEORS. If there are any "visitors from outer space," they are the meteors that fly into the atmosphere of the earth. On a clear night, especially at certain times of the year, these "visitors" streak across the sky, causing people to exclaim "look at the shooting star!" These falling bodies are not stars, but *meteors,* fragments of material varying in size from a grain of sand to a boulder of many tons. The glowing streak we see is not far off in starry space—just sixty miles or so up in our own atmosphere.

As the meteors are heated by friction with the air, they glow brilliantly. The heat is sufficient to cause most of the millions of meteors that enter the earth's atmosphere each day to vaporize or burn so that only their fine dust ever reaches the earth's surface. Those that do land in a solid chunk are called *meteorites.* The largest meteorite found so far has a weight of about thirty tons.

Larger meteorites were probably responsible for the well-known Meteor Crater in Arizona, which is a mile in diameter and six hundred feet deep, and for the recently discovered Chubb Crater in Canada, pictured on the opposite page. Meteorites are similar in composition to rocks. One common type is metallic, being made of iron and nickel. Another type is stony, being composed of basalt.

Billions of meteors are scattered throughout the solar system. Some travel alone; others travel in *meteor swarms.* It is thought that the swarms may have resulted from the breakup of a comet. When the earth passes through the path of one of these meteor swarms, we have a *meteor shower.* Showers are named after the constellation from whose *direction* in the sky the meteors seem to come. Thus, the Leonids are named after the constellation Leo.

Meteor showers may be watched by all, no telescope being needed for this spectacle. Look for the Perseids on August 10–14, for the Orionids on October 18–23, for the Leonids on November 14–18, for the Geminids on December 10–13.

Meteors today are more than a scientific curiosity. Scientists are concerned about the possible peril to space travelers of the impact of clouds of meteoric particles that may bombard space vehicles.

THE MOON. If a party of scientists ever land on the moon, their diaries might, in part, read something like this:

SEE PAGE 137

The world's greatest known meteorite crater, discovered in 1950, is located in the northern section of Quebec, Canada. The crater, which is almost perfectly circular, is 2½ miles in diameter and contains a lake. The smaller lakes nearby were apparently formed by meteorite fragments that fell around the main crater.

Meteorologist: Precipitation: none; clouds: none; wind: none; temperature of surface: very hot during the lunar day, reaching 214° F., about the boiling point of water, very cold during night, less than 270° below zero F.; barometric pressure: always zero; general appearance of sky: always black since there is no atmosphere to scatter the sunlight, stars always out; forecast: always the same, except when earth eclipses sun; unofficial reaction: a good place to visit, but not to live.

Physicist: Weight of 180-lb. man on spring scale: 30 lbs., only one-sixth as heavy as on earth; atmosphere: none, pull of gravity is not strong enough to prevent the escape of gases to space; transmission of sound: by radio only, no air to carry sound waves; radiation of sun: intense, strong ultraviolet and cosmic rays; equipment needed: air tanks, pressurized, insulated suits, dark glasses, walkie-talkie; distance back to earth: 222,000 to 253,000 miles; velocity needed to escape from moon and return to earth: 1½ miles per second (on earth escape velocity is 7 miles a second).

Geologist: Main types of land formations: marias ("seas"), mountain ranges, craters, rills, rays. Marias: large, gray, smooth areas, darker than rest of the moon —not seas, no water, no evidence that they ever were seas; naked-eye view of "man-in-moon" from earth due to these darker areas against lighter surface. (Investigate the theory that the marias are hardened fields of lava, caused by a chunk of rock 200 miles in diameter striking and heating the surface of the moon into a molten mass.) Mountain ranges: average height 5,000 to 12,000 feet; some 26,000 to 33,000 (Earth's Mount Everest is 29,000 feet); most mountains rugged, steep-walled, some rounded; most impressive mountain range: Leibnitz Mountains, near south pole of moon (shown at *top* of lunar charts and photographs). Craters: most beautiful crater, Copernicus, surrounded by a ring wall 12,000 feet high at highest point, diameter 56 miles, floor

A small portion of the lunar landscape as seen through a 200-inch telescope. The smooth areas, "marias" or plains, and several craters are seen in this photograph. The large crater, Copernicus, is partly darkened by the shadow cast by one of its walls. This view is one that may greet astronauts shortly before making a landing on the moon.

of crater depressed below level of surrounding territory; most craters have large central peaks. (Investigate to determine whether craters are caused by impact of meteors on surface of moon, like Meteor Crater in Arizona, or whether they are caused by volcanic activity—or, whether both of these influences have produced different kinds of craters.) Rills: Cracks in the moon's surface, some broad and flat, some narrow and deep like Grand Canyon. Rays: brilliant white streaks on the surface of the moon, up to 100 miles long; always emanate from some crater. (Investigate the rays to clear up the mystery of their origin.) Other geological investigations: Check surface of moon to find out the nature and the thickness of the dust layer; look for volcanoes and possible volcanic activity; investigate side of moon which is not seen from earth and compare with photographs taken by satellite in 1959; check rocks to see if any water is trapped in them.

Astronomer: Viewing conditions: excellent, good chance to study planets and stars without distortion or interference from an atmosphere; can observe at all times, day or night. Length of day and night: about two weeks each. Opportunity to observe earth: earth always visible from one side of moon, never visible on other side. General appearance of earth: looks like a big moon, diameter about four times that of the moon; oceans, continents, dark forests, white polar caps, clouds, great rivers visible; in moon's night, earthshine bright enough to read by; earth has phases: full earth, quarter earth, crescent earth, etc. Appearance of sun: bright disc against pitch-black sky. Corona visible, as is also the *zodiacal light,* a faint elliptical glow extending from the sun into space. (Note: Look for new star groups not visible on earth.)

Biologist: No immediate evidence of large plant or animal life, except ours. (Investigate carefully for possibility of microscopic spores of simple organisms.)

PHASES OF THE MOON

SEE PAGE 138 TO 139

Everyone who has ever watched the moon from night to night knows that it seems to change shape. If the moon is observed for a month, it may be seen *waning* from a full moon to a quarter moon to a thin crescent, then to the new moon ("no" moon) and then *waxing* to crescent, quarter, and full moon. These changes are known as the phases of the moon. Let us see what causes them.

The moon, like the earth, receives its light from the sun. Moonlight is thus reflected sunlight. Like the earth, the moon is an opaque sphere, so that only half of it is illuminated at any one time. However, since the moon revolves around the earth, we are not always in a position to see the lighted half. When we do see the whole lighted half we call it a full moon. When only half of the lighted part is visible, we see a quarter moon. When all of the lighted part faces away from the earth, we have "no" moon or a new moon. The demonstration suggested on pages 138–139 will help in an understanding of the phases of the moon.

If you are reading this at home now, you can understand the phases easily by doing the following. Hold an orange or any other round object in one hand, in such a way that your fingers do not obscure its surface. This object represents the moon.

A nearby table lamp represents the sun. Your head represents the earth. Face the lamp, holding the orange in front of you and slightly above the level of the top of your head. Observe that the side of the orange facing you is dark, representing the new moon. Now slowly describe a circle in the air with the orange, moving it toward your left. Look at it at all times to see how the portion illuminated by the lamp increases and then decreases.

It might be helpful to remind ourselves at this point that the moon always shows almost the same face or "man in the moon" to us on earth, but that this face is not always "lit up." If you paint a face on your orange and again wheel it through the air around your head, you can demonstrate this to yourself.

Before man reaches the moon, unmanned vehicles will unveil the secrets of its surface. The lunar spacecraft shown here is Surveyer, equipped with four television cameras. Drills will pierce the moon's crust to obtain samples for analysis, while other instruments will measure the moon's magnetism, gravity, impact of meteors, and other phenomena. Scientists on Earth will watch via television as this lunar laboratory performs its tasks.

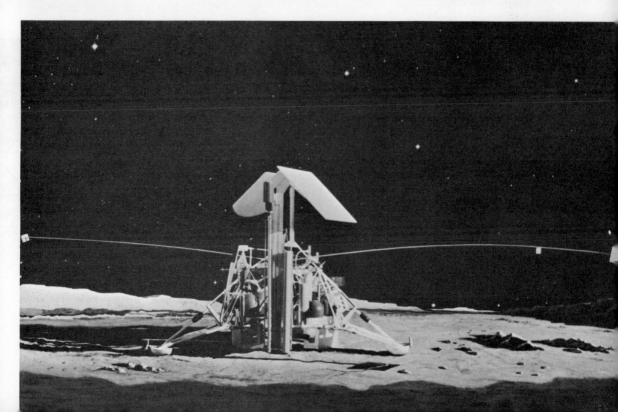

TIDES

The everlasting succession of low tide and high tide make the edge of the sea a constantly changing boundary. The range of tides varies widely in different localities, depending on the nature of the shore line and the ocean floor. Thus, in the open ocean the tidal range may be 2 or 3 feet. In Cape Cod Bay, on the other hand, the range may be as much as 10 or 11 feet, while in the narrowing Bay of Fundy of Nova Scotia the range may be as much as 60 feet.

For about six hours, the incoming or *flood tide* rises higher and higher, covering more and more of sloping beaches and climbing up on rocky shores. Then for six hours the falling or *ebb tide* recedes.

Two factors are responsible for the rhythm of the tides: the gravitational pull of the moon (and to a lesser extent the sun) and the rotation of the earth. Let us consider gravitation first.

The law of gravitation states in part, as we have seen, that every body attracts every other body in the universe. Thus the

earth attracts the moon, and the moon attracts the earth. The pull of the moon is relatively weak but is strong enough to have an effect on all parts of the earth—on the atmosphere and on the oceans as well as on the solid part. But the law of gravitation also states that the strength of the pull depends in part on the distance between the two bodies, being greater for closer objects. This has an interesting effect on the earth. The ocean on the side of the earth facing the moon is, because of its closer position, subject to more pull than the earth as a whole. As a result, it bulges several feet on the side closest to the moon. At the same time, there is another bulge in the ocean on the opposite side of the earth. This is more difficult to understand until we realize that the solid part of the earth is pulled harder (because it is closer to the moon) than the ocean on that side of the earth. The water on that side, therefore, also bulges away from the earth.

The water drawn into the two bulges must come from somewhere. It comes from the ocean areas between them, causing a

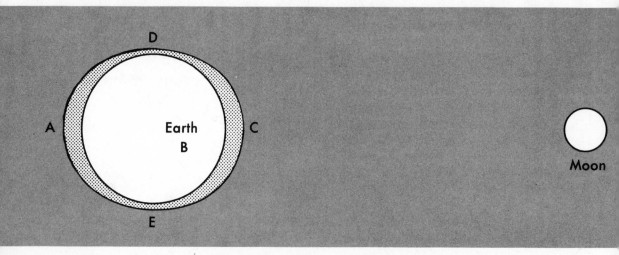

In this diagram earth and moon are viewed from a position in space "above" the North Pole. The ocean at C is attracted by the moon more than the earth (B), causing a high tide there. But the earth (B) is attracted more than the ocean at A, causing the ocean to bulge there also. Water is drawn into A and C from D and E, leaving low tides there.

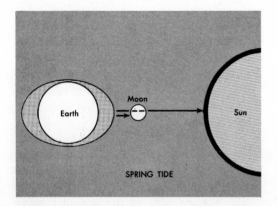

SPRING TIDE

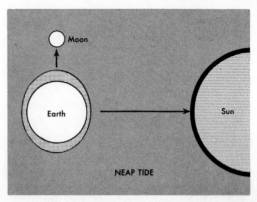

NEAP TIDE

The left-hand diagram illustrates how the sun and the moon work together to make the strong spring tide.

In the right-hand diagram the sun and the moon are working against each other to cause the weak neap tide.

depression there. Thus, at any one time, we have two bulges or *high tides* as shown in the diagram, and two depressions or *low tides* in the earth's oceans.

If the earth did not turn on its axis, we would have two permanent, stationary bulges and two similar depressions. But the earth completes a rotation every twenty-four hours, turning one place after another toward the moon's direct pull. As a result, the high tides and the low tides sweep around the earth to produce the tidal rhythm, high, low, high, low approximately every twenty-four hours.

We say "approximately" because the moon, too, is shifting its position as it moves in its orbit around the earth. As a result, the time between one high tide and the next is not twelve hours but an average of twelve hours and twenty-six minutes.

The United States Government provides tables and charts for mariners, showing times when high and low tides occur at many places along coasts. There are signs on many beaches for the benefit of swimmers, indicating the day-to-day schedule of tides. Ship's arrivals and departures are timed according to the tides to make certain that channels are deep enough for incoming ships and to prevent ships from having to

push their way out to sea against an incoming tide.

The following schedule is typical of tides:

	A. M.	P. M.	Time between high tides
Tues., July 31	1:03	1:38	12 hr. 35 min.
Wed., Aug. 1	2:08	2:44	12 hr. 36 min.
Thurs., Aug. 2	3:21	3:54	12 hr. 33 min.
Fri., Aug. 3	4:31	4:58	12 hr. 27 min.
Sat., Aug. 4	5:33	5:56	12 hr. 23 min.
Sun., Aug. 5	6:28	6:48	12 hr. 20 min.
Mon., Aug. 6	7:19	7:38	12 hr. 19 min.

The pull of the sun also affects tides. Despite its tremendous size, the sun is so distant from the earth that its tide-raising force is less than half that of the moon. This force may work with or against the moon's pull, depending on the relative position of the sun, moon, and earth. When the sun is in line with the moon, as it is during the periods of full moon and new moon, it *adds* its pull, thereby causing high high-tides and low low-tides. This tide is called a *spring tide,* although it has nothing to do with the spring of the year. Spring tides occur twice a month. They should be thought of as tides that "spring up" high.

When the sun pulls at right angles with respect to the pull of the moon on the earth, as it does when the moon is in its first and last quarter, it hinders the moon's efforts, producing tides that neither rise very high nor fall very low. These are the *neap* tides, also occurring twice a month.

ECLIPSES

SEE
PAGES
139
TO
140

Eclipses occur when the sun, earth, and moon are on a straight line in space. There are two kinds of eclipses, solar and lunar.

Solar eclipses occur when the moon passes directly in front of the sun, thus obscuring it from our vision. If you shut one eye and look at an electric bulb across the room with the other, you can hide its light with a penny held at the right distance from you. The penny (the moon) has eclipsed the bulb (the sun). Note that although the penny is smaller, it can eclipse the larger bulb because it is closer to you.

A friend observing you at this time would see the shadow of the penny on your open eye. Similarly, an astronaut in space would observe that the shadow of the moon falls on the earth during a solar eclipse. Since the moon is smaller than the earth and close to it, its shadow falls on only a small portion of the earth's surface, and is never more than 167 miles wide. However,

since the moon is moving around the earth, the path of its shadow may form a band thousands of miles long. (To return to the penny–bulb demonstration: If you moved the penny, its shadow would sweep across your head.) This narrow track is called the eclipse path.

A total eclipse of the sun is an exciting spectacle to watch. As you look through black film negatives (see page 110 for method and safeguards) you see a small, dark nick in the western edge of the sun that grows larger and larger. Just before totality, the sky is darkened considerably, and there is a strange hush. When the sun disappears completely, a pearly halo—the corona— appears around the blackened disc of the sun. A few stars appear. This period of total eclipse never lasts more than eight minutes. Astronomers, many of whom have traveled halfway around the world to see the eclipse, are in a frenzy of activity at this time, observing, photographing, and recording the event in their effort to learn more about the corona and the prominences of the sun. Then the moon slips off, and the western edge of the sun appears again and grows. The eclipse is over.

In any year, three to five eclipses of the sun can occur, but no more than three of these can be total. In a partial eclipse, only part of the sun is hidden by the moon. Since solar eclipses follow narrow paths across the earth, they are rare for a particu-

When the moon is at position B, it is in the shadow of the earth (an eclipse of the moon). When it is in position A, it casts a shadow on part of the earth and hides the sun from view there (an eclipse of the sun).

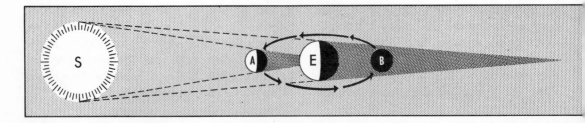

lar locality. In New York City, for example, a total eclipse of the sun occurred on January 24, 1925. This was the first eclipse of this kind there since the fifteenth century! The next total eclipse will occur there on October 26, 2144. The following are the dates and places of the total eclipses visible in the United States during the sixties and seventies:

1963, July 20	Maine, Alaska
1970, March 7	Florida, Georgia, South Carolina, North Carolina
1979, February 26	Idaho, Montana

Lunar eclipses occur when the earth is between the sun and the moon, thereby blocking off the moon's source of light and darkening it. As we observe an eclipse of the moon, therefore, we are watching the shadow of the earth pass across its face. An eclipse of the moon can be observed by all the people on that half of the earth that is in moonlight at the time. Therefore all of us have many opportunities to observe lunar eclipses in our lifetime. Lunar eclipses can occur three to five times a year, with a maximum of three total eclipses in that time.

Eclipses of the sun occur only during the period of the new moon, for it is only then that a sun-moon-earth line-up, in that order, is possible. Eclipses of the moon, on the other hand, occur only during the full moon, when a sun-earth-moon line-up may occur. Why is there not an eclipse of the sun and an eclipse of the moon every month? The answer lies in the peculiar track that the moon follows around the earth. If you can picture the earth and the sun sitting on an imaginary table in space, then the moon's path around the earth cuts through the table at an angle. Sometimes the moon is above the table and sometimes below it. It is only when there is a coincidence of the moon being on the table at the time of a new moon or full moon that an eclipse occurs.

HOW THE SOLAR SYSTEM WAS FORMED

The question of the origin of our solar system has intrigued astronomers for the past two hundred years and has resulted in a number of different theories. All the theories fall into one of two camps: some authorities envision a gradual evolution of the solar system; others a violent revolution. We will consider both.

The classic Nebular Hypothesis of the French astronomer, Marquis Pierre Simon de Laplace, proposed in 1796, is evolutionary in nature. This theory suggests that the sun and the planets were derived from a huge gaseous cloud or nebula, slowly rotating in space. This cloud extended beyond the limits of the known planets. Because of the gravitational attraction among its particles, the cloud contracted and, as it did, spun faster. You can demonstrate such an increase in speed by spinning yourself on a piano stool with your arms outstretched and holding some books and then suddenly pulling your arms and the books to your side. You will find that this "contraction" of yourself makes you go faster. As the nebula spun faster it threw off parts of itself, just as mud is thrown off the rim of a turning bicycle wheel. In this case, according to the theory, rings of gaseous matter were thrown off, revolving in the same plane as the nebula and in the same direction. The material in the rings collected, cooled, and condensed into spherical planets. On further shrinking of the central cloud, more rings were thrown off, one after another, accounting for all of the planets. According to this theory, satellites of the planets are thought to have been formed in a similar way while the planets were still in a gaseous state.

Another famous theory, violent in nature, is the Planetary Hypothesis proposed by the geologist T. C. Chamberlin and the astronomer F. R. Moulton, of the University of Chicago, in 1905. This theory postulates that a star came very close to our sun, exerting a powerful pull on it. Just as the moon causes tides on our terrestrial oceans, so did the passing star cause great tides to form on the sun. Great quantities of material were torn away by this tidal attraction. These then condensed into the separate planets.

Dissatisfaction with both of these theories, arising from increased knowledge, has resulted in a number of new hypotheses being proposed by scientists in this century. One of these is the Dust Cloud Hypothesis, advanced by Fred L. Whipple of the Harvard Observatory. This theory, evolutionary rather than revolutionary in nature, resembles the Nebular Hypothesis in some respects. In brief, it suggest that planets and stars were formed from immense collections of tiny particles floating in space. In such a cloud the mutual gravitational attraction of its particles caused it to condense, or contract. Within the huge cloud, minor turbulent motions caused streams of dust or sub-clouds to form. These minor clouds contracted further to become the various planets, while the major cloud condensed into the sun. The tremendous heat generated by the compression of material to form the sun made it white hot and promoted the 'atomic reactions, mentioned earlier in this chapter, which permitted it to shine as a star. The smaller planets, however, cooled off.

Although there is a good deal of of speculation in these and other theories, they are not wild dreams. Each theory is tested against these criteria:

1. Is it in accordance with known physical principles—with our knowledge of gravitation, heat, light, behavior of atoms?
2. Is the process within the realm of probability?
3. Does it account for our present solar system—its size, its motions, its members?

No generally accepted, adequate theory has yet been achieved. According to Whipple, "we are still groping in the haze of a poorly illuminated and ancient past."

This survey of the solar system contains a great many facts, which may be grouped together into some larger statements. Here are some of the important generalizations:

The sun is the center of a huge system of heavenly bodies that revolve around it. Included in the sun's family are planets, asteroids, satellites, comets, and meteors.

The mutual gravitational attraction between the planets and the sun prevents the planets from flying out of their orbits.

The sun is a nearby star; stars are distant suns.

The sun shines by virtue of its own atomic activities; the planets shine by reflecting sunlight.

Life on earth would be impossible if it were not for the sun.

Physical conditions vary on the different members of the solar system. Thus far, we have evidence of life only on Mars, and that is not conclusive.

All the planets move in the same direction in their nearly circular orbits around the sun.

The earth is the third planet from the sun. It is one of the smaller planets in the solar system.

Day and night are caused by the rotation of the earth on its axis.

The earth's rotation causes the apparent motion of the sun, moon and stars across the sky.

A year is the time it takes the earth to complete one revolution around the sun.

Seasons are caused by the tilt in the earth's axis and the revolution of the earth around the sun.

The principal effect of the moon on the earth is to cause tides.

Eclipses occur when the earth, sun, and moon are on a straight line in space.

Scientists differ in their theories about the origin of the solar system.

NOTE: Suggestions for things to discover for yourself about the sun and the planets will be found at the end of chapter 8A.

CHAPTER 7B

Teaching "The Sun and the Planets"

Too often the study of astronomy is confined to model- and chart-making and indoor experiments with flashlights, globes, and balls. Such aids are important but are no substitute for out-of-door experiences with the wonders in the sky, which help children appreciate that they live on Earth, a planet in space. One good look at the stars, or an observation of the moon with field glasses is much more valuable than dozens of diagrams of star charts.

For young children particularly, and to some extent for all children, there is great need to develop concepts basic to an understanding of space, i.e., concepts of distance, direction, length, weight, time, and motion. This may be thought of as developing "space readiness." It can be developed by experiences in the immediate environment, in the smaller space of a street for example, by comparing the length of a city block, of a clothesline; the distance to a smoke stack, to clouds and other objects in the daytime sky. Observing a cloud moving in front of the sun provides an opportunity to discover that clouds are closer to us than the sun. Pupils may estimate distances and, when possible, measure to see if they are accurate.

At all ages, arithmetic understandings are often necessary to the understanding of science concepts. For example, if pupils read that the earth is about four times as far across as is the moon, it is important that we attempt to bring meaning to this concept. Here models are helpful: a ball to represent the moon, a globe four times the diameter of the ball to represent the earth. Sometimes space distances are a little better understood if they are compared to some distance with which many of the pupils are familiar—for example, the number of miles to a distant city to which many of the pupils may have traveled. The concept of years of time may also be developed if pupils associate their own ages, or some other time span in their experience, with the unfamiliar and much longer time figure. Space exploration is continually providing motivation for the study of planets. Planets are in the news. So is the moon. In the future, some of today's children may indeed be space travelers. This situation adds interest to a study of what is in the sky.

Some broad problems for intermediate grades may be:

What is our solar system like?

Or,

How is our earth related to the solar system?

Smaller problems that are included in these but may be more appropriate, depending on children's interests, maturity, and abilities, are:

What makes day and night?
How does the moon and sun affect us?
What are the other planets like?

As in the previous chapter, we again make suggestions for use with beginning pupils. They have been used successfully in primary grades and at other levels as well, especially where pupils have had little science experience.

1. Try to find some prominent planet in the night sky.
2. Do experiments to see how the sun helps plants to grow. Place some plants in the dark and similar ones in the light, treating both groups of plants alike except for the light factor.
3. Observe shadows to see how they are made and how they change during the day. Record the length and position of a shadow cast by a stick on a large sheet of paper at 9 A.M., at noon, and later in the afternoon.
4. Watch the moon at night to see how it seems to change its shape over a period of several weeks or a month.
5. Feel things that are warmed by the sun and experience the difference in warmth in the sun and in the shade. Feel how clouds passing in front of the sun make a difference in the temperature.

These experiences for primary grades may be centered around such problems as: How is the sun important to us? What can we see in the sky at night?

Firsthand experiences are important at this level. The use of the senses adds greatly to the understanding, as time and distance are difficult concepts for young children to understand.

LOOKING AT THE PLANETS

It is scarcely possible to overestimate the importance of giving pupils an opportunity to look at the night sky through a telescope. If pupils studying about planets can actually see one, their enthusiasm will repay any effort a teacher makes to bring about such an experience. In the community, amateur astronomers with telescopes are often more than willing to let pupils look through their telescopes and, if properly briefed beforehand, will be very helpful to pupils. A nearby school or college may have a telescope. The suggestions given in chapter 3 for making field trips are applicable here. Parents and children may come together for such an evening meeting, to the enlightenment and delight of all concerned and perhaps the further interest of all parties.

Science News Letter[1] indicates periodically which planets are visible at any given time and where to locate them. It is helpful to go out of doors with children during the day at school and point to the section of the sky where they may expect to see the planets at night. It may help them, too, to learn where the planet will be on a particular night in relation to the moon (if there is one visible in the early evening) or to some easily identified star groups. If they can observe the position of the planet at the same time several nights in succession, they will easily see how it changes its position with relation to the constellations in the sky.

MAKING MODELS OF THE SOLAR SYSTEM

When pupils learn more about the sun and its family, they may profit from making a clay or paper cutout model of what they are learning. This activity is particularly useful in the fifth and sixth grades, when pupils know enough arithmetic to get approximately correct proportions of the sizes of various planets as well as their relative distances from one another and from the sun. From various sources pupils will get figures that tell distances and diameters of the various planets. Then they will have to decide on a scale that they can use in order to get all the members of the solar system into the classroom and in order to have the sun (the largest body) as well as Mercury (the smallest body) included. They may in fact need to use a larger area than the classroom, depending on the scale they select. Such a project as this might be started by asking pupils: "What figures will we have to know in order to make the model solar system? How can we adjust the figures to a scale?" Pupils should be urged to make their own plan and then to carry it out. Here is an excellent opportunity to let them try out their ideas and then to make them realize and remedy any mistakes they may make. It is important to note that distances in space are so great that it is practically impossible to use the same scales for the size of the planets *and* the distances between them.

A "Blackboard Planetarium"[2] illustrated here uses the facts on the chart to give pupils a better concept of distances in the solar system.

---

[1] *Science News Letter,* Science Service, 1769 N St., N. W., Washington, D. C. One issue each month contains a star map with interpretation.

[2] Adapted from *Earth in Space,* Board of Education of the City of New York, Publication Sales Office, 110 Livingston St., Brooklyn 1, N. Y. (50¢).

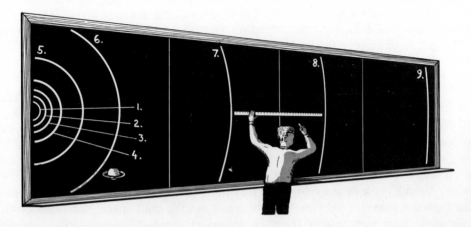

Such an activity as this affords an excellent opportunity for the meaningful use of mathematics. Better concepts of the vastness of space, relationships between heavenly bodies, and the place of the earth in the solar system can result when pupils solve the problems related to making this graphic representation.

FACTS FOR A "BLACKBOARD PLANETARIUM"

Number and name of planet	Distance from sun in millions of miles	Distance to be measured from left side of blackboard (Scale: 1 inch = 20 million miles)
1. Mercury	36	1¾ inches
2. Venus	67	3¼ inches
3. Earth	93	4¾ inches
4. Mars	140	7 inches
5. Jupiter	480	2 feet
6. Saturn	890	3 feet 8 inches
7. Uranus	1,800	7 feet 6 inches
8. Neptune	2,800	11 feet 8 inches
9. Pluto	3,700	15 feet 5 inches

DEMONSTRATING THE IMPORTANCE OF THE SUN

It is one thing to read or to hear that the sun is necessary for plant growth; it is quite another to try an experiment and see that this is actually true. Four plants (geraniums or any other house plants will do) as nearly alike as possible should be selected. They should be of the same size and should be growing in the same kind of soil and the same kind of pot. Two plants may be set in a dark place, the others in the sunlight. Both groups should be given the same amount of water and should be as nearly as possible in the same temperature, and the dark place should have ample fresh air. As far as possible, there should be only one difference in the environment of the plants—the presence of sunlight. After two weeks, the plants should be compared. Remember that pupils cannot generalize about *all* plants from their experience here. Moreover, some pupils may say, and rightly so, that the plants in the closet probably did not have exactly the same temperature, humidity, air circulation, etc. Consequently, only tentative conclusions can be drawn from the experiment. More refined experimentation would have to follow before final conclusions could be drawn. This is another example of keeping the scientific attitude in evidence.

LEARNING THE CAUSE OF DAY AND NIGHT

Because many science and geography books suggest how to demonstrate the cause of day and night, our description here will be brief. As a source of light, use either a flashlight, a floor lamp with a shade, or a lamp with a good reflector such as you may find in the school nurse's office. Use a globe for the earth. Remind pupils to imagine that they are living on the globe. A chalk mark on the spot where they live will help them get the idea more clearly. Darken the room, shine the light on the globe, point out the chalk mark, and begin slowly to turn the globe from west to east (counter-clockwise). Turn the globe around once on its axis so that pupils can observe what happens during one complete rotation. Then begin with the position of the chalk mark at sunrise, and let a pupil tell what he would be doing at different stages of the rotation—for example, "Now I am having breakfast," "Now I am on my way to school," etc. If the class is large, it may be advisable to let small groups take turns at standing close to the globe and light so that they can observe easily. Pupils should remember the following things in order to understand the causes of day and night:

> The earth is round, like a ball; consequently only half of it can be lighted at once.
> The earth gets its light from the sun. The lighted half has day; the unlighted half has night.
> The earth makes one rotation every twenty-four hours. This is one day and one night.

Pupils may make a chart indicating the number of hours of daylight and darkness during each of the months of the year, twelve rows across the chart—one row for each month—as illustrated on this page. From this chart, pupils may answer such questions as:

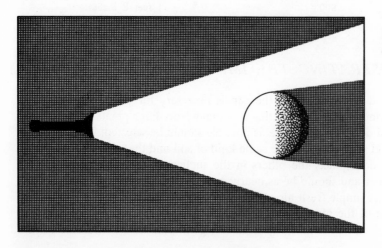

The flashlight illuminating the ball shows how only half of the earth (a ball-shaped object) can be lighted at one time.

HOURS OF THE DAY

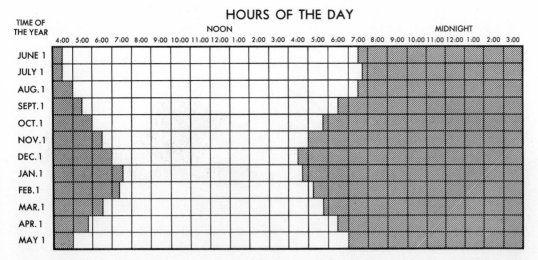

Making such a record of hours of daylight and darkness requires careful search and accurate recording of data. Each square indicates an hour. Newspapers, almanacs, radio broadcasts, and similar references may be used as sources of information. Pupils may devise other methods for making such a record.

"When do we have the most hours of daylight?" "When do we have the fewest hours of daylight?" "Is there much or little daylight on your birthday?" "When are the hours of daylight and darkness about the same?" The data for such a chart may be obtained from an almanac or from some daily newspapers, and some calendars.

LEARNING ABOUT THE CAUSE OF SEASONS

It is difficult to tell how much elementary pupils can understand about the actual causes of seasonal changes. It varies with the ability of the group. Probably the best we can do is to help pupils see that for any particular part of the earth, such as the United States: (1) in summer there are more hours of sunlight, and therefore more heating of the earth than in winter when there are fewer hours of sunlight; (2) in summer the sun is more directly overhead, it heats the earth more than it does in winter when it is lower in the sky and its rays strike the earth obliquely. Both these phenomena are observable.

Children can understand this phenomenon much better by actual experience with heat as shown in the illustration here.[3] Use two pieces of black paper placed on pieces of corrugated cardboard (because of its insulating properties). Place one to receive the sun's rays directly (90° angle); the other flat on the surface. On a sunny day place each in sunlight in the schoolroom. Let children feel and compare the warmth on both pieces after 2, 4, 6, 8, and 10 minutes and record their findings. There may be some disagreement among children about feeling the difference. How can we be more accurate and certain of the results? Place thermometers under each piece of black paper and read them after the same intervals.

---

[3] Adapted from *Weather,* Board of Education of the City of New York, Publication Sales Office, 110 Livingston St., Brooklyn 1, N. Y. (50¢).

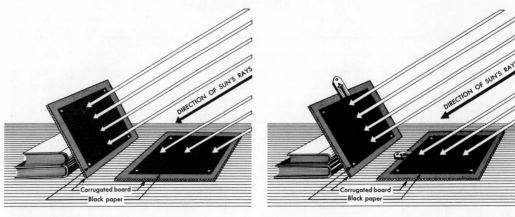

It is one thing to read or hear about the principle illustrated here and quite another to plan and carry out an experience such as this to show it. Performing the experiment without and then with a thermometer helps pupils to see the importance of accurate measurements.

The difference in length of days may be emphasized by asking pupils to recall the difference in light when they get up at 7 A.M. in September as compared with the same time in December. The chart of daylight and darkness hours that we have suggested will also help pupils to understand seasons. Here again, arithmetic serves as a tool for science. And the activity is another example of helping children to see the importance of collecting data over a long period of time before drawing conclusions.

Both of these experiences, one with the changes in length of day, the other with changes in the strength of the sunlight help children understand the cause of seasons. Along with these experiences a homemade planetarium has been found very successful in helping pupils to understand the cause of seasons as well as gain a "space view." Some of the older pupils can make it, with a little assistance from the teacher or another adult.

The following materials are needed: a wooden base, a light-bulb socket, a half-length of yardstick (or a wooden piece of about the same length), a small globe from the ten-cent store, a wooden spool, a long nail (one inch longer than the diameter of the globe), and a two-inch length of doweling (a piece of nail will do) that will fit into the spool.

One inch from the end of the yardstick, bore a hole large enough for the end of the light-bulb socket to pass through. Be sure that the hole is large enough to allow the yardstick to turn easily. Bore a hole in the other end of the yardstick for the dowel and fit it through the hole, allowing one inch to stick up above the yardstick (the spool will be placed over this). Glue the dowel into place. Punch holes in the globe at the North and South Poles and put the nail through these holes. Drive the nail into the spool so that the globe will be at a 23½-degree angle. Put the spool on the dowel, which is sticking up above the yardstick. Make sure that the spool can turn easily. Put the end of the light-bulb socket through the hole you made for it, and plug the lamp cord into the socket. The earth (globe) can be turned on its axis, and the yardstick can turn around the sun. Darken the room so that the only light available will come from the lamp (sun).

These demonstrations should be supplemented by several outdoor trips to observe the position of the sun during different times of the day and at different times of the year. This illustrates the point we have made before—that *experiments and demonstrations are*

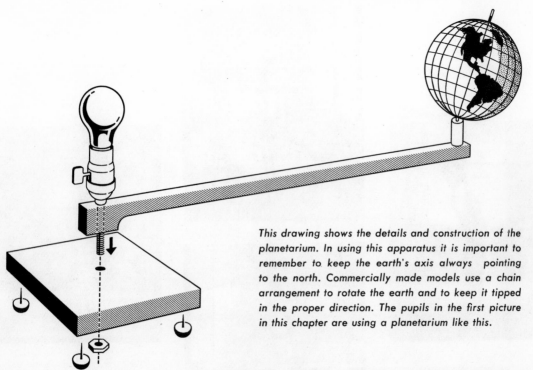

This drawing shows the details and construction of the planetarium. In using this apparatus it is important to remember to keep the earth's axis always pointing to the north. Commercially made models use a chain arrangement to rotate the earth and to keep it tipped in the proper direction. The pupils in the first picture in this chapter are using a planetarium like this.

done in order to help pupils understand a phenomenon or to solve a problem but not as ends in themselves. It is how well the pupils are helped to see the relation of the experiment or demonstration to the problem or phenomena that determines the experiment's value.

OBSERVING THE MOON

Even a small pair of binoculars is a great help in observing the moon if there is no telescope available. Especially after they have seen pictures of moon landscape and know what to look for, pupils are delighted at the sight of the moon through glasses. If any child has had the experience of looking at the moon through a large telescope, let him describe as carefully as he can how the moon looked.

Many calendars indicate the dates of the new moon and of the other phases. It is an interesting experience for pupils to observe these phases and draw pictures of the shape as they observe it on different dates. Have them indicate under their drawings the date, the time, and the part of the sky the moon was in (east, west, etc.). It is also interesting for them to note in newspapers, calendars, or almanacs the time of moonrise and moonset.

If pupils examine almanacs, they are almost sure to run across information about planting seeds in accordance with the phases of the moon. Despite the fact that we live in an age of scientific knowledge, there are still people who plant certain vegetables during certain phases of the moon. A discussion of what plants need in order to grow and some reading about superstitions will help pupils to form an opinion of such practices. *Superstition or Science*[4] is a helpful source of information on this subject.

---

[4] B. M. Parker, *Superstition or Science* (New York: Harper & Row, 1959), 36 pp.

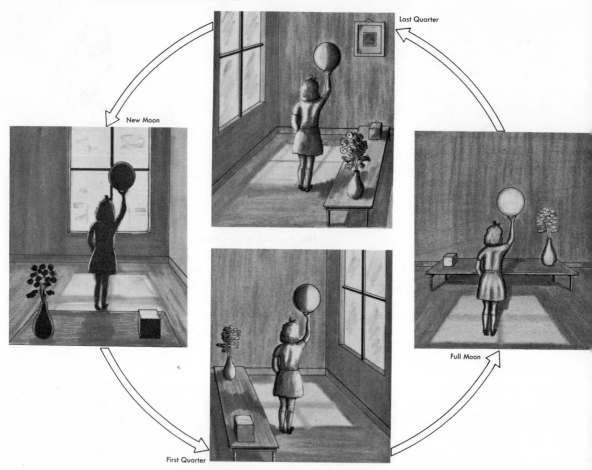

After pupils have observed the changing shapes of the moon as it revolves around the earth and have demonstrated what happens with appropriate equipment, they will do further observations of the earth's satellite with much greater understanding.

DEMONSTRATING THE PHASES OF THE MOON

Many pupils in the elementary school find it difficult to understand what makes the moon seem to change its shape as it travels around the earth. Even the demonstration commonly used, which we shall describe, is not always effective with all pupils. It is difficult for young pupils to transpose what they see in the demonstration to the conditions that exist in the sky.

To represent the moon, use a basketball or a ball of similar size. To represent the sun, use a lamp such as was suggested for use in learning the cause of day and night. Darken the room and turn on the lamp. Stand in the light of the lamp and hold the ball at arm's length, a little higher than the lamp (teacher demonstrates). Your head represents the position of the earth. Remind the pupils that to understand how the shape of the moon seems to change we must remember three things: (1) the moon's light comes from the sun; (2) the moon is ball-shaped and can be lighted on only one side; (3) the moon revolves around the earth once every month (approximately once every 27½ days). Pupils should be reminded also that they can see the moon only from the position of the earth—i.e., the teacher's head. (In this demonstration it is especially important that each pupil be given an opportunity to participate since only the demonstrator is in position to actually see the changes.) Begin by holding the ball in a position between the sun and the earth, a little higher than the head. This represents the position at new moon, when scarcely any of it is visible to us on the earth, because the light from the sun cannot strike the side of the moon we see. As you turn slowly toward the left, still holding the ball a little over your head, more of the moon will gradually become lighted. Stop a quarter of the way around and you are in the position of first quarter. Draw a chalk mark on the ball to outline the lighted part so that the shape becomes apparent. Keep turning in the same direction another quarter of the way around. Now you are in the position of full moon (remember to keep the ball a little higher than your head). Approximately two weeks have passed since new moon. Keep turning and observe the lighted part of the ball. It is now growing smaller. Turn another quarter of the way around and you are in the position of third quarter. Approximately three weeks of the month have gone. Keep turning in the same direction to the original position. A month has passed. The moon has changed from new moon to first quarter, to full moon, to third quarter, and back again to new moon.

This sort of demonstration needs to be done by each pupil, if possible, so that the idea will be clearer. It will help also for them to draw the several shapes on the chalkboard as they see them and to compare these with the shapes they see as they observe the moon at night.

Using a lamp to light up a basketball is a way of helping pupils understand what happens in the night sky, but pupils' right answers to the questions we ask them about the ball and light do not necessarily mean that they fully understand the cause of the moon's phases. It is quite a mental jump from the schoolroom demonstration out into the space where the phenomenon is taking place.

STUDYING AN ECLIPSE

An eclipse during a school year is reason enough to study astronomy, for nearly everyone is interested in such a phenomenon. Newspapers will carry pictures and accounts of the eclipse. Even if the eclipse is not visible locally, there may be considerable interest. The U. S. Naval Observatory supplies information about eclipses.

It is important to remember that while demonstrations such as this are indeed helpful in understanding the science principles, pupils need help in translating what they see here into an understanding of what actually happens.

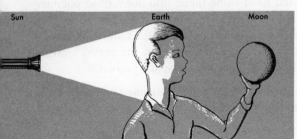

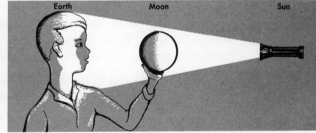

The demonstration used to show moon phases may also be used to show eclipses. An electric lamp, placed at one side of a darkened room, should be used as a source of light. The question may arise, "Why don't we have an eclipse every month as the moon travels around the earth?" It should be made clear that the earth, sun, and moon are not often in line and in the same plane. As shown in the drawing here, children will see that when their head (the earth) is between the light (the sun) and the ball (moon) and all three are in line, the shadow of their head falls on the ball and eclipses it (an eclipse of the moon). If the ball is now moved to a position between the head and the light they will see that the ball has cut off the light of the lamp (the sun). The shadow of the ball now falls on the child's face (an eclipse of the sun).

Ancient peoples regarded eclipses with great alarm. They gave all sorts of weird explanations and were superstitious about eclipses. Today most people realize that an eclipse is the result of natural causes and can be forecast to the exact minute. Pupils may be interested in discussing how the growth of knowledge of astronomy has been useful to us.

WATCHING FOR "SHOOTING STARS"

Pupils may be encouraged to watch the evening sky to see meteors, especially on the dates suggested in chapter 7A. If they do observe any, they should be urged to describe what they saw, including the date, the time, and the sky location. There are many superstitions about "shooting stars." For example, there is a saying that if you repeat "money" three times while you are seeing the star you will be rich. Knowledge of science and its methods should help pupils overcome superstitions, and this is one occasion when a discussion of superstitions may arise. It is often possible to borrow a meteorite from a local, state, or college museum. Pupils are greatly interested in such an object that has come from outer space. To hold in your hand a piece of material that has actually fallen from the sky is quite an experience. If they actually have one to feel and lift, pupils will be much more enthusiastic to do some reading "research" about meteors and meteorites. They will want to know whether it was found locally and what kind of materials it is made of. A museum may be able to supply such information.

PLANNING A SPACE TRIP

Some children like to write stories, and a group may like to write an imaginary story about a space trip.[5] They may plan to allocate various responsibilities to specific scientists such as: astronomers, navigators, commissary men, geologists, etc., each gathering material from reading and elsewhere that would need to be taken into account in planning the trip. Doing this involves: reading, selecting appropriate science facts, listing unsolved problems, judging validity of material, organizing material, etc. Other such stories might be written to discuss: "What might happen if the sun stopped shining on the earth?" "What is involved in making a round trip to the moon?" and other similar space problems.

NOTE: "Resources to Investigate" to learn about the sun and the planets will be found at the end of chapter 8B.

---

[5] E. MacGregor, *Miss Pickerell Goes to Mars* (New York: Whittlesey, 1951), 128 pp. Science fiction that will inspire further reading to find out what is fact and what fiction and inspire pupils to do some similar writing.

CHAPTER 8A

The Stars and the Universe

How shall we measure the universe? What kind of a yardstick shall we use for the immense spaces between the stars? Our imagination, already staggered by the millions and billions of miles within the solar system, searches for some new unit to apply to the vast reaches of the space beyond—for some measure that speaks in small familiar numbers.

We might try to use *time* to measure distance. The American Indians did that when they said that a certain place was two moons away. They meant, of course, that the distance was such that it would require two months of journeying to reach it, with the limited means of travel at their disposal. A way that we can use to make distances in the solar system comprehensible is to figure how much time a spaceship, moving at an average rate of 17,500 miles an hour (fast enough to circle the earth in one and a half hours), would take to reach the various points of interest in our planetary system. Thus we calculate that it would take only 11 hours on such a ship to reach the moon but about 7 months to reach the sun. These figures have had meaning to us ever since February 20, 1962, when John Glenn made three orbits around the earth, covering each orbit in about an hour and a half, and traveling at the speed of 17,500 miles an hour. That day changed the concept of distance for every person who watched breathlessly this historic flight from liftoff to touchdown. From that day on, we could think: at that (average) speed Glenn could reach the moon in 11 hours, the sun in 7 months.

These statistics—11 hours to the moon, 7 months to the sun—are manageable units for measuring distances within the solar system. But as we leave the solar system for deeper space, we get into difficulties if we use "spaceship time" to measure distances. The numbers get big again! We look for something that can zip through space at a faster rate, and we find it in a ray of light. Light takes time to travel from one point to another; we are not aware of this because it moves at the incredible speed of about 186,000 miles a *second*. Such a rate would send it seven times around our earth in one second.

Let us apply this speed-of-light scale to the distances of the moon and the sun from the earth. Light from the moon reaches the earth after a brief journey of 1⅓ *seconds*; from the sun, about 8 *minutes* is required. From distant Pluto, near the outermost bounds of our known solar system, 5⅓ *hours* would be needed.

Look at the stars some clear night. These, as we learned in the previous chapter, are distant suns outside our solar system—so distant that they appear as points of light in the blackness of night. The nearest star (and the brightest) that can be seen with the naked eye in the Northern Hemisphere is Sirius in the constellation Canis Major (Big Dog). Light from Sirius takes about 8 *years* to reach our eyes.

Astronomers use the speed of light as a convenient method for measuring the universe, with the *light year* as the basic unit. A light year is a measure of *distance,* not of time; it is the distance that light, traveling at the speed of 186,000 miles a second, traverses in one year (approximately 6,000,-000,000,000 miles). The star Sirius, then, is 8 light years away from us. Arcturus, another bright star, is 36 light years distant. Polaris,

the North Star, is about 650 light years away.

This use of time as a cosmic yardstick brings up a fascinating idea. When you look at the North Star, you are seeing the light that left it approximately 650 years ago. By now, Polaris may have moved to another place (even the so-called "fixed" stars of the ancients are not really stationary); it may have exploded and become cold and dark. Our descendants 650 years hence will know the whereabouts and the condition of the Polaris of the present.

So, when you look at the sky tonight, you are peering not only into the vastness of space but also into events of the past. You are looking not only far into distance but also far back into time.

THE STARS

DISTANCE, SIZE, COLOR.   Ask a beginner how many stars he sees on a clear night and he will answer "thousands" or "millions." Actually, only about twenty-five hundred to three thousand stars can be seen with the unaided eye from any spot on the earth at any time; some nine thousand stars can be seen throughout the year from the whole earth. Of course, with the use of telescopes and cameras millions of stars can be detected.

Another assumption of viewers is that the observed brightness of stars is indicative of their real brilliance. This illusion occurs because we have no perspective into the depth of space; all the stars appear to be at the same distance. Actually, Sirius appears bright because it is close; Rigel in the constellation of Orion appears dimmer than Sirius because it is about sixty times as far away. However, if all the stars were moved to the same distance from the earth, Rigel would shine 700 times as brightly as Sirius.

The apparent brightness of a star depends on three factors: its distance from the earth, its size, and its temperature. The nearest star (except the sun) to the earth is Alpha Centauri. Visible only in the Southern Hemisphere, this star is 4⅓ light years away. The most distant star visible to our eyes is about a million light years away. The most distant star that the powerful two-hundred-inch Mt. Palomar telescope can isolate as an individual body is 20 million light years away. The most distant star collections picked out by this telescope are estimated to be 2 billion light years away!

Stars vary considerably in size. Small ones, known as *dwarfs*, may be only 10,000 miles in diameter, about the size of the earth. A *giant*, like Antares, has a diameter 450 times that of our sun. In the range of stars from dwarf to giant our sun is considered an average-sized star.

If you look closely, you will see that stars are not all the same color. Some are reddish, some yellowish, some white, some bluish-white. The difference in color is due to differences in the temperature of the stars. If a piece of metal is heated, it first turns red, then orange, then yellow, then white. Blacksmiths used to get a rough idea of the temperature of the iron that they were heating by watching its color. Scientists have discovered that this holds true for stars also. The hottest ones appear bluish, those less hot white, cooler ones are yellowish, and the coolest are reddish. Our sun is a yellowish star of medium temperature. Betelgeuse, in Orion, is red. Rigel, one of the hottest, has a temperature of 100,000° F. Our sun has a temperature of 10,000° F. Cooler Betelgeuse has a temperature of about 4,000° F. All of these are the measurable *surface* temperatures; the interiors of stars are much hotter, running into millions of degrees.

The high temperature of the sun, as we found in chapter 7A, is not the result of burning but of violent atomic activity in which hydrogen atoms combine to form helium atoms, as in a hydrogen bomb. This is also true of the other stars of the universe.

MAGNITUDE.   We have seen how the apparent brightness of a star is determined by distance, size, and temperature. For convenience in viewing and identifying stars, astronomers classify them according to their *magnitude*. In speaking of stars, magnitude does *not* mean size, but apparent brightness. The smaller the number given, the brighter the star. Thus the *first-magnitude* stars are the brightest. These are two and one-half times as bright, on the average, as a second-magnitude star. A second-magnitude star is two and one-half times as bright as a third-magnitude star and so on. The faintest star that we can ordinarily see with the unaided eye is of the fifth magnitude, but occasionally we can see one of the sixth magnitude. Stars fainter than the sixth magnitude can be seen only with the telescope. At present we can photograph stars of the twenty-third magnitude with the Mt. Palomar telescope. These stars are about one five-millionth as bright as first-magnitude stars.

There are twenty stars of the first magnitude or brighter. Some of the more commonly known ones are Sirius, Vega, Capella, Arcturus, Rigel, Procyon, Altair,

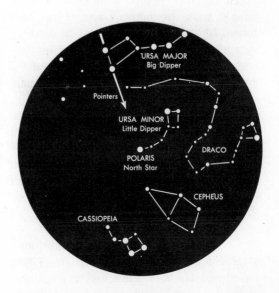

The constellations near the North Star are in view every hour of the night. They are easy to find and they provide a guide to other star groups.

Betelgeuse, Adalbaran, Pollux, Spica, Antares, Formalhaut, Deneb, and Regulus. Sirius, brightest of the first-magnitude stars, is not as bright as three planets—Venus, Mars, and Jupiter.

The original brightness scale was devised about 120 B.C. by Hipparchus, a Greek astronomer. Using a scale from 1 to 6, he catalogued 1,080 stars, using 1 for the brightest and 6 for the faintest stars. Later astronomers extended the scale upwards (with the help of the telescope, as we have seen) and downwards. Very bright Sirius has a negative magnitude, —1.4. The moon has a magnitude of —12.6 and the sun —26.7. There is nothing really "negative" about such brilliant objects. We have been forced to assign negative values to them because we have adhered to the method instituted by Hipparchus.

DOUBLE STARS AND STAR CLUSTERS.
Stars are like people—they are gregarious. They are often grouped in pairs, one revolving around the other. To be more accurate we should say that both revolve around their *center of gravity*, which is a point between the two. Several thousands of these double stars, or *binary stars*, have been found. Most binary stars cannot be detected except with the aid of a telescope or spectroscope. Bright Sirius is a double star; it waltzes around its invisible (to the eye) mate once every fifty years.

There are also larger groups of stars, *star clusters*, held together by gravitational attraction, which move together through space. The Pleiades are such a group. You can see at least seven of its members with the naked eye; with a telescope we find some 250 members.

VARIABLE STARS.
Some individual stars change in brightness and hence are called *variable stars*. Some vary in brightness at regular intervals. The cycle from bright to dim to bright again may take from a few hours to hundreds of days, depending on the star. One type of variable star is known as a *cepheid*, named for a notable fluctuating star in the constellation of Cepheus. Stars of this type brighten up and fade again like clockwork. The star Delta Cephei, for example, takes five days and nine hours to pass from its brightest phase down to its faintest and then back to its brightest. Also there are *irregular variables* which vary in brightness in an unpredictable manner.

"New" stars or *novae* are stars that have previously been inconspicuous and then suddenly flare up and become as much as seventy or eighty thousand times as bright. The name "nova" is inaccurate, since there is no evidence that these are new stars. We do not know what causes these stars to flare up. The appearance of a *supernova*, an extraordinarily bright nova, is a rare event. The Danish astronomer, Tycho Brahe, described a supernova that appeared on a November evening in 1572, when a previously unseen star flared up brighter than Sirius. The following night it was brighter than the planet Venus. It was so bright in the days that followed that it could be seen even in the daytime. By September of the following year it faded. Today it is no longer visible.

We know more about supernovae than novae, even though they are rarer, because they leave traces that we can study. For example, Japanese and Chinese records mention a blazing star that appeared in the year 1054. We have reasons to believe that the explosion of this star produced a cloud of starry material observable today as the Crab nebula, so named because of its crab-like appearance. The flaring of a star into a supernova is believed to represent an atomic explosion on a celestial scale.

It is believed that all stars are, in reality, variable. In recent years, astronomers have gathered evidence which leads them to believe that the stars in the sky are of widely varying ages. According to the current theory of stellar evolution, a star comes into being through the contraction of a mass of gas and dust, a *protostar*. This stage, which may be thought of as the star's childhood, is comparatively short. Then for most of its life the star is full grown (adulthood) and more or less stable. Most of the stars we see are, therefore, in this state. Full grown stars range from blue white (very hot) to red (cool) in color. The hotter stars give off their energy faster than the cooler stars, and are therefore shorter-lived. After a certain amount of energy has been lost, a star expands, becomes cooler and unstable, or variable in brightness. At a later stage (old age) a star may become a nova before fading away from sight completely.

MOTION. Alas for those who are looking for a firm, immovable rock in this giddy universe! Even the "fixed" stars are not fixed but are moving rapidly through space in various directions. Some are moving toward and some away from our solar system. Stars speed through space at the average rate of 25 miles per second. Despite this speed, stars very rarely collide with each other because space is so vast and the distances between stars very great. The speeds and the directions of hundreds of stars are known to astronomers. This drifting over periods of thousands of years causes even the shape of the star patterns—the *constellations*—to change. The Big Dipper will become an open scoop 100,000 years from now!

THE CONSTELLATIONS

When night falls, the glittering sky beckons to us to join in the ancient hobby of stargazing. Primitive people long ago traced pictures of familiar objects, animals, and humans in the pattern of stars. The American Indians painted them on buffalo skins. The ancient Greeks and Romans filled the heavens with their gods and heroes.

The resemblance of groups of stars, or constellations, to these imaginary figures may be difficult for us to follow. We may

prefer to think of the stars that make up Pegasus, for example, as a baseball diamond, with stars at home plate, first, second, and third base, along the right and left field foul lines, rather than as a white-winged horse. Whether we group stars on the basis of their mythology or in a more modern way, knowing the constellations is fun and also serves as a convenient guide for locating individual stars and other heavenly bodies.

The part of the heavens that we can see on any night is limited by the fact that we live in the Northern Hemisphere of an opaque globe. People living in the Southern Hemisphere look out on a different portion of the sky, seeing constellations that we never see.

Our view of the heavens is also influenced by the seasons, since the earth is in different positions in its orbit around the sun in the course of a year. Some constellations can be seen only in summer and some only in winter. Fortunately there are some star groups that are always visible—the constellations around the Pole Star (North Star). Among these are the Big Bear, the Little

An active imagination will help you make a bear out of this constellation of stars. Note that the Big Dipper is a part of this star group.

Bear, Draco, Cassiopeia (kăs′ĭ-ŏ-pē′-ya), Perseus and Cepheus. A good way to begin your acquaintance with the stars is to find in the northern sky the Big Dipper, which is part of the constellation of the Big Bear. Two stars that form the part of the dipper opposite the handle are known as ·the "pointers." A line drawn through these pointers and extending about five times the distance between them will lead you to the Pole Star, known also as Polaris.

Polaris is also at the tip end of the handle of the Little Dipper, which is part of the constellation of the Little Bear. Polaris, although not a very bright star, is the brightest in the Little Dipper. The two dippers are so placed that when one is upright, the other is upside down, with their handles extending in opposite directions.

If you trace a line from the pointers to the Pole Star and then extend it an equal distance across the sky you will come close to Cassiopeia. Five of the stars of this constellation make up a big W or M in the sky. Near Cassiopeia, the mythological Queen of Ethiopia, is her husband Cepheus. Cepheus forms a pattern not unlike a triangle mounted on a square. One of the most famous of the variable stars, Delta Cephei, is located in this constellation.

Come back to the Big Dipper and follow its *handle* this time to find the bright star Arcturus (ark-tū′rŭs), one of the few stars mentioned in the Bible. Arcturus, which means "Bear Driver," is located in the tail of a kite-shaped constellation, Bootes (Bŏ-ō′tēz), the Herdsman.

Pegasus, mentioned earlier, is one of the outstanding constellations in the autumn sky. Its three brightest stars, together with the brightest star in adjacent Andromeda, form the four-cornered figure known as the Square of Pegasus. In Andromeda, which extends away from the Square, is a hazy patch of light. This filmy wisp in the sky is actually made of 100 billion stars! We will have more to say of such collections pres-

The three stars in a line and the reddish color of Betelgeuse make Orion, the Great Hunter, an easy winter constellation to identify. Knowing the old legends about this constellation and the others make them more interesting to observe. Interest deepens as modern star knowledge is added, as, for example, the fact that Rigel is 21,000 times as bright as the sun.

ently. This one is notable because it is one of the very few visible to the naked eye.

A line of bright stars from Pegasus through Andromeda points the way to Perseus. One of the stars in this group is variable Algol, which has a three-day cycle of brightness and dimness. Perseus is also distinguished, as indicated in chapter 7A, because it marks the location of brilliant meteoric showers that occur in August.

Draco, the Dragon, may be difficult to find, since it does not have any first-magnitude stars in it and its hard-to-describe outline wriggles between the two dippers, curves toward Cepheus, and then toward Hercules.

Hercules, like Draco, has no bright stars. The ancients pictured Hercules as a kneeling figure with an upraised club ready to crush the head of Draco. A brilliant globular cluster of stars in Hercules may be seen with the naked eye and is a favorite of telescope viewers.

One of the brightest constellations and the most spectacular of the winter season is Orion, the mighty Hunter. The three stars that make up the belt of this figure, equally spaced in a straight row, are seen even by city dwellers who glance up at the sky. This belt is in the center of a nearly rectangular figure, making up the body of Orion. The giant sun Betelgeuse marks one corner of the rectangle, the right shoulder of the warrior. Blazing Rigel, diagonally across, marks his left leg.

Trace along Orion's belt to the brightest star in all the sky, Sirius, in the constellation of the Great Dog. Companion to this star is Procyon, in the nearby constellation of the Little Dog. Except for Sirius, Procyon, about eleven light years distant, is the closest to the earth of the larger stars visible in the Northern Hemisphere.

As we watch the sky on a pleasant summer night, the constellations appear to wheel across the heavens. This apparent motion is due, of course, to the turning of the earth on its axis. One star, however, appears fixed in the sky throughout the night. This is Polaris, which hangs over the North Pole of the earth, over one end of the axis on which the earth turns. All the stars seem to revolve around the North Star. Constellations close to it, such as the Dippers, appear to circle the Pole Star during the night. Stars more distant from Polaris trace bigger circles in the sky; those most distant appear to rise in the east and set in the west.

THE MILKY WAY

What is our address in the universe? What is the place of our solar system—the earth, the other planets, and the sun—in the starry sky? What, in short, is the structure of the universe, and where are we located in that structure?

If we turn to the constellations for an answer, we do not get much help. For the most part, these sky patterns are composed of stars that happen to lie approximately in the same direction from the earth. When we look upward, our eyes cannot discern the *depth* of space. No wonder the ancients thought that the sky was a round dome studded with twinkling lights. Careful observations and calculations by astronomers have revealed that although all the stars seem to lie in a single plane, some of them may be great distances beyond others.

The sun is one of the billions of stars in our Milky Way galaxy.

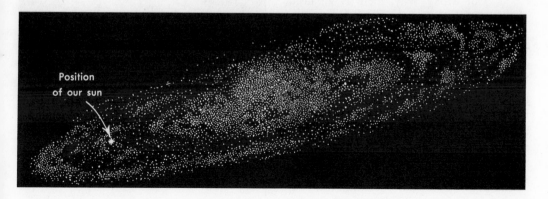

Position of our sun

The constellations in themselves do not reveal the three-dimensional structure of space. Then how are the stars arranged? If we look up at the heavens on a clear night, we see stretching across the sky a broad luminous band—the Milky Way. Examination even with a pair of binoculars or a small telescope reveals that the Milky Way is populated with millions of stars, so concentrated in depth in the direction in which we are looking that they make a "milky" band in the sky. The sky on either side of the milky band has many fewer stars, and the farther from the Milky Way the fewer are the stars. What does all of this reveal about the organization of stars?

Astronomers puzzling over this have concluded that we are in the midst of a huge disk or wheel-shaped collection of stars. They call this Milky Way system our galaxy (a word derived from the Greek *gala*, which means milk). Since we are *within* this disk of stars, our vision is somewhat obscured. It might help in our understanding if we think of our galaxy as a cherry pie in space, without the crust. Each cherry represents a gleaming star, one of these our sun. Think of the viewpoint of a cherry within the pie. Looking toward the edge of the pie, a thick conglomeration of cherries in the form of a band is seen; looking toward the top or bottom of the pie, few cherries are seen. Thus, in our cherry pie galaxy, we would see a "Cherry Way" extending in one direction across our view.

Our Milky Way, then, is an inside view of the great galaxy of stars in which we are situated. All the stars that can be seen with the naked eye and most of those observed with telescopes are a part of the Milky Way system, which contains about 100 billion stars. Unlike a cherry pie, however, there is ample space within our galaxy—enough to hold a million times as many stars as it does!

How big is our galaxy? To measure it, we again use the speed of light as our yardstick. We calculated previously that, if we traveled at the speed of light, it would take us a little over a second to reach the moon, 8 minutes to reach the sun, and 4⅓ years to reach the nearest star. Traveling at this speed—186,000 miles a second—it would take about 100,000 years to go from one edge of the galaxy to the other, and about 10,000 years to go across its greatest thickness. Our galaxy, then, is a wheel about 100,000 light years across, and 10,000 light years thick.

Just where is the solar system in this wheel? Astronomers say that we are 27,000 light years away from the center out toward the rim of the wheel, and in the central *plane* of the wheel. The whole galaxy is rotating like a pinwheel. All the stars are wheeling in the same direction around the center, but at different speeds. Despite the fact that our

This star cluster in Hercules is made of hundreds of thousands of stars, but the individual stars are not seen by the unaided eye because the cluster is so far away.

sun and its solar system are moving at 140 miles a second in a roughly circular orbit, it takes 200 million years to complete a swing around the center. Our solar system is also taking a trip all its own; it is heading in the general direction of the constellation Hercules at the rate of about 12 miles a second.

Perhaps a better understanding of our galaxy can be gotten by looking at another one, at a galaxy *outside* our Milky Way system. The best known of these is the Great Spiral in Andromeda, which is revealed by telescopes as a collection of 100 billion stars, with spiral arms like those of a Fourth of July pinwheel. Pictured on the first page of this chapter is the famous Whirlpool Nebula in the constellation Canes Venatici, showing distinct spiral arms. This, like the Andromeda Spiral, has been likened to our galaxy in shape and in its starry population.

THE UNIVERSE

Again we ask, what is our place in the universe? Just as a child becomes aware of larger and larger units—home, neighborhood, city, and so on—so have astronomers discovered a hierarchy in the heavens. Our galaxy of 100,000 light years diameter is only one of the billions of galaxies that make up the universe.

To come back to our original question about our address in the universe, the best answer we can give at this time is:

> Planet: Earth
> Star: Our Sun
> Galaxy: Milky Way
> Universe

One more thought about our "address in space." If you were to return to your home town aften an absence of several years, you would be astonished if you found that the distances between all the houses had increased so that your next-door neighbor was now a mile away, and the whole town was spread out over an area 10,000 times its original size. If for each house you substitute a galaxy, you are now prepared to understand what astronomers call an "expanding universe." The study of distant galaxies with the spectroscope, an instrument to be described shortly, indicates that the galaxies are fleeing from each other at a terrific rate, some at a speed of 60,000 miles a second or one third the speed of light! Astronomers have also found that the farther away the galaxies are from us, the faster they are moving. It should be made clear that the expansion in the "expanding universe" refers to the increase in the space between the galaxies and not to the size of the galaxies themselves. Thus our lonely address in the vastness of space becomes lonelier as our neighbors become more and more distant.

HOW THE STARS
ARE STUDIED

The basic equipment that man possesses for the exploration of the heavens are his eyes, his intelligence, and his imagination. To aid his senses, man has invented devices like the telescope, the camera, the spectroscope, and the radio telescope. With all of these, man has measured the distances and sizes of stars, estimated their temperatures, analyzed their composition, charted their motions, and described their evolution. Let us take a brief look at some astronomical instruments.

TELESCOPE. In 1928, George Ellery Hale, an American astronomer, made a plea for the construction of a new telescope. Hale based his plea on three unsolved problems of astronomy: the evolution of stars, the structure of the universe, and the constitution of matter. The Rockefeller International Education Board responded by making a

Many new discoveries about distant stars, star clusters, and the universe have been made with this 200-inch reflecting telescope at Mount Palomar in California.

grant of 6 million dollars that made possible the construction of a 200-inch telescope and led to the establishment of an observatory on Mount Palomar, California, in 1948. Thus, a new instrument, the most powerful of all telescopes, was added to man's devices for his study of the stars.

The Palomar telescope, like all others, gives man a bigger "eye" because it can gather more light than the human eye and because it can magnify the view. The Palomar telescope is an example of a *reflecting telescope,* using a large circular mirror 200 inches across (more than 17 feet!) to collect and focus the light of stars. The *refracting telescope,* on the other hand,

uses a lens to gather and focus light. Galileo used a refracting telescope to explore the heavens and to discover the plains, mountains, and craters of our moon, and the satellites revolving around the planet Jupiter. In both kinds of telescopes—reflector and refractor—the image is magnified by a lens in the eye-piece through which one looks.

The Yerkes refracting telescope— the largest of its kind in the world—has a light-gathering lens 40 inches in diameter. The telescope is 60 feet long and is located at Williams Bay, Lake Geneva, Wisconsin. Another famous refracting telescope is located at the Lick Observatory, on Mount Hamilton, near San Jose, California.

The Mount Palomar telescope, with its 200-inch, 14½-ton mirror, has the light-gathering power of a million eyes. It has already taken thousands of photographs of distant stars and galaxies. With it astronomers expect to photograph objects 2 billion light years away. Its major contribution so far to astronomical theory has been to correct our measurement of distances outside of our Milky Way galaxy. All older figures for the distances of distant bodies have been doubled. Thus, Andromeda is not 1 but 2 million light years away. Next to the Palomar telescope in power is the 100-inch reflecting telescope on Mount Wilson, near Pasadena, California.

Telescopes are usually placed on mountain tops because the air there is generally freer from dust, mist, and haze, and because the location is usually distant from the lights of cities. They are protected from the weather by a dome that opens to the sky. Motors turn the telescope so that it moves westward to make up for the eastward rotation of the earth. Thus, the heavenly bodies "stand still" for prolonged observation. In the vast architecture of a large modern observatory, the astronomer is a tiny figure, instructing his engineers by telephone how to keep the telescope steadily fixed on a particular point in the sky.

CAMERA. No longer does the astronomer spend much time looking through a telescope with his own eyes. Instead, he attaches a camera to the telescope and devotes himself to keeping the "picture" in view. The human eye, even when aided by a telescope, has limitations. It tires after a while. It is not sensitive to color in dim light. It cannot retain images very long, hence it cannot build up weak images into strong ones. The camera overcomes these limitations. It does not tire. Film can be made that is very sensitive to light and to different colors. Film can retain and build up weak images into strong ones, even if it takes several nights of exposure for the same pic-ture. As a consequence, we can photograph and detect stars through a telescope which are too faint to be seen through the same telescope with the eye.

Because of this, all large astronomical telescopes are used almost exclusively as cameras rather than as visual instruments. It is through the use of photography that scientists all over the world are working together, charting each section of the heavens in order to obtain a more detailed picture of the universe.

SPECTROSCOPE. How can we know the chemical composition of the stars? The answer lies in the fact that the light emitted by heavenly bodies, when analyzed, furnishes scientists with evidence of the kinds of atoms that are present there. Let us see how scientists analyze starlight.

When sunlight passes through one side of a glass prism, a rainbow of colors, called a spectrum, emerges from the other side. The white light of the sun is a mixture of different colors. The prism bends each of these colors at a slightly different angle and thus fans out the white light into its component colors.

A special instrument called a spectroscope combines the simple prism with a viewing lens. If sunlight is examined with a spectroscope the colors are segregated further into a long band that looks something like a piano keyboard in color, with the "white" piano keys ranging in order from red through orange, yellow, green, and blue, to violet, and with the black keys represented as black lines, not regularly spaced, separating the white keys.

Scientists have found that each of the known chemical elements, if heated until it glows, produces a different and characteristic "keyboard" of colors when viewed through a spectroscope. Thus, the element sodium produces two separate bright yellow "keys." No other element does this. If an astronomer finds evidence of these yellow lines in his spectroscope view of a star, he knows that the star contains sodium. Hydrogen produces a more complex series of lines, some very close together toward the violet end of the spectrum keyboard and others more widely separated at the red end. Calcium (the essential mineral in chalk) is responsible for two remarkably wide, prominent lines in the extreme violet section. Iron produces a chord of lines scattered throughout the spectrum.

Astronomers, knowing the color chord of each element, are able to determine the chemical make-up of a particular star by looking at its light through the spectroscope. Without going further into the details of spectroscopic analysis, let us enumerate some of the astronomical findings that have resulted from it:

1. *The sun is composed of many chemical elements; its main constituent is hydrogen.*
2. *Most stars have elements identical to those of the sun.*
3. *The elements or kinds of atoms glowing in the sun and the stars are the same as those found on earth. Incidentally, the element helium was first discovered in a spectroscopic view of the sun and later found on the earth!*

The spectroscope is a valuable astronomical instrument for other reasons:

1. *The spectroscope reveals the temperature of individual stars.*
2. *It tells whether the body emitting the light rays is solid or gaseous.*
3. *It reveals the presence of invisible gases between the visible source and us.*
4. *It reveals whether a body is approaching us or receding from us, and makes it possible to calculate its speed through space.*
5. *It tells whether a body is rotating.*

RADIO-TELESCOPE. All of us have had the experience of picking up static on our radios. Static is caused by a jumble of radio waves of different lengths. Your radio converts this jumble into "noise" or static, just as it converts regular broadcasts which are beamed over a single wavelength into the sounds of music or speech. Static may originate from man-made electrical disturbances, such as that caused by a nearby power line. You can produce static by rubbing your comb vigorously through your hair and then bringing it near a small radio which is tuned to a position between stations. The consequent electrical discharge (see chapter 21A) starts a radio wave. Static is also nature-made, occurring during lightning storms, and, as we learned in chapter 7A, during periods of great sunspot activity.

In 1931, Karl G. Jansky, an electrical engineer at the Bell Telephone Laboratories, was assigned to investigate the static interfering with short-wave broadcasts. These radio "noises," most bothersome during the day, also occurred at night. In the course of his investigation, Jansky picked up radio signals that he suggested might be coming from outer space. This theory was tested and confirmed by Grote Reber, a radio engineer, who built an aerial shaped like an upside-down umbrella, 30 feet in diameter, to scan the skies for radio waves. With this aerial and a sensitive radio, Reber plotted the first radio map of the sky. Reber's maps showed that the signals were strongest in the Milky Way region. His work much impressed astronomers.

Using improved *radio-telescopes,* as these sensitive radios were called, astronomers were able to focus on particular points in space where the signals were strong. These points were called "radio sources." Strangely enough, only a small fraction of the radio sources which were located corresponded to objects seen with conventional telescopes. Hundreds of these sources were noted and plotted on new radio maps of the skies.

The radio telescope is one of the new instruments used by astronomers for studying the universe. It detects radio waves emitted by heavenly bodies, including those which cannot be seen with light telescopes. Scientists of the National Radio Astronomy Observatory scan the sky with this 300-foot dish at Green Bank, West Virginia, in their search for new information about the universe.

The radio-telescope, then, enabled us to "hear" heavenly objects and detect celestial events that optical devices failed to reveal. Here was a new instrument for penetrating space. As interest mounted, new listening posts were set up all over the world to tune in on these astral waves and to discover more of these radio sources.

Radio-astronomy has made it possible to explore certain dark areas in the sky, in which interstellar dust has blocked the light from our conventional telescopes. With the radio-telescope we have found that galaxies are larger than we thought they were. The shiny arms of our own spiral Milky Way have thus been traced out into the dark. We have also found that what we have called "empty" space between the stars is not really empty—it contains hydrogen.

Radio-telescopes are penetrating deeper into space than optical telescopes, and providing us with significant clues about the structure of the universe, and about its past and its future. A new era in astronomy has opened.

SPACE PROBES. In chapter 7A we discussed the use of satellites and sky balloons, laden with astronomical instruments, in providing us with new information about the planets. High above the earth's disturbing blanket of air, space-borne instruments will also radio back information of objects and happenings outside our solar system:

about the "dark companions" of certain stars, about distant galaxies, about the composition of space. Some day they may announce the existence of other solar systems in space and of other planets which resemble Earth.

An Orbiting Astronomical Observatory (OAO), a 3,200-pound satellite, is to travel in a circular orbit about 475 miles from the Earth. OAO will carry about 1,000 pounds of experimental equipment, such as telescopes, spectrometers, and photometers.

PROJECT OZMA

The possibility of life on other worlds has long intrigued men. Recently, some astronomers have suggested that since the sun is but one of billions of stars, it is likely that some of the other stars may also have planets in orbit around them. They reason further that there is a likelihood that conditions on many of the planets are conducive to the evolution of life.

Because of these considerations, and because of the availability of a new tool—the radio-telescope—for exploring the universe, a project Ozma was launched in May, 1960. (Ozma is the Queen of the imaginary land of Oz.) The 85-foot radio-telescope of the National Astronomy Observatory was pointed at each of two target stars, Tau Ceti and Epsilon Eridani. These stars were selected because they are the nearest sunlike stars observable from the telescope site.

No signals of extraterrestrial origin have been obtained thus far, but the search is still continuing for signals broadcast by the possible inhabitants of possible other worlds in space.

From this survey of the universe, there are important generalizations that we can make. Some of the essential ones are:

Space in the universe is so great that astronomers measure it in light years.

Constellations are sky patterns of stars that happen to lie approximately in the same direction from the earth.

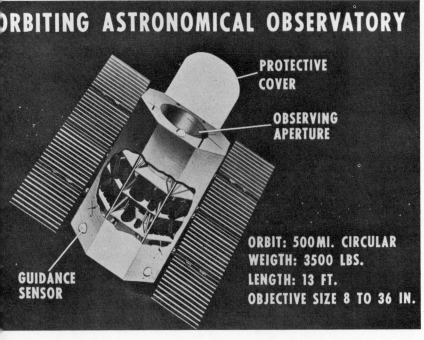

ORBITING ASTRONOMICAL OBSERVATORY

PROTECTIVE COVER

OBSERVING APERTURE

GUIDANCE SENSOR

ORBIT: 500 MI. CIRCULAR
WEIGTH: 3500 LBS.
LENGTH: 13 FT.
OBJECTIVE SIZE 8 TO 36 IN.

Unmanned observatories circling the earth will enable astronomers to "see" the planets and stars without the intervening screen of the atmosphere.

The apparent nightly motion of the stars is due to the turning of the earth.

The apparent brightness of a star depends on its distance from the earth, its size, and its temperature.

When we view the stars we are not only looking far into distance but also far back into time.

Our Milky Way is an inside view of the great disk-shaped galaxy of stars in which our solar system is located.

Our sun is one of 100 billion stars in our Milky Way galaxy.

The stars in the Milky Way are revolving around its center.

Other galaxies resembling ours exist.

The astronomical hierachy in which we live, according to the most recent knowledge is: planet, solar system, galaxy, universe.

Everything in the universe is in motion.

We live in an expanding universe, with galaxies fleeing from each other at terrific speeds.

The most important instruments for exploring the universe are the telescope, camera, spectroscope and radio-telescope. Space observatories carry astronomical instruments to positions where more information may be gathered.

Each year our knowledge of the universe increases.

DISCOVERING FOR YOURSELF*

1. Read several issues of "Science News Letter" (see bibliography, Magazines), to learn about some new astronomical discoveries.
2. Locate as many first magnitude stars as you can.
3. Observe a planet. Tell at what hour and in what sky location you saw it. Describe it and tell how it differs from any other object in the sky. Observe its position at the some hour for a period of a week or more.
4. Observe the moon through a pair of field glasses. Report your observations.
5. Do further reading about sun spots. Be prepared to discuss your findings from the standpoint of reliability and importance.
6. Find out when the next partial or full eclipses of the moon and sun will take place. Explain your procedure in obtaining the information.
7. Obtain and discuss the latest information about possible life on the planet Mars.
8. Try to observe meteorites in a local museum and find out their histories.
9. Observe the moon for a two-week period. Record the time of observation and location in sky. Keep a record (by making line drawings) of its appearance.
10. Find the North Star and make a drawing of the constellations near it that you can see on a clear night.
11. Make four observations of the Big Dipper at one-hour intervals on the same night. Make a drawing of your observations.
12. Look at stars, planets, and the moon through a telescope and describe your experience.

---

* This section tells how to discover for yourself about "The Sun and the Planets" as well as about "The Stars and the Universe."

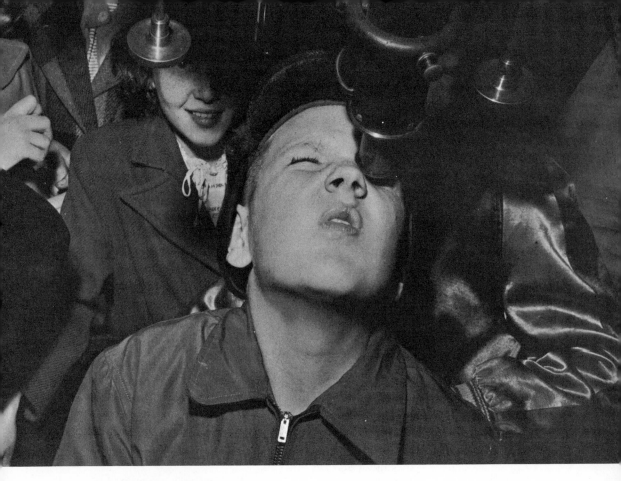

CHAPTER 8B

Teaching "The Stars and the Universe"

The stars have a new meaning today. They form a backdrop for the many exciting space adventures which are actually occurring with ever-increasing frequency. As millions of children across the United States watched the movement of the balloon satellite Echo across the sky, their interest in the stars and star groups was stimulated. With each new space conquest, children themselves are propelled into space—in thought, in imagination, in feeling.

We can help children know the stars and star groups by suggesting that they look at some that may be found easily in the sky. It is suggested that pupils look for just *one* star or *one* constellation on any evening. In this way they can begin to recognize some of the prominent features of the night sky, step by step. It is advisable to give children specific instructions about the hours, the direction, and how far up in the sky to look for each observation.

The following day, the children can describe what they have seen and make further studies from charts and books.

Many of the concepts of distance and size of stars are beyond the comprehension of many younger children. It is sufficient for them to know that these distances are great and cannot really be compared with any distances on the earth. The later elementary pupils are better able to begin to understand these great distances and sizes. Many of the general suggestions given for the previous chapter are also appropriate for teaching the material treated in this one.

Some suitable unit problems for the intermediate grades may be:

What are stars and constellations and how can we locate some of them?
How do stars differ from each other and from planets?

For beginning pupils, the following activities may be appropriate:

Observing how stars appear as the sky darkens.
Making drawings of the night-time sky.
Watching a particular star or star group for a half-hour to see how it appears to move with respect to any convenient landmark (building or tree).

LOCATING THE CONSTELLATIONS

Begin the study by locating some of the most easily identified star groups, one or a few at a time. Start with the Big Dipper, part of the constellation Ursa Major. If the teacher locates it herself, draws a sketch on the board in relationship to the school or other landmark, pupils can then more easily find it themselves.

The North Star is easy to locate from the Big Dipper. (See star map, page 143.) The two stars opposite the handle are the pointers. A line drawn through these stars away from the dipper's bottom for a length of about five times the distance between the pointers will locate the North Star. A simple map that the children have sketched will help them to locate

The Big Dipper is one of the easiest star groups to locate; since it may be used to locate the North Star, it is one of the most important in orienting a star gazer. Observing it at different times of the night helps pupils to understand the effect of the earth's rotation on what we see in the night sky.

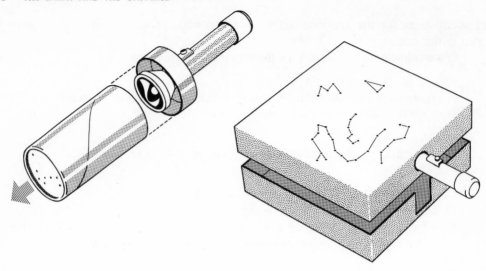

In studying the constellations, insert a flashlight into either a cereal box (left) or a large cardboard box to illuminate constellations punched in the other end. Each constellation is drawn on a separate top.

the North Star at night. Pupils may be urged to use a compass in determining the section of the sky where the North Star is located. If they find north, then look up to the sky about halfway from the horizon to straight overhead, they will see the star.

The constellation Orion is another interesting group. This is in the southern sky in the winter months, halfway from the horizon to straight overhead. Three bright stars mark Orion's belt. With the use of the star map, the rest of the constellation can be located.

Pupils generally have the idea that constellations are flat, not realizing that space has depth. A model of the Big Dipper will help to give them a better concept of the universe. The model as shown here in the drawing is made of clay balls suspended from a cardboard by strings. No attempt is made to produce the model to any specific scale but when pupils view the model from a distance they get the idea that the appearance of the Big Dipper is strictly an *earth* view. From other points in the universe it looks quite different.

A device for showing star groups is made from a cardboard box. Leave the cover on and remove one end of the box. Cut several pieces of paper the size of the end of the box, and on each piece make one constellation by punching holes to represent the stars. Use a flashlight to illuminate the inside of the box. When the constellation cards are held over the open end of the box, the light shines through the holes and the constellation shows up very well, especially if the room is darkened. The details about the kind of paper to use, the brightness of the light, the shape of the box, and so forth, may be worked out by the pupils.

Another easily made device is constructed from a cylindrical cereal box, as shown in the drawing. The constellations are made by punching holes in the bottom. Pupils will think of ways to remove the circular bottom piece and insert other similar pieces, each with a different constellation.

Constellations may also be represented on pieces of large paper placed against a bright window, with holes to represent individual stars.

Note: Some variations of the activities suggested in chapter 7B are appropriate for use in helping pupils understand more clearly the material on constellations and galaxies.

*RESOURCES TO INVESTIGATE**

1. A local telescope in an observatory or a smaller telescope owned by an amateur astronomer for viewing the moon and other objects in the night sky.
2. The evening sky to observe visible planets and to see the moon through binoculars.
3. The daytime sky to observe the moon—its shape and location in relation to the sun.
4. Meteorites in a local museum collection.
5. Magazine and newspaper accounts of current astronomical discoveries.
6. A local amateur astronomer to answer questions about astronomy.
7. Leaders of Scouts and 4-H Clubs to conduct evening trips to study the heavens.
8. Military and naval personnel in the community for information about the uses of the heavenly bodies in navigating and about constellations seen in other parts of the world.
9. Various persons in the community for field glasses to use in observing the moon.
10. Local planetarium, if there is one in your vicinity.

---

* This section tells about resources to investigate to learn about "The Sun and the Planets" as well as "The Stars and the Universe."

The Air and the Weather

Weather is a characteristic of the atmosphere in which we live. Hurricanes, thunderstorms, snowstorms, balmy breezes, hot spells, cold snaps, dense fogs, and rainbows are symptomatic of the ever-changing conditions within the earth's blanketing atmosphere. Weathermen probe the atmosphere carefully to find out more about the causes of weather, so that they may be able to forecast it with ever-improving accuracy. Ultimately, with this information, they hope to modify or control weather and climate for the betterment of mankind.

To understand weather, it is necessary to be familiar with the characteristics of the atmosphere, for it is in the atmosphere that weather occurs. To be weather-wise, it is essential to gather information about the air—its composition, temperature, humidity, pressure, movements, and other characteristics—and to combine this information into a comprehensive picture. Weathermen, or *meteorologists*, as they are called, measure these characteristics in many places around the earth and at many altitudes in order to gain a three-dimensional picture of the weather from the surface of the earth up to 100,000 feet. They make observations hour after hour, day after day, and thus are able to write a continuous story of the ever-changing weather.

We will see later just what kind of instruments are used for these measurements. First let us take a look at the atmosphere. We will consider the atmosphere carefully, not only because it is the setting for the kind of weather we experience daily, but also because its upper layers are now the environment of high-flying jet planes, of rocket ships, of man-made satellites, and of orbiting manned spacecraft.

THE ATMOSPHERE

Man lives at the bottom of an ocean of air. Covering the entire earth and extending upward for hundreds of miles, as shown on page 162, the atmosphere acts as a protective blanket, moderating the temperature and shielding us from harmful rays and particles from outer space which bombard our planet.

DISTRIBUTION OF AIR. The air in our atmospheric ocean is distributed so that it becomes thinner and thinner at higher levels. Mountain climbers are painfully aware of this at high altitudes. At 18,000 feet, or 3½ miles, there is only half as much oxygen (and other air constituents) in each lungful of air as at sea level. Half of the total weight of the air in the atmosphere lies below the 3½-mile mark, and half above it. Ninety-nine percent of the air is under the 20-mile level, leaving only 1 percent thinly scattered in the hundreds of miles above.

Scientists have divided the atmosphere into a series of layers, one on top of the other, in order to point up differences in temperature, chemical composition, pressure, and other properties at varying altitudes. If you consult different sources, you will find somewhat different atmosphere diagrams, or *profiles*, as they are called. Recent studies of the atmosphere with rockets and satellites are yielding new secrets of the earth's upper atmosphere, and causing scientists to modify earlier profiles. We present here a simplified profile, in which the atmosphere is divided into five layers: the *troposphere*, the *stratosphere*, the *mesosphere*, the *ionosphere*, and the *exosphere*.

THE TURBULENT SPHERE. The layer in which we live is the troposphere. This layer varies in height from 10 miles at the equator to about 5 miles at the poles, and is about 7 miles high in the middle latitudes. The word troposphere, which means "turbulent sphere," is appropriate, since all storms great and small and, indeed, almost all weather phenomena appear to occur in this layer. Another characteristic of the troposphere is the steady drop in temperature with increased altitude: the temperature drops 3½° F. for each 1,000 feet of ascent. In the troposphere the sky appears blue because the air and dust particles in it scatter the white light of the sun in such a way that its blue rays are bent into our line of vision (see chapter 23A). The blue skies we see are not far off in space; they are a phenomenon produced in the nearby troposphere, as too are the clouds.

At the upper boundary of the troposphere the temperature ceases to fall with increasing altitude; here the stratosphere begins.

THE STRATOSPHERE. This layer extends from the top of the troposphere to a height of 19 miles above the earth's surface. The air in the stratosphere is almost moistureless, and cloudless except for some ice-crystal clouds at a height of 13 to 18 miles. The temperature at the bottom of the stratosphere is 67° *below* zero F. (over the temperate zones). It remains at this temperature until about 14 miles above the earth and then begins to rise, reaching about −45° F. at 19 miles.

Winds in the stratosphere are strong and steady, but there are no up-and-down air currents. Men have penetrated the lower stratosphere in balloons and planes. In 1957, Major G. Simons, an Air Force balloonist, soared 19 miles above the earth, higher than anyone had ever reached in a balloon.

A concentration of a special form of oxygen, called *ozone,* appears 13 to 16 miles

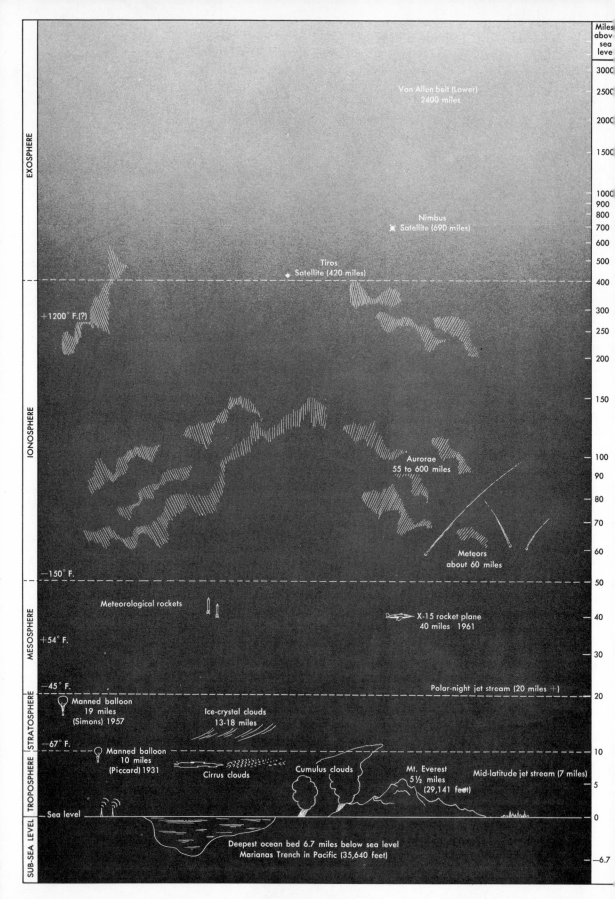

The earth's atmosphere.

above the earth. (Ordinary oxygen is composed of two atoms of oxygen—O_2—while ozone has three atoms—O_3—in each of its molecules. See chapter 16A for a discussion of atoms and molecules.) Ozone absorbs most of the powerful ultraviolet radiation from the sun, and in this way protects living things on earth from rays that in full strength would prove deadly. The ultraviolet rays that do penetrate to the earth's surface tan our skins, prevent rickets, and kill bacteria.

THE MESOSPHERE. By the time we reach the mesosphere we have passed 99 percent of the weight of the atmosphere. In the mesosphere, which extends from the stratosphere to 50 miles above the earth, the temperature continues to rise up to the 30-mile level, reaching 54° F. It then falls to a very cold −150° F. at the top of the mesosphere.

A large amount of ozone is produced in the mesosphere. The high temperature at the 30-mile level is caused by the absorption of solar radiation by the ozone.

In 1961, pilots flying X-15 rocket planes penetrated deep into the mesosphere, reaching heights over 40 miles above the earth.

THE ELECTRICALLY CHARGED SPHERE. The third layer above the earth is the ionosphere. Here x-rays and ultraviolet rays from the sun are absorbed by the scattered atoms and molecules of extremely thin atmosphere. As a result, many of these particles are shaken apart. Some of the fragments are electrically charged, becoming *ions*, from which the name ionosphere is derived. These ions make radio reception around the earth possible, since they reflect back to earth over and over again the radio waves used in regular and in short-wave broadcasting and thus make it possible for the signals to travel around the earth. In the ionosphere, too, radio reception may be interfered with. You recall from chapter 7A that, when storms are raging on the sun,

streams of electrical particles pour down from it on the ionosphere. During these solar flares, the ionosphere *absorbs* radio waves, instead of bouncing them back to earth. As a result, radio communication may be disrupted for days.

The fascinating and mysterious Northern Lights, or the *Aurora Borealis*, also originate in the ionosphere. It is believed that the aurora is caused by electrically charged hydrogen particles streaking down from the sun, which under the influence of the earth's magnetic poles strike nitrogen and oxygen atoms in the ionosphere and cause them to glow, thus producing the display of light.

In the ionosphere, which extends from 50 to 400 miles above the earth's surface, the air is incredibly thin, being 10 million times rarer than the air at sea level. Thin as it is, the air in the ionosphere offers enough frictional resistance to some of the meteors to cause them to become white hot and to be reduced to dust. The ionosphere (and to some extent, the mesosphere) serves, therefore, as a screen, protecting the earth from the millions of meteors that bombard it daily.

THE OUTER SPHERE. The exosphere begins at the upper limit of the ionosphere and extends outward about 10,000–18,000 miles until it is indistinguishable from outer space. In the exosphere, the air is so thin that molecules of it can travel almost an infinite distance without hitting each other.

One of the major achievements of the exploration of the atmosphere by satellite was the discovery of the existence of two belts of high radiation, known as the Van Allen belts after their discoverer. These doughnut-shaped belts, one inside the other, consist of fast moving electrons and protrons (see chapter 19A) which spiral in the lines of force in the earth's magnetic field (see chapter 21A). The center of one belt is 2,400 miles and the other 10,000 miles from the earth. Since the radiation in the

Van Allen belts presents a hazard to space travelers, the flight paths of manned spacecraft are planned to avoid these regions.

THE COMPLEX ATMOSPHERE. The more the atmosphere is studied, the clearer it becomes that it is an extremely complicated system. Meteorologists hope that when we discover the laws governing the changes in this system, and when we have perfected ways of recording minute by minute the significant data in the ever-changing atmosphere, we may then be in a position to foretell the later course of events with a high degree of accuracy. With the help of thousands of stations on earth, and in earth-circling satellites, and with the electronic "brains" of computing machines into which weather data may be registered and interpreted, the hope for dependable short- and long-term forecasts may become a reality in our own time.

COMPOSITION OF THE AIR

The air that enters your lungs with each breath is not one but many things. The two most abundant parts of air are nitrogen, which accounts for nearly four-fifths of the air, and oxygen, which makes up about one-fifth. Up to an altitude of 55 miles these primary components of air are uniformly mixed in a 4/5–1/5 proportion, even though, as we have seen, the air becomes thinner and thinner. Above 55 miles the proportion changes markedly.

Nitrogen, the chief constituent of air, is also an essential element in proteins, which are basic in the make-up of all living things. As we shall see in chapter 15A, some atmospheric nitrogen is made available to plants by action of certain bacteria in the soil.

Oxygen, a chemically active component of the air, is essential for respiration in plants and animals and for the combustion of fuels.

Carbon dioxide, making up only 3/100 of 1 percent of the air, is extremely important to life. Green plants absorb carbon dioxide from the air and combine it with the hydrogen in water molecules to produce the food essential for their life and eventually for that of all animals as well. This important process will be discussed in chapter 10A.

Water vapor, also found in small amounts, varying from zero to 3 or 4 percent of the air, exerts a profound influence on the distribution of life on this planet, since a region's capacity for supporting life is determined principally by the amount of water in the form of rain or snow that is available. Most of the water vapor is found in the lower 4 miles of the atmosphere. As we will see, water vapor plays an important part in the changing weather picture.

We have thus far accounted for about 99 percent of the air. The remaining 1 percent is primarily the gases argon, neon, helium, krypton, xenon, and hydrogen. Sprinkled in the air also is a varying amount of dust.

SUN, AIR, AND WATER

The drama of weather is better understood if we follow closely the roles played by the sun, air, and water. The sun is the leading figure in the spectacle, providing the heat energy that keeps the whole show moving. The air is the vehicle that circulates and transports all kinds and conditions of weather around the earth. Water appears in many forms—dew, sleet, fog, clouds, rain, and snow; it disappears from view as water vapor.

SEE PAGE 197 TO 199

SUN. From a distance of about 93 million miles, the sun warms the earth. If all parts of the earth were heated equally, there would not be much weather to talk about. But the sun's heat is not distributed equally. Let us see why:

1. *For one thing the sun's rays reach only half of the earth at any one time, the side in daylight. Since we live on a turning earth, there is a daily cycle of heating and cooling accompanying day and night.*

2. *Sunshine is not equally strong all over the earth. The fact that the earth is round means that different parts of its surface receive sunlight at different angles. Thus areas near the equator face the sun directly and receive more radiation than the belts farther away from the equator that receive more slanting rays. As a result, the equatorial regions receive more heat than the temperate, and the temperate more than the polar. (See chapter 7B for a demonstration of the principle involved.)*

3. *We saw in chapter 7A how the tilted axis of the earth and the yearly revolution of the earth around the sun causes variation in the amount of heat received at different times of the year, thereby causing the different seasons.*

4. *The amount of heat absorbed by any area of the earth depends in part on the kind of surface that is being heated. Water heats up much more slowly than land. Hence it is cooler in summer at the seacoast than in inland regions at the same latitude.*

5. *Even without the first four factors operating, the atmosphere of the earth, considered vertically, would exhibit variation in temperature. As we learned previously, temperatures drop off in the troposphere at the average rate of 3½° F. for every 1,000 feet of elevation. It may seem unusual that temperatures should drop as one gets nearer to the sun, until one considers that the few thousand feet involved are a very tiny percentage of the 93 million miles to the sun. Far overshadowing relative distance from the sun are two other factors:*

a. *The air at the bottom of the atmosphere, being denser, dustier, and more moist, is able to absorb more of the sun's radiation than air in the upper layers. This absorbed radiation is converted into heat, thus warming the air.*

b. *The bottom air is also heated from below by the earth itself. The sun's radiant energy is first absorbed by the rocks, soil, and water of the earth, and changed into heat. These warmed materials, in turn, heat the layer of air closest to the surface of the earth.*

It is apparent, then, that the amount of solar energy received and absorbed varies considerably from place to place and from time to time. This results in an uneven heating of the earth and has a profound effect on the weather.

AIR.   Weather, as we indicated at the beginning of this chapter, is a condition of the atmosphere, and hence of the air that makes up the atmosphere. In chapter 7A, we saw how the peculiar "weather" of the moon, or rather, the absence of weather, is due to the fact that it has no atmosphere. The earth's air acts as a huge insulator, holding in the heat absorbed from the sun's rays by the earth's surface. As an insulator, it moderates the temperature of the earth so that we do not freeze at night nor broil in the day.

The uneven heating of the earth results in an uneven heating of the air above it, so that all around the earth there are parcels of air, big and small, with different temperatures. *Because cold air is heavier than an equal volume of warm air, cold air sinks and pushes up the lighter warm air.* On a small scale, this happens in a room heated by a radiator. If the circulation of the air in a room is traced by means of smoke or streamers of tissue paper, it will

SEE PAGES 205 TO 206

be noted that the warm air above the radiator rises to the ceiling and then moves away, while the colder air near the floor moves toward the radiator to be heated in turn. (See diagram page 441 in chapter 18A.)

Thus, in a radiator-heated room we see that the difference in temperature in the air causes up-and-down movements, or air currents, and lateral movements across the room, a kind of homemade "breeze."

The same principle that explains the movement of air in a heated room applies, on a larger scale, to a summer seacoast. The sun beating down on the coastal land heats it, and consequently the air over it, more

than it heats the ocean and its overlying air. Because of this, the land behaves like the room radiator, and a circulation is started in which a "sea breeze" of cool air sweeps in from the ocean, pushing up the air warmed by the land which then rises and streams out aloft toward the ocean. At night, however, the land loses its heat more rapidly than the water. The air above it is chilled, while the ocean air is relatively warm. The colder air now sweeps from the land to the water, producing the "land breeze."

On a global scale, the hot equatorial regions may be thought of as the earth's "radiator." Air heated in the tropics accumulates and forms a warm mass of air. In the polar regions, the air is chilled to form a cold mass. A circulation is set up in the troposphere in which warm air rises over the equator and streams toward the poles, while cold air from the poles slips down toward the equator. This circulation is complicated by many factors, but it is clear that it provides a mechanism whereby the heat of the earth can be distributed, a mechanism that brings to us in the temperate zones air that has been chilled at the poles and air that has been heated at the equator.

During the daytime, the air over the sea is cooler than the air over the land. A cool sea breeze blows. At night, when conditions are reversed, a land breeze blows.

Summer day

Summer night

WATER. Although we talk of water "shortages," the amount of water on the earth is fairly constant, but it is not always available when and where we want it. The endless cycle of evaporation and condensation depicted in the diagram on page 167 keeps the water of the earth in constant circulation. Water evaporates from the soil, from leaves of plants, from the lungs and skin of animals, from puddles, ponds, lakes, and seas. In the process of evaporation, molecules of water bounce out of their liquid surroundings to mix with the other components of the air. This highly scattered, invisible form of water is known as water vapor. The heat provided by the sun and the fanning by the winds hasten evaporation, as anyone who has hung wet clothes on a line to dry knows.

SEE PAGES 200 TO 202

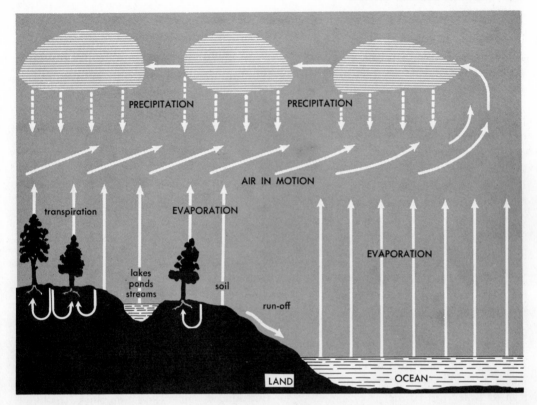

PRECIPITATION PRECIPITATION

AIR IN MOTION

transpiration EVAPORATION

EVAPORATION

lakes
ponds
streams
soil

run-off

LAND OCEAN

The endless cycle of evaporation and condensation keeps the water of the earth in constant circulation.

Aloft, a chilling of air containing water vapor causes the water molecules to clump together in tiny droplets to form a cloud. We see cloud formation on a small scale when we breathe out on a cold day and "see" our breath. If the light droplets in a cloud clump together, they become larger, forming heavier drops that fall as rain and return to the soil, streams, lakes, and oceans. Water vapor may return in other forms—as snow, dew, and frost. We will consider these and other forms of precipitation presently.

The water cycle, then, provides a means of circulating water from oceans, lakes, and seas to the land areas. The water cycle also serves as nature's water-purification system, since minerals, mud, debris, and other impurities in water are left behind when water evaporates into the air. The water that comes down is pure and clean.

MEASURING THE WEATHER

In order to describe present weather conditions accurately and to forecast future weather successfully, it is necessary to use weather instruments. Measurements of rainfall and snowfall, of wind direction and wind velocity, of the temperature, humidity, and pressure of the air must be recorded. The meteorologist collects such information from many points on the earth and as high into the atmosphere as possible. He keeps records and makes charts day after day, using these to forecast the weather.

SEE
PAGES
199
TO
200

MEASURING RAIN AND SNOW.
Probably the oldest weather instrument was
a rain gauge. Any straight-walled vessel,
such as a jar, served as a measure of the
amount of rain in any rainfall. A modern
rain gauge catches the rain in a funnel whose
mouth is exactly 10 times as big as the
opening of the cylinder into which it empties
as shown in the diagram on page 199. Thus
the amount of rainfall is magnified 10 times.
If 4 inches of rain accumulate in the collecting cylinder, the actual rainfall is 4/10 of an
inch.

Snowfall is measured directly by
plunging a stick into the snow at an average
open location. Snow varies in its yield of
water. The rain water equivalent of the snowfall is determined by melting a given portion
of snow. Light, fluffy snow with a good deal
of air in it may give only 1 inch of water for
15 inches of snow; a dense, packed snowfall
may yield an inch of water from only 6
inches of snow. The average is about an
inch of water for 10 inches of snow.

The Weather Bureau also uses a type
of gauge which weighs the amount of precipitation (rain or snow) falling into the
gauge. The weight is "translated" automatically on a chart into depth of water in
inches. If for example, 13 ounces of rain
were caught in the gauge, a recording pen
would indicate that 0.45 inches of rain had
fallen.

SEE
PAGES
207
TO
208

MEASURING WIND. Wind, as de-
fined by the meteorologist, refers to *horizontal* air motion, as distinct from vertical motion. To measure the wind is to determine its
direction and speed. The wind vane measures
direction. (It is more popularly called the
weather vane, since men have known for a
long time that wind direction has an important bearing on the weather.) A wind vane
points into the wind, that is, toward the
direction from which the wind is blowing.
For example, if a wind is blowing from the
west, the arrowhead points to the west.
Winds are named by the direction *from*

which they come. A wind blowing from west
to east is designated a west wind.

The speed of the wind is measured
by an instrument called an anemometer. A
common type used by weather bureaus is
the three-cup anemometer. Each cup is a
hollow hemisphere. The three cups are attached by spokes to a central pivot. The
wind spins the cups around as it would a
pinwheel, at a speed that is proportional to
the wind speed. The speed is transmitted
electrically to an indicator located inside the
weather bureau.

The direction and speed of winds
above the earth are determined with the aid
of balloons. These balloons, containing hydrogen or helium, are released into the air.
They are observed from the ground with a
theodolite, a telescope that enables the meteorologist to determine the balloon's position.
From these observations, the speed and the
direction of the wind at different levels of
the atmosphere can be calculated. A method
introduced in 1946 employs balloons
equipped with a radio transmitter which is
tracked by radar equipment on the ground.
This tracking method, known as RAWIN
(radio winds-aloft) is superior to the theodolite method because the balloon can be followed to greater heights and in all kinds of
weather.

MEASURING TEMPERATURE. The
weatherman uses his thermometer to tell the
temperature of the air. All significant readings are made in an enclosure open to the
air but shaded from the sun. (Reading a
thermometer with the sun beating on it will
merely show how effectively the thermometer is absorbing the sun's rays. It will not
give any significant figure, nor will it agree
with another thermometer of different size
or shape held in the same location. It is not
intended to be used in sunlight. A full discussion of the thermometer is to be found
in chapter 18A.)

It is extremely important for the
meteorologist to know the temperature at

different elevations above the earth. We will see shortly how he takes the temperature of the air aloft.

MEASURING HUMIDITY. The hygrometer is an instrument for measuring the water content of the atmosphere. One kind of hygrometer is the *wet- and dry-bulb thermometer*. You can understand the principle of this instrument if you recall two common experiences.

First, you may have noticed how slowly wet clothing dries on a humid day, how rapidly on a dry day.

Second, you may recall the coolness you feel on the skin of your hands or face as water evaporates from them.

The wet-bulb thermometer shown in the picture is one that has a moist cloth wrapped around its bulb. As water evaporates from the cloth into the air, the thermometer is cooled. If the air is dry, evaporation is rapid and the thermometer drops markedly. If the air is humid, evaporation is slow and the temperature falls little.

In short, we calculate the moisture content of the air from the rate of evaporation of a moist cloth. By comparing the temperature of the wet-bulb thermometer with that of an ordinary dry-bulb one, and by using the chart on page 170, the humidity of the air can be determined. The humidity referred to is the *relative humidity* and it is expressed as a percentage.

Just what is meant by relative humidity? If, for example, we say that the relative humidity is 100 percent, we mean that the air is as full of water vapor as it can be; if more water were added it would fall out of the air as mist or rain. Fifty percent relative humidity means that the air is holding only half the amount of water vapor that it could.

A glance at the chart shows that the percentages given are true for a particular temperature. In other words, the capacity of air to hold water varies with its temperature: warm air can hold more water vapor than

These weather instruments, which are used to determine relative humidity, are shielded from the sun but not from the air. The rate of evaporation of water from the "sock" of the wet-bulb thermometer is an index to the amount of vapor present in the air. The readings of the two thermometers are taken and the relative humidity of the air is computed. The fan provides ventilation, constantly bringing in "fresh" air.

RELATIVE HUMIDITY IN PERCENTAGES

Readings of dry-bulb thermometer

Difference in degrees fahrenheit between wet- and dry-bulb thermometers

	0	1	2	3	4	5	6	7	8	9	10	11	12	13	14	15
60	100%	94%	89%	84%	78%	73%	68%	63%	58%	53%	49%	44%	40%	35%	31%	27%
61	100	94	89	84	79	74	68	64	59	54	50	45	40	36	32	28
62	100	94	89	84	79	74	69	64	60	55	50	46	41	37	33	29
63	100	95	90	84	79	74	70	65	60	56	51	47	42	38	34	30
64	100	95	90	85	79	75	70	66	61	56	52	48	43	39	35	31
65	100	95	90	85	80	75	70	66	62	57	53	48	44	40	36	32
66	100	95	90	85	80	76	71	66	62	58	53	49	45	41	37	33
67	100	95	90	85	80	76	71	67	62	58	54	50	46	42	38	34
68	100	95	90	85	81	76	72	67	63	59	55	51	47	43	39	35
69	100	95	90	86	81	77	72	68	64	59	55	51	47	44	40	36
70	100	95	90	86	81	77	72	68	64	60	56	52	48	44	40	37
71	100	95	90	86	82	77	73	69	64	60	56	53	49	45	41	38
72	100	95	91	86	82	78	73	69	65	61	57	53	49	46	42	39
73	100	95	91	86	82	78	73	69	65	61	58	54	50	46	43	40
74	100	95	91	86	82	78	74	70	66	62	58	54	51	47	44	40
75	100	96	91	87	82	78	74	70	66	63	59	55	51	48	44	41
76	100	96	91	87	83	78	74	70	67	63	59	55	52	48	45	42
77	100	96	91	87	83	79	75	71	67	63	60	56	52	49	46	42
78	100	96	91	87	83	79	75	71	67	64	60	57	53	50	46	43
79	100	96	91	87	83	79	75	71	68	64	60	57	54	50	47	44
80	100	96	91	87	83	79	76	72	68	64	61	57	54	51	47	44

cold air. This is important in weather phenomena, for it means that if a given portion of air is chilled, its water-holding capacity decreases. Without any change in its actual water *content*, the relative humidity of such a portion of air increases, and, if it reaches 100 percent, water may be condensed out of it. This is just what happens on a warm summer day as warm, moist air rises in the morning to cooler regions above to form the thunderclouds of the afternoon.

How to calculate the relative humidity: Look at the relative humidity chart. If the air temperature as given by the dry-bulb thermometer is 70 degress and the wet-bulb thermometer falls to 64 degrees, the difference is 6 degrees. Look along the 70-degree line until you come under the number 6. The relative humidity is 72 percent.

Another instrument for measuring relative humidity is the *hair hygrometer*, which makes use of the fact that human hair shortens when the atmosphere is dry and lengthens when it is moist. Blond hair seems to work best. It is first treated to remove oils, and then a few strands of it are fastened into a device in such a way that the hair moves a pointer over a scale of humidity percentages. Readings are made directly, without the need to consult a chart, but this instrument is not quite as accurate as the wet- and dry-bulb thermometers.

MEASURING PRESSURE. It is most important for the meteorologist to know the air pressure because it reveals the inner workings of the air-circulating system within our atmosphere.

SEE PAG 203 TO 204

When we say that air has pressure, we mean very simply that air pushes or presses against things. We are not referring to breezes or hurricane winds but to quiet, untroubled air. We are not aware of this pressure because we live our lives in it and because it pushes in on us equally from all directions. Moreover, the air in our body cavities and the blood in our veins and arteries push our body structures outward with equal pressure. Let us change our elevation, however, as we do when we descend or rise rapidly in an elevator or in an automobile on a mountain, and our eardrums tell us quickly of the changing pressure.

What gives air its push, its pressure? To answer in one word, it is its *weight*. We live at the bottom of an air ocean that rests its weight on the earth. Let us think of just a small portion of the earth's surface, just one square inch of it. Let us assume that we were able to ascend slowly in a balloon from the surface of the earth to the top of the atmosphere, collecting all the air *directly over this square inch* into an empty (empty even of air) steel cylinder. On returning to earth, we would find that the cylinder would weigh fifteen pounds more than it did at the outset. There are approximately fifteen pounds of air weighing down on every square inch of the surface of the earth (at sea level). Or, to put it in other words, the *pressure* of the air at sea level is about fifteen pounds per square inch.

Air pressure, then, is due to the weight of air above us. Obviously it should be less on a mountain top, and it is; it is greater in a mine below sea level.

In 1643 Toricelli invented an instrument for measuring air pressure, the mercury barometer. To make a mercury barometer, a glass tube about 36 inches long, closed at one end, is filled with mercury. It is then inverted into an open jar containing more mercury. If this experiment is performed at sea level, the mercury will fall a few inches, but it will then stop. Approximately 30 inches will remain in the tube, as shown in the diagram. The space above the mercury is empty; it is a vacuum.

Why does the mercury not flow out of the tube? Toricelli's first thought was that this might be an example of Aristotle's theory that "nature abhors a vacuum." According to this line of reasoning, if all the mercury flowed out, it would leave a long vacuum in the tube, giving nature a great deal to abhor. But Toricelli noticed something that was to be of great significance in meteorology: *the height of the mercury column varied from day to day.* He reasoned from this that "nature would not, as a flirtatious girl, have a different horror of a vacuum on different days," and he looked elsewhere for an explanation. This brought him to the conclusion that we hold currently: the mercury in the tube is supported by the pressure of the air on the surface of the mercury in the jar. You might think of the mercury

A simple mercury barometer. Air pressure on the mercury in the dish supports the column of mercury in the tube. Increasing atmospheric pressure causes the mercury to rise; decreasing pressure allows it to fall.

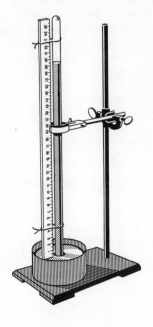

The dark pointer on the aneroid barometer indicates changes in the air pressure. The other pointer is set by hand so that changes for any period of time can be noted easily. The numbers correspond to inches of mercury. Evidently, the barometer shown here fell a bit more than half an inch since it was last set. The delicate mechanism inside the aneroid barometer case (see diagram below) consists essentially of a disk-like box from which air has been exhausted, and a connecting system of levers that operates the pointer to indicate the change in pressure.

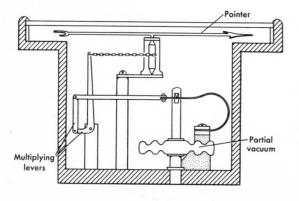

barometer as a kind of balance, in which the weight of the atmosphere on the mercury is counterbalanced exactly by the weight of the mercury in the tube.

Mercury is used in barometers because it is the heaviest common fluid available. If water were used, the barometer tube would have to be about 40 feet high! In meteorology, the pressure of the air is expressed in inches of mercury, which may seem to be a curious way of measuring pressure unless you think of the construction of a mercury barometer. The 30 inches represent the *equivalent* of a pressure of approximately 15 pounds per square inch.

Within a few years after the discovery of the mercury barometer, it was found that high air pressure was generally associated with fair weather and a low pressure with unsettled or rainy weather. We will discuss the relation of air pressure to the general weather pattern in more detail presently.

For the moment, let us try to find out *why* air pressure varies from day to day. The pressure of air, as we have discovered, depends on its weight. The weight of the air over any one place is not constant. It varies for two reasons:

1. *Its temperature changes: a mass of warm air is generally lighter than an equal volume of cold air.*
2. *Its humidity changes: a mass of moist air is generally lighter than an equal volume of dry air.*

The reason that moist air is lighter than dry air is that a larger percentage of it is water vapor. Water vapor is actually lighter than the other components of the air. In any region of the atmosphere, when water vapor is added to the air it pushes out of it—to a more distant region—an equivalent volume of the heavier nitrogen and oxygen.

The barometric reading, then, being dependent on the moisture and temperature of the air, is an important weather measurement. Also, since air will tend to flow from a region of high pressure to one of low pressure, knowing these high and low areas will enable the weatherman to forecast the circulation of air.

Mercury barometers are awkward to carry from place to place. A much more convenient type is the *aneroid* barometer shown on page 172. The word "aneroid" means "without liquid." Instead of a liquid, the aneroid barometer contains a disk-shaped metal box from which much of the air has been removed. As air pressure increases, it pushes the top of the box down; as air pressure decreases, the top springs up. This slight movement is conveyed by levers to a pointer that sweeps over a scale calibrated to correspond with the mercury barometer. Aneroid barometers are used in homes, on ships, and in airplanes.

THE FOUR "Rs" AND ONE "S." As long as the measurement of wind, moisture, temperature, and pressure was confined to the surface of the earth, our knowledge of

weather was severely restricted. Weather, like the atmosphere, is a three-dimensional affair. We must know the characteristics of the air at various levels above us if we are to have the full picture of the weather at work. The modern 4 "Rs" that we employ for this upper air study are the *radiosonde, reconnaissance, radar,* and *rockets.* To the 4 "Rs" we have now added an "S"—*satellites.*

The radiosonde is a balloon-borne instrument that measures temperature, humidity, and pressure at regular intervals as the gas-filled, unmanned balloon ascends to heights of approximately 50,000-75,000 feet. The measurements are converted into radio signals that are broadcast back to earth. (See illustration.)

The use of airplanes equipped with weather instruments for reconnaissance into the atmosphere, including flights into dangerous hurricanes, has given us vital information that could not be obtained in any other way.

An observer is preparing to release a radiosonde balloon, parachute, and instruments. A second observer is prepared to follow the flight of this instrument with a radio direction-finding device in order to determine upper-air wind direction and velocities.

Radar, originally used as an important instrument of navigation by ships and planes, was found to be useful as a weather detector. Radar screens are sensitive to raindrops, snowflakes, and layers of air of contrasting temperature or moisture content. Radar has been used successfully as a rain and storm detection and tracking instrument, showing the presence of atmospheric disturbances hundreds of miles away. We will see later how it has been used by the Weather Bureau for this purpose.

Meteorological rockets are now used to extend our observations of the atmosphere above the current limits of balloons, which carry instruments only up to a height of 20 miles. Recent research indicates that the atmosphere in the zone between 20 and 60 miles above the earth's surface (principally in the mesosphere) may have an important influence on weather. In 1959 a Meteorological Rocket Network was established to make systematic studies of the atmosphere above the balloon limit. From a number of stations in the United States and Canada, rockets are fired into the atmosphere. At predetermined levels, payloads of metallic strips, or a metalized parachute, both of which reflect radar waves, are ejected from the rocket into the atmosphere. As it descends, the metallic material is tracked by radar at the network station. From such observations, wind speed and direction are determined. In some rockets, sensitive equipment permits the detecting and transmission of information about the temperature and air density at these high altitudes.

On April 1, 1960, Tiros I, a meteorological satellite bearing two television cameras, was launched into orbit. By June of the same year, the cameras had taken and broadcast to stations on earth about 20,000 pictures of entire cloud systems in great detail. Tiros II and Tiros III which followed had notable careers. One of the historic achievements of Tiros III was the spotting of Hurricane Esther on September 10, 1961, *before it was detected by any other means.*

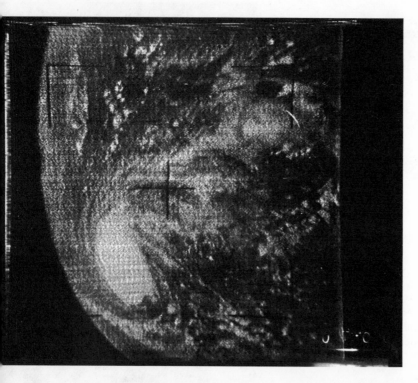

This is a portrait of Hurricane Betsy photographed by the satellite Tiros III on September 7, 1961. The eye of the hurricane is clearly visible and is approximately 200 miles in diameter. The surrounding mass of swirling clouds extends several hundred miles out. The picture was sent to ground stations by television.

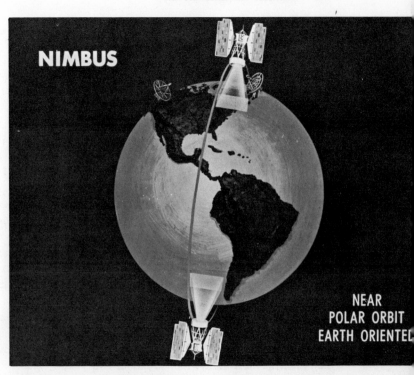

NIMBUS

NEAR
POLAR ORBIT
EARTH ORIENTEL

Weather satellites such as these will bring the entire world's weather under constant surveillance.

It is hoped that from the study of cloud patterns as seen from a satellite it will be possible to forecast hurricanes and other weather phenomena. In addition to photographing clouds, the Tiros satellites measure the radiation of heat from the earth—from ground, snow, and water surfaces, and from the tops of clouds. It is believed that data of the earth heat lost in this way may be significantly related to wind, temperature, and other weather characteristics. Ultimately more important is the role of meteorological satellites as research tools in deepening our understanding of the way in which weather systems develop and move.

Present plans call for the setting up of a complete multi-satellite network by 1965–1966 that is expected to bring the entire world's weather under regular surveillance. Nimbus and Aeros satellites are to be placed in orbit to provide cloud-cover pictures, and detect the birth and growth of hurricanes, cyclonic storms, thunderstorms, and tornadoes.

WATER IN MANY FORMS

SEE PAGE 204

Fog, clouds, dew, rain, frost, snow, sleet, and hail are the visible forms that water assumes. Water disappears from view when its molecules scatter into the air to become water vapor. When we "see" our breath on a cold day, we are viewing the result of the transformation of the invisible water vapor in the air from our lungs into a visible form: the molecules of water vapor in the exhaled air cluster together and condense into a small visible cloud. This example also reminds us that, in order for water vapor to condense, the air containing it must be cooled sufficiently. The more water vapor there is in the air, the less chilling is needed to condense the vapor.

DEWPOINT. We saw previously how relative humidity was a useful way of describing the water vapor content of the air. The *dewpoint* is also useful because it helps in determining whether condensation of this vapor may occur. The dewpoint may be defined as the temperature below which a given sample of air must be cooled before condensation will occur. It may also be regarded as the temperature at which a given sample of air will have a relative humidity of 100 percent. Let us see how the dewpoint is useful in understanding dew and frost formation.

DEW AND FROST.   When you enter a room after being outside on a cool day, a film of moisture often forms on your eyeglasses. This occurs because the chilled surface of the glasses cools the air nearest them below its dewpoint, and the vapor in the air condenses on the glasses. Dew forms in a similar way out of doors. Dew is caused when objects at or near the earth's surface become cooler than the surrounding air. Grass, leaves, automobiles, and outdoor furniture lose their heat more rapidly at night than does the air around them. If the air contains considerable moisture, these objects may cool the air to its dewpoint, causing the water vapor to condense on them. A clear night favors dew formation because then the earth radiates away its day-stored heat into the atmosphere. (Clouds act as blankets at night to prevent the loss of heat.) A night with little or no wind also helps dew formation, since winds stir up the atmosphere so that no one part of it is cooled sufficiently to permit condensation of water vapor by the cold surfaces.

Frost is formed in the same manner as dew except that the temperature of the objects upon which condensation occurs is below the freezing point, that is, below 32° F. The water vapor changes directly into feathery ice crystals. Frost is *not* frozen dew.

FOG.   Almost everyone has walked in a fog. Fogs are clouds touching the ground. Fog is composed of small droplets of water, about 1/1000 of an inch in diameter, which have condensed from water vapor, but which because of their small size remain suspended in the air.

Ground fogs are caused by the rapid cooling of the air near the earth's surface at night when the sun goes down. The conditions essential for this kind of fog are similar to those for dew formation, except that light winds, instead of a dead calm, help in mixing the cold air near the ground with air a short distance above. Ground fogs are often found in valleys, where cold, heavy air accumulates at night and in the early morning. When the sun warms the air, the fog disappears. This occurs because warm air can hold more moisture, and the fog droplets evaporate into it.

Advection fogs result when the warm, moist air from one region moves horizontally over a cool surface. Fogs like this are formed off Newfoundland, where the warm moist air over the Gulf Stream blows over the cold Labrador current. Summer fogs occur off California, when warm ocean air flows over the cold coastal waters.

CLOUDS.   The clouds aloft, like the fogs near the ground, are formed by condensation. We have to add only that each of the tiny droplets in a cloud forms around a very small particle of dust, ash, smoke, pollen, or salt. These particles are known as *condensation nuclei*.

Since ancient times, many systems have been devised for identifying cloud types. Today, in accordance with an international meteorological agreement, all clouds are classified according to two factors, form and height. Let us consider form first. Three basic cloud forms are recognized—*cirrus, cumulus*, and *stratus*. These are shown in the photographs on page 177.

Cirrus, meaning "curl," are the most delicate of all clouds. These clouds, sometimes called "mare's tails," are white, feathery, and filmy. They do not obscure the sun. Cirrus clouds are the highest of all clouds, averaging six miles in altitude. They are composed of ice crystals.

Cumulus, meaning "heap," are dense clouds that build up to huge heaps. They

Cirrus clouds are high clouds made of ice crystals.

Cumulus clouds of this kind usually come with fair weather.

Stratus clouds are generally thin uniform clouds that give the whole sky a gray tone.

have flat bases, are white and billowy above, and cast shadows on the earth. Cumulus clouds are formed in rising currents of air and are the characteristic clouds seen on fair days. When they tower upward a number of miles they are called thunderheads.

Stratus, meaning "layer," refer to clouds that cover the whole sky, obscuring the sun. They give us smooth gray skies. Stratus clouds are composed of water droplets in summer and ice crystals in winter. A fog is a stratus cloud on the ground.

These basic cloud *forms*—cirrus, cumulus, and stratus—are further classified by a system that takes *altitude* into account. This system includes high, middle and low clouds, and clouds with vertical development.

RAIN. The particles or droplets of moisture that make up most clouds are so small that they remain suspended in the air, kept up by light air currents. When cloud droplets grow in size and become heavy enough, they fall through the atmosphere as rain. We are still not sure what makes cloud droplets come together to form raindrops.

SNOW. It is often possible for the lower portion of a single cloud to consist of water droplets and the upper portion of snowflakes. In the snowflake portion, the temperature is below freezing, so that the water vapor there condenses directly into ice crystals. When the ice crystals grow sufficiently, they fall as snow. (Snow is *not* frozen rain.) When snow falls, its beautiful six-sided crystals may come down separately, or they may coalesce into large fleecy clots.

SLEET. Sleet is rain that freezes as it falls. If raindrops formed in a relatively warm layer of air pass through a layer with freezing temperatures, they freeze into small, hard, clear ice pellets.

GLAZE. Glaze is formed when rain falls on trees, streets, and other objects that are below freezing temperatures. The rain freezes into a coating of ice that sometimes becomes so heavy upon tree branches and telephone and telegraph wires that it causes them to break.

HAIL. Hail sometimes occurs during thunderstorms and can be produced only if there are strong currents of rising air. Hail begins as falling rain, but, when the rising air current carries the drops aloft to colder temperatures, they freeze into ice. They fall and may be swept up again. More water vapor condenses on the hailstones, and they therefore grow larger. This process may be repeated a number of times, so that it is possible for hailstones to be as large as hen's eggs. When they are so large that they can no longer be lifted by air currents, they fall to earth. Hailstones thus consist of a number of concentric layers that can easily be distinguished if the stones are cut in two. Hail often does much damage to crops. The largest hailstone recorded in the United States weighed one and one-half pounds.

WIND

The basic cause of winds, as we have seen, is the unequal heating of the earth by the sun. Heated air expands and hence becomes lighter. Cold air, being heavier, pushes in under the lighter air and forces it up. Since the earth is hottest at the equator and coolest at the poles, a global wind circulation is set up, with cold air moving toward the equator and warm air moving toward the poles as shown in the upper figure on page 179.

WIND BELTS. But the wind picture is not quite as simple as this. If it were, we would have, in the Northern Hemisphere, surface winds sweeping from the north to the south and winds aloft moving in the opposite direction. In the Southern Hemisphere, the reverse would be true. Thus all winds would be either north or south winds. The large-scale, sun-powered wind system just described is steered in different directions

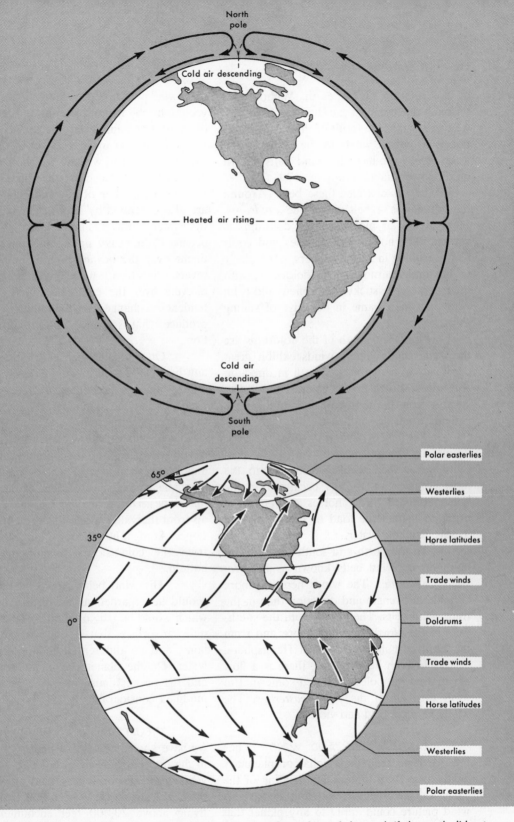

The diagram at the top shows how air would circulate over the surface of the earth if the earth did not spin on its axis. The earth's rotation deflects the winds to produce the wind systems shown in the lower diagram. (The added influence of land and water masses is not shown.)

by the rotation of the earth. Without describing the complex mechanism involved, we can say that the result of the earth's rotation is to deflect winds to the east and the west and to produce the wind belts shown on the lower diagram on page 179.

Let us consider these belts. Around the equator is a belt called the *doldrums*. Most of the air motion in the doldrums is vertical. The hot humid air rises and cools aloft, resulting in heavy showers, particularly in the late afternoon. The doldrums, with their oppressive, sticky atmosphere and calm winds got their name in the days of sailing ships.

North and south of the doldrums are the *trade winds*. These winds exhibit great constancy over the oceans, both in direction and speed. North of the equator they blow steadily from the northeast and south of the equator from the southeast.

The *horse latitudes,* like the doldrums, are characterized by vertical air currents rather than winds. According to the most common tale, ships becalmed in the horse latitudes threw horses overboard in order to lighten the load of the vessel and to save drinking water.

To the north and south of the horse latitudes are wind belts known as the *prevailing westerlies*. The winds here are more variable in strength and direction than in the trade wind belts. They blow from the southwest in the Northern Hemisphere and from the northwest in the Southern Hemisphere.

In both hemispheres, there is a flow of air from the poles, deflected somewhat to form the belt of the *polar easterlies*. The winds here are cold and violent.

LAND, WATER, AND WIND.   Thus far, we have seen that global or planetary winds arise from the unequal heating of the earth and are then steered into belts. This wind picture could apply to any planet that is heated at the equator, rotates like the earth and has an atmosphere. Earth's complete wind picture is determined by its special geography, by its land masses and its bodies of water. Land and water affect wind because they do not heat up or cool off at the same rate. On page 166 we saw how land and sea breezes are produced by the differences in heating and cooling of day and night. Winds are also generated by seasonal variations. In the winter, continents are colder than nearby oceans. Cold, heavy air sweeps from the continent over the ocean. In the summer, the reverse is true, with ocean-cooled air blowing over the continent. Such seasonal tendencies change the prevailing winds to produce what is termed a *monsoon* circulation.

On a smaller scale this happens near any body of water. The *lake breeze* that is felt in Chicago and the *sea breeze* in San Francisco, in the summer, are examples of the same phenomenon.

Mountain and valley winds are another example of how geography produces minor terrestrial winds. These winds result from the heating and cooling of the mountain slopes. During the day warmed air flows up from the valley along the strongly heated slopes. At night heavy cooled air drains down from the cold slopes toward the valley bottom.

The wind belts shown on page 179 should be regarded as an idealized picture which would be true only on a planet with a uniform surface, that is, one with no mountains, and no differentiation into land and water. On the planet Earth, the continents and the oceans cause the wind belts to be modified considerably.

THE JET STREAMS.   For many years, we have known of belts of high-speed winds in the upper troposphere, but only in recent years have meteorologists paid attention to them. During World War II, American pilots flying above 20,000 feet encountered unbelievably strong headwinds, often over 200 miles per hour. As airplane flight reached these altitudes and wind observations at higher levels were improved, the existence of these high-speed winds became more and more apparent. Speeds as high as 400 miles per hour were reported. These winds became known as the *jet stream*.

The jet stream has been likened to a narrow current flowing around the earth. The winds in this stream are not freakish winds but are an ever-present part of atmospheric circulation. During the International Geophysical Year, meteorologists refined and extended our knowledge of these high-altitude winds. Two jet streams in the Northern Hemisphere were studied: the Mid-Latitude Jet Stream and the Polar-Night Jet Stream. The Mid-Latitude Jet Stream lies roughly over the southern border of the United States at a height of about 7 miles above the surface of the earth, and continues at approximately this latitude around the earth. The Polar-Night Jet Stream, with its core at an elevation of at least 20 miles or more, crosses Northern Canada and also encircles the Arctic.

In the winter, both jet streams flow from west to east. In the spring, there is a shifting of direction and speed. The Polar jet reverses direction, and flows from east to west. The Mid-Latitude jet continues to blow from the west but becomes weaker, and it moves from the latitude of Texas to that of the Great Lakes. There are two similar jets, south of the equator, making four in all for the earth.

The exact part played by the jet streams in weather is not known, but the jet streams are associated with many weather phenomena. They probably play a role in steering storm and fair weather areas across the earth. The jet streams also put warm and cold masses of air into motion across continents. The behavior of jet streams shows enough regularity to be of value in long-range weather forecasting. The charting of jet streams is, of course, of vital concern to airlines.

AIR MASSES

If you have ever gone into a cool, dank cellar on a hot day, you were probably impressed by the contrast in temperature and humidity between the cellar and the outdoor air. In entering the cellar, you moved from one weather to another, from one kind of air to another.

The air in the cellar had acquired its odor, its dampness, and its temperature because it had stagnated there and taken on the qualities imposed by its surroundings. Something like this happens on a global scale.

When a large portion of the atmosphere comes to rest or moves slowly over land or sea areas, the air will tend to become similar in temperature and moisture to the underlying surface. If the surface is warm, the air above it will be warmed. If the surface is cold, the air above it will be cooled. If the surface is moist, the air above it will become moist; if the surface is dry, the air will lose moisture. A large body of air that takes its character from the surface beneath it is called an *air mass*. An air mass may cover hundreds of thousands of square miles and be miles high, but the temperature and humidity at any particular level is fairly uniform.

The place where an air mass originates is called a *source region*. There are two general source regions—the tropics and the snow- or ice-covered polar areas—for it is in these regions that huge masses of air stagnate long enough to acquire their identifying characteristics. After remaining for some time over the area where they form, air masses eventually begin to move, the cold ones drifting toward the equator and the warm ones toward the poles.

Air masses retain their identity and their characteristics even when they move far from their source regions. Some people claim that they can detect exotic aromas in air coming from the tropics, a thousand miles away. Only slowly and gradually are air

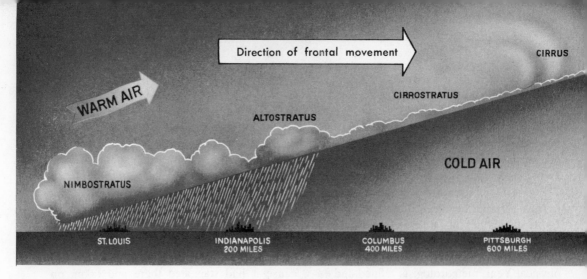

WARM AIR

CIRRUS

CIRROSTRATUS

ALTOSTRATUS

COLD AIR

NIMBOSTRATUS

ST. LOUIS

INDIANAPOLIS
200 MILES

COLUMBUS
400 MILES

PITTSBURGH
600 MILES

This is a vertical section through a warm front and the air masses associated with it, described in the text. A viewer in Pittsburgh would first be made aware of the approaching warm front by high cirrus clouds. This is followed by lower and lower clouds as the weather "picture" moves eastward. Finally the front passes, and Pittsburgh is in a warm air mass.

masses modified by the new surface conditions that they encounter.

The analysis of air masses has been made possible by the extensive use of radio-sonde, radar, reconnaissance by airplanes, rockets and satellites, all described previously, and by the establishment of weather observation stations over wide areas of the earth, even over the frozen arctic. Thus the meteorologist's view has expanded vertically and horizontally.

FRONTS. If the air masses are regarded as armies, then their battleground is the United States and other areas located in the temperate zones of the world. For it is in these zones that there is a meeting of warm and cold air masses; it is here that one air mass advances over the land pushing the other back; it is here that the *fronts*, a word borrowed by the meteorologists from the military, extend for hundreds and sometimes thousands of miles and mark the violent clashes of the opposing air masses. Wherever you are in the United States, you are in territory occupied by a warm or cool mass of air; the chances are that the present temperature will not last for very long—soon the advancing opposing army of air will make itself known by clouds, thunder, lightning,

and other special effects. When the front passes, you are again in occupied territory—occupied by the new "victorious" air mass. In the heat of the "battle," some mixing of opposing masses does occur; the front lines that originally may have been straight may be thrown into waves, reflecting local advances of warm air here and cold air elsewhere. But what is most remarkable during the clash is that, by and large, each air mass retains its own identity, its own distinguishing banners of temperature and humidity.

The diagrams on this and the opposite page depict some of the events occurring along a *warm front* and *cold front*, respectively. Each of these shows a vertical section of the atmosphere measuring six hundred miles, from St. Louis to Pittsburgh, and extending five or six miles upward from the surface of the earth.

Let us examine the warm front first. Warm air is on the march, pushing against the cold air. Since it is lighter, it rides up the cold air mass. You might think of the boundary as a kind of hill, not as steep as depicted in the picture, but one up which the warm air is traveling. As the warm air moves upward it is cooled; the moisture in it condenses, resulting in cloud formation and the precipitation of rain. The diagram on page

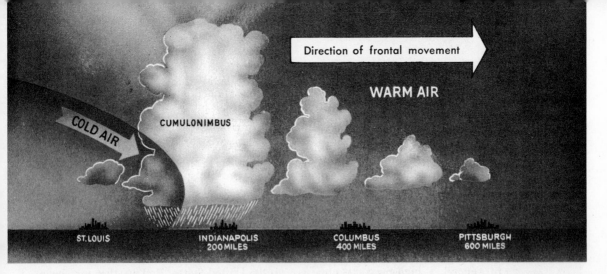

Cold fronts are steeper than warm fronts and move faster. The characteristic towering cumulonimbus clouds arrive rather suddenly. The weather changes abruptly when the cold front arrives.

182 will be better understood if one keeps *two* kinds of motion in mind:

1. *Warm air is moving up the slope.*
2. *The whole picture is sliding eastward over the map.*

Consider then a viewer in Pittsburgh. Within the next twenty-four to forty-eight hours, he may expect the weather picture to slide over him, since St. Louis's weather today is Pittsburgh's tomorrow. At present, he sees high, wispy, cirrus clouds, and since he is weather-wise he knows that this often is the harbinger of a warm front, with its attendant weather. As the hours go by, the eastward moving cirrus clouds are replaced by lower and lower clouds of the stratus type. When the heavy, low nimbo-stratus clouds pass overhead, rain falls steadily. Finally, the front that was originally near St. Louis passes Pittsburgh. A new mass of air is now over the city, with higher temperature and higher humidity. The sky clears slowly; the army of warm air is "occupying" the city.

The diagram at the top of this page shows the same area as before, but with a cold front in evidence. This time it is the cold air that is advancing toward Pittsburgh. The cold front differs in several respects from a warm front. The slope of the hill or front is steeper. The front moves more rapidly. The weather phenomena over a cold front are more dramatic, more sudden, more violent. The warm air is lifted above the advancing cold air to form towering *cumulonimbus* clouds, or thunderclouds. Thunderstorms occur along the front (see page 188).

A weather observer in Pittsburgh would not be given as much advance notice by the clouds as he would in the case of a warm front. High cumulus clouds appear on the horizon in the direction of Columbus, Ohio. As the front nears, rain falls with increasing intensity. As the front passes, there is often a fairly rapid clearing with a falling of temperature and humidity. A cold air mass now occupies Pittsburgh.

It is apparent that air mass and air front analysis, developed after World War I, are essential to an understanding of weather. *Highs* and *lows*, however, have been well known for many years as an important ingredient of the weather picture.

HIGHS AND LOWS

In the daily weather report given on radio and television, and in weather maps printed in newspapers, prominence is given to the highs and lows across the country. Just what is their significance?

A high refers to an area of high air pressure and a low to an area of low air pressure. In the description of weather instruments, we said that the barometer is important to the study of weather, noting that air pressure reflected the moisture content and the temperature of the air, and that differences in pressure resulted in a force which directed the movement of air.

In general a high-pressure area is characterized by clear, dry weather, while a low brings with it a host of weather changes, mostly bad.

Low pressure areas, or lows, are also called *cyclones* by the meteorologists. Cyclones should not be confused with tornadoes, which will be described later. A low may cover an area hundreds or thousands of miles in diameter. In a low, the lowest pressure is in the center, with pressure increasing away from the center. Winds blow in a counter-clockwise motion around a low (in the Northern Hemisphere) and veer toward the center.

In high-pressure areas, called *anticyclones*, the opposite conditions obtain: highest pressures are at the center, and winds blow clockwise and outward from the center in the Northern Hemisphere.

Cyclones, or lows, starting from the northwest, southwest, and southeast, move eastward across the country with the rest of the weather picture, usually ending their visit somewhere in New England. Lows move at the rate of 500 miles a day in summer and 700 miles a day in the winter.

The origin of cyclones in temperate zones has been determined to be related to a development in the front between warm and cold air masses. Lows occur at those places along the front where a kink or wave appears, as we will see later when we study weather maps.

Lows, being notorious for their stormy weather, attract most of the attention of the public, while highs are neglected. Highs generally bring good weather. One reason for this is that the air in highs, being heavy, is usually descending, which means that it is being warmed. Since warm air can hold more moisture than cold air (without showing it), this is a factor in making the air in highs dry and clear. Highs are also associated with the heavy, cold, continental air masses originating in the polar or arctic regions. These highs bring intense cold waves to the United States. Bad weather may occur at the cold fronts of these high-pressure areas, but good weather is soon to follow as the cold, high-pressure air mass takes hold. Anticyclones, like cyclones, move eastward across the country.

HURRICANES

A cyclone arising in the tropics may develop into a full-fledged *hurricane*, the most dangerous and the most destructive of all storms. Like its more harmless cousin, the cyclone or low, a hurricane is a low-pressure area, but its pressure is much lower. The winds spiral counter-clockwise toward the center, in the Northern Hemisphere, at furious velocities often exceeding 100 miles an hour. Rain falls at a heavy rate. The area covered by a hurricane averages only 200 to 400 miles in diameter as contrasted with the 1,000-mile diameter of a typical cyclonic low. In addition, hurricanes have a special feature of their own: a calm, clear, central "eye," about 15 miles in diameter.

The destructiveness of most hurricanes is due principally to the mountainous waves whipped up by these tropical storms, sinking and grounding ships, causing high seas that inundate low coastal areas, wiping out towns and cities.

The strength of the winds must be at least 74 miles per hour for a storm to qualify as a hurricane. Maximum wind speeds of 75 to 150 miles per hour are common in hurricanes striking a coast, and speeds up to 200 miles per hour have occurred in some hurricanes, according to estimates based on damage to structures.

All tropical cyclones originate near the equator, forming over all of the tropical oceans except the South Atlantic. In the western North Pacific, these storms are known as *typhoons*; in the Bay of Bengal and the north Indian Ocean as *cyclones*; in the South Pacific, eastern North Pacific, Southern Indian, and North Atlantic Oceans (including the Gulf of Mexico and Caribbean Sea) as *hurricanes*; in Australia as *willy-willies* and in China as *baguios*. The word "hurricane" is an American Indian word, claimed by some to mean "big wind" and by others to be derived from the name of the god of stormy weather.

The area of the most destructive winds along the path of a hurricane may be from 30 to 100 miles wide. As the storm develops and moves forward, it may traverse a path several thousand miles long from its birthplace in the Caribbean or tropical Atlantic until it blows itself out over the continent or in the North Atlantic.

While the winds of the hurricane are blowing at great speed around the center, the entire storm system may move forward very slowly, and sometimes even remain stationary for a short time. In the tropics, the forward speed of the entire hurricane is about 15 miles per hour; as it moves away from the tropics, the speed may reach 50 miles per hour.

HURRICANE POWER. The power of a hurricane has been estimated to be the equivalent of several thousand atomic bombs per second! How does it develop this power? The answer lies in the three fundamental weather factors that we stressed earlier in the chapter: heat, water, and air.

Heat poured down by the sun, day after day, warming tropical waters and the air above them, is the basic source of the power. The resulting evaporation of water from the oceans into the atmosphere is a process that traps and stores much of this heat. It takes a great deal of heat to change water into water vapor. This energy is not lost but is carried off by the water vapor in a latent or hidden form. The energy is released as heat again when the water vapor condenses into clouds. The enormous heat liberated stirs up the characteristic fierce winds of hurricanes.

A hurricane, then, may be thought of as a gigantic heat engine. Its fuel is the

The powerful winds of the September 21, 1943, hurricane pile up the waters of Biscayne Bay on Miami's North Bayshore retaining wall.

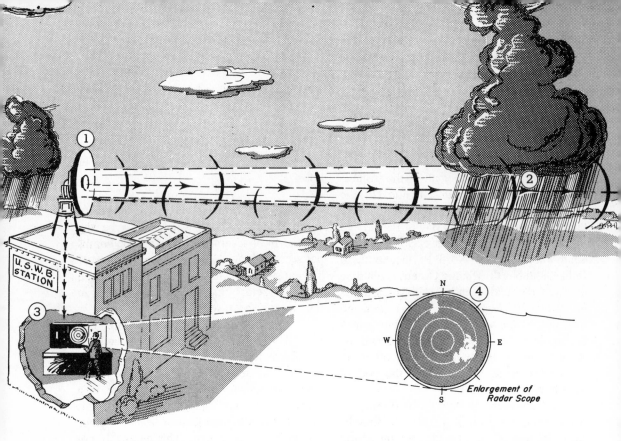

The principle of radar as it pertains to weather surveillance is shown here. Radio waves (large arrows) are emitted from the rotating radar antenna (1). A portion of this radio energy is reflected back (small arrows) from rain, snow, or hail particles in the storm (2). The waves are received by the antenna and sent to a radarscope (3). The storm areas appear as bright spots on a dark background, and their direction and distance from the station can be read on the radarscope (4).

hidden heat released by condensation of the water vapor in the air, and it releases its energy in the form of whirling winds. Conditions in the doldrums, where the strong sun beats over the ocean and the air is calm, promote the growth of hurricanes. The whole story of how a hurricane forms under these conditions is not known; meteorologists have offered a number of different theories to explain this violent phenomenon.

WARNING SERVICE. One of the important functions of the U. S. Weather Bureau is the Hurricane Warning Service, which was set up in 1935. In recent years, notable improvements in tracking and in

forecasting the movements of hurricanes have resulted from the use of radar observations at coastal stations, from the receipt of additional weather reports from reconnaissance aircraft, and from the more complete data obtained by radiosonde from heights up to 40,000 feet above the earth's surface.

In 1956, the Weather Bureau set up a radar network that will eventually blanket the United States, detecting and tracking not only hurricanes but also tornadoes and other severe storms. Radio signals sent out by radar bounce off raindrops and are reflected back to the sets, where they are electronically converted to the picture seen on the radar screen. The eye of hurricane Carla (September, 1961) first appeared on the Weather Bureau's radarscope at Galveston, Texas, when it was located over the Gulf of Mexico, 250 miles away. Carla was then tracked by radar for the next 46 hours.

By extending the radar network, which at present writing consists of 32 long-range and 64 medium-range radars, much can be done to prevent the loss of lives and the destruction of property that occur during violent storms. The value of satellites in detecting and tracking hurricanes was noted previously in the section on the weatherman's instruments. Data from satellite-borne instruments is filling the gaps in the detection and reporting of storm centers around the world, especially over the oceans.

TORNADOES

A tornado is a violent local storm with upward-spiraling winds of tremendous speed. Tornadoes are often mistakenly called cyclones; cyclones, however, as we have seen, are broad areas of low pressure, whereas tornadoes are raging storms. Tornadoes are much smaller in area than hurricanes, averaging only about 1,200 feet or ⅕ of a mile in diameter. The average distance traveled by a tornado is about 16 miles.

A tornado is recognized as a rotating, funnel-shaped cloud, extending toward the earth from the base of a thundercloud and colored from gray to black with the dust and debris that have been forced into it. All tornadoes have a common characteristic: the rapidly rotating winds that cause them to spin like a top. When it is near, a tornado usually sounds like the roaring of hundreds of airplanes.

The leading tornado states, judging by the number of tornadoes for the period 1916–1960, are Kansas, Texas, Oklahoma, Iowa, Nebraska, Missouri, and Arkansas. The destructiveness of tornadoes is due in part to their violent winds, which have been estimated to exceed 500 miles per hour. The maximum speeds of the internal winds of a tornado have never been measured directly, for the reason that no anemometer has yet survived the test. Dry straws have been driven through telephone poles from the impact of tornado winds.

The destructiveness of tornadoes is also due to the extremely low pressure of the whirling column of air, which makes it behave like a giant vacuum cleaner suspended from the sky, "sucking" in trees, houses, cars, animals, and people! Pressure as low as 25½ inches have been recorded (about 30 inches is normal). The low pressure that suddenly develops outside buildings may cause them to explode from the normal pressure inside.

Tornadoes move in erratic paths at speeds averaging 25 to 40 miles an hour. Most move from the southwest to the northeast. Tornadoes, however, have been known to come from any direction, even stopping their forward movements, turning, and looping their paths.

We are not sure exactly how tornadoes develop, but we do know some of the accompanying circumstances. Ordinarily, cold air, being relatively heavy, moves under warm air, as we saw in our study of fronts. Under special conditions, however, a layer of dry, cold air may be thrust over a mass of moist, warm air. Warm air forces its way up through the cold cap in corkscrew fashion. Cold and warm air mix, aided by strong winds aloft. A vortex is formed around a low-pressure center and thus becomes a tornado.

It is not possible to predict the exact spot where a tornado will develop, but the Weather Bureau is able to prepare a forecast which alerts people to the possibility of tornado activity in an area. The principal tornado forecasts are made in the Weather Bureau's Severe Local Storm Forecast Center at Kansas City, Missouri. In a typical situation, a study of the surface weather maps may alert the meteorologists in the Center to the possibility of a tornado threat. To check, they study charts showing upper air currents and other data which may confirm their suspicion. If warranted, a forecast is issued to the public that indicates the possible area of tornado activity. The first confirmation that the forecast is materializing may come from radar reports. The tornado activity is then tracked carefully by radar, and further reports are issued as needed so that all safety precautions may be taken along its path.

When a tornado passes over a body of water, a *waterspout* may result. The lower portion of the funnel cloud is made of spray, instead of the dust and debris found in a tornado over land. Actually there is very little water in a typical "spout." Most of it is fine mist or spray, with perhaps a few feet of water at its base.

THUNDERSTORMS

Thunderstorms are weather "factories." Pilots flying into them can expect to see a great many weather "products," including lightning and thunder, updrafts and downdrafts, heavy rain, snow, and hail, as well as ice formation on the wings of the plane. It is obvious that, for pilots, thunderstorms represent a severe and dangerous form of atmospheric activity.

Thunderstorms have their beginning in the rising of warm, moist air to higher, cooler levels, where the water vapor condenses to form towering thunderclouds, called also cumulonimbus clouds. Let us consider three different ways in which this happens. First, this hoisting up may occur, as we have seen on page 183, when an advancing cold front wedges itself under a warm, moist mass of air. An almost continuous line of thunderstorms may form along the front, which becomes known as a *squall line*.

A second cause of thunderstorm formation arises from the topography of the

land. Moist air blowing up the slopes of hills and mountains helps form cumulus and cumulonimbus clouds as it is chilled at higher levels.

Third, the local heating of the ground and the moist air above it on a warm, sunny day gives rise to the typical summer thunderstorm.

LIGHTNING AND THUNDER. When Benjamin Franklin sent a kite sailing in a thunderstorm, he demonstrated for the first time that lightning was electricity. The flash that ran down the string of the kite in this dangerous experiment behaved like man-made electricity. We will consider this particular kind, called static electricity, in chapter 21A. For the moment, it will do to recall some of our common experiences with static electricity. When we scuff our feet on a carpet and touch a metallic object, such as a doorknob, a spark jumps from our finger to the object. This is an electric spark, small but effective enough for us to feel. When we comb our hair, we hear a crackling sound as electric sparks jump. When we tear a piece of adhesive tape apart in the dark we can see sparks. In each case, a charge of electricity has been built up on a surface by rubbing or tearing; the electricity is then discharged in the form of a spark that jumps through the air.

The production of high electric charges in thunderstorms is a complex process, not fully understood. It is thought that the water droplets in a cumulus cloud are continuously torn apart by friction with the air. As a result, the droplets become electrically charged. Eventually, the thundercloud builds up enough electricity to cause a discharge. We see this as a flash of lightning. This discharge may take place within the cloud, between one cloud and another, or between the cloud and the earth.

As the lightning leaps through the air, it heats it and causes it to expand suddenly. This starts a tremendous sound wave, which reaches our ears as thunder. Why do we hear thunder after we see lightning? Light travels so rapidly, about 186,000 miles a second, that we see the flash practically as it occurs. Sound, on the other hand, travels relatively slowly, moving 1 mile in 5 seconds. It is possible to estimate the distance between yourself and a lightning bolt by counting the number of seconds between the flash and the thunder. Dividing this by five gives the answer in miles. For example, if you count 10 seconds between the flash and the rumble of thunder, the distance of that particular bolt is 2 miles.

A building of steel and concrete is practically lightning proof, because the electricity follows the steel down into the ground. The Empire State Building in New York City has been struck hundreds of times, without harm to anyone.

There is very little danger of being struck by lightning if one observes the following:

Inside a house, stay away from the chimney, since it is the tallest part of a house and the most likely to be struck. Contrary to popular opinion, it is as safe near a window, open or closed, as anywhere else.

Out of doors, avoid high ground. If you must stand under a tree choose a short one, and one which is in a group of trees, rather than a high or isolated tree. Caves and holes are relatively safe. Stay away from wire fences!

An automobile is very safe.

So-called "sheet" lightning, or "heat" lightning, consists simply of flashes from distant thunderclouds. Sheet lightning occurs when the electrical discharge is from cloud to cloud. The flashes are hidden, and only a large lighted area is seen. "Heat" lightning is the flashes of ordinary lightning so far away that the thunder is not heard.

THE WEATHER MAP

SEE PAGE 206

As interest in weather conditions grows, more newspapers and telecasts are using the weather map as a means of picturing the weather. On page 190 is a typical newspaper weather map, depicting conditions prevailing at 1:30 P.M. Eastern Standard Time on October 6, 1956.

Before the invention of the telegraph, such a map would have been impossible, for it is based on *simultaneous reports* from around the country. Indeed, the telegraph played an important role in the early beginnings of a weather service. After the first telegraph lines were set up in 1844, the operators, on opening their lines in the morning, sent messages describing the weather in their parts of the country. This practice showed that it would be practical to gather reports of developing storms and to warn of their approach. In 1870, Congress set up a national weather service to issue storm warnings and to keep records of the climate. As time went on, the Weather Bureau, as it became known in 1890, expanded its services to include flood warnings and to provide various kinds of weather information for farmers, fruit growers, ranchers, and foresters. With the development of aviation, demands for detailed weather data increased, and improved services were made available.

How is a typical weather map made? Weather observations of the temperature, air pressure, wind, and other conditions are reported every six hours to the Weather Bureau's National Meteorological Center at Suitland, Maryland, from 245 Weather Bureau offices and airport stations in the United States, 6 fixed stations in the Atlantic and Pacific oceans and 5 stations in the Arctic. The Weather Bureau network reports are supplemented by observations from the military and other agencies of the government, as well as from aviation services and merchant vessels of all nations. At the Center, a complete weather map is drawn up, which

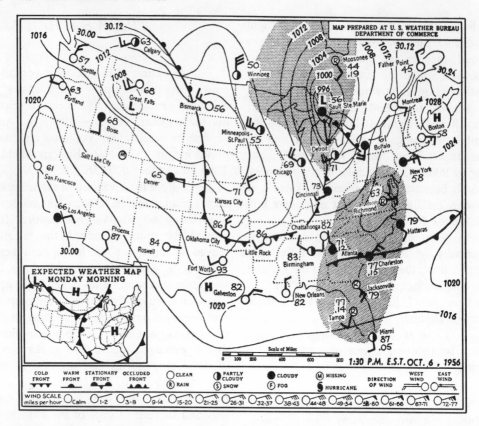

This map, prepared by the United States Weather Bureau, presents a comprehensive picture of weather all over the country. It is discussed in detail in the text.

is then transmitted in a facsimile machine to all the forecast centers in the country, in much the same way that wirephoto pictures are sent by newspapers.

To enable the forecaster to make his analysis and prediction, information is needed about weather conditions in the atmosphere to a height of several miles above the earth's surface. We have discussed how radar, airplane reconnaissance, and radiosondes carried up by balloons help gather upper air data. From this data upper level weather maps are prepared.

The weather map shown here is a simplified version of the map drawn up by the Weather Bureau. Let us examine it to see what it tells.

GENERAL WEATHER CONDITIONS. We note that the map tells of conditions prevailing at 1:30 P.M. on October 6, 1956. Each city included is represented by a circle, called the *station circle*. Within the circles, as indicated in the key, are symbols for the general weather conditions: clear, partly cloudy, cloudy, rain, snow, or fog. Thus we see that it is cloudy in Boise, partly cloudy in Birmingham, and raining in Richmond.

WIND. Extending from the station circles is the shaft of an arrow denoting wind direction. (The head of the arrow, not depicted, would point at the station circle.) The arrows fly *with* the wind. Thus the wind in Boise is from the south and is called a south wind, while in Denver the arrow shaft tells us that we have an east wind. The feathers, or markings on the tail of the arrow, show the wind strength, which as shown by the key, ranges from calm to 75 miles per hour. Thus, Winnipeg has winds of 44–48 miles per hour, while Phoenix has winds of 9–14 miles per hour.

TEMPERATURE AND PRECIPITATION. The figures near the station circle give the temperature and the precipitation, if any, in the six hours prior to the hour of the map, which is 1:30 P.M. Eastern Standard Time. Thus Tampa has a temperature of 77° F. and has had 14/100 of an inch of rainfall in the past six hours.

PRESSURE. The light, continuous lines seen on the weather map indicate the atmospheric pressure across the country. These lines, called *isobars*, are drawn through points of equal air pressure. If the reader were equipped with magic boots so that he could run the length of one of these lines in a flash, he would find that the air pressure was the same along the entire route (at sea level). The isobar shown in southern California has a number at its end: 30.00. This represents the air pressure as measured in inches of mercury. The number 1016, found at the eastern end of this isobar, off Florida, is another way of measuring air pressure, using units called *millibars*.

Around the map are a number of points designated by the letters H or L, which stand for high and low pressure areas, respectively. The most outstanding low is centered in Sault Sainte Marie. The isobars in this low drop from 1012 to 996 millibars, which corresponds to 29.89 to 29.41 inches. Another low-pressure area, not so clearly defined, is centered over Great Falls, Montana. High pressure areas are found near Galveston and Boston.

Note that the winds around a low blow counter-clockwise with respect to the center. Not too well illustrated on this map is the usual tendency of these winds to blow somewhat toward the center. The winds around highs behave exactly opposite. They blow clockwise and away from the center.

FRONTS. The position of the fronts of air masses on the earth's surface are depicted by the heavy lines with special markings on them. A cold front can be found beginning at a point west of Kansas City, extending south and then north up to Sault Sainte Marie. Here a warm front begins and extends a short distance in a southeasterly direction.

The wind arrows indicate that the cool mass of air behind the cold front is pushing south and east, while the air behind the warm front is pushing north and east.

The inverted V-shaped junction of the warm and cold front is a typical stage in the "battle" of the air masses. The advancing cold and warm air fronts seem to wheel around a point. Characteristically, a low pressure area is associated with this arrangement of fronts, and with it the inclement weather that is usually associated with lows.

The idea that low pressure areas develop as an outcome of frontal activity is referred to as the "wave" theory because of the undulating form taken by the fronts. This theory was first advanced by J. Bjerknes, a Norwegian meteorologist, in 1918. The reader is referred to books on meteorology for a fuller treatment of this theory.

FORECASTING WEATHER

Throughout the chapter, we have indicated some of the ways in which the weather may be predicted. In general, the weatherman looks backward to study the tendencies of weather of the past days and hours and then tries to project into the future. Weather maps are an important aid in summarizing this information, and may be compared to the "chart" of a patient's progress that the doctor studies.

The Weather Bureau is aided in making forecasts by the knowledge that the weather pattern shown on the map moves eastward across the country at the rate of about 500 miles a day in summer and 700 miles a day in winter. Hence the saying "Chicago's weather today is New York's tomorrow." The Weather Bureau is also aided by its knowledge of the special tracks that low pressure areas, or cyclones take as they swing across the United States. Lows, starting from the northwest, southwest, and southeast sweep across the country toward New England, bringing with them rain, drizzle, snow, and other associated conditions. Contrary to popular opinion, weather forecasts of considerable usefulness are possible for periods up to 24 hours.

THE REVOLUTION IN METEOROLOGY

A revolution in meteorology which is affecting weather forecasting is now in progress. It is too early at this writing to gauge the full impact of this profound change. Some of the elements in this revolution may be summarized as follows:

1. *Since the International Geophysical Year, the development and refinement of a wide range of measuring and transmitting tools have increased the amount of significant information and the speed at which such information is obtained. These tools include automatic transmitting weather stations (requiring no personnel), super-sensitive radar, high-level balloon flights, rockets, satellites and computing machines; also improved wirephoto and facsimile transmission of data.*
2. *Air masses, fronts, highs, and lows, while still important as a part of the fundamental pattern of weather, are being subordinated to data collected on a global basis and at many levels of the atmosphere. This data is treated mathematically in complex computers which are programed to take into account the many factors which contribute to the determination of the weather. It is hoped that this treatment of fundamental weather data will result in useful long-range forecasting of weather.*
3. *Meteorology is being linked more closely with specialized studies such as those of the oceans, the sun, the Arctic, all the way to atmospheres of other planets and the influence of radiations from outer space.*
4. *Meteorology is becoming a truly international affair. In the United Nations the cooperative efforts of all nations are demonstrated best in this area. This is natural, because weather flows from land to land without recourse to passports. Weather is part of our global environment, and consequently no true understanding and benefit can come from meteorology without the mutual support and complete cooperation of the nations of the world. To this objective, the work of the United Nations' World Meteorological Organization is dedicated.*

MAN-MADE WEATHER

One of the puzzling questions in meteorology is "How does rain form in clouds?" or, to state it more precisely, "Just how do the tiny droplets that make up a cloud join together to form raindrops and snowflakes?" In looking for an answer to this question, two scientists, Vincent Schaefer and Irving Langmuir of General Electric Research Laboratory, were puzzled by the fact that even in clouds with temperatures below freezing snow crystals often did not form.

They decided to conduct experiments with such clouds, called supercooled clouds. Schaefer found that, if he breathed into a home freezer compartment, he could produce a low temperature cloud like those found in nature. He found to his delight that, when he dropped a very cold substance like dry ice (solid carbon dioxide) into the freezer, the vapor cloud changed into millions of shimmering snow crystals. Other substances, provided they were 38° below zero F., or colder, also caused a fall of snow. In 1946, Schaefer went up in an airplane and scattered dry ice into a cloud and observed that long streamers of falling snow were produced.

At about the same time, scientist Bernard Vonnegut was investigating another technique for making supercooled clouds turn into snow. He found that silver iodide particles could induce the formation of ice crystals in clouds. As a result of all of these experiments, projects were initiated to test the value of cloudseeding operations in causing snow and rain and in dissipating unwanted fogs.

These studies indicated that precipitation could be increased in local areas where specific favorable conditions prevailed, but that large-scale changes of weather or climate by cloudseeding were not yet achievable. In a statement issued on July 4, 1962, the American Meteorological Society added that "application of numerical methods of forecasting by means of high speed computers, together with the use of model experiments in studying atmospheric processes, gives promise that some day it will be possible to predict with accuracy the short- and long-term effect of artificial interference with normal atmospheric processes." If disastrous windstorms and floods, such as those attending hurricanes, could be prevented, many lives would be saved and much misery avoided.

In 1961, hurricane Esther was seeded with silver iodide from a jet plane. Although it is premature to draw conclusions about hurricane control, there is some indication that as a result of the seeding, the energy of this hurricane was cut down appreciably.

WEATHER AND CLIMATE

The difference between weather and climate is chiefly one of *time*. Weather is the state of the atmosphere—its temperature, humidity, wind, pressure, cloudiness, etc.—at any particular hour or day. Climate is the history of these characteristics over a long period of time.

Climate may be defined briefly as "average weather." But an average may be misleading. For example, St. Louis, Missouri, has an average yearly rainfall of about 40 inches, while Bombay, India, has 74 inches. In St. Louis, however, the rainfall is evenly distributed so that no one month has less than 3 inches of rain. In Bombay, on the other hand, the rain falls in torrential cloudbursts during four summer months; the rest of the year is almost rainless.

The climate of a region is customarily described in terms of its year-round temperature and rainfall. Climate in any region is controlled by a number of factors:

1. *Latitude: distance from the equator*
2. *Altitude: height above sea level*
3. *The presence of land and sea masses*
4. *The prevailing winds: the winds that blow steadily across an area*
5. *The topography: mountains and plains*
6. *Ocean currents, such as the Gulf Stream.*

Space does not permit a discussion of how these factors influence climate, although some references to them are scattered through this chapter. For a full treatment of climate, the reader may refer to the bibliography for texts on climatology, meteorology, and earth science.

From our discussion of the air and the weather, certain fundamental concepts emerge. Some of these are:

Man lives at the bottom of an ocean of air.

Half of the air in the atmosphere is in the atmosphere's lowest 3½ miles.

Scientists divide the atmosphere into five layers: the troposphere, stratosphere, mesosphere, ionosphere, and exosphere.

In the troposphere, temperature falls about 3½ ° F. for every 1,000 feet of altitude.

Weather happens in the troposphere.

Air is a mixture of nitrogen, oxygen, water vapor, carbon dioxide, other gases, and dust.

Air is essential for life.

Changes in the atmosphere determine the weather.

The sun, the air, and water play leading roles in weather.

The sun is the prime source of energy for the weather "machine."

The unequal distribution of the sun's heat on the earth has a profound effect on weather.

Air serves to distribute heat and water around the earth.

The water cycle involves the circulation of water from oceans and lakes to the air, thence to the land, and then back to oceans and lakes again.

Since weather is a three-dimensional phenomenon, knowledge of the characteristics of the air at various levels is essential for a full understanding of weather.

Wind movements over the earth's surface follow a definite pattern.

Large masses of cold and warm air influence the weather of the world.

Weather in the United States is influenced by the interaction of cold and warm air masses.

More research is needed to determine to what extent man can control weather.

DISCOVERING FOR YOURSELF

1. Discover as much as you can about the use of weather satellites.
2. Clip a U. S. weather map and report from a daily paper. Interpret it by telling (a) the different things about air that are shown, (b) how the resulting forecast is made from the data given, (c) how conditions on the map have changed since the previous day.
3. Observe cloud formations on several successive days to discover how the clouds change from time to time, see what relation they have to the weather, and identify them.
4. Look out of a window and see what you can tell about the temperature and movement of air by observation. Observe birds, smoke, trees, people, and any other things that will provide clues.
5. Explain what makes the various air currents in your house—in the kitchen, near open windows, near air ducts, and elsewhere.
6. Try to find a toy or gimcrack that operates by use of air pressure or air currents, and explain its operation.
7. Look for places in your indoor environment where water evaporates and condenses. Explain the conditions that are responsible. Explain how these conditions are similar to those outside that cause precipitation.

8. Observe different kinds of thermometers that are in use in your home environment. Tell how they differ from each other and how they are similar.

9. Keep a record of the accuracy of the weather forecasts for a two-week period. Observe the elements of the scientific attitude discussed in Part I of this book. Write a paragraph setting forth your conclusions.

10. Visit a weather station to observe the instruments used and the records kept, and find out as much as you can about how the data are used to forecast weather. Find out how computers are used.

11. Select some weather "sayings" and try to test their accuracy by observation. Use the suggestions given in No. 8 in carrying out your observations. Write a paragraph setting forth your conclusions.

12. Learn to read a hygrometer, a barometer, and other weather instruments.

CHAPTER 9B

Teaching "The Air and the Weather"

The study of weather provides many opportunities to help children appreciate the use of mathematics as a tool of science. As they observe and record changes in temperature, length of day, position of the sun in the sky, and other phenomena, and as they make records and graphs of their observations, they employ mathematical skills in a meaningful way.

There are many simple experiments and experiences to help pupils to comprehend the essential concepts of air and weather. Several of the supplementary books in the bibliography contain experiments in addition to those described here. Pupils should understand that weather is the condition of the atmosphere; that various weather phenomena which they experience are caused by changes in the air around them. Children deepen their understanding of weather as they observe at first hand, as they measure and record the weather with various instruments, and as they experiment to determine the causes of weather changes. The example of using the wet spot on the blackboard to see that wind helps evaporation (pp. 48–49) illustrates a way of working with children to get them to plan and participate actively in the experimentation.

Unit weather problems for the early grades may be:

How does water disappear into the air and appear again?
What makes it rain and snow?
How does the weather bureau help us?
How can we observe and measure weather changes?

For later elementary grades the scope is, of course, enlarged, and the problems may be:

How does weather change from season to season?
How is weather different from place to place?
How does the weather bureau forecast the weather?
What makes changes in weather?
What causes the different kinds of precipitation?

Again we suggest activities that are useful in the primary grades but need not be confined exclusively to them.

1. Melt snow and ice to see that they are forms of water. Measure how much water there is in a glass of snow by allowing it to melt. Try samples of different snowfalls and compare results.
2. Keep a weather chart or clock to see that the weather changes often. (See page 198 for example.)
3. Do simple experiments to show that water evaporates into the air and that it condenses again. (See *Water Appears and Disappears,* listed in bibliography.)
4. Watch clouds at several different times to see how they change (in size, shape, color, movement) and to see the different kinds.
5. Make pin wheels and use them to see how the speed of the wind changes from day to day.
6. Keep a daily record of the temperature for a few weeks to see how it changes. Make a "red-ribbon" thermometer to learn how to read a thermometer (see books in bibliography for suggestions).
7. Listen to the radio weather report or watch it on television to find out what is reported. Compare the report with the weather observed.
8. Look out of the schoolroom window to try to decide what kind of day it is—warm, cold, wet, windy, cloudy, sunny, etc. Then go out-of-doors to check the observations. Observe that weather sometimes changes several times in a day.
9. Collect pictures showing different kinds of weather. Tell about how people and animals change their activities when the weather changes.
10. Go outside after a storm to see what the wind and water did and to see what is happening to the water.
11. Place a coffee can out-of-doors during a heavy rain to observe how much water falls. Bring it inside to see that the water will evaporate if left uncovered.

OBSERVING AIR AND WEATHER CONDITIONS

Too often the study of weather is confined to classroom activity, while real weather conditions are not observed. Ask pupils to be prepared to discuss these problems: "What is the weather like today?" "What can you tell about the air by using your five senses?" "What are the clouds like today?" Such observations as these help pupils to realize that they are studying something that is real. The discussion may raise several questions and problems about weather, for pupils are almost certain not to agree on all of their observations. By

Today's Weather

A weather clock such as this one helps young children to notice the weather and how often it changes. They will observe that the clock may need to be "reset" several times during the day.

using their senses they should report something about the air's temperature, that air is going from one place to another ("wind's blowing"), perhaps that the air "feels damp," and that they can feel the warmth of the sun on their faces. Their cloud description may indicate that the clouds are moving, that some are getting larger, some are disappearing, some are darker than others, etc. Pupils may learn to recognize some of the cloud formations pictured in the previous chapter.

While pupils are outdoors, they might be asked to estimate how high they think the air extends, how high they think the clouds are, and how fast they are moving. Later, pupils may try to find out how nearly correct their estimates were.

From discussion of the observations, many problems will probably arise. These may be written on the chalkboard and used as the basis for the study of weather. The teacher may add problems in order to broaden the study when this seems desirable. Problems will also be added as the study proceeds.

Younger children, with the help of the teacher, may read a real thermometer and then set a "play" thermometer in the room to correspond to the real reading. In so doing, they learn (a) that the temperature changes frequently, (b) that the higher the red line goes the warmer the temperature is and the lower it goes the colder the temperature is, (c) that high numbers mean warmer temperature, low numbers mean colder temperature. A "dummy" or play thermometer can be very useful in helping young children to read the real instrument. Draw the scale on cardboard. The ribbon is half white and half red and is sewed together to make a continuous band so that it can be easily moved to indicate different temperature readings. It may be made in any desired size.

A weather clock such as the one pictured here is a convenient way for young children to indicate weather conditions. Cut the large disk (see picture) from stiff cardboard and divide into sections as shown. Label the sections "rain," "cloudy," "snow," "fair weather," etc., and let the pupils decide on pictures to show each kind of weather. Pupils may help to draw the pictures and paste them on the disk. The pointers are also made of stiff cardboard and fastened to the center so that they can be moved like the hands of a clock. It may often be necessary to change the position of the pointers during the day. This will help pupils realize how often the weather changes.

MEASURING RAINFALL

Pupils may make a simple rain gauge to measure the amount of rainfall.[1] The picture here shows the completed gauge. The instrument can be made from an ordinary coffee can set in plaster of Paris. Because of evaporation, amounts of rainfall should be measured immediately after the rainfall.

Another type of rain gauge is made by inserting a cork and a funnel into the top of an olive jar. The building of such a gauge is an excellent opportunity to have children plan and design a scientific instrument to meet a particular problem. *Before* constructing it, it is well to review the use of the tin-can rain gauge. Children will recall that it is difficult to

A rain gauge can be made of a tin can set in plaster of Paris. A somewhat more elaborate gauge consists of an olive bottle with a funnel, with dimensions and markings as shown here.

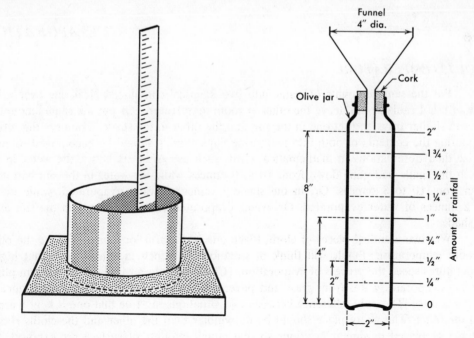

---

[1] G. O. Blough and M. H. Campbell, *Making and Using Classroom Science Materials in the Elementary School* (New York: Holt, Rinehart and Winston, 1954), p. 114.

read a rainfall of less than ¼ inch with the simple tin-can gauge. Discuss why this is so and ask the children how they might make an instrument to measure small amounts of rain. The use of a funnel, as shown in the illustration on page 199, increases the area for catching rain. This increase in area must be compensated for in the making of a scale, as shown in the illustration. Thus 4 inches of water in the collecting bottle represents ¼ inch of rainfall.

Children may use the rain gauge to compare readings at the school with those of the Weather Bureau. A discrepancy, of course, does not mean that either one is necessarily incorrect, since rainfall is not always exactly the same in the various localities covered by the weather report.

Older children may find out what the average rainfall is for each month of the year in their locality. They may summarize this information in a chart or graph. It is important that they understand that the average is obtained from the rainfall records of many years. They may compare averages of their locality with others in their state or in the United States. In this way, they begin to understand about climate which is "average weather."

LEARNING ABOUT THE WATER VAPOR
IN THE AIR

How water changes to vapor and gets into the air, and how it gets out are important concepts. The effects of temperature, wind, and amount of surface exposed on the rate of evaporation can be seen by experimenting.

EVAPORATION

ABOUT TEMPERATURE

Put the same amounts of water into two identical containers. Heat one over a hot plate or a hot radiator and leave the other at room temperature. Or put the same amount of water in similar trays and set one in the sun and the other in the shade. Compare the results by pouring the contents of both into measuring cups. Pupils should be encouraged to summarize their observations in mathematical terms such as: After six hours, the water in the tray in the shade had gone down from 10 to 9 ounces while the water in the sun had gone down from 10 to 8 ounces. Or, in the shade 1 ounce of water evaporated, while in the sun 2 ounces of water evaporated. Or, water evaporated twice as quickly in the sun as in the shade.

Wet two identical pieces of cloth. Place one in a warm location and leave the other at room temperature. Pupils will think of situations in which they have seen that higher temperatures speed the process of evaporation. (Clothes dry faster if placed in a warm place. The sun evaporates water from grass and pavements.) Again we stress the importance of using a control. The only difference between two situations must be that one is kept warmer than the other. The warm place should be no windier than the other and the cloths should be hung or placed in similar positions so that equal amounts of surface are exposed. We should stress also the importance of not drawing sweeping conclusions from observing *one* experiment.

ABOUT WIND

Fanning a wet spot on the chalkboard (see pp. 48–49) is a useful experiment. Examples of application are: blowing on wet ink to dry it, the wind's helping to dry wet pavements, hair driers, etc.

ABOUT AMOUNT OF SURFACE EXPOSED

Wet two similar handkerchiefs. Leave one crumpled up and one spread out. Compare the results after several hours.

Put the same amounts of water in a tall olive bottle and in a saucer. Compare the results mathematically as described in the experiments on temperature. Applications: wet bathing suits and towels should be spread out to dry; water spilled on the floor evaporates faster if spread out.

As we have frequently indicated, pupils can themselves originate useful experiments. In response to the teacher's suggestion that pupils try to think of experiments to show that heat and wind help evaporation, a third-grade boy gave this report of a home experiment:

> I started with three pieces of cloth about a foot square and used one eighth of a cup of water to wet each one. I hung one over a hot-air register, one at room temperature, and one with an electric fan blowing against it. The one over the hot-air register dried in 20 minutes; the one near the electric fan dried in 25 minutes; the one at room temperature dried in an hour and 30 minutes.

He pointed out the importance of having the pieces of cloth the same size and with the same amounts of water in them and the necessity of timing the evaporation. Note also that two factors are in operation, wind and heat, and consequently further experimentation is in order before definite conclusions can be drawn.

CONDENSATION

There are many experiments that show how cooling makes water condense out of the air. Place some ice in a tin cup, stir for a few moments, and note the droplets of water on the outside surface. Let pupils formulate theories as to where the droplets come from. If they think that they "leaked" through, let them test this theory by putting hot water in another tin cup to observe the results. After they have decided that the air is the only possible place from which the drops could have come, they must answer the question, "What was done to make the water come out of the air?" The answer appears to be that the cup cooled the air in contact with it. Pupils may perform this experiment on several different days to note that condensing is more noticeable on some days than on others.

Pupils may observe condensation taking place: on cold water pipes and faucets, on pitchers of cold liquid, on a cold window or a cold mirror from their own breath, in the air on a cold day when they "see" their own breath, etc.

After pupils have done these and other experiments, suggest that they go to the window and tell how many different kinds of places they can see from which water is evaporating. Do the same for condensation. Then name places in the schoolhouse where these two processes take place. The experiment described on page 18 suggests a way of showing that plants give off water into the air.

Ordinarily pupils at the elementary level do not concern themselves about how relative humidity is calculated. Pupils can, however, read a hair hygrometer, which gives a direct reading of the relative humidity, and understand the meaning of the term "relative humidity" even though they do not go into *how* the percentage is determined. Those who wish to make a simple hygrometer may consult Blough and Campbell, *Making and Using Classroom Science Materials* (pages 114–115).

If their home furnaces are equipped with humidifiers, pupils might find out where they are and how the humidifying tanks are filled. If the school building makes any provision for getting additional moisture into the air, the school custodian will be able to explain the process.

There are many homes with damp basements where calcium chloride is used to take water from the air. This compound is sometimes sold in hardware and household-supply stores under trade names. It is dry when first exposed but soon becomes damp as water from the air accumulates in it.

As these experiments and observations go on, it may be advisable to keep a record of the important science concepts that pupils have learned so that they can later be put together and used to understand weather phenomena. The breadth of these concepts will depend on the experience, interest, and intellectual maturity of the pupils. Here are examples of important ideas pupils should have encountered from the experiments and observations in evaporation and condensation:

Water evaporates into the air from many places.
Heat helps water evaporate.
Wind helps water evaporate.
Cooling of the air may cause water to condense.
Water condenses on many cool surfaces.

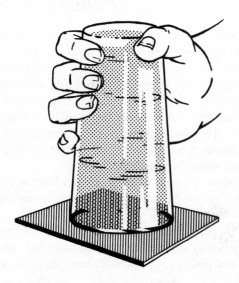

Pupils recognize that air pressure is a very real force when they see that it can keep water from running out of a glass turned upside down. Be sure to use a card that will not bend easily and perform the experiment over a pan in case of accident. (See photograph p. 203).

EXPERIMENTING WITH AIR PRESSURE

The realization that air exerts pressure and that this pressure changes is important in understanding the causes of weather and its changes. Although the connection between air pressure and weather condition is somewhat difficult for elementary pupils to comprehend, the idea of air pressure itself may be made quite evident. There are many simple experiments that help pupils to see that air actually has pressure. A simple one is to take a full glass of water, lay a piece of cardboard over it, hold the cardboard firmly to the glass, and invert it over a basin or the sink. The air pressure on the cardboard keeps the water in the glass. Some children may object to this demonstration, saying that the cardboard simply sticks to the glass. This seems plausible and should not be summarily rejected. A partial answer to this comment is to ask what would happen if several small holes were made in the cardboard. The water still stays in; air pressure prevents it from falling out.

The following experiment shows more spectacularly an effect of air pressure on the surface of a can. Get a hot plate or other source of heat, a clean, gallon varnish can, a stopper to fit tightly into the can opening, and a little water. Place a couple of tablespoonfuls of water in the can and heat it until the water boils vigorously and a cloud appears around the opening. You have now driven the air out of the can, leaving the can full of steam. Place the stopper into the can tightly. Set the can on a window sill if the weather is cold, or cool it with a piece of ice or with cold water. Watch it. You are condensing the steam inside of the can, leaving a partial vacuum in it. In a short time the pressure of the air on the outside crushes the can. It is interesting for children to calculate the weight of the air pressing on the can. It usually amounts to more than the weight of the whole class of fifth graders. Here again is an opportunity for the purposeful use of arithmetic in finding the area of the can and in multiplying accurately. The use of the round number of 15 pounds per square inch, and round number of the can measurements is suggested.

It is interesting for pupils to investigate places where "suction cups" are used—coat hangers, sink plungers, etc., since they work because of air pressure.

Aneroid barometers (see page 172) are now found more and more as standard equipment in an elementary school or as home weather instruments. Pupils should learn

Pupils should be urged to find or think up other experiments that illustrate principles such as this one on air pressure. If the equipment is left available, more pupils can see for themselves.

to read the barometer scale, in inches to the first decimal place. The printed words on the dial, such as RAIN, CHANGE, FAIR, etc. have only limited significance. (Some students might keep records to judge the reliability of these designations.) The barometer measures only one thing: air pressure. A movement toward high pressure *usually* indicates the approach of clear dry weather. A movement toward low pressure *usually* indicates the approach of bad weather.

Pupils should keep records and compare their readings with those of the Weather Bureau. Pupils should learn also that a barometer is a scientific instrument and not a toy; that it is for the purpose of supplying information; that it is a delicate instrument and must be handled carefully.

As they progress with their study of air and weather, pupils may want to keep track of barometer readings given in the newspaper and on the radio.

At this point, pupils may add to the list of concepts about air such statements as:

Air has pressure.
We can measure the pressure of the air.
The pressure of the air changes.
When the barometer goes up, the weather is generally expected to be fair. When it
    goes down, unsettled or stormy weather may be expected.

LEARNING ABOUT THE WATER CYCLE

With this topic we begin to put together what pupils have learned about evaporation and condensation in order to understand some of the causes of rain and other forms of precipitation. Heat a kettle and, when the steam begins to come from the spout, hold a cold plate or pie tin in the cloud. Watch the water condense. Incidentally, it becomes natural for children to use the words "condense" and "evaporate" in their conversation.

The covered terrarium in the schoolroom is an excellent place to observe the water cycle. The water evaporates from all of the wet things in the terrarium. When the moist air cools, the water vapor condenses on the glass. Another very simple way to show the same idea is by using a clean, dry glass jar. Place an inch or so of water in the bottom. Screw the lid on. Set the jar so that part of it is in the sunlight. In a short time the vapor which evaporates from the source will condense in droplets on the cool glass.

In using the materials described in the previous paragraphs, it is important that the pupils see the relationship between what happens to these materials and what happens outdoors. Thus in the kettle demonstration, the heating device represents the sun, the steam a cloud, the cold plate cold air, and the drops rain. In the terrarium, the analogies are more apparent, except that the cooler sides of the terrarium represent the cold temperatures experienced aloft.

OBSERVING CLOUDS

Too often we study clouds in the schoolroom, where there are none. But there is no reason why we should not take pupils outdoors to look at them. The weather bureau's chart of clouds (see footnote, page 206) is a great help in identifying them. Through their

This convection box, which may be made at school or purchased from a supply house, is used to show how wind is caused by the unequal heating of the air.

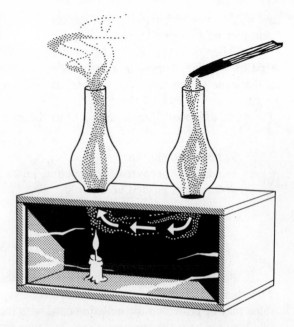

reading, pupils at this stage are in a position to answer some of the questions they asked on their first observing trip. They should know the answers to such questions as: "What are the clouds made of?" "What happens when they disappear?" "How high are different clouds?" "What kinds of weather are they likely to bring?"

LEARNING THE CAUSE OF WIND

Children learn from reading and class discussion that the earth is not heated equally in all regions. The equatorial regions are heated more than the temperate zones, the temperate more than the arctic. How does unequal heating produce winds? A convection box (see drawing) may be used to help pupils see how winds are caused. The box has two openings in the top, each covered by a glass chimney. The front is covered by a sliding glass. Under one of the holes is a candle, which heats the air around and over it. The surrounding cooler heavier air pushes in and forces the warmed lighter air up the chimney. This circulation of air is a small-scale wind. Of course, you cannot see the wind, but if you hold a smoking splinter of wood or piece of damp paper above the cooler chimney, you will see smoke being carried *down* that chimney, across the box, and *up* the other chimney. (The word "tracer" is a useful one to use to describe the role of the smoke in this demonstration.) Caution should be exercised in the use of this apparatus, since it involves the use of matches. Pupils should never light a match unless an adult is present.

To carry the principle of this demonstration to the cause of winds on the earth, develop the idea that the burning candle represents the equatorial regions of the earth. The large winds of the earth start blowing as the heated air in this region is pushed up and starts flowing toward the poles. Cold air from the poles flows toward the equatorial regions.

After children have observed the currents in the convection box, they are ready to apply what they have seen to the schoolroom where they are sitting. Why is the ceiling the hottest place in the room? With the door closed, open a window at the top and at the bottom and hold a stick with tissue paper streamers tied to it at each of these openings. Why is the wind coming *in* at the bottom and going *out* at the top?

After this experience, the children are ready to try to explain what is making the wind blow today. They can answer such questions as "What heats the earth?" "Is it heated to the same temperature everywhere? If not, why not?" "Would the wind blow toward the warmer place or toward the cooler?"

At this point, pupils may add to the lists of concepts about air such statements as:

Wind is moving air.
Winds blow because of the unequal heating of the earth.
Warm air is pushed up by colder air.

STUDYING A WEATHER MAP

Pupils can use much of the information they have learned in order to interpret some of the things that weather maps show. Many newspapers carry weather maps (see page 190), which may be posted on the bulletin board with the forecasts. As pupils study the maps they will discover how the measurements of temperature, air pressure, wind direction, wind speed, and precipitation are indicated. They become familiar with the symbols used.

Pupils may try to determine how the forecasts were made from the maps. Excellent helps in learning about weather maps as well as other weather materials are available from the Superintendent of Documents, Washington 25, D. C.[2]

Keeping track of the accuracy of the local weather reports over a period of time is an activity interesting to children. Reports may be taken from the radio, from newspapers, or by telephoning the local weather bureau, if there is one that gives such information. A committee may be appointed to provide the report each day and to decide whether or not it has been made accurately. This is a fine opportunity to stress the importance of making accurate observation, withholding judgment, and other elements of a scientific attitude discussed in part one. For example, if the forecast is for rain in the *vicinity* of the school and it does not rain *at the school itself,* further investigation is necessary before a decision can be reached.

VISITING A WEATHER STATION

In many localities, a visit to a weather station is taken when upper elementary school classes study weather. The effectiveness of these visits is increased with a little more planning and by looking more carefully at our objectives. The general objectives discussed in chapter 2 are the guideposts that help us plan for the trip to the weather station. The suggestions in chapter 3 for making field trips are also important to remember. Specifically, pupils go to the weather station to learn more than they already know about weather fore-

---

[2] *Cloud Code Chart* (cloud figures), 10¢; *Instruments Used in Weather Observing* (leaflet), 5¢; *Hurricane Warnings* (leaflet), 5¢; *Tornadoes: What They Are And What To Do About Them* (leaflet), 5¢; *The Hurricane,* 20¢; *Aviation Weather Leaflets* (16 leaflets), 75¢; *Code Figures and Symbols,* 10¢; *Weather Forecasting,* 25¢; *The Weather Bureau at Work,* 10¢. Sample copies of the Washington weather map are available free from Chief of the U. S. Weather Bureau, Washington 25, D. C. See also *Price List of Publications Number 48,* Superintendent of Documents, Washington 25, D. C.

Pupils may like to experiment with other materials than those suggested here. See books in bibliography for other ideas of how to make and use weather instruments.

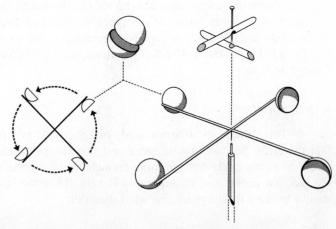

casting, to increase their interest in scientific procedures, to satisfy their curiosity about some of the materials they have seen pictured, and to increase their appreciation for the work of scientists.

Here are some specific questions for which pupils may want to find the answers at a weather station: "What things do the scientists learn from the instruments?" "How are these facts put together?" "How do the instruments work?" "How is the weather map made?" "Who uses the weather reports?" "Who pays for maintaining the weather station?" Arrangements may be made to send the pupils' questions to the station in advance of the visit so that the men in charge may have an idea of the kinds of information the pupils need.

SETTING UP A WEATHER STATION

Sometimes pupils can set up their own weather station to gather data on wind direction, air pressure, temperature, etc. Weather instruments may be assembled, and pupils may use them to try to make their own forecasts. Of course, their forecasts may not be accurate, because the pupils do not possess sufficient experience and knowledge, but a greater understanding and appreciation of the work of the weather bureau may be gained through this activity. They should realize that the data from one station is not enough to forecast weather with any amount of accuracy, even if these data were more correct than theirs. The above pictures show some of the weather instruments that may be made. The barometer and rain gauge have already been described.

ANEMOMETER

This wind gauge is made from two hollow rubber balls cut in halves and nailed to the ends of crossed sticks. The anemometer may be fastened to a post or a part of a building where the wind reaches it unobstructed. An electric fan may be used to test ease of operation before it is installed outside.

Again we have an instrument in which pupils may see the use of mathematics in science. If one of the half balls is painted red, it will not be too difficult to count the number of turns made per minute. Knowing this, pupils will be able to compare relative wind speeds on different days, in a relative sense. Thus 90 turns a minute on one day compared with 45 turns the next means that the wind speed on the first day was twice that of the second.

Interested students may also be able to determine the actual speed in miles per hour. Assume that each cup moves at the speed of the wind. From the radius, the circumference of the circle described by the cups is determined to be, let us say, 5 feet. If a cup makes 90 turns a minute, it covers 450 feet a minute, or 27,000 feet an hour. This comes to about 5 miles an hour.

WIND VANE

This consists of an arrow made of light wood and placed on a pivot. It is important that the arrow be carefully balanced and that the pivot hole be large enough to permit the arrow to swing freely but not large enough to permit the arrow to tilt. A washer between the wooden arrow and its support will help the arrow to move more freely. A compass should be used to determine the wind direction.

Wire wrapped around the arrow as needed will help to balance it so that it can swing freely. Pupils will need to experiment with this construction in order to produce an effective instrument.

RESOURCES TO INVESTIGATE

1. Local newspapers for weather maps and weather forecasts.
2. Local or nearby weather station to observe weather instruments and to learn how data are used in forecasting.
3. Local farmers, nurserymen, and fruit growers to learn how the weather bureau helps them and how they protect their crops in extreme or unusual weather.
4. Truck drivers and men who work on boats, for information on how they learn about sudden weather changes and what the weather bureau does for them.
5. Airports to observe weather instruments and to learn how information is gathered and disseminated.
6. Newspaper accounts of unusual weather conditions such as tornadoes, hurricanes, frosts, etc., for explanations of causes and results and other information about these conditions.
7. United States Weather Bureau and its branches for samples of weather maps and any other available information.
8. Local small-craft owners for barometer and other weather instruments and for accounts of how they get weather warnings and other weather information.
9. Newspaper accounts of recent advances in meteorology, such as the use of Tiros satellites to send data from a viewpoint in space.

Living Things

PART THREE

CHAPTER 10A

The Nature and Variety of Life

Life is all around us. A drop of water from a pond teems with thousands of tiny plants and animals. In the meadow nearby, the soil is alive with bacteria, molds, and worms; the weeds are home to a multitude of insects. The air above is not only the domain of birds but also the carrier of countless spores of microscopic life and the pollen of the higher plants. Life is found almost everywhere—even on frozen tundras, on dry deserts, and in hot springs. Life exists in the ocean deeps, on wave-battered shores, in sunless caves, and on windswept mountain peaks.

WHAT IT MEANS TO BE ALIVE

The forms of life are many and varied. Bread molds spreading their cottony growth, jellyfish contracting their umbrella-like bodies, dogwood trees bursting into bloom, fireflies sparkling on a summer night are all living things. What makes these different forms alike—and alive?

All can reproduce their kind; all can respond to stimuli; all can secure food and obtain energy from it, or transform it into living material for growth; all can dispose of their wastes. Let us consider some of these characteristics of living things.

REPRODUCTION. The bread mold scatters its spores so successfully that a piece of bread exposed to the air almost anywhere on the earth will be invaded by these reproductive bodies, which, if conditions are favorable, will develop into new cottony molds. Bacteria multiply so rapidly that within a day one becomes millions. An oak tree produces thousands of acorns, each capable of becoming a new tree. The female oyster produces nine million eggs each season. The female housefly lays up to six hundred eggs at a time. One female fly in April could have five and one-half trillion descendants by September if all survived. Mammals, such as deer, elephants, and squirrels, have smaller numbers of offspring. What they lack in numbers, they make up in parental care, in intelligence, and in other characteristics which insure their survival.

SENSITIVITY. A living thing is sensitive. It responds to outside forces, or *stimuli.* The leaves of the geranium plant growing in its pot on the window sill respond to the rays of the sun by turning toward the light. The roots of a plant respond to gravity by growing down, just as the stems respond in the opposite fashion by growing up. The trained hunting dog can flush a pheasant from its cover, led there by its highly developed sense of smell. A flying duck hawk sights its prey and unwaveringly plummets down at speeds up to 80 miles an hour for the kill.

USING FOOD FOR FUEL. Both plants and animals are able to secure food, but the

methods used vary so much that it will be more profitable to discuss this later, when they are considered separately. All living things use food as fuel for their "engines." In a series of complex chemical changes, the energy stored in food molecules is slowly released. This process enables a seed to break through the soil and even split rocks, or a beaver to gnaw down trees and build a dam. In brain cells, the energy derived from food helps an engineer to design a rocket ship that will reach the moon.

The use of food for energy in living things is often compared to the burning of a fire. In both processes, complex molecules are broken down into simple ones with a release of energy. However, there are two important differences that should be noted. In a fire, a great deal of heat is produced in a short time. In living things, the "burning" takes place slowly at low temperatures. Secondly, in a fire, the energy is released in the form of heat and light. In living things, however, very little of the energy is expended in this wasteful way; the energy is used for the many processes of life such as movement, transmission of nerve impulses, etc.

GROWTH. One of the qualities of the living thing is growth. An acorn becomes a massive oak tree. Bamboo in tropical jungles may grow a foot overnight. The newly hatched chick weighing a few ounces develops into a full-grown chicken that tips the scales at 6 or 7 pounds. A human baby that weighs, at birth, about 7 pounds matures into a grownup weighing 140 pounds or more. Where does this increase come from? Part of the food taken in by the living thing is converted into living substance called *protoplasm.* Growth, then, means an increase in this complex chemical material of life. Within a plant or animal, the protoplasm is found in separate building blocks, or *cells* (see diagram). As a living thing grows and builds more protoplasm out of the food it consumes, it also increases the number of cells of which it is composed.

The cell, the building block of life, is made of living protoplasm. The typical cell contains a nucleus surrounded by streaming cytoplasm, and is covered by a thin cell membrane. Plant cells, in addition, have a protective cell wall outside the membrane. Cells multiply by splitting in two. They then grow to their original size by converting food into protoplasm.

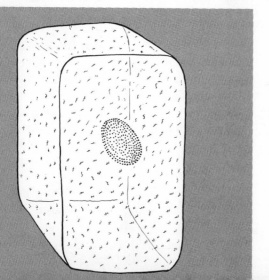

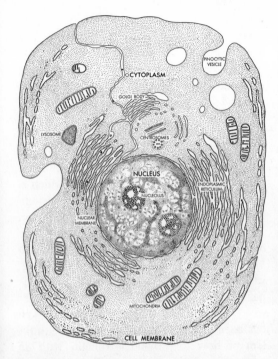

This modern diagram of a typical cell is based on what is seen through the electron microscope which magnifies 100,000 times and more. Aided by such magnifications and by the revelations of chemistry, the biologist now sees the cell as much more than a drop of protoplasm—he sees it as a highly organized molecule factory.

The most rapid growth in mammals takes place early in life. The human baby may double its weight in its first six months. Never again will it grow so fast. A tree, however, continues to increase in size, building one ring or layer of wood each year. Some animals, such as the lobster, also grow as long as they live.

SECURING OXYGEN. Deprived of oxygen, almost all living things, plant or animal, die. Oxygen is required for the release of energy from food, necessary for all life activity. Not all living things, however, obtain their oxygen directly from the atmosphere. Some, such as fish, lobsters, clams, and other forms of aquatic life, extract the oxygen from the air that is dissolved in the water in which they live. You can see this air

if you allow a glass of cold water to stand in a warm room for a few hours. Bubbles of air form on the sides of the glass. The animals just mentioned are equipped with special devices, such as gills, to extract the dissolved oxygen from the water. Warm-blooded animals—the birds and mammals—require the most oxygen, since they must produce heat constantly to maintain their normal body temperature. Oxygen consumption is very high in the smaller birds, such as the hummingbird, whose body temperature is normally 130° F.

Certain kinds of microbes do not require oxygen for the release of energy from food. Yeasts, which are tiny plants, may secure energy by fermenting sugar; that is, by splitting sugar into alcohol and carbon dioxide. Certain bacteria also are able to obtain energy from foods in the absence of oxygen.

WASTE DISPOSAL. The wastes of the living organism generally are poisonous to it. In order to live, the organism must continually rid itself of these wastes. Simple animals, such as the one-celled protozoa that live in the water, simply expel their bodies' liquid wastes into the water through their covering membranes. In complex animals, the kidneys, skin, and lungs (or gills) assume the vital job of getting rid of liquid and gaseous wastes, such as water, salts, urea, and carbon dioxide. Solid wastes are discharged from an opening at the end of the food tube.

CENSUS OF THE LIVING

The *taxonomists* (scientists who study the family tree of living things) list some million and a half *species*, or kinds, of living organisms in their catalogues. Most of these are small organisms seldom noticed by the average person. The insect group includes, by far, the major number of species, 700,000 having been described and named to date. New kinds of insects are being discovered at the rate of nearly 2,000 a year!

The two broad groups of living things are plants and animals. These two divisions, the plant and animal *kingdom*s, are sub-divided into major groups. In the animal kingdom, the major groups are called *phyla*. Classification in the plant kingdom has been undergoing revision in recent years with the result that the term "division" is now replacing the category "phylum." We will not go into the complexities and divergencies of modern plant taxonomy, but will identify the characteristic kinds of plant life. It would be helpful to read chapter 14A, which deals with the evolution of the various forms of life, in connection with the brief survey of plants and animals which follows.

THE PLANT KINGDOM

THE SIMPLEST PLANTS. The plant kingdom includes all of the commonly recognized plants as well as many that are strange and unknown to the ordinary person.

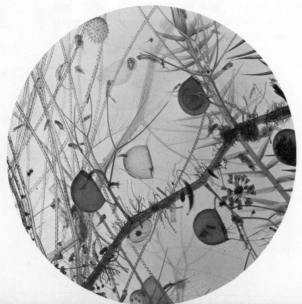

A drop of pond water examined under the microscope reveals a world of tiny plants and animals. These have been skillfully depicted in this exhibit of glass models at the American Museum of Natural History.

Algae are simple plants which lack true stems, leaves, and flowers. All algae contain chlorophyll, the green coloring matter which enables them to be food-makers. Algae vary in size from microscopic, single-celled forms to the 200-foot-long, many-celled giant seaweeds, or kelps, which live attached to rocks at the edge of the sea.

Algae for microscopic study may be obtained by scraping the green film which is sometimes seen on the walls of an aquarium. Pond water is a rich source of many algae. The green, silky threads found near the edge of a pond may be those of the beautiful *Spirogyra*. (See magnified view of Spirogyra, with spiral chlorophyll structures, on this page.)

Chlorella is a microscopic alga which has been proposed as an answer to the problem of how to provide astronauts with an adequate supply of food and oxygen (see chapter 24A). Chlorella would be grown in tanks in spaceships, under artificial light. The oxygen released by these microscopic plants would freshen the air for the astronauts. A crop of the excess Chlorella would be harvested regularly and used as food. The wastes produced by the astronauts—carbon dioxide, liquid and solid wastes—would be used to supply the plants with materials essential for their growth.

Bacteria are tiny one-celled plants. Most bacteria do not have chlorophyll, and consequently cannot manufacture their own food. They obtain food from other living things or from dead plants and animals. Some bacteria, for example, live parasitically on plants or animals, causing disease. Bacteria are also of great benefit to living things. Every plant and animal is a storehouse of valuable chemicals. If these chemicals remained locked up within the organisms after death, there would soon be a scarcity of them for the living. Bacteria cause the rotting or decay of dead plants and animals, thus restoring their essential chemicals to the soil. These chemicals, nitrates for example, then become available again for use by green plants and eventually by animals. It is probably true that without bacteria, most life on the planet Earth would disappear.

The *fungi* include a variety of groups of plants lacking chlorophyll: yeasts, molds, and mushrooms. Fungi play a similar role to that of bacteria; they are typically organisms which promote the decay of plant and animal materials.

Yeasts, like bacteria, are microscopic, one-celled plants. Some yeasts produce a chemical change in sugar, causing it to break down into alcohol and carbon dioxide gas. Man has put this to practical advantage. Yeasts ferment the sugar in crushed grapes into alcohol, making wine. In bread-making, the carbon dioxide produced by the action of living yeast plants "raises" the dough and so helps make a light, tasty bread.

Molds are commonly seen growing on fruit, bread, and in other places where they are not wanted. Molds have recently taken on added importance because extracts from them have been found useful in fighting bacteria harmful to man. Penicillin, streptomycin, and neomycin are but a few of the growing list of *antibiotics*, as these substances are called, that man has extracted from certain molds.

The edible *mushroom* is known best by its stalk and cap, which is actually the reproductive part of this fungus plant. There is no simple rule for telling edible from poisonous mushrooms. The only way to be sure is to *know* the particular mushroom you pick to eat by *all* of its characteristics.

One of the first questions to be answered by the first astronauts to land on Mars will probably be, "Are the greenish patches we saw from Earth made of lichens?" A *lichen* is a strange plant since it is really two plants growing together: an alga and a fungus. Lichens are found as greenish-gray patches on rocks and on soil.

THE MOSSES. All the members of this division of the plant kingdom possess chlorophyll. Mosses have no true roots, stems, or leaves such as are found in the more complex flowering plants. The size of these plants is severely limited because they lack a good conducting system of tubes for the distribution of food, water, and minerals. These tubes, found in the higher plants, are needed to carry vital supplies long distances from the soil. Hence, a moss plant more than a foot high would be a rarity.

THE FERNS AND THEIR RELATIVES. The ferns are the first plants—in the gamut of simple to complex—equipped with well-developed roots, stems, and leaves and an

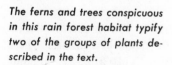

The ferns and trees conspicuous in this rain forest habitat typify two of the groups of plants described in the text.

efficient conducting system of tubes. This enables them to grow to great size. The heyday of the ferns in the early days of life on earth is described in chapter 14A. In the Carboniferous period, ferns were the most highly developed plants on the earth, comparable in size to our present forest trees. Horsetails and club mosses, small relatives of ferns, also had their heyday in this period, reaching heights of 75 and 100 feet.

Ferns reproduce by means of spores. If you turn over a fern leaf, you will frequently find brown spots there. These contain the spore cases, within which are numerous minute spores.

THE SEED PLANTS.   The seed plants are the most complex of all plants. They include all of the common herbs, shrubs, and trees. Differences in the method of seed production determine the separation of the seed plants into two major groups.

In one group there are no flowers, and the seeds are generally produced in open cones, as in the pine tree. This group, known as the *gymnosperms* ("naked-seed"), includes the yew, hemlock, spruce, fir, cypress, sequoia, and redwood. It was once thought that the giant redwood qualified for the distinction of being the oldest and largest land plant now on the earth. It is now believed that the Big Tree of Tule in Mexico has this honor. It is at least 5,000 years old, and its trunk diameter is 50 feet.

The flowering plants, called the *angiosperms*, bear their seeds inside of closed seed cases. Angiosperms generally have thin, sheet-like leaves, in contrast to the needle-like or scale-like leaves of the gymnosperms.

There are over 250,000 kinds of flowering plants. They are found as small herbaceous plants, and as vines, shrubs, and trees. It was from this group of plants that people long ago selected those with useful qualities for cultivation. A large part of our food is derived from seeds, particularly the grains. From ground grain comes the flour that makes the "staff of life"—bread. Our clothing is woven from plant fibers, such as cotton and linen. When we become ill, we often heal ourselves with plant extracts. Although modern chemists can synthesize many drugs, we still depend on plants for such vital drugs as digitalis for regulating the heart action, opium and its derivatives for relief of pain, and cocaine and its derivatives for anesthesia. Modern chemical industry uses cellulose, which the plant makes as a covering around its cells, as the raw material for such products as rayon and the cellulose-base plastics.

We should not overlook the esthetic appeal of flowering plants, which bring a rainbow of colors and many exotic odors to the planet Earth.

THE ANIMAL KINGDOM

What in common speech is called an "animal" is usually one of the four-footed, fur-bearing mammals, such as a sheep, a dog, a horse, or a cow. These are simply the most familiar animals. There are many quite different forms equally entitled to be called animals. Initially, we note that animals fall readily into one of two types. Some have a backbone, and some do not not. The animals without a backbone are called *invertebrates*; those with a backbone are the *vertebrates*. The vertebrates loom large in our minds because they are familiar animals and are generally large. However, of all the different kinds of animals, only 5 percent are vertebrates; the remaining 95 percent are invertebrates.

PROTOZOA.   The simplest of the invertebrates are the one-celled animals. These are called *protozoa* (prō′tō-zō′à), a name that means "first animals." They are too small to be seen with the unaided eye, so it is not surprising that they were not discovered until the microscope was perfected. Antony Van Leeuwenhoek, the Dutch lensgrinder of the seventeenth century who invented the microscope, was the first person to see protozoa. He called them *animalculae* (small animals), which they literally are. Among the thousands of kinds that have been described since that time, there is an amazing diversity. Some are without a fixed shape and possess few parts. Such a one is the ameba, widely studied today in high school biology classes (see photograph). Others have intricate structures, including devices such as hair-like or whip-like projections by which they propel themselves. Most live as independent animals, but some are parasites.

2. *SPONGES.* The sponges are the first phylum of many-celled animals. Their sac-like bodies are living waterways. Currents of water sweep in through microscopic pores that cover the entire surface. Minute food particles are strained out of the water, which is then swept out through a large opening at one end of the animal. The natural sponge used in homes and in industry is the dried and cleaned skeleton of the sponge animals.

In the sponges we have the beginnings of cellular *specialization*; certain cells take food out of the sea water and then pass it along to others that specialize in protection, mechanical support, and reproduction.

3. *CORALS AND THEIR RELATIVES.* Extending part way around the continent of Australia is the famed Great Barrier Reef. This is a huge growth of coral, a member of the *coelenterate* (sĕ-lĕn′tēr-ȧt) phylum of animals. The reef is built of the skeletons of thousands of generations of the coral animals that lived and died in the warm seas. The corals and their relatives, the sea anemones, the jellyfish, and the Portuguese man-of-war, are alike in having a body which is essentially a hollow sac, with a single opening surrounded by tentacles. The tentacles are used for capturing tiny animals. There is more co-ordination among the cells of coelenterates than in the case of the sponges. Coelenterates

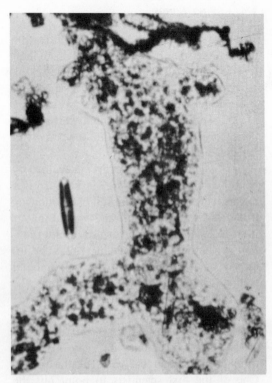

An actual photograph, taken through a microscope, of a living ameba. This one-celled animal changes its shape as it streams along, and feeds by wrapping itself around its food.

also have structures that are specialized for feeding, locomotion, digestion, and reproduction.

4. *WORMS.* We have included here three different phyla of animals—flatworms, roundworms, and segmented worms. People are generally only familiar with the segmented worms, such as the earthworm and the sandworm. Most of the other worms live at the expense of other animals, including man, as parasites. Examples of parasitic flatworms are the tapeworms and the flukes. The roundworms are widespread over the earth. A spadeful of garden soil teems with millions of them. Some roundworms are parasitic on other animals. The one of chief importance in the United States is the hookworm. The scientific name of this worm is indicative of its role. It is *Necator americanus,* which means "the American killer." Hookworms were the scourge of the southern states. They

enter the body from the soil by burrowing through the soles of the feet. They make their way to the small intestine, where they hook on, feed, and reproduce. The eggs pass out with the feces and develop into worms.

Another parasitic round worm is the pork worm, which is taken into the body with insufficiently cooked pork.

The segmented worms are typified by the common earthworm. This burrower makes its way through the soil by swallowing it and digesting the plant and animal matter in it. In doing this, it performs a useful function in agriculture. Tunneling up, it brings the lower layers of soil with rich mineral content into the upper part, making the minerals available for plant growth. Also, the progress of the worm through the soil makes the soil porous, so that water and air, which are essential to plant life, can percolate through and reach the roots of the plants. One of the first scientists to point out the significant contribution of the earthworm was Charles Darwin, who estimated that earthworms brought eighteen tons of soil to the surface of an acre each year.

5. MOLLUSKS. The mollusks are the second largest phylum of invertebrates, numbering about 100,000 species. Their tasty, soft, fleshy bodies have made them an important source of food to man. Some of the better-known mollusks are oysters, snails, and octopuses. The mollusks with a one-piece shell include the snails, conches, and whelks. Many people collect the colorful and decorative shells of these animals. Some are used in making jewelry and ornaments. The mollusks with two shells are represented by oysters, clams, and scallops. Oysters are the makers of the treasured pearl. When a foreign particle gets into its body, the irritated mollusk secretes a pearly material around the particle. Man takes advantage of this reaction and induces oysters to make pearls. A particle of sand or other substance is put under the shell, and the oyster proceeds to build a pearl around it. The third group of mollusks include the nautilus, the squid, and the octopus. These are jet-propelled animals. They usually move by taking in water and ejecting it forcefully to the back through a narrow tube or funnel. This pushes them rapidly in the opposite direction from the squirted water. They can steer themselves by turning the funnel in different directions. Squids are among the largest of all animals. Some giant squids have been found, measuring more than 50 feet in length These are probably one of the animals responsible for the age-old legends of "sea monsters."

6. THE JOINTED-LEGGED INVERTEBRATES. Of all the major groups in the animal kingdom, this one, the arthropods, contains by far the largest number of different kinds of species of animals. All the arthropods have an external skeleton and jointed legs. There are five main classes in this tremendous group.

The crustaceans (krŭs-tā′shănz) include crayfish, lobsters, shrimps, and crabs. With a few exceptions, these animals breathe with gills, and most of them inhabit the sea. They range in size from microscopic water fleas and barnacles an inch wide to the 35-pound American lobster and the Japanese spider crab, with a span of 20 feet between the tips of its first pair of legs. This group is an important source of food for human beings.

Centipedes and millipedes have many legs, not hundreds and thousands, as their names imply, but several dozen. Centipedes have one pair of legs attached to each body segment, while the millipedes have two pair on each segment.

Spiders and their allies have four pairs of walking legs and are generally air-breathers. Included in this group, called the arachnids (à-răk′nĭdz), are not only the spiders but also scorpions, ticks, and mites. The king or horseshoe crab is also an arachnid, a relative of the extinct trilobites that are discussed in chapter 14A.

The insects have three pair of legs and their bodies are divided into three parts: head, thorax, and abdomen. They are the largest group in the animal kingdom, represented, as indicated previously, by 700,000 separate species. There are 112,000 known kinds of butterflies and moths alone! The insects as a group have penetrated almost every niche of the earth, adapting themselves to an amazing variety of environmental conditions. Insects live in frigid and in tropical zones, in desert and in rain forest, on prairie and on mountain top. They are meat-eaters and plant-eaters. Some ants grow fungus gardens in their underground tunnels, thus providing themselves with food. Termites eat wood. Mosquitoes suck the blood of mammals. The young larvae of one kind of fly inhabit the digestive tube of a horse. The corn borer destroys man's food while it is still growing in the fields. The clothes moth destroys his clothing and the termite his wooden home. The anopheles mosquito carries the protozoan that causes malaria. But there are some insects that are helpful to man. Bees, wasps, and butterflies help in the pollination of flowers of many plants which we depend on for food. The products of the honeybee and silkworm are used directly. Some insects help to keep harmful insects under control. An example of this is the dragonfly, which devours flies and mosquitoes.

7. *STARFISH.* The spiny-skinned animals, or *echinoderms*, are typified by the starfish. All of the starfish and their relatives live in the ocean. Despite their name, the starfish are no more kin to fish than are the shellfish, such as oysters and crabs. In addition to their spiny skins, starfish are noted for their system of water tubes. Water is drawn into an opening in the body and then forced under pressure into thousands of small cylinders called *tube feet* that protrude from its arms. These feet have suckers at their ends. The starfish moves itself from place to place by applying and then releasing its tube feet on

This seascape is a study in contrast. The active vertebrate fish, a Blue Striped Grunt, swims near the invertebrate coral forms, which are rooted in their underwater home. The fish has a flexible internal skeleton; the coral a hard, unmovable, external skeleton.

the surface on which it is moving. The tube feet also help in feeding. Starfish feed chiefly on clams, oysters, scallops, and mussels.

In addition to the starfish, the echinoderms include animals with such self-descriptive names as brittle stars, basket stars, sea urchins, sand dollars, sea cucumbers, and sea lilies.

8. ANIMALS WITH BACKBONES. The most highly developed group of animals is the backboned animals, the vertebrates. These are characterized by an internal bony skeleton. There are five main branches of backboned animals, each in a group designated as a *class*: fish, amphibians, reptiles, birds, and mammals. We will consider them briefly here, since they will be referred to frequently in the latter part of this chapter and the next four chapters. *Fish* have scaly skins and two-chambered hearts, breathe by means of gills, lay eggs without a shell, and are cold-blooded. A cold-blooded animal is one that does not maintain a constant body temperature; its temperature varies with the temperature of its environment. Fish, amphibians, and reptiles are cold-blooded. Cold-blooded animals become sluggish and frequently hibernate when the temperature drops. Birds and mammals are warm-blooded, maintaining the same temperature at all times. The ability to do this makes these animals relatively independent of outside conditions, so that they can remain active in very cold weather.

Amphibians include frogs, toads, newts, and salamanders. These animals, in most cases, spend part of their life in water and part of it on land. The young, or tadpoles, breathe through gills, but the adult uses its lungs and moist skin to breathe. Amphibians have three-chambered hearts and moist skin, lay eggs, and are cold-blooded. Some few of them are used by man for food, and many are useful because they feed chiefly on insects. Some, such as the mud puppies or hellbenders, never leave the water; some, such as the frogs and the newts, divide their

time between water and land; some, such as toads, some frogs, and salamanders, spend most of their adult life on land. But almost all mate in the water, and the young of almost all amphibians are born there.

Reptiles breathe through lungs, have three- or four-chambered hearts and scaly skins, lay eggs covered by a tough shell, and are cold-blooded. Typical reptiles are snakes, lizards, alligators, crocodiles, and turtles. Some of these are used for food by man; others are prized for their skin or shell. Some of the reptiles, notably certain snakes, make venom with which to poison their prey. The poisonous snakes in the United States are the coral, copperhead, water moccasin, and rattlesnake. Despite their deadly venom, rattlesnakes kill few people in this country because of the animal's retiring disposition. Given a chance, a rattlesnake will silently glide away rather than join in battle with man.

Birds have achieved mastery of the air. Birds have feathers and four-chambered hearts, breathe through lungs, lay eggs covered with a hard shell, and are warm-blooded. Birds are the warmest of all animals, with average temperatures of 100° F. to 110° F. If you have ever held a live chick in your hand, you are well aware of how warm birds are. This need to keep warm makes birds large eaters. Many of the smaller birds, such as the warblers, will eat their own weight of food in a day. Birds are of great value to man in helping to keep insect pests under control. The birds of prey, such as hawks and owls, are now recognized as important aids in helping to keep down the numbers of four-footed vermin, such as mice and rats. Birds are also an important source of food to man.

The *mammals* are warm-blooded animals that are covered with hair, and nurse their young on milk from mammary glands. They are distinguished for the complexity of their brains, which is greatest in man. Within the mammal group there is a wide variety in structure and in ways of living. Some mammals, such as the bat, whose forelimbs are fitted for flight, have taken to the air. Other mammals, such as the whale, live in the ocean but must rise to the top to breathe in air with their lungs. Some mammals, such as the hoofed camel, deer, and horse, are vegetarians. Others, such as the lion, tiger, and wolf, are flesh-eaters. The animals with the greatest development of the brain are the monkeys, apes, and man. Mammals vary widely in size from the tiniest rodents to the sulphur-bottom whale, the largest animal that ever lived, past or present.

In this brief survey of the plant and animal kingdoms, we have stressed the economic importance of the various forms of life to man. In so doing, we do not wish to leave the impression that the different plants and animals have evolved for the particular purpose of serving man or that they should be considered solely in this light. Each is a living thing, from bacteria to man. Man is but one of the multitude of living things on this planet.

THE METHOD OF CLASSIFICATION

Biologists classify living things according to this scheme:

Kingdom
  Phylum
    Class
      Order
        Family
          Genus
            Species

To understand this system, let us see how it is used to classify a human—literally, to put him in his place.

Kingdom: Animal, *of course. We are one of 1¼ million of them.*

Phylum: Chordates. *Most of the animals in this group are better known as vertebrates, animals with backbones, which include fish, amphibia, reptiles, birds, and mammals.*

Class: Mammals. *Man is one of 6,000 in this hairy, warm-blooded group that feeds milk to its young.*

Order: Primates. *Man is a distinguished member of this order, which also includes monkeys, lemurs, and apes.*

Family: Hominidae. *This group includes not only present-day humans but also ancient prehuman forms such as Peking Man. (The word "family," when used in classification, has nothing to do with our everyday use of this word.)*

Genus: Homo. *A small group that includes Neanderthal Man and humans.*

Species: Sapiens. *This group is limited to human beings only. It includes all men living on earth today.*

An examination of this method of classification reveals that as one proceeds from kingdom to species, there are fewer and fewer kinds in each group and the kinds of living things in each group are more and more alike.

This method of classification also provides a scientific way of naming an organism. The name consists of the genus and species designation. Thus man's scientific name is *Homo sapiens.* This "two-name" system of naming plants and animals was invented by Linnaeus, a Swedish botanist, and described in his book, *Systema Naturae,* published in 1735. This method provides a name for every organism, a name internationally accepted and recognized. At the same time, the name fits the living thing into its natural place in its kingdom. For example, the common house cat has the name, *Felis domestica;* the lion is *Felis leo;* the tiger, *Felis tigris.* This system of naming reveals that these three animals belong to the same genus, that they are all closely related.

We do not have the space here to go into the criteria which taxonomists use in deciding where a form of life belongs, but we would like to underscore the fact that high on the list are the structural details of the organism.

FOOD FACTORY FOR
THE EARTH

Climb to the top of a hill and look out over the countryside. The dominant color of the meadows, the valleys, and the hillsides is green. This is no accident, for green is the color of chlorophyll, the stuff that makes life on earth possible. It is this green pigment that enables every plant possessing it to take in two of the commonest substances, water and carbon dioxide, and through its internal chemistry transform them into sugar. In plants, we take this process for granted. But if you were looking at a glass of carbonated water (which is nothing but water and bubbles of carbon dioxide gas) and suddenly the water and bubbles disappeared and just as suddenly a lump of sugar appeared in the

bottom—you would say, "magic!" Yet green plants perform this chemical "magic" every day. (Chemical changes will be discussed more fully in chapter 16A.)

The main food factory of common plants is located in the leaves. A leaf is well adapted to do its job. The broad upper surface (see diagram) is a vast absorber for taking in the sun's rays, which supply the energy for the food manufacturing process. Immediately below the upper *epidermis*, as the layer of cells comprising the leaf surface is called, is a closely packed group of cells that are conspicuous for the large number of chlorophyll bodies within them. These "palisade cells," as they are known, are active food-makers, as are also the "spongy cells" beneath them. The sun's rays coming through the semitransparent epidermis reach the chlorophyll bodies in the palisade and spongy cells. The raw materials for food-making come to these cells from two places. On the lower surface of the leaf are found numbers of microscopic openings, each between two *guard cells*. These openings are the *stomata* of the leaf. Changes in the size of the guard cells cause the stomata to open or close. Air

The food factory of the earth. Diagram of a section view of part of a leaf.

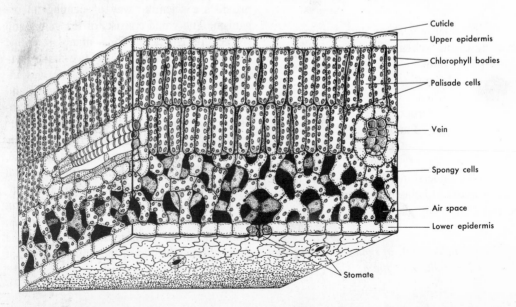

Cuticle
Upper epidermis
Chlorophyll bodies
Palisade cells
Vein
Spongy cells
Air space
Lower epidermis
Stomate

passes through the stomata into air spaces inside the leaf. The gas carbon dioxide is then taken out of the air by the food-making layer of cells. Meanwhile, water is absorbed from the soil by the millions of minute cells projecting from the plant's root, the *root hairs*. From the root hair cells, water moves to the tubes inside the root that transport the water up through the stem into the leaf. At last the water reaches the food-making cells. Here the green chlorophyll has trapped some of the energy of sunlight. The energy is used to make sugar from atoms supplied by molecules of water and carbon dioxide. A valuable by-product, oxygen, also results from this chemical process. (See the chemical equation for this process on page 403.) The oxygen is released by the leaf through the stomata to the air. In this way, the atmosphere of the earth is freshened with some 400 billion tons of oxygen each year, replacing the oxygen used up by living things.

(The knowledge that green plants take in carbon dioxide and release oxygen during sugar-manufacture should not make us forget that *in the process of respiration, plants, like animals, take in oxygen and give off carbon dioxide.* It is *untrue* to say that "plants breathe in the opposite way that animals do.")

The plant cells can change the sugar into starch for storage or combine it with other materials to build substances such as proteins and vitamins. Sugar can also be converted into fats (in animals as well as plants). Thus, the sugar-making process in green plants produces the primary material of all foodstuffs.

The scientific name for this essential process of sugar-making is made up of two words that emphasize the key aspect of the action: photo, which means "light," and synthesis, which means "putting together." *Photosynthesis,* "putting together by means of light," is exactly what happens in the process. In recent years, scientists have succeeded in duplicating part of this process in test tubes. Perhaps some day they will be able to manufacture food in large quantity from abundant chemicals. Until that day, we will have to continue to depend for our food upon the action of chlorophyll in the living cells of plants, with the energy supplied by the sunlight, and with carbon dioxide and water as the raw materials.

BIOGRAPHY OF A PLANT

GERMINATION. Germination, the development of a seed into a plant with roots, stem, and ·leaves, is a crucial period in the life of a plant. Lacking certain conditions,

SEE PAGES 35 O 38

SEE PAGES 242 TO 245

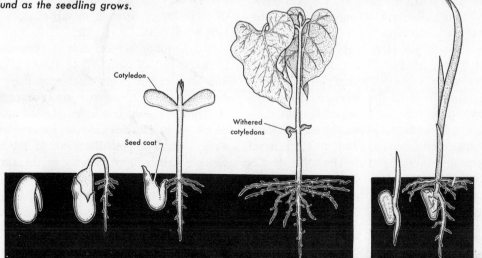

Left: *Stages in germination of the garden bean. The two cotyledons provide food until the plant is able to make its own.* Right: *Germination of the corn seed. The single cotyledon of the corn seed remains underground as the seedling grows.*

Cotyledon

Withered cotyledons

Seed coat

the seed will fail to germinate. These requirements are food, oxygen, suitable temperature, and water. The food supply is provided in the seed. There is enough food to last until the roots are established in the ground and the first green leaves exposed to the sun are ready to carry on photosynthesis. Oxygen is essential for the burning of food and the release of energy. The soil in which plants grow must be porous to allow air to circulate down to the roots. The warmth needed for germination is supplied by the sun, which warms the ground. Water is essential for the germination of the seed. Water softens the hard seed coat so that the soft parts within may push through as they develop. The plant cells take in water, become active, and reproduce by cell division. This permits the kind of rapid growth that makes the seeds seem almost to burst from the ground overnight. All chemical activity in the cell, such as digestion of stored starch into sugar, requires water as a medium in which to occur. Water is also needed as a vital component of the new protoplasm forming in the cells of the rapidly growing plant.

With the softening and swelling of the seed coat, the first part of the embryo breaks out. This is the part that will form the roots. Roots serve to obtain sufficient water and to anchor the plant in the soil. In seeds such as the bean (see illustration, p. 223) the root-making part forms an arch. This arch soon breaks through the soil. Thereupon, the arch straightens out, and the two food halves of the seed, the *cotyledons,* are thus pulled out of the ground. Protectively sandwiched between the cotyledons are the first leaves. Once above ground, the cotyledons separate. The food stored in the cotyledons is slowly digested and transported to other parts of the seedling. The leaves grow, turn green, and start making food.

In seeds that have only one cotyledon, such as corn (see illustration, p. 223), development is a bit different. The roots develop first, but then a spear-like sheath emerges that encloses the first leaves. Its spear shape

permits it to push through the soil readily, while protecting the tender leaves within. Soon this spear point shows above ground, and the leaves unfold, turn green, and start making food. In these plants, the main bulk of the seed, containing the food for the embyro, remains below ground. The food is soon used up, and the seed remnants shrivel as the seedling grows.

The water, minerals, and carbon dioxide that the plant takes in are used in food manufacture and in building the living substance—protoplasm. The plant thrives and enlarges. The stem reaches higher and higher, and more and more leaves are formed. Soon, enough food has been made so that flowers can be produced. Before considering flowers and their role in reproduction, let us take a look at stems and roots.

STEMS AND ROOTS. Stems serve to conduct water and minerals from the roots to the leaves and manufactured foods from the leaves to the flowers and roots.

Water moves up in a continuous stream from the soil to the roots, stems, and leaves, and thence to the air. This movement is accomplished in one set of tubes in the plant. In a tree, these water-carrying pipes are located in the *sapwood,* or the outer portion of the wood. Foods are conducted down from the leaves to other parts of the plant through another set of tubes located in the inner part of the bark. Between the wood and the bark lies the *cambium,* a thin sheet of dividing cells that contribute to the growth of the stem by forming new bark cells and new wood cells.

Girdling a tree, that is removing a complete ring of bark and cambium from it, kills the tree, for it severs the pipelines that carry food, and it destroys the layer of cells responsible for the continued life and growth of the plant. The cambium grows new layers each year, adding to the girth of the tree. Since it grows more actively in the spring, there is a marked difference between the spring growth and that of the rest of the year.

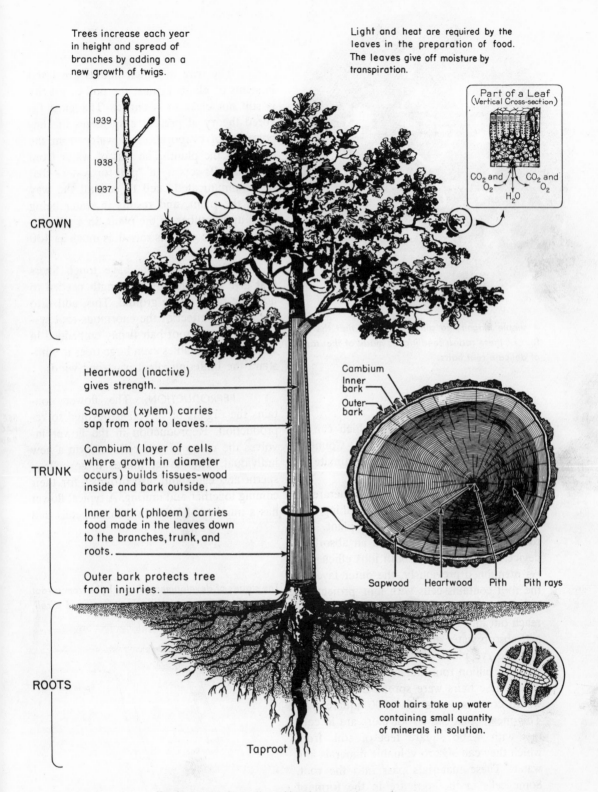

Trees increase each year in height and spread of branches by adding on a new growth of twigs.

1939
1938
1937

Light and heat are required by the leaves in the preparation of food. The leaves give off moisture by transpiration.

Part of a Leaf
(Vertical Cross-section)

CO_2 and O_2 CO_2 and O_2

H_2O

CROWN

Heartwood (inactive) gives strength.

Sapwood (xylem) carries sap from root to leaves.

Cambium (layer of cells where growth in diameter occurs) builds tissues-wood inside and bark outside.

Inner bark (phloem) carries food made in the leaves down to the branches, trunk, and roots.

Outer bark protects tree from injuries.

Cambium
Inner bark
Outer bark

TRUNK

Sapwood   Heartwood   Pith   Pith rays

ROOTS

Root hairs take up water containing small quantity of minerals in solution.

Taproot

The buds, root tips, and cambium layer are the growing parts. The tree takes in oxygen over its entire surface through pores on leaves, twigs, branches, trunk, and roots.

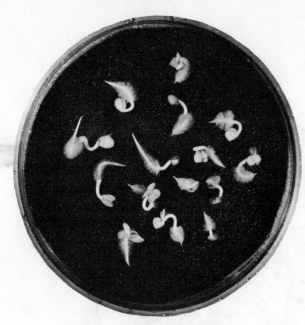

A simple magnifying glass will show that the fine fuzz of these radish seedlings is made of thousands of delicate root hairs.

The way in which liquids are lifted in stems of plants against the pull of gravity is still not clear to scientists. The most favored theory at present emphasizes the importance of evaporation of water from the leaves of the plant. The loss of water from the leaf cells sets up a "pull for water" that is "communicated" cell to cell all the way down the plant, and results in water being lifted up the tubes of the plant. In a tall redwood tree the water is raised as much as 400 feet.

The larger roots have tough fibers that give them the great strength needed to hold the plant in the ground. This, added to the gripping effect of the enormous root system, with each root hair firmly embedded in soil particles, enables even large trees to withstand the buffeting effect of strong winds.

This results in *annual rings*, which can be seen when a tree is cut across. Counting these rings gives an accurate estimate of the age of the tree.

We have described the structure of the leaf in the section on food-making. Let us now look at the root of the plant. The root is both an anchoring and an absorbing device. It is built to do both jobs efficiently. As mentioned previously, the outer layer of the root contains cells with long projections called root hairs. These microscopic "hairs" reach out into the soil to a surprising degree and absorb water and dissolved minerals. In a single rye plant, it was found that there were 14 billion root hairs. If the surfaces of all of these hairs were spread out flat, they would cover an area of 4,300 square feet. This means that these root hairs are in contact with 4,300 square feet of soil, from which they can absorb valuable minerals and water. These materials pass into the root. Some cells in the root are in the form of tubes that carry the absorbed materials to all parts of the plant by connecting with similar tubes in the stem and leaves.

REPRODUCTION. The flower contains the organs of the plant devoted to reproduction. Reproduction in the flower involves the union of two cells to form a new individual. The flower makes these cells—sperm and egg—and also provides for their coming together and uniting. A typical flower has a number of brightly colored petals that

SEE PAG 248

The stages of development of root hairs from a root of timothy. Each root hair is an extension of a cell.

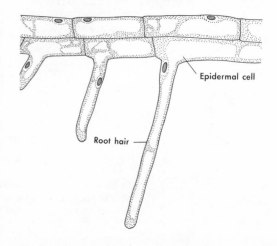

Epidermal cell

Root hair

often have a distinctive odor. The color and odor serve to attract insects needed for *cross-pollination*, which is the transfer of pollen from one flower to another of the same kind. Some flowers do not require insects to carry their pollen, but use the wind for this purpose. Wind-pollinated flowers make huge amounts of pollen, which compensates for the pollen wasted by this hit-or-miss method. Some flowers are *self-pollinated*, the transfer of pollen taking place within the flower.

The part of the flower engaged in pollen-making is the *stamen* (see diagram). The top part of the stamen is an enlarged sac, called the *anther*, where the pollen is formed. Supporting the anther is a long, thin stem, the *filament*. The pollen grain is a microscopic structure containing the male reproductive cell, the sperm. To succeed in its function, the pollen must be carried to the *pistil* of a flower of the same kind. The pistil generally consists of three parts. The broad, enlarged, lower portion is the *ovary*. Within it are produced the *ovules*. Inside each ovule is an egg, the female reproductive cell.

The six stamens and the single pistil are easily seen in this lily flower.

Above the ovary is a slender stem-like part called the *style*. The enlarged top of the style is the *stigma*. The stigma, equipped with hairs and a sticky secretion, holds any pollen grains which may land on it. The pollen grain starts to grow a tube that extends down through the style and into the ovary. Finally it reaches a special opening in the ovule. The sperm cell of the pollen grain passes into the ovule through the channel thus made and unites with the egg cell. This union of the sperm and the egg is called *fertilization*. The fertilized egg resulting from this union will develop into an *embryo*, a baby plant.

After fertilization, the flower seems to wither. Parts no longer needed, such as petals, stamens, and parts of the pistil, shrivel or fall off, but the remaining parts of the flower grow to many times their original size. The fertilized egg develops into an embryo. The ovule develops into a seed. The ovary develops into a fruit. A fruit, then, is a ripened ovary containing seeds. That is why the tomato is really a fruit even though people customarily call it a vegetable.

The flower contains the reproductive organs of the plant. Depicted here are the characteristic structures found in most flowers.

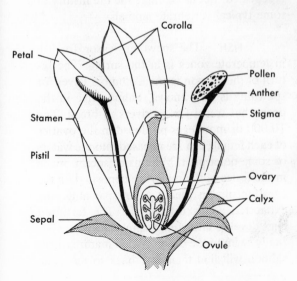

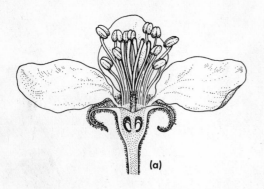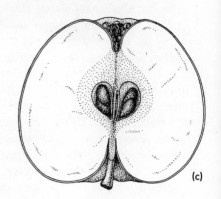

The apple blossom produces the apple. Note how some of the floral parts become less conspicuous or drop off as the ovary ripens to become the core of the seed-carrying fruit. (A) Flower of apple. (B) Older flower, after petals have fallen off. (C) Section of the mature fruit.

There are many different kinds of fruits. They include edible varieties such as apples, string beans, green peppers, and cucumbers, as well as inedible varieties such as milkweed pods, rose "apples," winged maple fruit, and sycamore "buttonballs."

A seed is made up of the young plant, a food supply, and a protective coat. The embryo has two parts, one of which becomes the roots and the other the stem and leaves. As the seed dries, its food supply is concentrated or "dehydrated." This makes seeds a prime food for human beings. The most important plant foods are seeds, such as corn, wheat, rice, barley, oats, and beans. In addition to their food value, plant seeds furnish such valuable substances as oil, for example, linseed oil, and drugs, such as opium from the poppy seed.

LIFE CYCLE OF SOME ANIMALS

Someone once defined a chicken as a machine that an egg uses to make more eggs. We may not accept this definition, but we do see in it the emphasis on the continuity of life: egg to adult to egg and so on.

The life of most animals begins when an egg and sperm join. The fertilized egg resulting from the union of these two sex cells begins to divide into many cells and to form an embryo. The embryo continues to develop, ultimately becoming an adult, either male or female. Sperm produced by the male and eggs by the female unite, and the cycle is repeated. Let us examine the life history of some typical vertebrate animals.

FISH.   The spawning season for fish in temperate zones is in the spring. The return of the salmon to the Columbia River for spawning is well known. Salmon live in the ocean but travel far up rivers to breed. The 10,000 or more eggs produced in the ovaries of each female fish are released into the waters of some quiet pool. Millions of sperm, made in the testes of the male, are deposited on the eggs, fertilizing them. After spawning, the exhausted adults usually die. The fertilized eggs develop into young salmon, which eventually swim to the ocean. When mature, these salmon will find their way back to the same

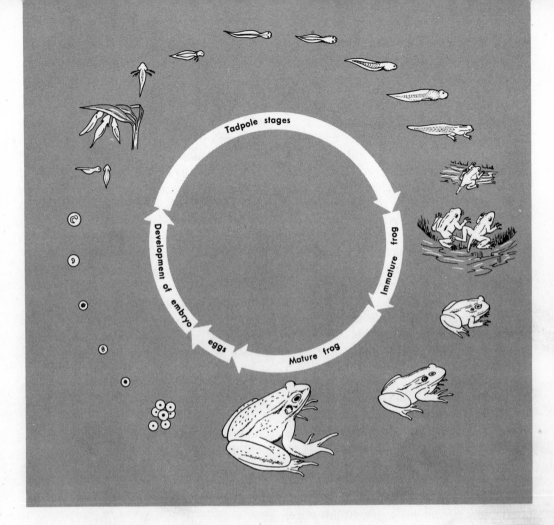

The gradual metamorphosis of the frog illustrates how completely some animals change as they develop. The frog's fishlike ancestry is revealed in its early stages of development.

stream where they were spawned and continue the cycle of reproduction.

Some fish, such as many of the tropical fish with which people stock their home aquaria, seem to bear their young alive. This is only apparent since the fish actually lay eggs, but these eggs after fertilization are retained within the body of the female to complete their early growth. These "live bearers" are not live bearers in the sense that mammals are, since there is no direct connection of the tissues of the growing embryo with those of the female. Hence neither food nor oxygen can be supplied from the blood stream of the mother, as is the case in mammals.

FROGS. Frogs mate in the spring, the male typically clasping the female until the eggs are expelled. The male then fertilizes the eggs in the water by discharging sperm over them. Mating thus increases the chances of sperm meeting eggs. After mating, the pair separate, having no interest in their offspring. What the eggs lack in safety, they make up in number, anywhere from several hundred to several thousand eggs being laid by one female, the number depending on the species of the frog. Moreover, each egg is amply stocked with yolk, which supplies the developing embryo with food until well after hatching has occurred.

SEE PAGES 249 TO 250

Each egg is embedded in a clear jelly-like sphere. All the eggs laid by the frog stick together in a mass; this provides some degree of protection against fish and other pond enemies. The development of the egg from its very first stages to adult frog is interesting and may be watched easily if some of the eggs are placed in a jar or aquarium with some pond water. While still inside the jelly, the egg changes into a tiny embryo that wriggles occasionally. After about ten days to two weeks the tadpole wriggles out of the jelly, which by now has started to disintegrate.

The tadpole breathes through gills, which are flaps of tissue with thin outer membranes and a rich supply of blood. As the pond water streams over the gills, oxygen dissolved in the water passes through the thin membrane into the blood stream. At the same time, the excess carbon dioxide waste in the blood is discharged through the gills into the water.

The tadpole grows, eating bits of plant material that are in the pond. Its tail grows into a fin capable of moving the tadpole rapidly through the water. At this stage, the developing frog is indeed very much like a fish. This is no accident, for the frog, like all higher vertebrates, reveals in its early development traces of its fish-like ancestry. After some time, hind legs and then front legs develop; the material of the tail is broken down and absorbed by the frog to build other parts of its body. The gills are replaced by lungs; other internal changes occur. The frog changes its diet, eating only living worms and insects.

The common leopard frog completes this change or *metamorphosis,* as it is called, in a few months. The bullfrog, on the other hand, remains a tadpole for two years, only then changing into an adult frog.

The frog is a cold-blooded animal. In the colder parts of the country, at the approach of cold weather, its activity slows down, and the animal hibernates in the mud at the bottom of the pond where it lives. In this torpid state, all body functions are reduced to a minimum. Living on food stored during the lush days, it is able to survive until the warm days arrive again. The moist skin of the frog is thin enough to permit the passage of oxygen from the pond water into its blood and the release of carbon dioxide.

REPTILES. In land animals, fertilization is internal, that is, the sperm reaches

This snapping turtle is taking its first look at the outside world.

the egg while it is inside the body of the female. This is essential, since the sperm and eggs require a moist environment to survive. Consequently reptiles, birds, and mammals must have internal fertilization. Reptiles lay eggs covered with a soft, leathery shell. Some, like the turtle, deposit the eggs in sand and then depart, providing no further care for the young. The sun warms the sand and incubates the eggs. The newborn turtle is ready to fend for itself and soon starts off in search of food. In some snakes, like the common garter snake, the eggs after fertilization are retained in the body of the female. The young snakes hatch from the eggs inside the mother and then leave the body of the female.

BIRDS. Birds reproduce in essentially the same way as reptiles. Fertilization is internal; development, however, is always external. The shell is porous, permitting oxygen to pass through it from the air to the developing embryo. The bulk of the bird's egg furnishes a complete "diet" for the embryo. Man appreciates this and consumes millions of such eggs, mainly from the domestic chicken. The bird warms the egg by the heat of its own body. After twenty-one days (in the case of the ordinary chicken) the young chick is hatched. It breaks through the shell and makes its way out. It is quickly able to maneuver under its own power and begin the unending search for food. Many birds hatch out in a helpless state and depend on their parents for food for some time.

MAMMALS. In mammals, the minute egg is fertilized within the body of the female; it then attaches itself to the mother. Here it remains for the period of development. The mother and the embryo develop a special membrane, the *placenta,* through which food and oxygen are supplied to the developing embryo. The wastes of the embryo also pass through this membrane into the blood stream of the mother. There are, however, two mammals that lay external

eggs: the remarkable duck-billed platypus and the spiny anteater. Most mammals take care of the young after they are born. They supply food for the young and protect them. In man, this period of care for the young is longer than in any other animal. Out of this instinct arise some of the noblest sentiments of man.

SEE PAGE 250

Some of the important generalizations of this chapter are:

Life exists almost everywhere on earth.

Living things use food for energy and for growth, dispose of their wastes, are sensitive to their environment, and can make others like themselves.

Living things are built of basic units called cells.

Within the cell there is an architecture of many special structures that carry on the activities of life.

There is a huge number of different kinds of plants and animals on the earth.

The modern system of classifying living things is based on their structure.

There is great variation in the structures and in the ways of living of plants and animals.

Living things need food, water, and oxygen in order to stay alive and to grow.

Plants with chlorophyll manufacture the food essential to the existence of living things on the earth.

Living things reproduce their kind in a variety of ways.

Some living things, such as protozoa and bacteria, reproduce simply by splitting in two.

Most plants and animals reproduce by producing sperm and egg cells that unite to form a new organism.

Living things go through a series of stages in their development from fertilized egg to adult.

DISCOVERING FOR YOURSELF

1. Incubate some chickens' eggs; examine them as they develop.
2. Visit a greenhouse to find out how plants are supplied with what they need for growth, and investigate any experiments with plant growth that are taking place.
3. Visit a garden-supply shop to find out the new types of fertilizer and new methods and types of pest control.
4. Collect and examine current seed and nursery catalogues to discover new varieties of fruits, vegetables, and flowers. Learn as much as you can about the processes by which these were produced.
5. Find out about hydroponics (raising plants without soil).
6. Make a collection of plants to show protective adaptations, and explain how the adaptations help the plant in its environment.
7. Make a collection of flowers to show adaptations for cross-pollination. Explain how the structures of the flowers function with reference to insects and wind and any other agents of cross-pollination.
8. Visit an orchard or a nursery to find out how plants are cared for (pruned, protected against weather changes, kept free from damaging insects, etc.).
9. Sprout five different kinds of seeds. Plan an exhibit to show likenesses and differences in the ways in which these seeds change as they germinate and begin to grow.
10. Dig up five different common weeds or other plants. Wash the root systems and examine them. Explain what you have discovered about adaptation to environment and the functions of the various plants' roots.
11. Collect six different kinds of insects to discover how they are alike, how they are adapted to different environments, how they get food, how they protect themselves, and how they reproduce.
12. Observe a mammal, a reptile, a bird, a fish, or an amphibian to see how it gets food, is adapted to a specific environment, protects itself, and changes as it grows.
13. Collect frogs' and toads' eggs and watch the young develop.
14. Investigate at first hand the plant and animal life associated with any of the following: pond, vacant lot, swamp, lawn, woodland, stream, beach, field. Start a card file, listing on each card the name of the organism, date observed, and any outstanding characteristics that interest you. Sort the cards into the groups suggested in this chapter.
15. Study one square foot of lawn, swamp, or forest floor. List all the plants and animals you can discover there. Observe it over a period of time for changes.
16. Make a collection of any group of plants and animals that interests you. First determine availability of material, method of preserving and storing, what plants and animals should not be collected. Arrange your collection in any way that makes it useful. This may be on the basis of scientific classification or illustrating adaptations of the organism.

CHAPTER 10B

Teaching "The Nature and Variety of Life"

No picture, or model, or pickled or otherwise preserved specimens can really substitute for living material when children are studying plants and animals. The responsiveness, the ability to grow, the capacity to reproduce and the other characteristics of living things make them interesting and exciting to children.

This chapter and the three that follow all treat the important ideas about living things. The subject matter of animal and plant life may be organized around such unit problems as:

What do plants and animals need in order to grow?
How do plants and animals depend on each other?
How do living things change as they grow?
How do plants and animals reproduce?
How do plants and animals get food?
What plants and animals live in our neighborhood?

Children should observe living plants and animals and make many observations that will help them understand the underlying science principles. There are many opportunities for field trips, for observations by individuals and small groups, and for group activities that involve planning and working together. The information gained through these activities should be related and organized into important generalizations. We are interested not so much in teaching isolated facts about birds, trees, and butterflies as in developing important understandings useful in interpreting living things in relation to the environment. We are interested in teaching how the insect-eating habits of certain birds affect plant life, how the trees in a particular area play a vital role in providing a home for animals, how they are essential in protecting the soil from erosion, how they reproduce. We are very much interested in helping pupils learn to enjoy the out-of-doors and develop a desire to explore it. The conservation phase of this study is of utmost importance.

Although a few of the activities listed below are described in greater detail later in the chapter, they are included here because experience indicates that they are especially appropriate for younger children.

1. Explore the gardens of the neighborhood to see growing plants and to make other observations.
2. Grow plants in the schoolroom and observe changes: how buds open, leaves get larger, flowers appear, and new plants are made.
3. Let large seeds sprout to see how a seed develops into a plant. Keep a record of the observations in the order in which they happen. (Use large reading glass to help pupils make observations.)
4. Plant seeds to see what they need in order to sprout. (See discussion of experimenting in part one.)
5. Find out how fast corn seedlings grow by keeping daily records. Measure growth with a ruler or by cutting out strips of paper each day to represent height—paste the strips of paper next to each other to make a kind of graph.[1]
6. Take a walk to see different plants: look for different kinds of trees, shrubs, vegetables, weeds, and flowers. Compare them to see how they are alike and how they are different.
7. Plant a small garden to discover the different sizes and shapes of seeds, how seeds are planted, how long it takes them to come up, how they change as they grow, and how they need to be cared for. (See page 244 for further discussion.)
8. Keep a pet to observe how it gets food, how it grows, and how it protects itself. (See pages 238–239 for further details.)
9. Observe animals in the neighborhood to see: what they eat, where they find their food, how they eat, where they live, how they take care of their young, how they protect themselves.
10. Look for ways in which we use animal and plant materials in our daily living— for food, clothing, shelter.
11. Make a collection of different plants that are used for food and for clothing.
12. Grow plants from bulbs to see how they change as they grow.
13. Look carefully at different flowers to see how they are alike and how they are different from each other. (Use large reading glass and large flowers.)
14. Visit a greenhouse to see different kinds of plants, to see how plants are cared for and how new plants are started.
15. Bring in a pail of soil from the floor of a woods in spring. Put it in a wooden box (like a greenhouse flat) or an empty aquarium, water it and watch for the appearance of plants and animals.

---

[1] For further details see: *Growing Seeds,* Elementary Science Study, 108 Water Street, Watertown, Mass.

16. Observe a setting hen to see how the eggs are cared for, observe the eggs as they hatch, and watch the young chicks change as they grow.
17. Dig up dandelions, clover, and other plants to see what the roots look like and how they differ from each other.
18. Raise caterpillars in jars to see how they grow and change in appearance.
19. Take a walk to listen for the sounds of birds, insects, and other animals.

EXPERIMENTING TO SEE WHAT PLANTS NEED

When pupils are considering the problem of what plants need in order to grow, they may list things they think are needed and then consider the question, "How can we set up experiments to show that plants need water, sunlight, good soil, and a proper temperature?" Pupils can plan the experiments themselves, make a summary of the plan on the chalkboard, and then carefully follow the plan and note the results. They should decide first of all exactly what question they are trying to answer by means of the experiment. Here is an example of such a procedure as a fifth-grade class mapped it out:

PURPOSE OF THE EXPERIMENT

To find out whether plants need sunlight.

OUR PLAN

Bring four small geranium plants that are alike. (George will bring them.)
Be sure that all plants are healthy and that they are all growing in the same kind of soil.

This simple experiment or variations of it may be used to show that plants grow toward light. Pupils may use different kinds of seeds or plants and place them in varying conditions. Similar plants should be grown uncovered to indicate the difference in growth.

Set two on the window ledge where they will be in sunlight part of the day and set the others in the dark clothes closet.

Water all plants every other day with the same amount of water. (Perry and Albert will do this.)

Put labels on the plants so that no one else will move them and spoil our experiment. (Alice will make the label to say, "Please do not touch.")

Every three days bring the plants together and compare them for growth, for color, and for anything else that we can see.

This plan evolved only after lengthy discussion and with some caution from the teacher about making sure that the experiment would produce reliable results. The pupils understood the reasons for including plants that were not subject to the experimental conditions (darkness). They saw that these plants (the control) served as a basis of comparison. As they put it later, "If we didn't have the plants in the *light*, we wouldn't know whether darkness or something else made the closet plants wilt." In drawing conclusions pupils were urged not to decide from this one experiment that *all* plants need sunlight. Several pupils volunteered to perform a similar experiment at home.

After the experiment was finished and pupils had reported on their home experiments, the class took a trip around the schoolyard to see places where plants did not grow well—*perhaps* because of the lack of light. They found a board on the grass, turned it over, and discovered that the grass was dead under it. They observed places where plants were growing toward the light. In a shaded place, they found plants that had grown much taller and more spindly than the same kinds of plants growing in direct sunlight. It is important for children to understand that some plants, by nature, require less direct sunlight than others.

When the pupils returned from this trip, one of them found in a book an experiment that was designed to show how plants grow toward the light. They planted radish seeds in soil in two 4-inch flower pots. After the seeds sprouted, the pupils cut a round cereal box in half to make a cardboard cylinder that fitted over the growing seeds in one of the flower pots and excluded all light. Then they cut a round hole in one side of the box near the top. This was the only source of light. The young plants covered with the box grew toward the hole where the light came in. The other pot was left uncovered. The pupils frequently compared the two. They observed that the plants in the uncovered pot grew toward the window and that the other plants growing in their schoolroom also turned toward the light.

Pupils can themselves think of other experiments to show that plants need light. The experiments with the geranium and with the radish seeds show two ways of approaching the experimental idea with pupils: in one, the pupils themselves devised an experiment; in the other, they found an experiment in a book that served their purpose. In both cases, it is important to remember that the method used in performing the experiment is just as valuable as the knowledge gained from it. In both cases the setting up of the "controls" as a basis for comparison was a critical and essential part of the experiment.

Too often we go on to some other topic after the experiment has been performed. Important learning comes about, however, when we begin to *apply* the results of the experiment to everyday observations in the real world of living things.

We have illustrated a method used in experimenting to see that plants need light. Their need for the other essentials (water, good soil, air, and proper temperature) may be demonstrated in similar ways. (See bibliography for specific books that give more details about plant experiments.)

Plants and their need for and use of water may be studied in the following ways:

Sprout some radish seeds on moist blotting paper and look at the rootlets through a magnifying glass. The "fuzz" on the rootlets is made up of the root hairs through which water enters the plant. Discuss the advantage of a plant's having thousands of root hairs instead of a single root. Ask children to guess what the length of all the hairs would be if they were attached end to end.

Plant about a dozen lima bean seeds. After the shoots have come above ground and the first leaves have appeared, try this experiment to see what happens when the root hairs are broken. Pull two or three of the plants out of the soil. Replant them in other soil. Lift two or three of the other plants out of the soil with a trowel, being careful not to disturb the roots at all. Replant them also. Leave the remaining plants. Observe all three groups of plants. The plants pulled up by the roots will probably wilt, because when they were pulled up many of their root hairs were torn off. New ones had to be formed before the plant could get water. The plants that were lifted gently, with the soil disturbed only a little or not at all, will not wilt. The remaining plants are left so that the pupils can see what happens if these plants are not disturbed at all.

When water once gets inside the plant, it must be carried to the leaves, for it is there that the manufacturing of food takes place. By the use of stalks of celery and some red ink, pupils may observe how water goes up the plant. Try to have children *propose* the use of ink by first showing just the celery stalks and a glass of water and then asking them how they might detect the rise of water in the stalk. Use celery stalks with yellow leaves, if possible. With a sharp knife, cut the bottom from the stalks of celery. Put just enough red ink into a glass of water to color the water a bright red. Place the celery stems in the water and set them in the light. Observe the leaves from time to time. After two or three hours, break one of the stalks and look for the tubes that are carrying the colored water to the leaves. Look closely at the leaves and you will see the red liquid in the veins. The red color makes it easy to see the parts in which the water is moving. It is useful to introduce the word "tracer" here: the colored ink makes it possible to trace the course of the water. (This is

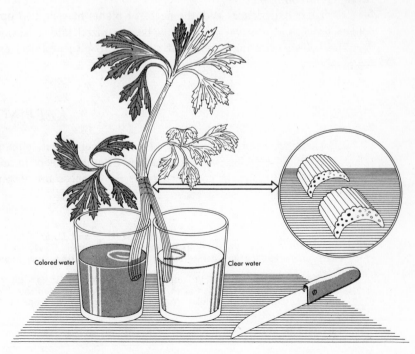

The nature of the transportation system of the plant is more easily understood by observation of this experiment. Pupils may try other plant stems as well as flowers in order to trace the path of liquids as they are carried within the stem.

Colored water

Clear water

similar in principle to the use of radioactive atoms to trace the flow and use of materials in living things.) An interesting variation of this experiment is shown in the drawing here. The celery stalk has been split part way so that the difference can be noted.

OBSERVING PLANTS IN DIFFERENT PLACES

Not all plants require the same amounts of the essentials. Pupils can see this by observing different kinds of plants—growing in the schoolyard, in the schoolroom, in gardens, along fences, and in the woods. Some of the plants that illustrate variation in these needs are mosses, ferns, lichens, cacti, water plants, ivy, geraniums, and other house plants. A trip to a greenhouse for the purpose of learning how the gardener takes care of various plants is a good learning experience. Pupils will see that some plants are given more water than others, some kept shaded and some placed in direct sunlight, some planted in one kind of soil and some in another. Mosses and ferns will be found growing under the benches in the greenhouse, whereas cactus plants grow in bright sunlight in a warm place. Such conditions as these must be seen to be fully comprehended. It is one thing to read about them, quite another to see them. This is an example of a trip that is made for one specific purpose —to solve specific problems. If it is not possible for the whole group to make the trip, a committee armed with the questions to be answered may go on Saturday or after school and report the results. Pupils may go by themselves or with their parents to make the observations. It is important for them to make appointments if they wish to have help from personnel at the place visited.

Outdoor observations will be a great help also in seeing how different kinds of plants react to different growing conditions. Certain plants are able to grow even on a barren playground, some in shaded places, some in a swamp. A woods is a good growing place for certain plants; others grow better in an open meadow. Observing the conditions in these various places helps pupils to understand how plants vary in their needs and how they adapt to different conditions.

These experiences with the needs of plants may be tied up with the problem of how plants grow, and the two topics may be organized into a learning unit. The experiments may be tied up with the planting of a garden to give practical experience with the growth of plants.

KEEPING A PET ANIMAL[2]

There are many reasons for keeping a pet rabbit, guinea pig, or hamster[3] in the classroom. Pupils can observe what one kind of animal needs in order to live and grow. Here are some things to keep in mind, whatever the purpose for keeping the pet animal: (1) It

---

[2] G. O. Blough and M. H. Campbell, *Making and Using Classroom Science Materials in the Elementary School* (New York: Holt, Rinehart and Winston, 1954), pp. 62–67. Gives details, including food chart, about feeding and caring for animals, and describes how to make cages for different kinds of animals.

[3] These animals are rodents and are popular for use in laboratory experiments and as pets in school. Hamsters may be purchased at local pet shops. See also *Hamster Raising*, Catalogue No. A. 1.35: 250, and *Raising Guinea Pigs*, Leaflet No. 466, Superintendent of Documents, U. S. Government Printing Office, Washington 25, D. C. (5¢).

The cage should suit the animal. The insect cage (right) is made from an ice cream carton and wire cloth. Staples are used to fasten the wire screen to the cardboard (see center cage). The cage for snakes (left) contains an ash tray for water and a branch for the snake.

should never be kept in a schoolroom unless it can be made comfortable. (2) Unless an animal is accustomed to captive life, it should never be kept for a long time. (3) Children should plan in advance for the needs of the animal and share responsibility for its care. (4) Children should exercise care in handling the animal, and animals should not be handled too much.

Each animal should have:

1. Enough space to move around and be comfortable in.
2. An environment as nearly like his natural habitat as possible.
3. A place to hide from sight.
4. Proper food, clean water, and good ventilation.
5. A cage that can be kept clean and free from odor.
6. Adequate food, heat, etc., over weekends.

Taking care of animal pets should not become a chore and responsibility of the teacher. If several animals are kept, each member of the class should assume some responsibility for their care during the course of the year. These responsibilities are real, and it makes a difference if they are not carried out correctly—one of the important prerequisites for helping pupils learn to assume responsibility.

As pupils observe the animal, they may make a list of the things the animal needs in order to grow.

As children keep a pet animal, there may be an opportunity for purposeful use of mathematics. The children might weigh the pet periodically and, if feasible, measure its dimensions. The making of tables and graphs clarifies and defines more exactly the growth of the animal. The children can express their observations mathematically with such statements as: "Our pet gained 4 ounces last week," or "Our pet gained 2 pounds during its first month in the classroom, but only 1 pound during the second month," or "The graph shows that our pet gained slowly when it was first brought to school but then its weight shot up rapidly. Now it is slowing down again."

FEEDING ANIMALS

The feeding of animals in the classroom sometimes presents problems. Here are specific suggestions of kinds of foods for animals as well as some advice based on classroom experience in coaxing animals to eat various things.

ANTS
Dead spiders or insects, bread crumbs, small food scraps, cracked rice, sugar and water, crumbled nut meats, honey or molasses, and water. Place on top of soil where ants live, either on the soil or in a small dish.

BIRDS, TAME
Prepared bird foods, cuttlefish bone, lettuce, water cress of chickweed, carrot, apple, pieces of bread, hard-boiled egg, grit of some sort. Special food is needed during moulting season (consult pet store). Fresh water every day.

BIRDS, WILD
Wild-bird seed, small flower seeds, peanut butter, grains, bread broken into small pieces, suet, apple, bread, unsalted nuts, raisins, grit, cranberries, sunflower seeds, and fresh water.

A very satisfactory food for out-of-doors birds in winter is known as bird pudding. It is made of suet, wild bird seeds, and other kinds of seeds, raisins, unsalted nuts. Heat the suet until it liquefies. Let it cool and then stir into it the ingredients listed above. As it begins to thicken, pour the pudding mixture into paper cups, pine cones, or other bird-feeding devices. Be sure that the mixture is packed under the scales of the cones. The cones may be tied to branches of trees where birds will find them. The cups may be put into feeding trays and fastened so that the wind will not blow them away.

BUTTERFLIES
Fresh, thick sugar-and-water solution. Will sometimes take nectar from flowers.

CATERPILLARS
The leaves upon which the animals were found feeding. Give fresh leaves daily. Experiment with various kinds of leaves. (See also moth larvae.)

CHAMELEONS
Any small moving insect. When hungry, they will eat bits of hamburger on a string moved before their eyes. Chameleons cannot drink as many animals do. Dewdrops are their source of water. Green branches with their stems in water should be kept in the case and frequently sprinkled with water.

CHICKENS	Commercial chicken feed, vegetables, meat scraps, grit, water.
CRAYFISH	Chopped meat, water plants.
CRICKETS	Pulpy fruits, lettuce, bread, peanut butter, crushed seeds.
DUCKS	Commercially prepared feed, chicken feed, vegetables, grit, plenty of water next to food.
EARTHWORMS	Obtain their food from the soil.
FROGS	Earthworms, meal worms, caterpillars, nearly any living insects, soft grubs. Small bits of ground meat if it is moved in front of the animal on a toothpick or thread. (See also tadpoles.)
GOLDFISH	Commercially prepared fish food, ant eggs, ground-up dog biscuit, a small pinch of oatmeal or cornmeal. Do not overfeed. Do not give more food than they will eat immediately.
GRASSHOPPERS	The leaves they were eating when found. Celery, ripe bananas. Experiment with different kinds of foliage.
GUINEA PIGS OR CAVIES	About the same foods as rabbits eat. Do not feed potato parings. Clean drinking water.
GUPPIES	Food commercially prepared, especially for guppies and other tropical fish.
HAMSTERS	Dog biscuit plus a small supply of fresh vegetables, such as carrots, cabbage, and lettuce, and bits of fresh fruit, sometimes a little meat. Nuts, corn, oats, wheat, and other grains. Peas can be used to vary the diet. Water is necessary but, if enough green food is given, use less water. The animals must have dog biscuits, pellets, or grain every day to keep their teeth sharp.
HORNED TOADS	Ants, meal worms.
LIZARDS	Flies, crickets, meal worms.
MOTH LARVAE	*Cecropia:* leaves of willow, maple, apple, and many other trees. *Polyphemus:* leaves of willow, oak, apple, plum, birch, basswood, and other trees. *Promethia:* leaves of wild cherry, ash, lilac, tulip, and sassafras trees. *Luna:* leaves of hickory, walnut, sweet gum, and several other trees. *Cynthia:* lilac, sycamore, cherry, and others.
MOTHS	Sugar-and-water solution.
NEWTS	Parts of dead insects, ant eggs, finely ground beef.
PRAYING MANTIS	Living insects.
RABBITS	Rabbit pellets contain the foods rabbits need. If the pellets cannot be obtained from a pet or feed store, feed wheat or buckwheat mixed with soybeans or peanuts. Rabbits eat various kinds of green vegetables— not wet—a little chopped clover, some greens, a little dry bread now and then. Wild rabbits get water from dew-covered grass; tame rabbits must be given water. Feed twice a day. Do not overfeed.
RATS (WHITE) AND MICE	Small grain, bread crusts, vegetables, egg yolks, meat scraps, breakfast foods, water.
SALAMANDERS	Insects, small bits of ground meat moved before their eyes on a toothpick or thread, earthworms, meal worms.

SNAILS, LAND	Lettuce, celery tops, spinach, or any soft vegetables, grapes, apple.
SNAILS, WATER	Fish food, lettuce, aquarium plants, spinach, shredded shrimp.
SNAKES	Earthworms, many kinds of insects, small pieces of meat wriggled in front of their noses, eggs. They need not eat every day. Some will not eat in captivity; some do not eat for weeks at a time. Do not keep if they will not eat. Let them escape into suitable environment.
TADPOLES	Water plants or green scum. Much food is obtained from the water. Cooked oatmeal, cooked spinach, cornmeal, lettuce or spinach leaves, and bits of hamburger put into water in small quantities.
TOADS	Insects, tiny bits of meat moved before their eyes, earthworms, meal worms.
TURTLES	Commercially prepared foods, nearly all kinds of insects, bits of hard-boiled eggs, lettuce, berries, meal worms, earthworms. Place the food for turtles on the water. Many of them eat only under the surface of the water. Do not overfeed.

RECOGNIZING POISONOUS PLANTS

Pupils should learn to recognize plants that are dangerous to touch or eat. The most that can be hoped for at the elementary level is that pupils learn to recognize and avoid such plants. For example, it is hardly to be expected that pupils learn how to distinguish poisonous mushrooms from edible ones, for most teachers are not qualified to teach the distinction. Poison ivy and poison sumac should be recognized by everyone and at all times of the year. There are many pictures of these plants available (see page 243) for observation and display, and if there are any such plants near the school grounds they should be plainly marked with their names, and all pupils should learn to identify them.[4] If samples of the plant can be sealed in glass jars for observation, pupils can learn to identify them more readily.

OBSERVING SPROUTING SEEDS

Sprouting seeds can teach many things about how plants grow. Large seeds are best, because their germination and growth may be observed easily. In many communities, beans, corn, and other seeds may be brought from home by the children. Some of the experiments with growing seeds may be done as class projects, but it is desirable for each child to have seeds of his own to watch each day and to compare with those of other pupils. Often pupils enjoy doing some of the experiments at home and bringing the results to school. In one class, each pupil brought a different kind of seed, watched it sprout, and compared results: "How are the seeds alike?" "How are they different from each other?"

Seeds may be sprouted in a number of different ways: on moist blotting paper or cotton in a covered flat plate or dish; next to the glass in soil in a glass tumbler so that pupils

---

[4] *Poison Ivy and Other Poisonous Plants*, Audubon Nature Bulletin. National Audubon Society, 1130 Fifth Ave., New York 28, N. Y. (15¢). *Poison Ivy, Poison Oak and Poison Sumac,* Farmers Bulletin No. 1922 (5¢). *Poison Ivy*, Health Information Series, No. 65, 1960 (10¢). Superintendent of Documents, U. S. Government Printing Office, Washington 25, D. C.

Although there is considerable variation in the appearance of poison ivy leaves, shiny leaves arranged in groups of three is characteristic. The most common type has leaves with smooth edges (left), but plants with lobed edges (right) are also widely distributed. There are several kinds of poisonous plants in various parts of the United States. It is important to be able to recognize such plants.

can watch the roots grow down and the stem grow up; or directly in soil.[5] It is quite easy to make a diary record that tells exactly what happens as the seeds sprout. The record may be illustrated by simple drawings to show how growth takes place, or pupils may find drawings in books and other sources to compare their sprouting seeds with the drawings.

Urge pupils to examine seeds to see their structure. Beans are good to examine, because the parts are large and can be easily seen. Each child in the group should have one or more seeds to examine. Soak the seeds in water overnight (to hasten germination). Leave them on moist blotting paper for one or two days or until the germinating parts can easily be distinguished. The children can use toothpicks to take the seeds apart. They may look for the three parts of the seed (coat, tiny plant, stored food). After they have identified the parts, they may discuss the function of each part. As they observe seeds sprouting, they can verify their conclusions. They may examine other seeds also to find the three parts.

Pupils may devise experiments to find out whether a bean seed could grow into a plant if the stored food were taken away from it. (Lift the tiny plant out from between the halves of a soaked bean, plant it, and see what happens.) It will die, of course, because the first food for the plant is that stored in the seed. They may try to determine what happens if one half of the food material is removed, leaving the tiny plant attached to the other half. They may also set up an experiment to discover which part (the stem or the root) comes out of the seed first as it germinates.

If pupils want to test seeds to see whether they will germinate if planted in their school garden, they may set up an experiment, try to sprout the seeds on moist blotting paper, and even calculate what percentage or fraction of the seeds sprouted—an excellent occasion to make use of mathematics.

---

[5] For further information, see Blough and Campbell, *Making and Using* (*op. cit.*), pp. 74–80.

We must find out —
1. Is our soil still too heavy (too much clay)?
2. Is the soil acid (sour) or alkaline (sweet)?
3. Will the seeds we collected from the garden last fall germinate (sprout)?
4. Are the garden tools in good condition? Is the tool room in order?
5. Which classes want garden plots?
6. What are we going to plant?
   Vegetables must mature by June 1. (Be ready to harvest)
   Flowers must be fall bloomers.
      (Our pansies, bulbs, iris, roses, poppies, lilacs and shrubs
      will give us flowers until school closes in June.)
7. What must be our first work when we can go out to the garden?

Which question will you help to answer?

Do you want a garden?
Please sign

Problems to be solved must be identified long before planting time. Here soil samples are being examined. The success of the gardening venture depends on how well the learning situation has been set up and how much opportunity has been provided for pupils to learn scientific principles.

PLANTING A GARDEN

Through the experience of planting and caring for a school garden, pupils can learn much about how plants grow, but in order to produce a truly valuable science experience much planning must be done. Weeks before the time for planting, discussion should begin in order to settle such questions as "Why shall we have a garden?" (For pleasure, to give flowers and vegetables to other people, to learn about growing plants, to grow vegetables to eat, to make our schoolyard more attractive, etc.) If this problem is discussed at the beginning, pupils may use these aims to evaluate their progress and results. They may also discuss the questions "What shall we plant in the garden?" "What must we do to the soil in the garden before it is ready for the seeds?" "What kinds of tools do we need and where shall we get them?" "Where and how can we get the seeds for planting?" In their planning sessions, pupils will raise and answer such questions as these and others. The school garden should provide real opportunity for problem-solving—children decide on the problems, make and carry out their plans, and then evaluate their work.

The following sources are helpful in planning and planting a successful school garden: (1) The county agricultural agent, a high school agriculture or biology teacher, or a greenhouse owner can help to test the soil so that pupils can decide whether it needs fertilizer and whether the drainage is proper. (2) Seed catalogues can help children decide what to plant, by the illustrations and by the descriptions, which tell how long the plants take to mature, what kinds of soil they need, etc. (3) Seed packages contain directions for depth and time of seed planting. (4) Interested parents who are experienced gardeners may be willing to give assistance and advice. (5) Inexpensive government publications and other

In carrying out the gardening plans that they made, these pupils are using their knowledge of soils and plant growth. Each pupil is responsible for a specific phase of the gardening. The care and patience exercised here will show up as these seeds sprout and grow.

published materials about gardening and insect-pest control might be helpful.[6] (6) Many people save flower and vegetable seeds from the previous year's harvest; parents may supply such seeds for planting in the school garden.

In school gardening, it is important to remember that (1) there is considerable mathematics involved in gardening—number of rows, distances apart, number of plants that will fit into a given space, amount of space for each pupil, etc; (2) there is ample opportunity to help children learn cooperation and thoughtfulness in sharing tools, seeds, and plants; (3) a garden is an ideal place to evaluate a plan. If the rows are straight and even, if the plants are not crowded, and so forth, the plan has been successful. Evaluation should be made on the basis of all of the reasons for making the garden—not merely in terms of its yield.

The gardening experience provides a practical application of what has been learned through observing, reading, and experimenting.[7] Specifically, it shows what plants need in order to grow, how they change as they grow, how long it takes various plants to mature, how plants grow under different conditions, what happens when plants are too crowded, how plants of different kinds reproduce, and how plants change as the seasons change.

---

[6] Write to Superintendent of Documents, U. S. Government Printing Office, Washington 25, D. C., for Price Lists No. 41 (*Insects*) and 44 (*plants*). Also see bibliography for some good books on gardening for use by children.

[7] See Blough and Campbell, *Making and Using* (*op. cit.*), pp. 80–87, for details about gardening.

Sprouting seeds indoors for future outdoor planting provides an opportunity for observing plant growth firsthand, for following directions carefully, for transplanting, and for observing a plant through its entire life cycle.

RAISING PLANTS INDOORS

If the schoolroom is sunny or if there is some other suitable room, growing plants indoors for later outdoor planting is a good learning activity. Cabbages, tomatoes, peppers, zinnias, and marigolds are best planted in flats (shallow boxes) filled with good soil. The flats may be purchased or built by pupils from wooden boxes. The soil should be fine and the seeds planted and cared for according to the directions on the packages. Some schools have good growing facilities and even supply pupils' home gardens with seedlings raised in school.

Sow seeds thinly and cover them lightly with fine soil. Water them frequently enough to keep the soil damp but not wet. A piece of glass placed over the seed container will retain the moisture and aid in the growing. Seedlings raised indoors do better if they are fed once a week or so with a solution of plant food in water. Garden supply stores, florists, hardware stores, and many other sources sell different kinds of plant food. Follow the directions on the container.

As soon as seeds germinate and are growing well, water them only in the mornings and only if the soil is dry. When the plants are about two inches high, if they are growing too thickly, they should be thinned by transplanting every other one into another flat. Before the plants are set outside, they need to be prepared for this change. Give less water and set the flats outside for a few hours each day. Keep them out for a longer time each day for a week or two.

The plants that are commonly grown in schoolrooms furnish good material for plant study. Their possibilities are often overlooked. Geraniums, coleus, ferns, ivy, begonias, bulbs of different kinds, cacti, and other plants may be observed to discover the answers to such questions as "Where do the new leaves grow?" "Which plants grow fastest?" "How are they all alike in their growth?" "Are seeds formed on any of them?" "Are there spores on the ferns?" "Do they all need the same amount of light and water?" Particularly helpful references on indoor plants are listed in the bibliography.

Since most schoolrooms contain plants, the following specific suggestions may be helpful to teachers and pupils:[8]

---

[8] Quoted by permission from *Living Things*, Board of Education of the City of New York, Publication Sales Office, 110 Livingston St., Brooklyn 1, N. Y. (50¢).

Sufficient water. Plants should be watered only when the soil feels dry. However, when adding water give the soil a thorough soaking, not just a sprinkling.

Good drainage. The pot or box should have holes in the bottom to allow excess water to escape. (The roots of a plant require air. Water which remains may prevent air from entering the soil.) Saucers or aluminum pie plates under flower pots will protect the woodwork and catch drained water. Plants may be watered by adding water to the saucer until the top of the soil is moist. (Empty the saucer of any water which remains after the soil is moist.)

Suitable temperature. Plants should not be placed on hot radiators or in hot or cold drafts. Protect plants over cold weekends.

Proper light conditions. Experience is the best teacher here. A geranium, for example, needs a good deal of sunlight. Cactus also thrives in sunlight. Begonias and some ferns, on the other hand, should not be kept in direct sunlight for many hours at a time. Most plants will grow well with only a few hours of sunlight. No green plant will do well in a dark area.

Good soil. While each plant has its own soil requirements, any good garden or potting soil will usually be satisfactory. The addition of sand will make the soil more porous. If the soil dries too quickly, peat moss or humus can be added. Commercial fertilizer may be used, but only according to the directions on the package.

Note: When transplanting, take care to avoid injuring the roots.

Other care. Leaves should be showered or washed with a sponge from time to time. Insect pests can be removed by washing or by using specific insecticides.

FINDING OUT HOW SOME PLANTS REPRODUCE WITHOUT SEEDS

Seeds are but one of the several ways by which plants reproduce. In some plants, a part such as a root, stem or leaf may be separated from the plant to start a new one. Pupils can plan experiences to discover some of the other ways. Some plants reproduce by bulbs. If a bulb is cut open, a series of fleshy layers may be seen as well as the bud of a stem. Narcissus and other plant bulbs may be grown in the schoolroom if the simple directions that accompany them are followed.

New geranium plants may be started from cuttings (slips) from the older plants. Take off most of the large leaves and put the cutting in moist sand until roots develop. New ivy plants may be started in this way or by putting the cuttings in water until roots appear. Pussy willows brought to school and placed in water often start roots and may be planted to grow into willow trees if there is a suitably damp place.[9]

Children can watch underground stems of the potato grow into a plant by putting a potato in some good soil. If several are planted, pupils may dig them up now and then to see where the roots develop and where the stems come from and to note that the potato itself is shriveling up, partly because it is supplying food to the growing shoots. If the potatoes

---

[9] *Plant Propagation in the Classroom; Outdoor-Indoor Adventures with Wild Plants; How To Select and Care For Indoor Plants,* Audubon Nature Bulletins, National Audubon Society, 1130 Fifth Ave., New York 28, N. Y. Practical help in growing plants (15¢ each).

are left growing, pupils can watch the shoots come above the ground and see the leaves develop. If a potato is left in a closed container on the table without being planted, pupils can see the sprouts begin to grow and note how differently the potato develops if it has no soil.

A strawberry plant, either wild or cultivated, growing in rich soil in a large flowerpot will send out runners. New plants grow out from these runners.

These activities with bulbs, cuttings, and potato and strawberry plants are further examples of simple experiences often overlooked but nonetheless important if we want to make science a living thing for children.

FINDING OUT HOW FLOWERS MAKE SEEDS

Perhaps the best way for children to discover the seed-making role of flowers is to watch one kind, *alive*, day after day on a small plant, bush, or tree. If they can begin with a flower bud, they will see it swell and open up. They will observe the anthers grow, split open, and expose their load of dusty pollen. A magnifying glass is most useful in revealing the minute structures and the beauty within a flower. Children will observe the sticky tip of the pistil ready to receive the pollen. As the flower matures, they observe the base of the pistil (the ovary) swell with its developing seeds. As other parts of the flower shrivel and drop off, the ovary grows larger into a full-sized fruit, laden with seeds.

Even a cut flower, standing in water, will reveal some stages in its development toward seed production. *The advantage of beginning with living plants is that it permits the children to make their own discoveries, to record changes as they observe them. This is in marked contrast to the method of presenting children with a flower and having them identify its parts, and then trying to have them understand the complexities of its structure and its functions.*

The process of discovery comes as children are permitted to observe living things engaged in the processes of living. Later they may consult books, charts, and other references to deepen and extend their understanding. They will then have both an experiential and scientific basis for finding answers to such questions as: What does the pollen do? How do bees help some flowers in seed-making? Where is the part that becomes the seed? How does the pollen get to the seed-forming part?

Flowers from a garden and from house plants may be examined as soon as they begin to fade. Pupils should be urged to bring from home flower specimens that show seeds forming. After the seeds have been formed, the seed container may be opened to show the seeds inside. Pumpkins, squash, melons, peas, beans, morning glories, and marigolds are interesting to examine because they grow seeds. On some of these, dead parts of the blossom may still be seen hanging from the seed-bearing part.

RAISING SILKWORMS

When children are learning how animals change as they grow, silkworm-raising is an interesting experience. They can watch the eggs hatch, see the young larvae eat, watch the larvae grow and change their skin, see them make cocoons, watch the moths emerge and mate, and see the eggs being laid to start the cycle over again. All of this can happen in a schoolroom in about two months. Leaves of mulberry trees are essential foods for silkworms.

Silkworm eggs are not expensive and may be purchased from biological supply houses.[10] They are accompanied by directions for raising them. If the eggs arrive before mulberry leaves have developed, they may be kept in a cool place until the food is ready. Eggs hatch in 7 to 10 days after they are taken from the cool place. The silkworm larvae eat for about a month and then form cocoons. In about 2 weeks the moths emerge. They mate almost immediately, and the females lay eggs; then the adults die. A few moths will lay enough eggs to supply the whole neighborhood, and pupils often like to take them home and raise silkworms during the summer. Eggs may be kept cool for extended periods.

The following general plan for raising silkworms, used in a fifth-grade class, suggests one way to proceed:

1. Box of eggs was opened and children looked at them with magnifying glasses. Several questions were asked about them. These were recorded on the chalkboard for future answering.
2. Teacher asked, "What things do we have to plan for if we are to raise silkworms?" (Food, place to keep them, schedule of feeding and so forth.)
3. Good reader from the class read the leaflet that came with the eggs, while pupils listened to hear suggestions useful in meeting the needs they had pointed out.
4. Class discussed leaflet material and made plans by volunteering for various jobs —bringing food, preparing food, and so on.
5. Class listed sources of information they planned to get that would help them answer such questions as "How do they change as they grow?" "How is the silkworm like other animals in the way it grows and how is it different?"

Many of these same procedures may be used in studying any caterpillars pupils bring in. Pupils should be encouraged to bring some of the leaves they find the caterpillars on and to try out different kinds of leaves if they are not sure of the food of the caterpillar. The caterpillars may grow, shed their skins, and spin cocoons, or in the case of butterfly larvae produce chrysalids. These may be kept until, with good luck, the adult insects emerge.

RAISING TADPOLES

Wherever frogs and toads croak in the spring, there are eggs for the taking. Hatching them in the schoolroom is not difficult and is very helpful in showing children how some animals go through their development from egg to adult.[11]

Frogs' eggs are laid in clumps, toads' eggs in long strings. Both may be scooped up from ponds or quiet waters in spring and brought to school for observation. Bring only a few eggs. Toads and frogs are useful animals if left in their environment, and here is a specific occasion to teach conservation. If they are kept in glass jars (gallon pickle or jelly jars are good), they can be observed easily, or if there are no fish or turtles in your aquarium,

---

[10] *Rearing the Silkworm Moth,* Turtox Service Leaflet No. 18; *Insect Metamorphosis,* No. 34; *Moth Cocoons,* No. 38. General Biological Supply House, 8200 South Hoyne Ave., Chicago 20, Ill. (4¢ per copy).

[11] *Frogs and Toads,* Audubon Nature Bulletin, National Audubon Society, 1130 Fifth Ave., New York 28, N. Y. Information about frogs and toads and how to raise them (15¢).

the eggs and tadpoles may be kept there. Bring some water plants with the water from the pond. The young tadpoles will eat algae or decaying bits of plant and animal material that will be in the water plants. As they grow, they will also eat tiny bits of hard-boiled egg, but if the water is taken from the pond it will probably contain the necessary plant food for them.

The length of time for hatching and the rate at which the tadpoles develop depend in part on the kind of eggs. Some kinds of frogs mature faster than others. The rate of hatching and development also depends on the temperature. This provides an excellent opportunity for setting up a carefully controlled experiment. Divide a batch of eggs into three equal parts. Place one batch in a jar of water in a cool place. Place another batch in a similar jar in a warm place. A third may be kept at room temperature. Except for temperature, all conditions are kept the same. Thus if it is necessary to place the cool batch in a dark cellar, the other two batches should also be in darkness. Day-by-day records of changes in size and appearance should be kept.

Here is a general plan used by pupils as they observed the eggs and tadpoles.

1. A library committee assembled and made available reading material from books and encyclopedias about frogs and toads and their development.
2. Pupils observed the eggs to see how they changed as they hatched. They made large drawings on the blackboard to show these changes.
3. They observed the tadpoles to see how they moved, how the legs formed, what happened to the gills, and what happened to the tails (see page 249). They kept a record of the dates of these changes.
4. They compared their observations with the information they had read and made an outline of the most obvious and important changes that the animals underwent.
5. They compared the development of toads and frogs, silkworms or other caterpillars, and other animals.

WATCHING ANIMALS CARE
FOR THEIR YOUNG

It is surprising how many kinds of animals with young are available for pupils to observe. Pupils can make a list of animals that are known to live in the community and then make arrangements to do as much firsthand observing as possible, later reporting their findings to the class. Some places that pupils may visit, as a class, in small groups, or individually, are: the zoo, a pet shop, a kennel where dogs are bred, a place where canaries are raised, a fur farm, a dairy farm, and the schoolyard or park to see birds, squirrels, and other animals. Pupils may be encouraged to find out how fish, reptiles, insects, and amphibians, as well as the mammals we have suggested, care for their young.

In order to guide the observations, the class may prepare a series of questions such as "How are the young fed?" "How are they protected?" "How long will they stay with their parents?" "Do both parents help to take care of the young?"

A good beginning in sex education has been made when children observe the birth of puppies and kittens, watch the mother care for them, and frankly discuss with their parents and teachers what they have seen. Intelligently answering the questions children ask, helps to satisfy their curiosity in a normal fashion and provides opportunity for parents and teachers to enter naturally into discussion of sex matters.

WATCHING ANIMALS EAT

Feeding time at the zoo is always a popular hour for observers as well as for the animals. At the zoo, pupils can observe how different kinds of animals eat, and they can see how animals are adapted for food getting. Observing zoo animals also provides examples of various ways in which animals protect themselves from their enemies, unusual adaptations for food-getting, and living in various environments.[12]

There are also many opportunities in and around the school and the home for pupils to observe how animals get their food. Pupils may list all the animals that they might possibly watch, make a plan for observing them, and then report their findings. Here is a list of animals studied by a third grade: snails, earthworms, fish, silkworms, carnaries, chickens, dogs, cats, frogs, horses, cows, sheep, and squirrels. Each animal was observed to find out "what kind of food it eats, what parts of its body helps it to eat, and any other interesting things about the way the animal eats."

SETTING UP AN AQUARIUM

An aquarium in the schoolroom is very helpful in the study of animal life. Fish, snails, tadpoles, and small turtles may be kept very easily. Different kinds of water plants also are interesting to observe.

An aquarium set up by the teacher before school begins in the autumn is never as much fun for the children or as useful to them as one they plan and make themselves. Children often volunteer to bring fish to school from an outdoor pool, and this motivates the making of the aquarium. If this happens, the planning may begin by letting the pupils discuss such questions as "What kind of place shall we make for the fish?" "What materials shall we need?" "Where can we get them?" "How shall we use them?" There will be opportunity to share, to contribute to the group, to work together, and to assume responsibility. What is more, the tangible result of this cooperation will be in evidence for a long time if the aquarium is a good one.

Here are the things you will need: a container, some sand, some small stones, a few water plants, a few snails, and the fish. The container may be of almost any size or shape, but one that is rectangular and holds three gallons or so is preferable. It can be purchased locally or ordered from a supply house.[13] Many supply houses furnish detailed directions for stocking and caring for an aquarium. Begin by scrubbing the aquarium thoroughly. The sand may come from a variety of sources: the beach, a sand bar of a river, a builders' supply yard, or a pet shop. Wash it by running water through it until the water is clear. Water plants are usually most satisfactory when purchased from local ten-cent stores, pet shops, or biological supply houses, although it is possible to get them from ponds or from lakes or from an outdoor garden pool. Buying water plants at a pet shop may be an interesting experience for a young child or for a committee. While they are there, they may also buy some snails. You will need only a few. You'll soon have more.

---

[12] G. O. Blough and M. H. Campbell, *When You Go to the Zoo* (New York: Whittlesey House, 1955). Details of animal adaptation for food-getting.

[13] *Starting and Maintaining a Balanced Fresh-Water Aquarium,* Turtox Service Leaflet No. 5; *Plants for the Balanced Aquarium,* No. 11; *Feeding Aquarium and Terrarium Animals,* No. 23; *Aquarium Troubles: Their Prevention and Remedies,* No. 48. General Biological Supply House, 8200 South Hoyne Ave., Chicago 22, Ill. (4¢ per copy).

Having assembled the materials, plan with the children how the materials are to be put together.[14] Be sure that the water is free of chlorine or other chemicals that may be harmful to water life. If you are using city water, pour it back and forth from one container to another to let chlorine from the water escape into the air or let it stand for a day in a container before placing plants and animals in it. After putting the sand in the bottom of the aquarium, set a saucer or plate on it so that when you pour the water in, it will not disturb the sand. Half fill the aquarium with water, put stones around the base of the water plants to help hold them down, and finish filling the aquarium. Put in the fish and snails. Later you may wish to add tadpoles or other suitable water animals. After the aquarium is finished, it may be covered with a piece of glass to prevent the water from evaporating.

Although goldfish are commonly used in aquariums, other kinds of fish may also be used. Tropical fish, however, need considerable attention; the water temperature must be kept nearly constant, and, for other reasons, they do not lend themselves to the usual schoolroom aquarium unless the teacher or some pupil has made a hobby of raising such fish.

After the aquarium is set up, if the proportion of water plants and fish is correct, the aquarium needs little attention, because the plants and the animals are mutually dependent on one another. The plants in their food manufacturing process give off oxygen to the water and use carbon dioxide. The animals use this oxygen in their breathing and give off carbon dioxide. When such a balance exists, it is not necessary to change the water unless something contaminates it. It is often necessary to experiment to discover the proper proportions of plant and animal life. Overfeeding is one of the chief causes of death of fish. Further information about aquariums is contained in *The Fresh Water Aquarium*.[15]

An aquarium is useful in helping to solve many of the problems that arise in the study of plants and animals. Children may observe animal life to see how the animals are fitted for life in the water, and they may watch both plants and animals to see how they grow and how they change as they grow.[16] An aquarium is also useful in stimulating children to ask questions such as: What are the bubbles coming out of the plant? Where did all of the new snails come from? Why does the fish open and close its mouth? Why do the fish sometimes come to the top of the water?

MAKING A TERRARIUM

A terrarium is a land habitat made of small plants, moss, stones, and rich soil for such animals as small toads, frogs, small snakes, turtles, or salamanders. The general procedure suggested for use with children in initiating an aquarium project is also appropriate in making a terrarium.

The container may be of almost any general shape or size, from a gallon glass jar to a large aquarium tank. An aquarium tank that leaks may be adequate for use as a terrarium.

A trip to a wood lot to gather material is good experience for careful observing and for learning conservation. Take only a little moss of different kinds, a few varieties of wood plants, some rich soil, and anything else that you think will give the terrarium a "woodsy"

---

[14] G. O. Blough, *An Aquarium* (New York: Harper & Row, 1959), 36 pp. A book to consult in making and using an aquarium in the elementary school. Easy reading.

[15] *The Fresh Water Aquarium*, Audubon Nature Bulletin, National Audubon Society, 1130 Fifth Ave., New York 28, N. Y. Clearly written, illustrated material about making and maintaining an aquarium (15¢).

[16] Blough and Campbell, *Making and Using* (*op. cit.*). Further details about aquarium-making.

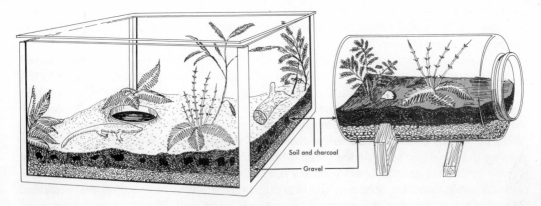

A terrarium may be planted in almost any shape or size container. The gallon jar at the right is set in a round groove in a wooden block. The original can cover may be used to cover the opening, or some transparent paper may be placed over the opening and held on by a rubber band.

A sixth grade pupil helps a kindergartener build a terrarium with soil, mosses, other plants, gravel, and charcoal. The older pupils have learned how to build indoor gardens and have volunteered to assist the kindergarten teacher and her pupils in this project.

touch. Do not collect rare plants but use this situation to help pupils learn good conservation practices. Placed in the bottom of the terrarium, some pieces of charcoal from a campfire will absorb gases and help to keep the soil from becoming sour.

Cover the bottom of the terrarium container with coarse gravel or sand, bury several pieces of charcoal in it, and then add rich soil from the woods. Plant the small plants in this and cover the remaining soil with the moss. Brightly colored stones placed here and there where the different pieces of moss meet in the terrarium add interest. Sink into the soil and moss a small dish to hold water, and cover the terrarium container with a piece of glass, which the school custodian can cut to the size of the container. When you have finished planting the materials, sprinkle the plants with water, put water in the dish, and the habitat is ready for a small animal. It will probably not be necessary to add water. Water will evaporate and condense as the temperature changes, so that it seems to "rain" in the terrarium. Observing this is very useful in studying air and weather as well. There are, of course, many variations of this procedure in making terraria which may be used to reproduce in miniature different kinds of habitats and to meet the requirements of different kinds of animals.[17]

USING THE MICROSCOPE

Many elementary schools are now in possession of one or more shining new microscopes, and many teachers and supervisors are wondering what to do with them. Although it is not good policy to permit apparatus to determine the curriculum, it is worth considering the potential of the microscope in the study of living things. First, one or two general rules:

1. In general, the younger the child, the lower the power that should be used.
2. Move step by step from the visible world to the microscopic world (naked eye—5 power magnifying glass—10 power magnifying glass—25–50–100 power microscope.)
3. The microscope should serve as a tool in the understanding of some large problems—and not be used as an end in itself.

Now a few suggestions for things to see:

1. A drop of water from a stagnant pond to see tiny plants and animals there.
2. A thin strip of tissue from an onion to see cells.
3. Pollen from flower, to see the thousands of grains in a small bit of pollen.
4. A bit of yeast in water to see thousands of living yeast plants. (high power)
5. A thin strip of material from the outside of a leaf to see the many openings (stoma) in it.
6. A bird's feather to see the way in which it is "hooked" together.
7. Some snail eggs to see evidences of their development.

---

[17] *The School Terrarium*, Turtox Service Leaflet No. 10. General Biological Supply House, 8200 South Hoyne Ave., Chicago 20, Ill. (4¢ each).

B. M. Parker, *Garden Indoors* (New York: Harper & Row, 1959), 36 pp.

The Terrarium, Audubon Nature Bulletin, National Audubon Society, 1130 Fifth Ave., New York 28, N. Y. Very helpful bulletin on building and maintaining a terrarium (15¢).

8. Water fleas (Daphnia) obtained from pet shops to see their heart beat, their digestive tract, their reproduction.

9. Parts of insects, to see the compound eyes, pads at ends of legs (flies), etc.

RESOURCES TO INVESTIGATE

1. Garden clubs for information and for a possible resource person to assist with school gardening.

2. Seed catalogues for pictures and for information about seeds, soil preparation, and the care of growing plants.

3. County agriculture agent and high school agriculture or biology teacher for help in doing plant experiments and answering questions, and as general resource persons.

4. Florists, nurserymen, and gardeners for soil and other supplies and for information about growing things in the classroom and in outdoor gardens.

5. Hardware dealers for supplies, seeds and seed catalogues, information about fertilizer.

6. Pet shops and dealers for information about care of animals and for supplies.

7. Animal hospitals for information about care of animals and for other assistance.

8. Successful farmers for information about local crops and how they are planted and cared for.

9. Forester to learn about how tree seeds are gathered and planted and how the young trees are cared for.

10. State Agricultural College and experiment stations for information about plant-growing experiments and similar information.

11. Zoos for information about housing and feeding of animals.

12. Museums and botanic gardens for a better understanding of the orderly classification of plants and animals.

13. Local resources for the study of living plants and animals in their environment: parks, ponds, lakes, streams, swamps, fields, woodland, vacant lots, lawns, home gardens, trees on streets, seashore, rivers, etc.

CHAPTER 11A

Living Things and the Seasons

SEE PAGES 268 TO 269

The tides of life ebb and flow with the seasons. Changes in life parallel the changes in the sun's position. In the spring, the sun warms up the earth. Moisture is released from the bondage of frost and is absorbed by the roots of plants. The energy of the sun's rays is trapped by green leaves to help in the manufacture of food. The animal world begins to stir out of its winter sleep as the earth warms up.

In the temperate zone, the most marked seasonal changes come in the spring and in the fall. During the winter cold, life seems to be at a standstill. In reality it is not. There are slow changes in both plant and animal life, but these are hidden from the casual view. As the sun moves higher in the sky with the advance of spring, these processes accelerate and one day make their presence known. The first spring flowers seem to appear overnight. The first robin is welcomed by winter-weary human beings. While the snow is still on the ground, the sap begins to run in the maples.

Summer is the season of full growth. The trees and herbs are in lush foliage. The rearing of young is the main concern of many animals. Food is stored by both plants and animals against the coming cold season.

Fall finds the migrating birds on their way back to warmer climes. The broad-leaved trees shed their vernal dress after one brave splurge of color. The hibernators find the dens they will use for their long winter snooze. Those animals that remain active may change their fur to fit the temperature and sometimes the color of their surroundings. With winter, activity slows to its lowest

256

ebb. Only a few hardy animals are seen about, and the plant world is dormant in the frozen soil.

Most insects, in fact, spend the winter as eggs. With the warming of the air, the eggs hatch out and the larvae start foraging for food.

ANIMALS IN SPRING

Spring is the time of renewal. The animal world comes out of its winter lethargy. Among the first of the new animals to be seen in our northern spring are the migrating birds. Weeks before, they begin their northward flight, and, by the first days of March, the earliest arrivals are with us. The proverbial robin, and, soon after, the song sparrow, purple grackle, and red-winged blackbird lead the van. By May, the migration is at its peak. The numerous species of warblers, the thrushes, and the various sparrows are in full force, heading for their nesting grounds. At this time, one is amply rewarded by getting up before the sun and out to the countryside or city park to hear the early morning symphony of the birds. Male birds parade their fine feathers and engage in the acrobatics of courtship. Then starts the earnest business of building the nest, laying the eggs, and caring for the young. This will occupy many birds until well into the summer.

The primal urge to reproduce their kind is strong in most animals at this season. Fish and frogs spawn, and soon the waters teem with the new generation. Our spring peeper is one of the first of the frogs to lay its eggs. It heralds its mating time by its clear sweet piping in March.

Insects emerge from their overwintering states and begin anew the cycle of life. Some insects have survived the winter in adult form. Among the butterflies, a mourning cloak may be seen sailing over snow banks in the earliest spring days. This is an adult of last fall that has hibernated, something very unusual among butterflies. Ordinarily, the adults die in the fall, leaving behind only the eggs that they laid or immature forms which developed from the eggs.

SEE PAGE 72

PLANTS IN SPRING

The tulips, lilies, crocuses, and other flowers of Easter are to city dwellers the welcome affirmation that spring has come. Country people, or even city folk who have a park close by, see floral heralds of spring much earlier. Among the very first to flower is the plant that has taken its name from the skunk, the skunk cabbage. While the snow is still on the ground, this hardy green flower pushes its spike up through the mud where it thrives, the hooded flowers appearing before the cabbage-like leaves uncurl. The odor, from which it derives its name, may not attract human beings, but it does attract flies and other insects, which are necessary for its pollination. The spring beauty rises from the leaf litter on the forest floor, and later Solomon's seal, yellow bellwort, and the wild geranium make their appearance.

The buds on the trees become visibly swollen at this time. Shortly after, the leaves will seem to burst forth overnight. However, this is not merely an overnight growth. The leaves within the bud were made by the tree the summer before. If you open a leaf bud in the winter, you will find there tiny but complete leaflets. What happens in the spring that makes their emergence so rapid is the rush of newly obtained water. The water fills the cells of the tiny leaves, swelling them so that they force the bud scales apart and emerge. In many trees, as in the red maple, the flower buds open before the leaf buds, bedecking the bare branches with colorful flowers before the green and yellow leaves appear.

SEE PAGE 272

As water is made available in the soil, sap begins to run in the sugar maples. Spring is the time of maple-sugaring in our northeastern states, particularly New York, Ver-

This fierce-looking caterpillar is making a meal of oak leaves.

mont, and New Hampshire. A hole is bored through the bark of the sugar maple tree. The sap oozes out through a hollow tube inserted in the hole into buckets attached to the tree. It is collected and then boiled down in huge evaporators to make maple syrup. Some of the syrup is boiled again until most of the water is gone, and solid maple sugar results. The richly sweet taste of the first chunk of maple sugar is a memorable childhood delight for those fortunate enough to have lived in sugar maple country.

ANIMALS IN SUMMER

Summer is the lush time. Food is plentiful, the earth is warm, and the days, are long. But, even in the midst of plenty, preparations are made for the lean days to come. It is not altogether accurate to say that living things "prepare" for the coming of winter. To "prepare" generally means a conscious action that anticipates a future condition. The "preparations" referred to in this chapter are built-in, automatic behavior patterns, with no conscious planning implied. In the animal kingdom, this means storing away food to be used during the cold winter days when food is scarce. Some animals, such as the squirrels and chipmunks, store

up nuts and other food in caches where they may find them in midwinter. Other mammals who spend the winter in a long sleep must store food, too, but they store it within their own bodies. The black bear gorges himself during the summer and early fall and stores up fat to be used during hibernation. The woodchuck grows so fat and becomes so slow that by autumn he falls easy prey to the farmer's rifle.

The birds that will migrate south in the fall, also busy themselves storing within their bodies some extra nourishment, although many of them will feed on the way as they migrate. However, some birds cross large bodies of water, such as the Gulf of Mexico, and they need the added food to sustain them during this flight.

The cares of raising a family occupy many of the higher animals, notably the birds and mammals, during the summer. Among the birds, the young must be fed and they must learn to fly. There are some birds that are able to take care of themselves as soon as they hatch out of the eggs. The common chicken is a good example of this. So is the killdeer. Most of our song birds, however, are born helpless. The parents spend the daylight hours endlessly hunting out food, much of which is given to the young. In some species, the food is predigested by the parent birds and then regurgitated into the open mouths of the fledglings. Some birds shirk the duties of parenthood. The cowbird deposits its eggs in the nests of other birds, frequently of small birds such as warblers. When the eggs hatch out, the much larger cowbird crowds out the rightful family and pirates the food that should go to the offspring of its foster parents.

The cold-blooded vertebrates show little care for their young. Most lay their eggs and then depart. The young must face the hazards of the world alone as soon as they hatch from the egg. Young tadpoles emerging from their jelly capsules feed on plant fragments in ponds and grow fat, later developing hind and then front legs and becoming tiny frogs. As frogs, they change to an animal diet, eating insects and worms.

The mammals devote considerable care to their offspring. The most primitive mammal, the opossum, gives birth to young that are only partially developed, each being smaller than a honeybee at first. They must then be transferred to a pouch on the underside of the mother to finish their development. Long afterwards, they may be seen clinging closely to the mother as she journeys about in search of food. The opossum is the only American pouched mammal, or *marsupial*. Other marsupials are found mainly in Australia, examples being the kangaroo and the wallaby.

The more common mammals, such as deer, foxes, rabbits, and, of course, our domestic animals, such as sheep, cows, and horses, keep their young close to them during infancy. The young are fed and protected until such time as they are independent. Summer is the family time.

PLANTS IN SUMMER

With the coming of summer, the sounds of spring are hushed in the forest. The fullness of foliage casts dark green shadows over the forest floor. The burst of blossoms is over, except for a late show put on by a few plants such as the touch-me-not and the pokeweed.

Inside the cells of green leaves, atoms are juggled to form molecules of sugar, starches, proteins, and other products essential for plant life. Roots are pushing deeper into the soil and stems are extending their growing ends. Under the bark of trees, new layers of cells are being added to the growth initiated in the spring which will result in the formation of a new annual ring.

As the summer wears on, the foods manufactured by leaves are stored in twigs, trunks, and roots. This stored food will provide the energy required for the plant's growth in the spring to come. At the same time, food is also being sent through the ducts of the plant into the fruit and seeds, thus providing the material needed to start new generations of plants.

Deep in the soil, microscopic agents of decay—molds and bacteria—are busy in the never-ending process of decomposition of dead plant and animal material. These non-green plants complete the mechanism of decay started by termites, ants, snails, and other soil creatures, thereby replenishing the soil with materials essential for the green plant world above.

ANIMALS IN AUTUMN

Fall in the temperate zone is a time of "getting ready" for winter. The change of seasons is gradual, one blending imperceptibly into the next. Similarly, the "preparations" for the next season by living things are gradual.

MIGRATION. Among the birds, the earliest migrants begin to journey south in July. These include some of the shore birds. Generally, the last to arrive in the spring are the first to leave in the fall. The southward movement occurs in waves. If the weather should suddenly turn cold, there will be a

SEE PAGES 294 TO 296

heavy exodus of birds. If the weather remains balmy and summer-like, the migrants leave in small groups. By the turn of October, the warblers and the thrushes are in full flight to their southern winter havens. In mid-October, the geese and ducks and other water fowl stream along the flyways to the warmer climates. In favorable spots, where food is available and there is some protection against the cold, some birds that normally migrate may remain throughout the winter. A good example of this is found in large waterfowl ponds in some city parks. Every year, a number of mallard ducks and Canada geese take advantage of the food that is provided and remain in the park during the winter instead of joining their comrades in moving south. Occasionally they will be joined by one or two stragglers of other species, who find the park pond a welcome refuge in the midst of an extensively built-up urban area.

When November arrives, the migration is about over. Those birds that go south have gone. Those birds that will winter over are here, busily hunting for food. It is not strange that few of the winter residents are insect-eaters since most of the insects have by this time succumbed to the cold, and only next year's eggs remain. The chief exceptions are those birds that feed on insects and insect larvae living in the bark of trees. The woodpeckers remain as cheery representatives of their tribe. They and the nuthatches, chickadees, and occasional brown creepers busy themselves searching out the bark for insects hidden there. Since these insects are harmful to our trees, these birds do a large service to us in protecting against this damage. The sparrows and other seed-eaters comprise much of the rest of the bird population at this time. Sometimes a robin who can change its diet of insects to one of seeds, which are more readily found at this season, lingers on. (Bird migration is described more fully in chapter 12A.)

HIBERNATION. The animals that do not migrate either hibernate or are equipped to withstand the cold of the frigid season. SEE PAG. 273 The frogs and other amphibians bury themselves during the late autumn, in the mud at the bottom of their ponds, and go into a state of suspended animation. Tadpoles, much like the fish that they resemble, fre-

In late autumn, the chipmunk begins gathering acorns to store in its den.

quently remain active and swim about during the fall and winter. The reptile world becomes torpid with the cold and goes into hibernation. Some turtles, such as the mud turtle, dig into the mud of ponds and there remain during the winter. Snakes seek out a hole in a tree or a crevice in the rocks and there diminish their rate of living, or *metabolism,* to the point where they can exist without requiring food. At times, if the weather becomes unseasonably warm, snakes may emerge to bask in the sun's warm rays. Fish have remarkable abilities to withstand the cold. It is not unusual to find fish swimming about actively in the water beneath the ice, and one can fish in winter by digging a hole in the ice and dropping a line into the water beneath.

Some of the furry host—the mammals—hibernate even though they have protection against the cold. It is not enough to have a fur coat to keep one warm. It is also necessary to obtain sufficient food. Those mammals that can subsist on the meager plant food available can remain active during the cold months. The deer foraging through the snow for acorns is an example of this. The common black bear, on the other hand, has gorged himself during the summer and early fall and stored up much fat. Late in the fall, the bear holes up in a protected nook and sleeps a good part of the winter away. If the weather becomes warm, the black bear may come out for a short time. Invariably it returns to hibernate until the first warmth of the spring. It is interesting to note that the bear's cubs are born during hibernation. By the time spring arrives, the cubs are quite large and frisky. They will remain with their mother, however, until fall at least.

Some of the fur-bearing animals change their coats with the season. The brown that protected them during the summer, by allowing them to blend with the background, would be an easily seen color when the snow is on the ground. Thus the snowshoe rabbit sheds his brown hairs and by the end of fall has taken on a white fur. The winter coats of fur bearers are generally heavier than their summer coats.

PLANTS IN AUTUMN

With the waning sun of autumn, the plant kingdom begins to fade from the scene. The late-flowering plants have been pollinated and have formed their seeds for the next generation. The annuals, those plants that survive for one year only, turn brown and shrivel. The perennial herbs, which live

Left: *The winged fruit of the tree of heaven (ailanthus) is adapted for wind dispersal.* Right: *The fruit of the beggar-tick is provided with hooks that aid in its dispersal by animals.*

The silken threads of milkweed seeds help in their dispersal by the wind.

from year to year, lose much of their above-ground structure, leaving only roots or under-ground stems..

THE SCATTERING OF SEEDS. Many of the seeds and fruits are a colorful part of the autumn scene. Formation of the fruit with its seeds is only the first step in the propagation of plants. The seed must reach a place suitable for it to grow next year. If the plant is a perennial one, living year after year, it is not enough for the seeds to be dropped to the ground in the selfsame spot. The older plant with its established root system would pre-empt the water in the vicinity, depriving the new plant of the water that it needs. Even if it were able to get the water for germination, the seedling might die for lack of vital sunlight. The older plant with its spreading mantle of leaves would shade the immature plant and prevent it from carrying on the essential process of photosynthesis. This conflict with the older plant is avoided

by the scattering of seeds. Examination of the varied devices and agencies of seed dispersal is an excellent study in adaptation. We shall consider how seeds are adapted for dispersal by wind, by animals, by water, and by mechanical means.

For many seeds, the wind is the distributing agent. Some wind-dispersed seeds and fruits are equipped with fine, feathery plumes or tufts of hair that act much as a parachute does. The seed is sustained in the air long enough for the wind to blow it to some distance. Familiar examples of plants whose seeds are so equipped are the cattail, milkweed, aster, dandelion, goldenrod, and the sycamore tree. Children are familiar with the ethereal, gray sphere of dandelion seeds, each equipped with a delicate parachute. They take delight in seeing how few puffs it takes to dislodge all of the seeds. Other seeds are adapted for wind journeys by having wings. The familiar "polly nose" of the maple tree is an example of this type. Other common winged seeds are those of the ash, elm, tulip, pine, and Ailanthus trees. Wind dispersal is sometimes accomplished by the movement of the entire plant, which, when mature, rolls along the ground and drops its seeds. This happens in the tumbleweeds, which include amaranth pigweeds, Russian thistle, and some grasses.

Seeds that are adapted for dispersal by animals may have an edible fruit with seeds whose coats are indigestible. In this case, as in the apple, the fleshy, edible part of the fruit is eaten by some animal, such as a deer, together with the seeds. The indigestible seed coat prevents destruction of the seed in the juices of the animal's digestive system. Ultimately, the seeds are eliminated with the other food wastes. By this time, the animal will probably be distant from the site where the fruit originally grew, and so the plant is spread. The scattering of edible nuts, such as walnuts, acorns, and hickory nuts, depends on a slight variation of this process. If the animal eats the nut, of course, the seed is destroyed. But many animals, such as squirrels and chipmunks and field mice, bury such nuts in the ground for future feeding. Those nuts that the animals forget may grow the following spring and further colonize their species.

Animals help scatter seeds in another way. Some seeds have hooks that catch on the fur of an animal as it brushes by the plant. Later on, the seed is brushed off, but by this time the animal may have carried the seed a long way from the mother plant. The common cockleburs, burdocks, "sticktights" of the burr marigold, and "beggar's ticks" are examples of seeds that hitchhike on the fur of animals, or the clothes of humans, for that matter.

Water is an agent in the scattering of seeds. Seeds and fruits are often transported over short distances by the washing of rain along the ground or over long distances by streams. The classic example of a water-dispersed seed is the coconut. The coconut as it comes from the tree is a massive fruit whose outer part, or husk, is made of myriads of interwoven fibers in which air is trapped. (This outer part is removed before the coconut reaches the market.) This is buoyant enough to support the heavy inner nut that contains the embryo. The covering of the coconut is waterproof, another necessity of a water-borne seed. How effective this device is may be seen from the fact that the coconut palm is one of the first plants to appear on newly created coral islands or atolls in the south Pacific. There is no doubt that some of these coconuts float for thousands of miles on the ocean surface.

Some seeds are scattered by being propelled from the plant. An example of this is found in the witch hazel tree which blooms in the fall, when the nut-like fruits formed from flowers of the previous fall are also evident. These have an interesting seed-scattering device. As the fruit dries, the cover suddenly breaks open, and the small black seeds are shot out to some distance in a way similar to the shooting of an orange seed from between the fingers.

LEAF FALL. The color spectacle of fall is provided by the deciduous trees, the broad-leaved trees that shed all their leaves in the fall. Many of these assume colors that vie with the rainbow. The change in color is accomplished partly by the addition of new pigments and partly by the unmasking of colors that were always there. Some of the colors, such as the reds and scarlets of oaks and maples, illustrate the former and are due to chemical changes in the leaf. Other colors, especially the yellows and browns, displayed by birches, poplars, elms, and most garden plants, illustrate the latter and are the result of loss of chlorophyll, which colors most leaves green during the spring and summer months. With the green gone, the underlying pigments become visible.

Leaf fall is an adaptation for conserving water. The broad leaf gives off large quantities of water to the air when it is active. This water must be replaced from the soil, or the tree suffers severe damage and may die. In the winter, the soil water is unavailable in the frozen ground. The detaching of the leaves prevents a water loss that would be fatal. Toward the end of the summer, a separation layer of special, cork-like cells begins to form across the base of the leaf stem. This layer gradually grows, cutting off circulation of sap to the leaf. Eventually the loosened leaves separate from the twig and flutter to the forest floor. It is said of this happening that trees are remarkable surgeons: they tie off their veins *before* performing an operation.

Some trees, such as certain oaks and beeches, form an incomplete layer of cells between the leaf and the twig. As a consequence, the leaves remain on the branches all winter. It is not until the buds begin to swell in the spring that the old leaves fall off. Such leaves are dead, however, and have ceased to make food.

The evergreen trees, or conifers, such as the pines, hemlocks, firs, and spruces, retain most of their leaves during the winter. Such trees *do* shed their leaves, but not all at one time. Usually, one-third of the leaves are shed each year. Such trees have special adaptations to prevent excessive water loss even though leaves remain on the trees all winter.

BUDS. When the fallen leaves have SEE PAGE 272 left the tree branches bare, it is easy to see the leaf or flower buds that were made during the summer. The leaves, or flowers, as the case may be, are encased within the bud scales. The scales are tough and waterproof and so can protect the delicate structures within during the severe months of winter. Some buds, such as those of the willow tree, also have a cover of fuzzy hairs to avoid excessive loss of water. Buds of some poplars are coated with a sticky wax for the same purpose.

The nuthatch partakes of the free meal left for it on this winter feeding station.

Buds containing flowers are particularly susceptible to cold. They are in no great danger when in the dormant condition. Danger arises when a premature warm spell causes the buds to develop rapidly, so that the flowers are in blossom when a freeze occurs. With the blossoms open, their delicate structures are no longer covered by protective scales. Below freezing temperatures are fatal to the flowers of almost all fruit trees. Cherry, apple, pear, and peach crops have been ruined by low temperatures that kill the flower parts that produce the fruit.

ANIMALS IN WINTER

Winter in the temperate zones is the SEE PAGE 270 TO 271 quiet time. It is the time that tests the vitality of plants and animals. Now survival hangs by a delicate thread. Not only is food scarce, but all living conditions become precarious. The greatest danger of all is cold.

Even those animals that have hibernated and so reduced their requirements to the minimum may freeze to death. The few mammals that are abroad in midwinter must forage unceasingly for food. When the snow covers the ground, the plant-eaters may find it hard to reach the roots on which they customarily feed and may turn to eating the bark of trees. This in turn may kill the trees if the animal succeeds in girdling the trunk, that is, gnawing a circle completely around the tree. Deer are frequently hard hit by cold winters. In many northern states, the game wardens set out special food to keep these animals alive during the winter. When the snow drifts to great heights, it is sometimes necessary to resort to a spectacular airlift to supply such stranded animals. The same must sometimes be done to save herds of range cattle cut off by huge drifts.

Even the predators find lean pickings at this time. Wolves, foxes, coyotes are limited in food resources because many of their usual prey are in hibernation or are sticking closely to their burrows and dens. The extra fat gained during the lush days of summer may help to tide over such animals until food becomes available in the spring. In particularly hard seasons, predators may be emboldened by hunger to invade built-up areas and prey upon man's domestic animals.

Winter birds eat voraciously to keep their bodies warm. A piece of suet nailed to a tree or a tray of bread crumbs placed out-of-doors is appreciated by the hungry birds, particularly when snow covers the ground.

Most of the cold-blooded animals are hibernating, since their rate of living is regulated by the temperature. Snakes, toads, frogs, insects disappear from the scene to hibernate over the winter. Insects winter as eggs, larvae, pupae, or adults in their many habitats—under the bark of trees, in the mud of ponds, in the soil. Moth larvae or pupae are wrapped in their silken cocoons. The thousands of eggs of the praying mantis, packed together in a straw-colored egg case, wait for the warm days in May and June to hatch into tiny mantids.

PLANTS IN WINTER

With their leaves shed and the severed tubes sealed, the broad-leaved trees are able to conserve what water they have through the winter. The evergreens can retain their needle-like leaves because these have a thick waxy coat of *cutin*, which reduces the loss of water. Even though the sun shines weakly during the winter, the evergreens are able to make some food by photosynthesis and thus supplement what was made during the warmer months. One winter condition that puts a severe strain on trees is freezing rain. Under certain conditions, rain that falls may freeze on the branches to such an extent that the sheer weight of the ice breaks the boughs. Snow piled on the branches may do the same thing. Although these two phenomena may produce picturesque scenes for the photographer, they

are a menace to the trees unless their fibers are elastic enough to bend under the weight without breaking.

Everything appears to be in a death-like sleep. As winter wears on, restless human beings venture out-of-doors, to look for signs of life. If they dig up some frozen soil and place it in a jar indoors they will be amazed at the changes that occur as the soil warms up. Seeds begin to sprout and insects emerge. A few twigs cut from forsythia or from some other woody plants and placed in a jar of water indoors will burst their buds weeks before their time, putting on a premature spring show for winter-weary eyes.

Some of the important generalizations from this chapter are:

Living things depend on the sun for warmth.

Green plants require sunlight for food manufacture.

Living things are able to adapt themselves to changes in temperature, light, and availability of food and water.

In the temperate zone, some animals, mainly birds, migrate in spring and fall.

Spring is the reproductive season for most animals.

Many hibernating animals store summer food for winter use.

Seeds are adapted in various ways for dispersal by wind, animals, and water.

Some plants store food in roots, stems, or leaves.

Some animals change their fur color in the fall.

Broad-leaved trees shed their leaves in the fall, thus conserving water.

Animals active in winter are adapted for securing food and protecting themselves against cold.

Cold-blooded animals reduce their rate of living, or metabolism, in their winter hibernation.

DISCOVERING FOR YOURSELF

1. Observe a specific tree branch carefully over as long a period as possible to determine how it changes with the seasons. Do the same with other selected specific plants and note the changes. Keep records that may be used later to draw conclusions.

2. Observe an animal such as a squirrel or a bird at various moments over a period of time and try to decide which actions can be attributed to changes in seasons. List your findings. Spring or fall in temperate climates are the best times for such observations.

3. Observe birds in your vicinity during spring or fall months to determine how the kinds and number seem to vary with the seasons.

4. Construct a winter feeding shelf for birds. Keep a list of the birds that are attracted. Keep a log of the times various birds appear, and try to determine what kinds of foods attract various birds.

5. Provide different kinds of food for a wild animal such as a squirrel. Observe what happens to the food, and try to decide whether or not this action is in any way related to seasonal behavior.

6. Gather twigs (during the dormant period) from various trees or shrubs. Bring them indoors, place the stems in water, and observe the results. Examine the buds with a magnifying glass on successive days, and try to draw some conclusions from the observation.

7. Collect various kinds of caterpillars, feed them, and observe any changes that take place.

8. Collect various kinds of seed cases. Examine them to determine methods of seed dispersal; observe arrangement of contents; examine with a magnifying glass.

9. Visit a pond or any other natural setting at different times to determine changes in plant and animal life associated with changes in the season. Keep a record which includes date, temperature, appearance and disappearance, changes in habits and structure of specific plants and animals.

10. In the winter dig up a square foot of soil, to a depth of 4 or 5 inches. Bring it indoors and place it in a box, aquarium, or any other available container which can be covered. Observe emergence of life—insects, worms, sprouting seeds, etc.

CHAPTER 11B

Teaching "Living Things and the Seasons"

Dramatic seasonal changes heighten children's interests in living things. For this reason, spring and fall are usually the best times, in temperate climates, to concentrate on studying the seasons because of the more obvious and rapid changes.

Very young children find it somewhat difficult to encompass a whole season in their thinking; they are affected more by what happens on a single day, or here and now, than by the complete picture of the seasons. Thus, the effect of a snowfall on trees, of a heavy wind-storm, of rain or earthworms, are the kinds of things they will want to investigate; here, they can see cause and effect relationships. As children mature, they are able to observe events over a longer period of time and to discover significant trends in the series of happenings.

The following activities involve careful observation by primary pupils, and contribute toward the understandings listed at the end of chapter 11A; they are not concerned with the study of one specific animal or plant, and they do not concentrate on identification.

1. Observe a specific tree or other plant at many times of the year and keep a record of the changes. See page 272 for further discussion.
2. Look around the schoolyard to see signs that tell us that colder weather is coming: observe plants and animals and tell what has been observed.
3. Look at pictures that show conditions in spring, summer, winter, and autumn and discuss: "What do you think the animals and plants are doing in each of these pictures?" "Are these same things happening near us?"

4. Bring into the schoolroom in spring some twigs of different trees and bushes and put the stems in water to watch the twigs change Tell what they see happen. Open buds to see how they are made. (Use a magnifying glass.)

5. Keep cocoons to watch the moths emerge.

6. Keep caterpillars, feed them, and watch them change.

7. Watch the birds at a feeding station to see, what they eat and try to tell what kinds of birds they are and how they are able to eat different kinds of foods. (See pages 270–271 for further discussion.)

8. Collect seeds and seed cases to see how seeds spread by wind, animals, water, and other means.[1]

9. Look for animal tracks in the snow. Try to discover what animal made them.

10. Observe a pet animal to see if it undergoes any seasonal changes.

TAKING A FIELD TRIP TO OBSERVE SEASONAL CHANGES

To observe changes in living things and the relationships of these changes to the season, several outdoor trips may be made during the school year. Obviously, children all over the United States will not be able to observe the same things when they go on trips, for in the southern states the changes made by living things as the months go by are somewhat different from those in the central and northern sections of the country. The suggestions given here will therefore have to be modified in accordance with the climate.

On an autumn trip, pupils may keep in mind this broad question: "What changes can you observe in plants and animals? Primary-grade pupils, as indicated earlier, may make one series of trips to observe only plants and another to observe animals. Pupils in the higher grades may observe both plants and animals on the same trip. Pupils will need to call up past experience and observe many times before they can draw any conclusions. Pupils may observe some of these plants: grass, trees, shrubs, flowers, weeds, and vegetables. They may observe animals such as: insects, birds, squirrels, and frogs. Here are some of the kinds of things that pupils may observe about plants on their autumn trips in temperate climates: Many plants are storing food. Some are making seeds. Some plants die. Some lose their leaves. Some make buds. About animals, they may observe: Some animals are getting heavier fur. Some are building homes. Some are migrating. Some are storing food. It will probably take several trips to see all these things.

During the winter, another trip or two should be taken over the same area to see what has happened since the last trip and to note any evidences of plant and animal life that show winter adaptations. In the spring several more trips to the same place may be taken to observe changes. Taking the trip to the same place and observing the same living things each time, if possible, helps pupils to keep track of the happenings more easily than if the trips are made to different places. A rather complete record of observations during each of the visits will help refresh pupils' memories as the successive trips are taken. There is, in this case, a real reason for making a record. The records made over this long period of time will supply data to be used in answering the question: How do animals and plants change as the seasons change? The final record will be made up of sentences such as: Some

---

[1] *Seeds and How They Travel,* Audubon Nature Bulletin, National Audubon Society, 1130 Fifth Ave., New York 28, N. Y. (15¢).

trees lose their leaves in autumn. They grow buds. The buds open in the spring. Some are leaf buds. Some are flower buds.

Taking "science walks" with children is not a new idea to elementary school teachers. These walks will be much more profitable if pupils are urged to observe very carefully, to report their observations accurately, to be thorough in their investigations so that the results can be relied upon, to interpret their observations and put them together to make a generalization, to do additional reading and investigating to substantiate their observations, to bring back specimens to examine more carefully, and to make their observations over a period of time long enough to insure accuracy.

Young children like to express their ideas in pictures. Making drawings of the seasonal changes and telling their schoolmates what the pictures show are instances of using art expression where it counts. Children may collect pictures from magazines and elsewhere that show how living things change with the seasons. The composition of a story based upon such pictures may be a very valuable science-language-arts experience.

Making a picture story is an occasion for pupils to work together in small committees and then pool their findings to make a more detailed presentation. Various groups may choose to draw or find pictures that illustrate some of the following statements: Insects change in autumn. Birds change in autumn. Plants change in autumn. Animals and plants change in our schoolyard. Fur-bearing animals make changes.[2]

Each of these pictures may be shown to the class and accompanied by talks explaining them. Afterward, the children may discuss: "What important things have we found out about living things and the seasons?" This is another occasion for stressing that animals and plants do not actually *prepare* for winter in the same sense that we ourselves get ready for winter by putting up storm windows and getting our warm clothes out of moth balls. We *know* that winter is coming. Our experience tells us that we shall need certain things because of the changes. We can *plan ahead*. Animals and plants do not plan ahead. They behave according to their instincts.[3]

LOOKING FOR ANIMAL TRACKS

If there is a park or woods nearby or if the school grounds are extensive, it is interesting to children to make a trip to observe animal tracks.[4] In many places, tracks of cats, dogs, squirrels, rabbits, and mice may be observed. A study of these tracks may help to tell where the animal was going and whether it was running or walking. There may be someone in the community—a hunter, perhaps—who can help in interpreting some of the observations. Although the pupils may be unable to interpret their observations dependably, they can learn that many animals are abroad even during cold weather—a fact of which many of them are not aware. These observations help also in making the idea of adaptation to seasonal changes more meaningful.

---

[2] *Winter Sleep; How Wildlife Survives the Winter,* Audubon Nature Bulletins, National Audubon Society, 1130 Fifth Ave., New York 28, N. Y. (15¢).

[3] G. O. Blough, *Soon After September* (New York: Whittlesey House, 1959).

[4] *Fields in Winter,* Cornell Science Leaflet Vol. 33, No. 3, January 1940. New York State College of Agriculture, Cornell University, Ithaca, N. Y. An inexpensive publication that is most useful to a teacher.

Track Stories in Mud, Sand and Snow, Audubon Nature Bulletin, National Audubon Society, 1130 Fifth Ave., New York 28, N. Y. (15¢).

INVESTIGATING SUPERSTITIONS

There are countless superstitions about animal life. Some of them, such as the one about ground-hog day, are well known. A newspaper clipping on ground-hog day is bound to provoke discussion that may well become the subject for investigation. This is a good opportunity to help develop a scientific attitude. Alert children raise such questions as: "How could a ground hog know which day is February 2?" "Suppose he saw his shadow in one county and it was cloudy in the next county, what would happen then?" The weather reports for February 2 and for the six weeks following are available for many years past. Investigating these reports and seeing that there is no connection between the action of ground hogs and weather make an interesting activity for children. Pupils should be encouraged to observe the weather and plants and animals during the current year to see what is happening. This may lead to debunking other superstitions, such as the one about planting in the dark of the moon.

FEEDING SQUIRRELS AND
OTHER MAMMALS

One way to learn about the food animals eat and where they store it, is to feed them and find out what they do with the food. If squirrels or chipmunks live near the school, children may bring nuts, corn, and other seeds for them, feed them, and observe the results. A real interest in observing animals may result from such an activity. Young children are amazed to see how many trips to a hollow tree or to a hole in the ground an animal will make. They are also surprised to see how much food animals will take. This may be a time to stress evidence which indicates that animals cannot anticipate weather conditions and that often the amount of food stored by an animal depends on how much is available. Chipmunks, for example, will carry away quarts and quarts of shelled corn whether they need it or not.

MAINTAINING A BIRD-FEEDING STATION

Maintaining a bird-feeding station may prove a very enjoyable experience if it is done carefully and planned well. On the other hand, if the feeding station is not well placed or is not stocked with proper food, the experience may be disappointing. Books that describe bird-feeding stations often mislead children, for they depict cardinals, bluejays, woodpeckers, chickadees, and other winter residents all clamoring for food. Such a rushing business is usually not done by a school bird-feeder—certainly not the day after it is installed.

There are many kinds of bird-feeders that pupils can make.[5] Some are trays fastened to a window; some may be hung from pulleys and pulled away from the window on a line; some can be fastened to trees or posts.

---

[5] *Attracting Birds*, Rev. 1947, Catalogue No. I. 1.72:1 (10¢). *Homes for Birds*, 1942, Catalogue No. I 1.72:14 (10¢). Order from Superintendent of Documents, U. S. Government Printing Office, Washington 25, D. C. Additional information may be obtained from the National Audubon Society, 1130 Fifth Ave., New York 28, N. Y.

See also G. O. Blough, *Bird Watchers and Bird Feeders* (New York: Whittlesey House, 1963).

A bird feeder outside a first-grade classroom in Indianapolis is near trees and shrubs so that birds come near enough to find the feeder. Bird visitors are observed, their visits and habits are recorded, and pupils take turns keeping the feeder stocked with different kinds of food to attract different kinds of birds. Reading and other language arts skills are used in connection with this activity. One winter season, these pupils issued a bulletin each week to inform the school about the bird visitors.

Here are some hints about making and maintaining a feeding station: The school custodian, a boy from an upper grade, or, in many classes, the pupils themselves can make the feeding station. The local biology teacher may make suggestions about placing it. Be sure that the station is out of reach of cats. Water, especially in dry and freezing weather, helps to attract birds. Various grains, bird seeds, sunflower seeds, bread crumbs, apples and other fruit, and suet are satisfactory foods. Be sure that the wind does not blow the food from the station; keep the station well stocked; and remove any uneaten food if it is spoiled. The feeder should be in a sheltered place but in view of the schoolroom window, if possible.

Pupils like to experiment to see what kinds of foods different birds eat. This activity presents opportunity for the use of scientific attitudes. Pupils should not generalize from one instance, should not decide without careful observation, and should withhold conclusions until there is sufficient evidence from observation and reading to justify them. For example, the fact that birds have not eaten sunflower seeds on the feeder for several days is no reason for deciding that birds do not like sunflower seeds.[6]

[6] G. O. Blough and M. H. Campbell, *Making and Using Classroom Science Materials in the Elementary School* (New York: Holt, Rinehart and Winston, 1954), pp. 67–72. Gives many examples of ways to feed birds in winter and illustrates many different kinds of bird-feeding stations.

OBSERVING CHANGES IN INSECTS

If there is a woods or park where there are dead trees and logs, pupils may be able to find hibernating insects under the bark or in the cracks. They may be able to find bunches of insect eggs and cocoons there also. They may see the shiny band of the tent caterpillar eggs on wild cherry and apple trees. If the ground is not frozen, they may dig down into an ant hole to see whether they can discover any ants.

Children often bring cocoons to school and like to keep them and see the moths emerge. This can be a very exciting and instructive experience. If cocoons are scarce in your neighborhood, they may be purchased from a biological supply company quite inexpensively, accompanied by directions for their care.[7] Cocoons are best kept in a wire cage of some kind so that they may be easily observed when the moths emerge from them. A satisfactory cage may be made by using a plant pot and some window screen. Make a wire-screen cylinder about a foot long and a little narrower than the diameter of the plant pot. Fill the plant pot with soil. Stand the wire cylinder up on the soil and push it down into the soil so that it will stand erect. Cover the top of the cylinder with a thin piece of wood. If the cocoons are fastened to twigs, as they often are, you can stand them up; otherwise, you may fasten them to the inside of the screen or lay them on the soil. A terrarium is also a good place to keep cocoons. They should be moistened occasionally, to simulate the conditions of rain or snow they would encounter outdoors.

If male and female moths of the same kind emerge at the same time, they will mate. The female will lay fertile eggs, and the larvae can be raised to spin cocoons if they are fed the right kind of leaves and are properly cared for. (See discussion of silkworm-raising, pages 248–249.)

OBSERVING TREES

The structure of a bud and the changes that take place as it opens are very interesting to observe, but they are often unnoticed by most children and adults. Small twigs of trees and shrubs may be brought to school and examined to answer such questions as "What covers the outside of the bud?" "What is on the inside?" "How are all the buds alike?" "How do they differ from one another?" Some of the buds may be cut open with a sharp knife. In early spring, each child may bring two or three twigs, put them in water in a separate container in a sunny window, and observe them each day to note the changes. Here is another activity for which a magnifying glass comes in handy. Toothpicks may be used in taking buds apart to study their structure. Pupils may be surprised to discover that maples, oaks, and other trees have flowers that are very beautiful. Twigs of apple trees are interesting to keep indoors. The buds are large, and the flower buds open as the leaves develop.[8]

Children will find it interesting to observe periodically a specific tree for the whole school year to see such things as: how the leaves change during the year; what birds, insects, and other living things inhabit it; what seeds and fruits are produced and what happens to them; what characteristics help to identify it; how it changes as the seasons change.

---

[7] *Moth Cocoons*, Turtox Service Leaflet No. 38. *How to Make an Insect Collection*, No. 1. General Biological Supply House, 8200 South Hoyne Ave., Chicago 20, Ill. (4¢ per copy). This company sells cocoons.

[8] *Trees and Their Twigs; Trees and Their Leaves*, Audubon Nature Bulletins, National Audubon Society, 1130 Fifth Ave., New York 28, N. Y. (15¢ each).

STUDYING HIBERNATION IN FROGS

In the winter, frogs bury themselves in the mud in ponds. All of their body activities are slowed down. The heart beats very slowly; breathing takes place only through the moist skin of the animal. The frog draws upon the food stored in its tissues to maintain life.

Children can actually see hibernation by placing some frogs in water that has been chilled to near the freezing point. Stir some ice cubes into a jar of cold water. Place some active frogs in the jar. (As a control put others in water at room temperature.) In a short time the frogs in the cold water will dive down, expelling air from their lungs to reduce their buoyancy. Transparent third eyelids slip over their eyes. They will stay at the bottom as long as the water is icy. Frogs can be induced to hibernate at any time of the year. If the hibernating frogs are now removed from the cold water and placed in warm water, they will become active in a few minutes.

This demonstration is always an exciting one for children but it has a number of other values too:

1. It indicates that hibernation is not a result of planning or preparation; rather it is an automatic response to a particular environmental influence.
2. It reveals how we can understand "nature" better—by controlled experiments in which we test one factor at a time.

RESOURCES TO INVESTIGATE

1. The surrounding environment to note seasonal changes in individual animals and plants.
2. Pets to see how they change with the seasons.
3. Local bird enthusiasts and Audubon Club members for information about bird migration, birdbanding, and other activities.
4. Individual trees on the schoolground or nearby to be observed for seasonal changes.
5. Ponds and streams to observe water animals during the seasons.
6. State Conservation Department for information about birdbanding, bird refuges, wildlife preservation, game laws and how they vary with the seasons, and other similar information.
7. Florists, nurserymen, and gardeners for information about seasonal changes in plants and about pruning, root and bulb storage, and so forth.
8. National Audubon Society, 1130 Fifth Ave., New York 28, N. Y., for pictures, bulletins, and other helpful material.
9. Vegetable market to observe examples of food storage in plants used by man.
10. A farm to observe and learn about care and feeding of farm animals at different seasons; also to learn about the relation between farm crops and the seasons.

CHAPTER 12A

Animal Ways

An important fact about animals is that they move. The salmon migrates hundreds of miles to lay its eggs. The swift spends almost all of its life on the wing—gathering food and nesting material, and mating in the air. The army ant advances its columns to raid the countryside for food, moving as much as 1000 feet from its temporary headquarters in one foray. Freedom of movement is the rule for most in the animal kingdom.

Much of animal activity, as in the instances just cited, represents inherited, unlearned patterns of behavior. These patterns are built into the sense organs, the nerves, the muscles of animals. They are characteristic of the species. In addition to these broad, instinctive behavior patterns, there is, however, some degree of experimentation, of learning, of adaptation to particular environmental conditions. Naturalists report that the

crow who apparently is posted as a "lookout" while his comrades are feasting in a cornfield learns to distinguish between an unarmed man and a man with a shotgun, giving a warning call when the latter appears.

Naturalists such as John Burroughs, Henri Fabre, William Beebe, Edmund Teale, and others have contributed much to our knowledge of animal ways, devoting their lives to the study of animals in their native haunts. However, the layman as well as the specialist can participate in this outdoor adventure. The fascinating antics of animals are open for all to see in their own backyards.

Clearer understanding of the internal mechanisms involved in behavior has developed as a result of carefully controlled experiments in laboratories with thousands of kinds of animals—from protozoans to man. These experiments have answered such questions as: What triggers the hibernating instinct in frogs? What sense enables spiders to detect prey in their webs? How are birds able to find their way over trackless seas? How can animals see at night? How does a bee communicate to other bees the location of some flowers from which it has been gathering nectar and pollen?

Some animals live solitary lives, others live in social groups or communities. We will discuss both of these ways of living, and then consider how animals build homes, obtain food, secure protection, and engage in courtship.

HERMIT ANIMALS

Examples of a solitary existence are to be found in all branches of the animal kingdom. The shark that terrorizes the sea is a lone hunter. True, when the victim is found, the sea soon swarms with other sharks, but there is no concerted effort here, no working together, which is the essence of social organization. The tiger stalking his prey in the jungle does so alone. The nearest approach to group living comes during the time of raising the young, when the family group may remain together. Usually, as soon as the young are able to fend for themselves, the family is dispersed. Lions may consort together in a group called a *pride*, but even here the individual acts as a unit, each unto himself. The individual lion seeks out his target and makes the kill by himself. Wolves, which are known to hunt in packs, do not usually live together. They band together only to bring down an animal too large for a lone wolf to tackle. Most fish are solitary animals. Some fish travel in schools, but these are not social groups in which the members assist each other.

HONEYBEES

Some animals live together in a social organization. By the division of labor within the social group, they gain increased protection and efficiency. The highest development of this mode of life occurs among the social insects—bees, wasps, ants, and termites. The honeybee that is seen gathering nectar from

SEE PAGES 292 TO 294

Female worker bees perform the many duties required in the colony. Among these are the building of beeswax combs in which they rear the young and store food.

the flowers is quite different in habit from a solitary insect, such as a housefly. The honeybee is part of a colony of thousands that centers around the single queen bee. The queen is literally the mother of the entire hive; her sole function is to produce eggs. After receiving sperm from a male during the marriage flight, she settles down to the business of making a family.

The queen bee can control the production of either fertilized or nonfertilized eggs. After the initial insemination by the male, the sperm is stored in a special sac. As the eggs are produced, they can either be united with a sperm to make a fertilized egg, or they can develop without fertilization. The unfertilized eggs develop into males. The males do no work in the hive and so are known as *drones*. The fertilized eggs become the female workers.

The workers perform a variety of jobs, all concerned with the well-being of the hive. Some are nursemaids who care for the queen and the eggs she lays. The eggs are put into individual compartments in the hive, which are built by another kind of worker. Each hexagonal cell is a marvel of space utilization. When the larvae hatch out, they are tended by the nursemaids. Whether the larva becomes another worker or a queen depends on how it is fed. The larvae that will become worker bees are fed for three days on bee jelly, which is made in the stomachs of the nurse bees and then secreted from their bodies. For three more days, they are given pollen and honey. After six days, the future workers eat another food, called beebread. This is mainly pollen to which a small amount of nectar is added. Prospective queens, on the other hand, are fed throughout their larval stage on royal bee jelly. This is a material secreted by certain glands of the nursemaid bees. Apparently this different type of feeding is responsible for the change into a queen bee. The queen is raised in an especially large cell.

Other workers form a sanitary squad that keeps the hive clean. Still others forage for pollen and nectar, the raw materials from which honey is made. Painstaking investigations, particularly by the Austrian scientist, Karl von Frisch, have revealed the remarkable way in which bees returning from a trip broadcast news to other bees in their hive about the location of flowers from which they have been getting nectar and pollen. When the bee returns to the hive, it performs a definite dance pattern. In effect the dance communicates to other bees the angle of the flight path in relation to the position of the sun! As the day wears on, and the sun moves across the sky, the dancing bee changes her dance to adjust to this movement, and consequently continues to communicate the correct beeline. The convolutions of this dance also convey to the other bees the distance of the desirable blossoms.

Some bees act as a police department, keeping the hive safe against possible invaders and maintaining order in the hive. There are even workers who serve as an air-conditioning corps—they stay near the hive entrance and, by the fanning of their wings, force air in and out of the hive. In cold weather, the bees in the hive are kept from freezing by the body heat generated by the rapid vibration of their wings. The sole function of the male drones is the fertilization of the queen, but only one of the drones in a hive enjoys this privilege. For this momentary contribution they live a life of apparent ease in the colony.

Bees are important to mankind. The honey that they make, although useful, is not very significant as compared with the total amount of food that we consume. But without bees many plants would be unable to produce seeds and fruit. Bees inadvertently help in *cross-pollination*, that is, in carrying pollen from one flower to another flower of the same kind of plant. The legs of the worker bees are equipped with enlargements called pollen baskets, in which they carry pollen to the hive to use for food. Watch a bee flying from flower to flower and you may see the pollen baskets on the hind legs packed full of pollen. When full, the baskets look like two big lumps on the legs. If the pollen baskets are full, the hind legs hang down when the bee flies. In the process of securing pollen for their own use, bees accidentally pick up and deliver pollen from flower to flower.

It is very important that every rural community have either wild or domesticated bees to help carry on plant reproduction. Some beekeepers rent colonies of bees to fruit growers. The hives are transported to a blossoming orchard and left there for a time so that the bees can do their work of cross-pollinating.

Bumblebees have a simpler communal life than that of the honeybee. Among bumblebees, only the queen, tucked away in a hollow tree or stump, lives through the winter. Mating occurs in the previous autumn, and the queen lays eggs as soon as the warm spring sun brings her out of her winter hibernation.

ANTS

Ants display an interesting variety of community lives. There are hundreds of species of ants. Some ants are large and some small. Some build nests ten or twelve feet high, while some have little homes only a few cubic inches in volume.

Some kinds of ants have as many as eight castes. There are, first of all, the sexually mature males and females, which are capable of reproduction. This is their only function, although one specific male and one female in each colony are the only ones active at one time. The other potentially reproductive males and females seem to be reserves that are called upon only if something

happens to one or both of the reproductive team. These reserves upon occasion found new colonies.

Another caste is that of the nurse-maids, who look after the larvae and pupae. They are highly efficient. When you break into an anthill, you can often see nurses rushing about trying to carry the white pupae to safety. Incidentally, most ants' eggs are tiny and can scarcely be seen without the aid of a magnifying glass. What people generally call the "eggs" are actually the pupae.

The food gatherers form another caste. They are responsible for keeping the group supplied with food. One kind of ant, for example, keeps cows, puts them out to pasture, and milks them. The ant cows are aphids (plant lice). The ants guard and care for these aphids. They even carry them up from their underground tunnels and place them on the leaves from which they can get food. The ants "milk" the aphids by stroking their bodies with their antennae. This causes the aphids to give off a sweet liquid that the ants eat. In return for this provender, the ants protect the aphids from their enemies, such as the ladybird beetle. Thus both the ants and the plant lice profit from the relationship. Another species, the farmer ant, cultivates a kind of fungus that it eats.

Many ant species have a soldier caste, with comparatively huge heads and sickle-shaped jaws. Their sole function is to protect the group. Sometimes they wage war on their neighbors. The losing ants, in a battle between two ant communities, may be turned into slave laborers by their conquerors. Other castes are the refuse-disposers, who keep the colony clean, and the constructors, who build the anthill.

As with bees, the actions are carried on instinctively. In some respects the communal life of ants and bees is more complete than that of human beings, but ours is a reasoned, planned, and ever-changing scheme. Most of us have some choice in what we do for our life work, whereas ants have none. They are firmly bound to an inherited, instinctive pattern of behavior. Man, in contrast, may change his social patterns.

HIVES OF BEES AND NESTS OF WASPS

The hive of the honeybee is a feat of highly skilled engineering. The individual cells are six-sided, a design that makes economical use of the material available. The honeycomb is made of wax secreted by the bee and manipulated by the workers to form the cells.

The country boy spotting a common wasps' nest looks upon it with respectful eye for he knows full well the fiery weapons that its inhabitants carry. The scientist looks upon the nest with a different kind of respect. Here, ingenious materials are manufactured and employed in a manner to make an efficient home for the colony. The outer envelope of the nest is a flexible, sturdy material like brown paper, made by the wasp by chewing up particles of wood. These insects are the first known paper-makers. Insulation is insured by numerous, loosely overlapping layers of the paper pulp in broad scales. The air thus enclosed acts as a heat-insulating blanket. The shape of the nest gives the largest amount of room in the smallest wrapper. The cells within the nest are also formed with an economy of space and material.

In contrast to the social wasps, the mud-dauber wasps lead a solitary life. The mud-dauber wasp builds its nest under eaves, under bridges, and inside sheds, barns and houses. The female of the most common species seeks the edge of a pool where she mixes mud and saliva into a pellet of mortar. She carries the mortar to the building site and constructs a mud cup made up of a series of tube-shaped cavities or cells. The female places several spiders, which she has paralyzed with her sting, into a cell. She then deposits an egg in the cell, and seals it with more mortar. The egg hatches into a larva, which has a fresh supply of spider meat to eat until it is grown.

SEE PAC 292

ANT AND TERMITE NESTS

The ant nests, whether large or small, is a series of tunnels or galleries, usually hollowed out in the soil. The ants called the

The female mud-dauber wasp builds a number of these mud cells. It places inside each several spiders which it has paralyzed, and an egg. It then seals the cell. The hungry larva that emerges from the wasp egg finds a meal of fresh spider "meat."

mound-builders build their homes of soil and grass. The carpenter ants live in logs, cutting out their chambers and passages with their sharp mandibles. The honey ants build a separate chamber in which workers called *repletes* hang from the ceiling. Other workers gather nectar, and, returning to the nest, regurgitate it into the repletes. The repletes become fat and swollen with food. They serve as living storage casks, which are "tapped" as needed during the winter season by the other ants.

Termites, which, like ants, are social insects, build tunnels similar to those of the ants, always starting from the soil and then working up into woody structures above ground. They must maintain their contact with the earth to survive. They do this by way of a special connecting tunnel. The tunnels are made of a mixture of a mucus-like cementing secretion and wood particles.

BIRDS' NESTS

Birds build nests that vary in structure from those so crude that they are almost unrecognizable as nests to those so elaborately constructed as to be worthy of the most skillful craftsman. All sorts of materials are used, from sticks and stones to hair and moss and even snake skins. Nests are located in every kind of place—on the ground, on tall cliffs, and in the highest trees.

Nests are built according to the size and type of young that will live in them. The sizes varies from the 1½-inch nest of the hummingbird to that of the eagle, which may be more than 7 feet across. Robins and orioles, whose young require much care, are careful builders. Herring gulls do not need much of a nest since the young can take care of themselves soon after hatching. These birds lay their eggs in a hollow in the rocks. A killdeer's nest amounts to nothing more than a slight hollow in the earth, sometimes with a few sticks in it. Young killdeers are able to run about soon after they are hatched.

The location of the nest is related to the habits of each kind of bird. Nests built by meadow larks, bobolinks, and other grassland birds are found on the ground. Here, accessibility to food seems to be the advantage, but at some sacrifice of safety. Nests

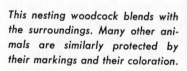

This nesting woodcock blends with the surroundings. Many other animals are similarly protected by their markings and their coloration.

that are built on the ground must be carefully concealed if the eggs or young birds are to be safe. Birds have many enemies, among them cats, skunks, raccoons, snakes, foxes, and other birds.

Many common birds build in the crotches of tree branches, where the nests will be partially hidden by the foliage. Eagles, hawks, and crows build in the tops of the highest trees or upon cliffs. They depend for safety on height and inaccessibility rather than concealment. Great blue herons build their nests in the tops of tall trees. It is quite a sight to see these huge birds standing up on their nests and feeding their young.

In making nests, birds use materials close at hand. Grassland birds use surrounding grass. Robins, orioles, and other birds use such materials as twigs, string, and mud. If you put out colored yarns and string so that birds can find them, you will find, if you examine the nests later, some skillful weaving with these materials, especially by orioles. Hawks and eagles build crude nests composed of sticks.

Some birds use hollow trees for nests. Among these are bluebirds, screech owls, titmice, woodpeckers, and nuthatches.

Ordinarily, birds do not use the same nest year after year. Nest construction follows mating, which takes place at different times for different birds. Owls and hawks mate early. Their offspring can be fed on young animal life (rabbits, rats, field mice, etc.), which is abundant in early spring. Birds that feed their young on insects mate later. When the young are born there is a sufficient supply of insects to feed them.

Birds' eggs take various lengths of time to hatch, but most hatch after about three weeks of incubation. During the period of incubation, the mother bird is confined to the nest to keep the eggs warm; she leaves only for a few moments to get water and to exercise. In many species of birds, the mother is fed during incubation by the father, who is kept busy bringing food to the nest. The eggs are carefully drawn up into the feathers of the mother bird for greater warmth. She turns them at frequent intervals. If the eggs are not turned, the young birds may be crippled or have some body parts which are poorly developed. The young birds are usually fed by both the male and the female.

Children sometimes like to bring birds' nests to school. Of course, spring and summer are not the times to disturb nests. It is perfectly proper to collect them in the fall or winter, because few of them are ever used again. They can be studied just as well at this time of the year as in the spring. More about collecting birds' nests is found in chapter 12B.

HOMES OF SOME ANIMALS

SQUIRRELS. Squirrels have places in hollow trees where they store nuts and where they spend a large part of their time during the cold winter months. Sometimes red squirrels have a home underground as well as one in a tree. Gray squirrels often build summer homes of sticks and leaves in the crotches of trees, in which the young are born and raised. On very cold days in winter, the squirrels are likely to stay in a hollow tree or in some other protected place.

BEAVERS. Beavers build rather elaborate homes in swamps or ponds, which are often artificially formed by dams made by the beavers of sticks and mud. To the uninitiated, beaver homes look much like the piles of brush left by woodcutters. Near these homes, branches with edible bark are anchored to the bottom of the pond so that the beavers can swim out under the ice in winter and obtain food. The homes have underwater entrances but contain an above-water shelf upon which the beavers can rest. Beavers breathe with lungs and therefore cannot stay under water for long. Several beavers work together to make these homes, and many beavers may live in one colony.

Several beavers may be found living in such a home as this, built in water held back by the dam, which may be seen beyond the lodge. Inside this house, beavers find shelter and protection from their enemies.

MUSKRATS. Muskrat homes are beehive-shaped and are made of marsh plants. Like the home of the beaver, the muskrat home has an underwater entrance and an above-water shelf. Muskrats store food for winter use. During the warm months, muskrats live in burrows in a steep bank rather than in houses. The young are born and are brought up in these burrows.

RATS AND MICE. Rats and mice, whether living in the woods or in buildings, have nests of soft material made from plants. Here the young are born and are kept until old enough to look after themselves. Anyone who has ever found the nest of a field mouse or a house mouse knows how much material is accumulated to make a suitable home for the young.

WOODCHUCKS. Woodchucks are very diligent burrowers. In many parts of the country, almost every field has one or more woodchuck burrows. The tunnels go three or four feet down into the ground and branch out into many feet of runway. Although the dirt is all pushed out near one of the entrances, there is always at least one alternate escape route that is almost impossible to find. The woodchuck keeps this exit as inconspicuous as possible. It has no attention-attracting pile of subsoil, and often it is constructed beside a large stone or in a clump of tall grass or weeds.

In the burrow, the woodchuck hibernates in winter and spends much of his time in summer. There he is relatively safe, although a predatory animal may catch him too far from the burrow while he is searching for food. Then it is a question of which runs faster. The woodchuck feeds on clover and on grasses. The entrances to woodchuck burrows are hazardous to plow horses since they may step into them and break their legs.

SKUNKS AND RABBITS. Animals such as skunks and some kinds of rabbits like to appropriate woodchuck burrows for themselves. Skunks, because of their scent glands, have no great difficulty obtaining possession. Skunks also have homes in haystacks, under stone fences, in hollow logs, and under buildings. Rabbits have no offensive or defensive weapons except speed, and they either occupy abandoned burrows or do with homes of the most rudimentary variety. Sometimes these are mere hollows in the ground and sometimes they are built in brush and rock piles. If you are walking in a field and happen to scare up a rabbit, try to find the place where it was sitting. It is likely to be a hollow that provides some shelter. In cold winter weather, these spots are most skillfully formed to make good windbreaks.

CHIPMUNKS AND PRAIRIE DOGS. These animals build rather extensive burrows underground. Chipmunks dig such burrows, being very careful to carry away all dirt from the entrances. Prairie dogs, found in large numbers in the western states, live in colonies that sometimes contain as many as a thousand members. The tunnels in their burrows are quite long and often connect with those of other members of the colony.

RACCOONS. Raccoons build their nests in hollow trees, in which the young are born and reared. The entrance is always a considerable distance above the ground.

FOXES. Foxes have elaborate dens where the young are reared. After the off-

This Orange Garden Spider has killed a grass-hopper that landed in the web, first enmeshing it in silk and then biting it.

spring have been weaned, the mother brings small animals to the den as food. A fox family consumes so much meat that the mother must hunt a great deal of the time. When foxes are plentiful, the rabbit, partridge, and pheasant populations are greatly reduced. If the natural food cupboard becomes too bare, the vixen may have to raid the farmer's henhouse. If pursued, she will never go to the den where her young are but will travel about the country until her enemies have been eluded.

TWO INTERESTING HOMES

SPIDER WEBS. One of the engineering masterpieces of nature is the spider's web. The web is often used as a trap for the unwary insect who is to be the spider's food. It is made of a silk-like fiber secreted by special glands of the spider. Though exceedingly thin, these strands are strong. Different species build different and characteristic webs, so that a spider can be identified by the web it weaves. When the web is completed, the spider takes up a strategic position in it. The vibrations of the web advise him of the entrapment of a victim. Then the spider quickly sallies forth, pounces on its prey, paralyzes it with its poisonous bite, and binds it with sticky threads. The spider then proceeds to suck the juices of its prey.

CADDIS FLY CASES. The larvae of these insects live in streams and ponds. The larva of one kind of caddis fly cements a tube from small pebbles and grains of sand that it finds in the water. Another type makes a "log cabin" case out of twig fragments. This case is the house of the caddis fly until it emerges as an adult; it is constructed to admit food and protect the young fly from water currents.

If the log-cabin caddis fly larva is taken out of its case and put in a jar of pond water, it will build a new case out of the available materials. Some have been reported to use fine bits of transparent film or cellophane that were placed in the jar by curious investigators.

ANIMAL DIETS

There are three principal kinds of diets: carnivorous, herbivorous, and omnivorous. Correlated with each diet are special kinds of behavior and special body structures. *Carnivorous animals* feed on other animals. They possess a variety of weapons for offense: fangs, talons, sharp beaks, poison stings. Carnivores are strong and fleet. Most fish are carnivorous; so too are hawks, owls, snakes, wolves, raccoons, and seals.

Herbivorous animals subsist on plant food. Herbivores are generally more gentle than carnivores; their habits and structures are correlated more with defense than offense. The mouth equipment of herbivores is specialized for cutting, scraping, grinding, and sucking, all of which are useful in dealing with tough plant tissues. Cattle, Japanese beetles, seed-eating birds, plant lice are among the many herbivores.

Omnivorous animals have a mixed diet: they feed on both vegetable and animal matter, dead or alive. Many kinds of worms, crabs, lobsters, insects, bears, and raccoons are omnivorous. The habits and structures of the omnivores lie somewhere in between those of the carnivores and the herbivores. Man is an omnivore.

WAYS OF PROTECTION

COLORATION. The color of an animal may make the difference between life and death. The woodcock, abruptly stopping its flight and remaining motionless on the ground, may escape the hunter because it blends so well with its leafy background. The helpless fawn is safe from hungry eyes because its mottled color merges with the background of fallen leaves and stray shafts of sunlight when it "freezes" in its tracks. Some animals change color with the season. The weasel is brown in the summer and matches the underbrush where he moves. In winter, the coats of some varieties of weasels turn white and match the snow. Most fish are dark-colored above—an enemy looking down at them from above finds them difficult to discern against the dark of the waters below. The light-colored underside makes them less visible to predators below them, viewing them against the lighter surface and sky above. The common flounder illustrates this well. Its upper surface is a dark, muddy brown, closely simulating the brown mud of the bottom where he customarily abides. The other side is almost white. Frogs are colored in similar manner. The dark, olive green of the upper parts makes them hard to see against the murky bottom of the pond or lake where they live.

MIMICRY. The masquerade is an effective way of avoiding discovery by an enemy. This art of camouflage is most highly developed in the insects. The famous walking stick looks as twig-like as an actual twig. The Kallima moth looks just like a leaf, complete with veins and all. The queer leafhoppers, sometimes called brownies, closely resemble thorns on a branch in both coloration and structure. The harmless hog-nosed snake, rearing up and expanding its neck to make itself look like a venomous viper, is revealed for the fraud that it is by a simple tap on the side of its head, when it will try another trick, turning over on its back and playing dead.

TASTE AND ODOR. An offensive odor can be a good defense. Witness the skunk. This animal is practically without fear. Where it walks, all others give it wide room. In its scent glands, just beneath the tail, it manfactures a potent fluid so powerfully obnoxious that even the human being respects it. When in danger the skunk can eject this fluid at its tormentor. It would be a brave animal that would invite this retaliation. Snakes and other animals when caught will frequently emit their body wastes, whose powerful and disagreeable odor may discourage their attacker.

Some animals avoid becoming regular fare for predatory animals because of their vile taste. The weasel, in addition to its fighting temper, has a musky odor that tempts few carnivorous animals. Man does not hunt gulls the way he does ducks and other water fowl because they have an unpleasant taste. Many insects are free from attack by birds for the same reason.

ARMOR. Porcupines have a unique protective device. All of the body except the underside is thickly covered with quills that are easily detached. Contrary to popular belief, the quills cannot be shot out. When in danger of attack, the porcupine rolls up in a sort of ball so that its soft, unprotected belly cannot be easily reached by the enemy. An unwary dog or wolf who attacks a porcupine gets his muzzle full of quills. The quills are equipped with back-pointing barbs like fish hooks, and so are very difficult to pull out. The porcupine is a slow-moving animal and can be easily captured by man. Generally it takes to captivity readily and soon becomes quite tame.

The turtle, with its shell completely covering its body, is exceptionally well protected. With its head and legs pulled in, it is almost invulnerable. A mammal in armor is the armadillo. This strange animal has its body covered with horny plates. When frightened or attacked, it curls into a ball with its head tucked in, the plates on its back protecting it like armor. The snail with its shell is a well-known example of an animal that carries its house around with it. By withdrawing into the shell, the snail is safe against most hazards.

SPEED. Many herbivorous animals, such as the deer and the gazelle, depend principally upon speed for escaping their foes. The rabbit also depends upon fleetness of foot to remain alive. This, coupled to its protective coloration and the startling ability to stop and remain motionless in mid-flight, enables it to escape the keen eye of its predators. Field mice also scurry about with short bursts of high speed, although they rely mainly on easy access to their numerous holes and burrows in the ground for survival.

MIGRATION

BIRDS. The migrations of birds are fascinating and puzzling. When the birds that have frequented our backyards, parks, and woods leave in the fall, it is natural to ask "Where do they go?" "How are they guided in their flight?" "Will the same individuals return?"

SEE PAG 29 TO 296

Although there is still much mystery associated with migration, there are some obvious advantages that are derived from this annual round trip between breeding grounds and winter quarters. The migratory habit enables a bird to enjoy northern summers while avoiding the severity of northern winters. In flying south, the birds escape the depletion of the food supply caused by the disappearance or hibernation of insects or the covering of seeds or other ground foods by a mantle of snow and ice. Another unfavorable condition in northern climes is the shortened day, with fewer hours of light to obtain food at a time when the birds need more food to maintain body heat against the cold.

In the spring, the northward flight to regions that are uninhabitable earlier in the year gives the migrants more space and food for themselves and their offspring.

We know the advantages of migration, but that does not explain the mechanism that starts a bird on its long trip. A recent view takes as its major premise the fact that the quantity of light and the length of day have a direct stimulating effect on birds. The proponents of this theory point out that birds such as swallows and shore birds start their southward movements when the food supply in the north is *most* abundant. Similarly north-bound robins and bluebirds leave an abundant food supply in the south in the spring.

The calendar regularity of arrival and departure leads defenders of this theory, called *photoperiodism,* to conclude that the increasing light in the spring and the decreasing light in the fall are the stimuli that trigger the migratory response in birds. This theory, however, has some limitations and does not explain migration in some species.

Many other questions about migration remain unanswered. Why do the same species always follow the same route north and south? Why should the arctic tern, the champion "globe-trotter," start out from beyond the Arctic Circle and fly south until it passes beyond the tip of South America to Tierra del Fuego, only to turn around in the spring and fly back again to the polar north? How does a young bird, newly hatched out during the spring, know the flyway by which its species always travels, even though it does not migrate with the older birds? It is easy enough to say "instinct" and feel that we have answered the questions. But scientists are not satisfied with such glib answers, which merely substitute a word for an explanation, and these and other mysteries of bird migration are being studied at the present time.

Bird migration routes have been traced by means of birdbanding. Birds are trapped in one place and small aluminum identification rings are fixed to their legs. The birds are then released. Banding does not harm the bird in any way. A record is kept of the banding and if the bird is later trapped elsewhere, the information can be tabulated and analyzed and the routes accurately mapped. Birdbanding has revealed that, in some species, one of the parent birds frequently returns and nests in the same tree, bush, or box that it used in the previous season. These records also show that the

same individuals migrate year after year over the same route, making the same stops on the way.

The unerring accuracy in the flight of birds has long challenged our curiosity. The great shearwater, for example, which ranges the entire Atlantic Ocean, returns each fall to the islands of Tristan da Cuna, which are mere specks in the sea. What is the "sense of direction" that enables the birds to do this? How do birds find their way?

Elaborate cage experiments have shown that starlings, which fly by day, use the sun as a compass. Homing experiments have revealed that rivers and mountains also serve as guides, especially when the day fliers near their destination.

But how do night-flying birds find their way? Recently Dr. Franz Sauer, a German scientist, made the astonishing discovery that the Old World warblers which he studied under experimental conditions in a planetarium navigate by means of star patterns! (See illustration on page 286.)

Birds, then, navigate by the sun and the stars. This is not simply a matter of aiming at a target. We recall that both the sun and the stars move across the sky. The birds under investigation were able to adjust their courses to the change in position of these heavenly bodies during the day or the night. This means that they have a kind of built-in time clock that enables them to change their course hour by hour.

We do not know just where this astoundingly accurate orientation system is located inside a bird, nor have we proven that all birds navigate in this way.

But experiments such as those described with birds (and earlier in this chapter with bees) should make us pause before we say that animals guide themselves only "by instinct." To brush off all intelligent-looking but unlearned behavior simply as an "instinct" tends to obscure the mechanisms operating in such behavior. A more rewarding approach to the understanding of

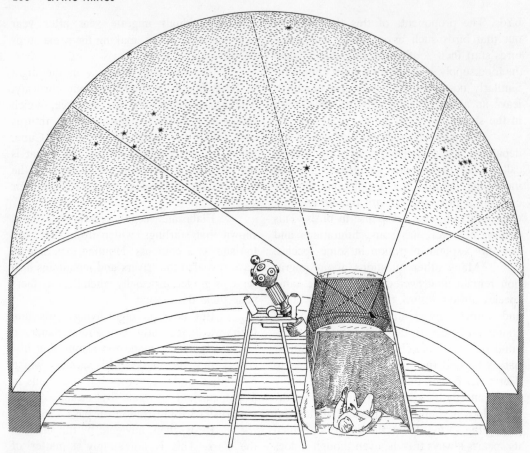

This amazing experiment, conducted in a planetarium, indicates that night-flying birds navigate by the stars. The experiment is performed under a 20-foot dome. The dome and bird cage are shown in cross-section. A felt cloth from the bottom of the cage to the floor cuts out light from below. The sector of the sky visible to the bird is indicated by solid lines. The sector visible from the opposite side of the perch is shown with broken lines. "Flight direction" means the direction in which the bird faces.

animal behavior is to try to discover the kinds of stimuli that animals respond to, and to search for the mechanisms working inside animals which make such responses possible.

BIRD FLYWAYS. In 1935 Frederick C. Lincoln, as a result of his studies of bird-banding data, discovered the existence of four great flyway systems. These are pictured and described in *Migration of Birds* (Circular 16; Fish and Wildlife Service, U. S. Department of the Interior), a booklet written by Dr. Lincoln and available from the Superintendent of Documents in Washing-ton, D. C. for thirty-five cents. The terms "flyway" and "migration route" have been used interchangeably in the past, but the modern definition of a flyway given in this booklet is: a "vast geographic region with extensive breeding grounds and wintering grounds connected with each other by a more or less complicated system of migration routes. Each flyway has its own population of birds. . . ." Four great flyway systems have been found over North America: the Atlantic flyway, the Mississippi flyway, the Central flyway, and the Pacific flyway.

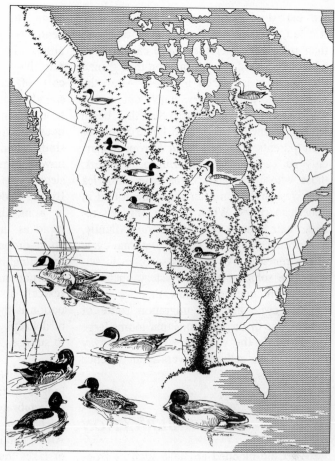

The Mississippi flyway is one of the four great flyways for birds. These flyways cover practically the entire width of the North American Continent and extend from the Arctic Coast to South America.

The same booklet concludes, "Long before the white man came to America the birds had established their seasonal lanes of migration throughout the Western Hemisphere. The economic, inspirational, and esthetic values of these migratory species dictate that they be permitted to continue their long-accustomed and still mysterious habits of migration from clime to clime."

LEMMINGS. The most notable migration of mammals is that of the little rodents called lemmings. One species, the Norway lemming, periodically mass in huge numbers and start migrating, stopping at nothing—swimming lakes, invading cities, and marching into the sea. Of course, many perish. The explanation has been offered that their food supply becomes exhausted and so they have to search for new sources. How-

ever, it has been pointed out that during such mass migrations there is little shortage of the customary food of the animals. The matter is still unsolved.

EELS. The ways of the eel have been the subject of speculation for a long time. For thousands of years people caught eels in fresh-water ponds and rivers, but never saw any evidence of their breeding. In the late 1860s, the Danish biologist J. Schmidt discovered that eels breed in the ocean. Mature eels from the rivers of Europe and America congregate and reproduce in the mid-South Atlantic Ocean, in an area known as the Sargasso Sea.

Later, after years of painstaking research participated in by investigators from several nations under the leadership of the United States Bureau of Fisheries, more of the eel story was uncovered. Eels were trapped, marked with identifying tags and then released. Later they were caught elsewhere, and from the information thus gained the puzzle was pieced together. After the young eels, called *elvers,* hatch out in the warm waters of the Sargasso Sea, they begin a long journey back to the home rivers of their parents. The eels from European parents go eastward to the European rivers; those whose forebears came from America turn west and soon afterwards are found in American rivers. When mature, the eels retrace their journey back to the mid-Atlantic, to reproduce and thus keep the eternal cycle of life renewed. As happens so often in science, the solution of one mystery opens up many more questions. Now that we know the life cycle and the migration route of the eel, one of the questions that looms large is, "How do the young eels find their way back to these selfsame rivers from whence their parents came?"

HIBERNATION

Cold-blooded animals, such as frogs and snakes, hibernate during the winter in the colder climates. The bodies of these animals become torpid, since they have little ability to regulate their body temperature. This is fortunate, because their food supply diminishes at that time almost to the vanishing point. The only way to survive until the spring is to place the body in a state of suspended animation. Metabolism goes on at the lowest ebb, just barely enough to keep the flame of life flickering in these cold-blooded animals. In the warm-blooded animals that hibernate, the torpor of their winter sleep serves to conserve the food stored in their bodies.

HUMMINGBIRD. A strange form of hibernation has recently been discovered in the hummingbird. This minute feathered creature has an extraordinarily high metabolism, that is, it burns food rapidly, which heats its body to unusually high temperatures. The hummingbird lives at a faster rate than any other bird or mammal, at the cost of enormous food consumption. It spends most of its waking hours gathering food, mainly nectar and insects. But how does it avoid overnight starvation? Recent studies, under carefully controlled conditions, have shown that as soon as the bird goes to sleep its rate of metabolism drops markedly. By the middle of the night the bird is living at a metabolic level only one-fifteenth as rapid as the daytime rate, and its temperature drops 20 to 30 degrees. In fact, the hummingbird at night shows many signs of hibernation. It is completely torpid and scarcely able to move. This overnight hibernation is the means by which the hummingbird keeps alive without eating from sunset to sunrise.

LUNGFISH. Perhaps the most prolonged instance of suspended animation in a vertebrate is found in the lungfish. This queer fish, species of which are found in Africa and in South America, lives in streams or lakes that dry up for part of the year. As the water dries out, the fish incases itself in a ball of mud, leaving a small opening through which air can come. Gills would be of no avail for breathing under such circumstances; the fish has modified its swim bladder into a crude sort of lung. This enables it to obtain sufficient oxygen to remain alive during its torpid period. Large city aquaria sometimes feature exhibits of a lungfish incased in its mud ball, which hibernates for several years and is still alive within its protective cover.

COURTSHIP

Animal behavior connected with mating has excited wonder for a long time. Earlier explanations have relied heavily on attributing human ways to other creatures.

The twentieth-century biologist cannot be persuaded by such answers. He must seek to explain animal behavior in accordance with mechanisms that are known to guide and control the animal's actions. Why do some animals engage in such absurd and fanciful posturing preliminary to mating? Why does the female have to be stimulated in so elaborate a fashion? What factors enter into the male's performance?

Studies of many animals indicate that courtship is a form of animal communication —a kind of signal system for the transmitting of "information" between potential mates. The information transmitted includes calling attention to the location of the individual, its sex, and its readiness for mating. The signals employed may be visual, auditory, tactile, chemical, or a combination of these devices. They serve as stimuli which elicit a typical response in the potential mate.

The display of brilliant neck feathers in the form of a bib by the twelve-wired bird of paradise, and the opening of its bill to show the brightly colored interior of its mouth is an example of visual communication. The European wild rabbit male walks stiff-legged away from the female and elevates its tail, thus revealing its white underside. Male and female fireflies of any particular species signal by flashing their "lights" at an interval and with a brilliance that is characteristic of that species. In this way, mating of fireflies of the same species is insured. In general, visual communication involves characteristic colors, forms, and movements.

Sound signal systems are well known in the familiar songs of birds and in the choruses of frogs and toads. In both birds and in the amphibia, the male is generally the singer. Crickets also communicate by sound signals. One investigator sent the male cricket's calls over a telephone and observed females moving toward the receiver.

Many species use touch in courtship. For example, in one kind of newt the male rubs the female's flanks with his snout and lashes water at her with his tail. In the three-spined stickleback, a small fish, the male taps the base of the female's tail with his snout. This stimulus causes the female to release her eggs. The same response may be obtained in a laboratory tank by tapping the female stickleback's tail with a glass rod.

Chemical stimuli are used by the females of many species of moths. The female produces a chemical in her abdominal glands which can stimulate the antennae of males which are as far as a mile away. The scent of the female drifts downwind; the response of the male is to fly upwind.

It is evident from the foregoing that many signaling devices are used in sexually reproducing animals, and that these play a decisive role in insuring reproduction and, consequently, survival of the species.

The foregoing material may be summarized by the following generalizations:

Animal behavior is based on inherited, unlearned patterns of behavior, but it is modified by the environment.

Some animals live solitary lives, independent of others of their own kind.

Some animals live in social groups, in which there is cooperation and division of labor.

Communal life reaches its highest complexity among some insects.

Animals make and use a variety of homes.

Animals differ widely in their ways of getting food.

Animals and plants depend on each other in many different ways.

Animals use various methods to protect themselves.

Animal behavior is better understood as we discover the particular stimuli which animals respond to, and the mechanisms inside animals which make responses possible.

Some animal actions still puzzle scientists.

DISCOVERING FOR YOURSELF

1. Find a deserted paper wasp nest; examine it thoroughly to see what you can discover.

2. Dig into an ant colony. Use a magnifying glass to observe the animals when they are disturbed. Find out as much as you can by observation, then read to verify your discoveries.

3. Observe honeybees to see how they get inside flowers, how they get out, how they get nectar and pollen; observe their structure.

4. Find the homes of mud-dauber wasps on the ceilings of garages or other outbuildings. Open them up and examine the contents.

5. Observe the building of a bird's nest. Try to discover what materials are used, how they are used, and how long the building takes.

6. Visit an apiary and observe the activities in a beehive. Ask the beekeeper to describe his work and to tell you about bees.

7. Try to locate a bumblebees' nest and observe the insects.

8. Obtain a sample of wood from a termite exterminating company. Examine the wood.

9. Read a book dealing with the behavior of animals. Look in your own environment for examples of animal activity described in the book.

10. With the aid of a magnifying glass, watch a leaf infested with aphids (plant lice) for ten minutes. Write a report of what you see.

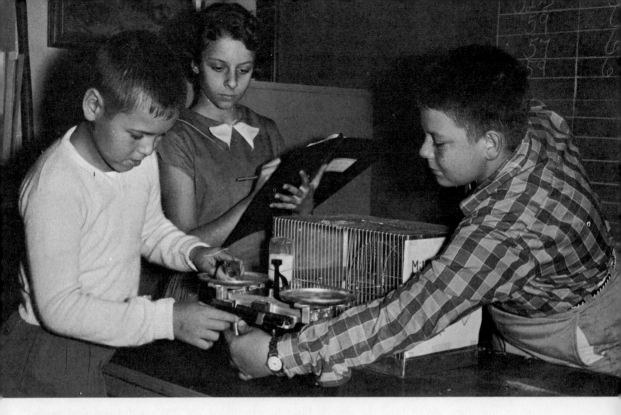

CHAPTER 12B

Teaching "Animal Ways"

Many of the activities suggested in this chapter provide opportunity for observing animal life in order to develop appreciation as well as to give information. They are closely related to the previous chapters in that they are planned to expand concepts concerning living things. We emphasize again that it is important to help pupils put information together into meaningful concepts that will be helpful in interpreting things they see.

Children's responses to animal life often give us a clue for procedures to follow in the study. Their delights, their fears, their questions, and their general reactions are all important. Young children take particular delight in furry animals. Most children are interested in knowing how animals eat, build homes, play, care for their young.

Every experienced teacher knows that animals are especially interesting to primary-grade pupils. The following activities are appropriate for young children:

1. Keep an animal pet, watch it eat, see how it protects itself, watch it drink, and learn as much as possible about how the animal is like other animals and how it is different from them.
2. Watch ants or, if possible, bees to discover what they are doing as they travel about from one place to another.
3. Watch a bird build its nest to see how it carries the material, where it finds the material, how long it takes to finish the nest, and other interesting things.[1]

---

[1] *Bird Nests,* Audubon Nature Bulletin, National Audubon Society, 1130 Fifth Ave., New York 28, N. Y. (15¢).

4. Examine a deserted bird's nest to see what it is made of and how the materials are put together.
5. Collect pictures that show different places where animals live. Find the answers to: Do any of these animals live nearby? In what kinds of places do they live?
6. Take a walk to look for places where birds might or do build their nests— inside trees, on the branches of trees, in cliffs, on the ground, and other places. Look for different kinds of materials that birds could use in building.

EXAMINING A MUD DAUBER'S NEST

Mud-dauber wasps are commonly found under eaves of buildings, under bridges, on ceilings in garages, and in similar places.[2] Examining them provides an opportunity for pupils to try to learn by firsthand observation *before* they do any reading. After they see a picture of the nests so that they will know what to look for, children can themselves often bring several nests to school for examination. This is a good opportunity for pupils to work in groups, for it is hardly likely that there will be enough specimens for everyone to examine. Pupils may carefully break the nests open on pieces of paper so they will not lose any of the contents. Magnifying glasses are very helpful in examining the material. Questions such as the following will direct pupils' observations and may be used for later discussion: "Can you tell anything about how the nest is built by examining it?" "What did you find inside the nest?" "How do you think these things got into the nest?" "What do you think will happen to them?" (Pupils will probably be able to identify spiders and mud-dauber wasps at various stages of their development.) After pupils have made as many observations as possible, they may pool their findings in a class discussion, perhaps reporting by groups. All their observations and conclusions will be tentative until they are checked by reading.

It is important to stress with children that the mud dauber does not *plan* so that the young larvae will have food. There is no "looking ahead" involved. The mud dauber is born able to act in this way. This same point should, of course, be stressed in the study of the habits of other animals, particularly since some of the reference books children use may be misleading in this respect. The procedure described here is also appropriate for the study of other similar living things that pupils find in their environment. It is important to stress the advantages of animals' habits and of the things the animals do, even though the animals do not actually plan their activities.

KEEPING BEES IN THE CLASSROOM

It is a most exciting activity in an elementary schoolroom to keep a swarm of bees and observe their ways. This is not very difficult, and the interest and enjoyment of the children is reward enough for the trouble. Here is a sketch showing how to build a small "beehive" that has glass sides so that pupils can observe the bees at work. One end of the hive extends outdoors under the window so that the bees can come and go just as they would from any other hive. If the exit from the hive is on the first floor of the building, it should not open directly onto the playground; if it does, there is some danger of the pupils getting stung by the bees.

---

[2] G. O. Blough, *Who Lives in this House?* (New York: Whittlesey House, 1957).

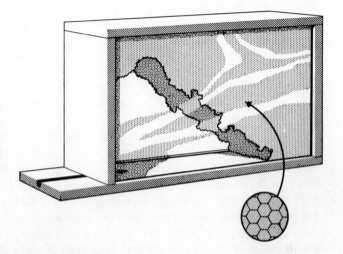

This observation hive is relatively simple in its construction. Consult a beekeeper for the standard dimensions of a comb rack and make this frame to fit the rack. The magnified insert shows the honeycomb that bees construct upon a wax foundation that must be placed on the comb rack. The extended strip fits under the schoolroom window.

The hive is built to fit around a standard frame, which you can obtain from a beekeeper in your community. Get a frame first, so that you will see how to fit it into the hive. The frame you use will have honeycomb, honey, developing bees, mature bees, and a queen on it. Almost anyone who keeps bees will be interested in helping a school obtain some for observation. The beekeeper will often be a useful source of information and may let pupils come to see the bees at his apiary. The observation hive is not difficult to make. The school custodian, a father of one of the pupils, an older boy from an upper grade, or the woodworking teacher can help to make it. If you wish to purchase one, a bee supply house[3] will sell one already made, with or without a stock of bees.

In such a glass-sided hive, pupils can observe all the activities commonly carried on in a real beehive. A magnifying glass aids in the observation. The story of what they see happening in such a hive has been written with great interest and success by many pupils. One school built its language-arts program for several days around the observations and recording the pupils made of the hive. Another school kept a diary of interesting happenings, beginning with the making of the hive. Other groups of pupils were invited to see the hive and to hear about it. Parents, too, were interested. After the study is over, or at the end of the school year, the bees may be returned to the beekeeper.[4]

Although the main emphasis in studying bees is on how animals live in groups, the interdependence of living things is equally important. This aspect may be a logical outgrowth of the bee study.

We have stressed the importance of increasing the child's appreciation for things around him. It is through such observations as we have described that pupils grow in appreciation of the living things in their environment. If you should ever find that, as the result of such experiences in school, pupils in your class observe bees at work in their gardens at home and are interested in watching them carefully to see how they enter flowers, leave them,

---

[3] A. I. Root Company, Medina, Ohio, sells observation hives. It also supplies booklets on bees and beekeeping (single copies free to teachers). The company publishes two very useful books on beekeeping: E. R. Root, *ABC and XYZ of Bee Culture*, 1962, 725 pp.; and *Starting Right With Bees*, 1960, 100 pp.

[4] *Life of the Honey Bee; What Good Are Insects?; How Insects Benefit Man;* Audubon Nature Bulletins, National Audubon Society, 1130 Fifth Ave., New York 28, N. Y. (15¢ each).

fly to others, and eventually go back to their hives, you may feel that you are beginning to achieve your objectives.

In connection with the study of bees it is important to remember that you are helping pupils not only to study life in a bee colony but also to organize these learnings into important generalizations about social animals as contrasted with solitary animals.

STUDYING ANTS AND SPIDERS

A convenient observation house in which to watch life in an ant colony can be made from a clear glass quart jar that has a screw top. A block of wood placed in the center of the jar will keep the ants from tunneling too far to be seen. Illustrations of two other more elaborate ant houses are shown here. Any available size glass may be used for this ant house. The plasticine walls are about ¾ inch high and 1 inch wide. One piece of glass fits under the walls, the other above them. This one is lifted off to feed the ants. The entire structure is set in a shallow pan of water to keep ants from escaping. The other house is made of a frame of two pieces of glass (12″ x 10″), cloth tape, 4 sticks about ½″ x ¼″ and two blocks to hold the frame upright. A fourth piece of wood forms the top, and two medicine-dropper-sized holes in the top permit entering. Remove the top to feed. Use a magnifying glass for observation.[5] Stock the ant house by digging into an anthill. Be sure to get plenty of ants, a queen, some eggs, and some soil.[6]

Wrap black paper around the outside of the glass jar to make it dark inside, and remove the paper when you want to see the ants. Feed them bread crumbs, sugar, and various other things, experimenting to find out what they like. Give them a little water, in a small dish on top of the soil, and not too much food. The story of "What We Saw the Ants Do" is an interesting one for children to write and illustrate.

Spiders are fascinating creatures to watch, and web-making is an operation that is awe inspiring. Pupils may be encouraged to search for spider webs that are in the process of construction to observe the operation and then to observe how the web functions in the capture of food for the spider.

STUDYING BIRD MIGRATION

In many localities, it is possible to observe flocks of birds gathering before they migrate. Migrating ducks and geese can often be observed, and children should be encouraged to watch for them.[7] A group of pupils who want to find out about migrating birds or about birdbanding may make a report that will stimulate a discussion of "Where and how

[5] Julius Schwartz, *Through the Magnifying Glass* (New York: Whittlesey House, 1954).

[6] *Ants*, Turtox Service Leaflet No. 35, General Biological Supply House, 8200 South Hoyne Ave., Chicago 20, Ill. (4¢ per copy).

Live Insects in the Classroom, Audubon Nature Bulletin. National Audubon Society, 1130 Fifth Ave., New York 28, N. Y. (15¢).

From G. O. Blough and M. H. Campbell, *Making and Using Classroom Science Materials in the Elementary School* (New York: Holt, Rinehart and Winston, 1954), pp. 52–53.

[7] *Mysteries of Bird Migration*, Audubon Nature Bulletin, National Audubon Society, 1130 Fifth Ave., New York 28, N. Y. (15¢). (With maps.) *Migration of Birds*, Fish and Wildlife Service, U. S. Department of the Interior (Circular 16), 1950, 102 pp.

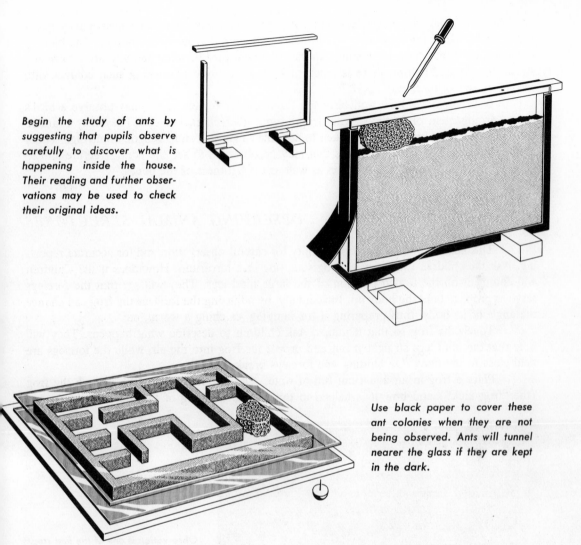

Begin the study of ants by suggesting that pupils observe carefully to discover what is happening inside the house. Their reading and further observations may be used to check their original ideas.

Use black paper to cover these ant colonies when they are not being observed. Ants will tunnel nearer the glass if they are kept in the dark.

birds migrate and how scientists are learning more and more about migration."[8] (The bibliography suggests books that give extensive information about bird migration.)

With the information about bird migration, pupils often find maps that show routes. They are interested to know in what places the birds of their locality spend the winter and how far the birds must fly to reach these places. They are also interested in finding out whether there are mountains or bodies of water that the birds must cross. These questions stimulate map study and may make use of information gained in geography and social studies.

There may be an authorized birdbander in your neighborhood who will have a great deal of interesting information for your class. A trip may be made to see how the birds are caught, to learn how they are banded and how the records are kept, and to hear about data

[8] For additional information, write to Fish and Wildlife Service, Patuxent Research Refuge, Laurel, Maryland.

that the birdbander may have discovered. A high school biology teacher nearby may know the name of one of the thousands of birdbanders scattered around the country. The biology teacher himself may have interesting experiences about bird banding and migrating to relate. As we have stated before, there is much to be said in favor of making such contact with secondary school teachers.

In order to see how well birds are fitted for air travel, pupils may observe a bird's shape, arrangement of feathers, wing length, and other characteristics. They may examine the bones of a dead bird or of a chicken to note their lightness and strength. Some high school biology teachers have bird skeletons that may be observed to see the bone structure and to note the general shape of the skeleton as well as the lightness of the bones.

OBSERVING ANIMAL STRUCTURES

This activity provides an opportunity for careful observation and for accurate reporting. Ask the children to observe a frog squatting in a terrarium. How does it sit? Children will comment on the folded position of the large hind legs. They will see that the forelegs serve as props to hold the body up. Incidentally, by adjusting the forelegs the frog can change the angle of its body, thus preparing it for jumping, catching a worm, etc.

Touch the frog so that it jumps. Ask children to describe what happens. They will note that the hind legs straighten out and propel the frog into the air, while the forelegs are held close to the body. On landing, the forelegs break the fall.

Place a frog in an aquarium full of water. Observe how the hind legs push the frog (the "frog kick") and how it is helped in this by the webbing of the toes. (If the frog is

Observation is one of the first steps to discovery. "What can you discover by looking?" is a logical question when children bring something to school to show to their classmates. Are these pellets that show something about the food of owls? If they are, what can you find out about the eating habits of owls by examining them?

placed in icy water, as described in chapter 11B, it will hibernate. This may be used to illustrate one effect of temperature on the "ways of animals.") Other animals may be observed in a similar way to see how their structures function in movement.

OBSERVING ANIMAL BEHAVIOR

The question "Can animals learn?" will provoke a flood of answers from your pupils, who will be only too happy to relate how their pet dog, cat, turtle, fish, or other animal, learned how to do something. An experiment that can be easily conducted is to see if fish in an aquarium can learn to respond to tapping by coming to the surface. Each time fish are fed (and this should not be more than once every two days) the feeding is preceded by tapping the aquarium glass with a coin. After some days (or weeks) the fish may respond to the tapping by coming to the top. As a control, the fish in a similar aquarium should be fed without the tapping and then compared with the others to see if they respond to the tapping.

Experiments like this, and observations of animal behavior will open up many other questions. Children will begin to understand that much of animal behavior is unlearned or inherited, while some is learned.

The behavior of mealworms, which are easily raised in a classroom, was studied by a sixth-grade group.[9] They asked and investigated such questions as: How do mealworms "explore" a box? How does a mealworm sense the presence of a wall so that he can follow it? How does a mealworm find bran? Pupils can, through careful observations, formulate some interesting hypotheses and attempt to evaluate them.

OBSERVING ANIMAL COLOR

Protective coloration of animals is always fascinating to children, and some planned observations of this phenomenon may be very rewarding. Children may be encouraged to: observe moths, butterflies, grasshoppers to see how blending of color and shape conceals the animals. Frogs, fish, birds, and mammals will furnish other examples, beginning with squirrels on autumn leaves, nuthatches on tree trunks, frogs on logs. Urge children to make as many observations as they can in parks, woods, ponds, creeks, lawns, and any other places.

RESOURCES TO INVESTIGATE

1. Zoo for information on the care and feeding of young animals, care of injured animals, and other matters.
2. Local beekeeper for information about habits and care of bees.
3. Exterminators for samples of termites and other insects and for information about their homes and habits.
4. Local parks, wood lots, and similar areas to see animal homes and to observe home-building by birds, squirrels, insects, and other animals.
5. Different types of local wild animals—hawks, owls, squirrels, for example—to note adaptations for food-getting and general habits.

---

[9] *Behavior of Meal Worms*, Elementary Science Study, 108 Water Street, Watertown, Mass.

CHAPTER 13A

The Human Body and How It Works

Man wonders over the restless sea
The flowing water and the sight of the sky
And forgets that of all wonders
Man himself is the most wonderful.

Since St. Augustine wrote these words in the fourth century A.D., man's knowledge of himself has increased enormously, but so too has his wonder. This wondering has led him to scrutinize himself intently, to examine the minute details of his body structure, and to unravel the many mysteries of the body's functioning.

HOW MAN STUDIES HIMSELF

Man views his body in many ways. The older view was concerned mainly with the body's gross structures—its systems and its organs, its bones, muscles, and blood vessels. Today we study the body alive. We record the fluctuations of the heartbeat electrically on a graph. We observe the rhythmic waves of the food tube through a fluoroscope. We inject a radioactive substance into the blood stream and follow its progress through the body with a Geiger counter.

We place bits of the body's tissues under the microscope, and the magnified view thus obtained reveals the billions of building blocks of the body—the cells. We use the most refined techniques of chemistry to detect the molecules of living material inside each cell, and to discover how the activities of these molecules in cell "laboratories" make life possible. We use the tools and techniques of the biologist, chemist, and physicist to unravel the many mysteries of life hidden in the minute structures within the cell.

With these tools and techniques we have made great progress in the many fields of research that have contributed to man's health. In the last hundred years we have detected the microscopic organisms that are responsible for many of man's diseases—bacteria, protozoa, and viruses. We have found how to combat these diseases with serums, vaccines, drugs, and antibiotics. We have discovered the role of the hormones, important chemicals released into the blood stream, in regulating the development and the functioning of the body. We have discovered the vitamins, essential components in the foods we eat.

We study the heredity and the environment of man to see how each of these influence his development. We see in his heredity, not without some difficulty and uncertainty, the contribution of his parents, grandparents, and more distant ancestors. We investigate the impact of his surroundings, which include not only climate, food, shelter, but also the social forces in human society. Finally, we see man as a part of the continuing story of life that started some two billion years ago.

CELLS

The human body, like all living things, plant or animal, is built of structural units called cells. Each cell, as we saw in chapter 10A, is a tiny glob of living protoplasm. Cells of the body come in many shapes and sizes. They are fitted to do many jobs—to protect and cover the body's surfaces, to receive and transmit nerve impulses, to contract and to relax, to manufacture special chemicals, to store foods, and to perform dozens of other services. A body cell, unlike an ameba (a one-celled animal) is not independent. It is affected by its relation with other cells and by the behavior of the whole cellular community—the body—of which it is a part.

BLUEPRINT OF THE BODY

Let us take a close look at the body to see how it is built and how it works. The body is made up of a number of obvious large parts, such as the limbs, the eyes, the ears, and internal parts such as the stomach and liver. Such large parts of the body, called organs, have a special job to perform. The legs are used to carry us from place to place. The eyes respond to light, enabling us to see. The arms and hands are used for doing all sorts of jobs, including grasping, lifting, and turning. The heart pumps the blood around the body. The stomach is active in a special phase of digestion. Each organ performs an essential task.

Let us select a convenient organ, like the forearm, and examine its structure. On the outside is skin. Within the arm you can feel the hard, supporting framework, the bones. If you wiggle your fingers while clasping the forearm with the other hand, you can feel the muscles that activate the fingers. When the skin is cut, even with the merest scratch, blood flows out. You have undoubtedly struck your elbow (the "funny bone") sometimes in just the right way to get a tingling sensation. You have unwittingly stimulated the nerve that is near the surface at that point. The various parts of the arm—skin, bones, muscles, nerves, blood vessels—are held together by connective bands.

Organs are composed of different kinds of tissues. Thus, in the arm, there is blood tissue, muscle tissue, bone tissue, outer skin or epithelial tissue, nerve tissue, and connective tissue. Like any good organization, the tissues must cooperate with each other to perform the work of the organ. Another way of saying this is that an organ is a group of tissues working together to perform a major function in the body. Let us examine the tissues more closely to see how they are constructed and how they work.

MUSCLE TISSUE.   To understand better how a muscle performs, shred a bit of

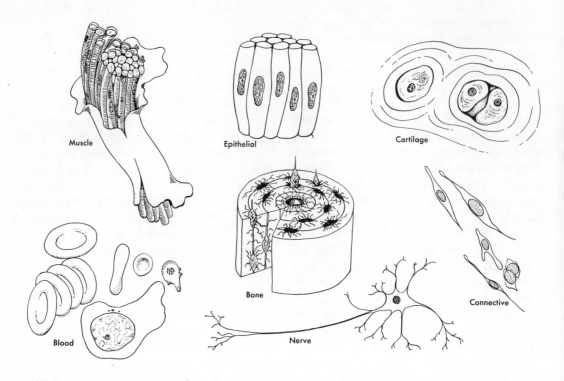

Each tissue cell is uniquely fitted for its job: the long, thin fibers of fused muscle cells that can contract quickly; the brick-like cells of epithelium, functioning as a protective wall; the freely moving cells of blood tissue; the long, complex cells of nerve tissue with their specialized receiving and sending parts; and the scattered cells of bone and cartilage, with their tough intercellular material.

uncooked meat (muscle tissue) from an animal and view it under a microscope. You will see that it is made of many long fibers, composed of muscle cells which are fused. Each fiber has hundreds of delicate threads which can contract quickly. Millions of muscle cells shortening at the same time cause the whole muscle to do its job—to shorten and to pull. That is why the bulge appears on your arm when you bend your elbow. All of the voluntary muscles of our body, that is, those that we can move at will, such as those found in the arms and legs, are composed of such cells.

The heart is essentially a hollow muscle, although its cells differ somewhat from those found in the muscles of the arm. A third type of muscle tissue is found in the parts of the digestive tube, such as the stomach and small intestine, and in the arteries and veins.

EPITHELIUM.   An example of the covering type of tissue is found in the outer layers of the skin, called *epithelium*. Here the cells are packed closely like bricks, thereby serving as an effective wall to keep body fluids in and foreign bodies out. The epithelium of the skin is only paper thin, but we are painfully aware of its importance when a bit of salt gets into a cut. The outermost cells of the skin's epithelium are dead and are shed continuously. What is commonly called dandruff is bits of epithelium flaking off from the scalp, a perfectly normal process if it does not occur excessively. As dead cells are lost from the outside, new ones are continuously forming underneath.

Every organ of the body has its own epithelium covering. Around the heart, for instance, is the epithelium called the *pericardium*. In addition to covering body parts, epithelium is a primary chemical factory of the body. Many glands contain epithelial tissue, which manufactures and secretes the useful products of the gland—enzymes and hormones, for example.

BONE AND CARTILAGE. The supporting tissues of the body are bone and cartilage. Bone is hard because of the deposit of minerals, mainly calcium phosphate, in the spaces between the bone cells. At birth, as is well known, our bones are not hard. The soft supporting tissue in them (except in the skull bones) is cartilage. The original cartilage is later replaced by bone, but in some parts of the body the cartilage is permanent. The outer ear, for example, and the tip of the nose, as well as the ends of all long bones, are made of cartilage. This is useful in places where strength must be combined with flexibility. Cartilage (you may know it as "gristle") is also found in the windpipe, where rings of cartilage serve to keep the passageway open. In cartilage tissue, as in bone, the material deposited *between* the cells carries on the supportive or protective function of the tissue.

Milk is an excellent source of the bone-building minerals—calcium and phosphorus. That is why milk has such an important role in children's diet. Bone is formed continuously in childhood. The bone minerals are constantly being torn down and rebuilt, even in adults. Most of the calcium of the body is in the bones, but calcium is also needed for the contraction of muscles and for the clotting of blood. When the amount of calcium in the blood falls below a certain level, the blood "borrows" some from the bones. This automatic calcium-transfer system is one of many "feedback" processes that occur in the body.

BLOOD. Blood tissue is unique in that its cells can move freely in a liquid. This is an asset for a material that must be readily transported to every minute part of the body. The liquid part of the blood is *plasma*. This is mainly water in which is dissolved many important substances, as we shall see later in our study of blood circulation. The cells of the blood are of three types—red cells, white cells, and platelets. The red cells' job is to carry oxygen around the body. One of the primary jobs of the white cells is to fight off invasion by harmful organisms, such as bacteria. Platelets help in the clotting of blood.

NERVE TISSUE. Nerve tissue contains the longest cells in the body. Some of these may be as much as three feet long, such as the cells from the skin of the foot that carry sensory messages to the spinal cord. However, these cells are so thin that a bundle an inch thick might contain 25,000 of them. Nerve cells come in a variety of sizes and shapes, but are all designed to carry messages called *nerve impulses*. One type that we might describe, the kind that carries impulses to muscles, has an antenna-like receiving part, a controlling and nutritive part, a long wire-like part, and a branched transmitting part, as shown in the diagram.

Some nerve cells provide incoming paths for messages from sense organs and thus provides us with information. Others carry the outgoing messages from the brain and stimulate body activity in muscles and glands. The headquarters of all nerves is the spinal cord and the brain. The brain is made up of an astounding number of nerve cells, an estimated thirty trillion.

CONNECTIVE TISSUE. Connective tissue does what its name implies: it connects the tissues of the body and holds them together. This binding type of tissue is found everywhere in the body. The white strands seen in roast beef and ham are connective tissue. Among the special types of connective tissue are tendons and ligaments. Tendons are the cords that connect muscles to bones. When the muscle contracts, it pulls on the tendon and in this way moves the bone to which the tendon is attached. If you place the fingers of your left hand on the inside of the right elbow and then flex the right forearm, you will feel the tendons moving back and forth at the joint. The cords you see on the back of the hand when you straighten your fingers are also tendons. They connect the finger bones to the muscles in the forearm. The most famous tendon in the body is the Achilles' tendon. You can feel this tough tendon in the back of the ankle. The calf muscle lifts the heel by its tendon of Achilles.

Ligaments are usually broad, flat bands of tough, elastic tissue that connect bone to bone, thus holding the bones in place at the joint. Ligaments can stretch and then return to their original size. If a ligament is torn, the joint may become dislocated, that is, one of the bones may be displaced from its normal position.

TISSUES, ORGANS, AND SYSTEMS. All of the tissues we have examined are made of cells. We may say that a tissue is a group of similar cells working together for a specific job. Of course, different kinds of tissues work together for a larger purpose. Thus, as we have seen, the arm contains muscle, nerve, bone, blood, and other tissues, working together to make possible the functioning of the arm. The same is true for all the organs of the body, such as the heart, the stomach, the liver, and the kidneys.

Efficient housekeeping in the body requires the division of work into different departments, just as the city government or a large industrial plant does. These departments of the body are called systems. Thus, all of the organs concerned with preparing food for the use of the body are part of the digestive system. The circulatory system handles transportation of materials throughout the body. The respiratory system is made up of the organs that supply oxygen and get rid of certain wastes. The excretory system

is the sanitation department of the body, ridding the body of its wastes. The nervous system has as its primary job controlling the body.

NUTRITION

The food you eat today becomes the "you" of tomorrow. The body has the remarkable ability to select needed chemical substances from the beans, beef, milk, and lettuce you consume, and to convert them into just the kind of substances needed to make the body's own flesh and bones. Even when you have ceased growing, food is essential for the repair and replacement of worn-out tissues. SEE PAG 324 TO 326

Food is needed also to stoke the "furnaces" in the cells of the body. When "burned" there, food releases the energy that is needed for all the body's activities.

FOOD ESSENTIALS. A trip to the supermarket provides convincing evidence of the tremendous variety of foods that are available for human consumption. This variety, however, is misleading: there are only a few kinds of essential substances in all of these foods. These are the carbohydrates, fats, proteins, minerals, vitamins, and water.

The common carbohydrates are sugar and starch. They are similar chemically, and both are changed into the same substance —glucose—by digestion. Carbohydrates constitute the prime fuels of the body. Fats and oils are the other large class of fuel nutrients. Pound for pound, fats produce about twice as much energy when burned in the body as do the carbohydrates. In cold climates, such as the polar regions, the people rely heavily on fat intake to supply the heat needed to maintain normal body temperature. Eskimos, for example, eat large amounts of blubber, the fat of the whale.

Water, minerals, and proteins are essential for the structure and the workings of the body. Water is taken in directly in the form of water, or as part of food, since foods have a great deal of water in them. Minerals are required in small amounts. These are provided by the food we eat, if our diet is a good one. The role of calcium and phosphorus in building bones has been mentioned previously. Other minerals serve other vital functions. Iron, for instance, is an essential constituent of hemoglobin, the oxygen-carrying pigment in red blood cells. Liver is an excellent source of this element. Iodine is required for proper functioning of the thyroid gland. Fluorine has been included in the list of needed minerals (and is now added to drinking water in some localities), since it seems to be a factor in preventing tooth decay. Common salt (sodium chloride) is also an essential ingredient of the diet. Proteins, the most complex of the food substances, are abundant in meat (muscle), eggs, cheese, and beans, and are essential in building protoplasm, enzymes, hormones, and other essential body materials.

The vitamins are found in foods in minute amounts. Unlike most of the other food essentials, the vitamins are not used directly as fuels or growth materials. Instead, they act as *regulators* of chemical activity and of growth in the body. At first, the chemical nature of the vitamins was not known and so they were designated by the letters of the alphabet, as Vitamin A, Vitamin B, etc. With increased understanding of the chemical structure of these substances, their specific chemical names are gradually replacing the less exact earlier terminology. Thus, Vitamin C is called ascorbic acid. Vitamin B has turned out to be an entire group of vitamins, with more than a dozen thus far separated and identified out of this complex group.

The proper place to obtain the vitamins that the body needs is from food. A good diet will supply all of the nutritive needs of the body. Vitamins in concentrated form should be taken only on the advice and under the supervision of a physician.

DIET.   Diet is one of the most popular subjects of ordinary conversation. Oddly enough, people generally mean a special diet, such as a reducing diet, when they mention the word. In reality, *diet* means the foods that a person customarily eats. The primary rules of diet are: (1) Sufficient food must be eaten to supply the body's energy needs; (2) A properly varied diet is needed to supply the materials for the growth and functioning of the body.

The word "calorie" is frequently misunderstood. A calorie is not a substance in food. It is simply a measure of heat. A calorie is the amount of heat needed to raise the temperature of a liter (a bit more than a quart) of water one degree centigrade. In other words, to speak of the calories that a portion of food contains is merely to indicate how much heat will be produced when that food is burned. A few examples of the approximate daily calorie requirements of human beings are: a workman doing heavy manual labor 4,000 calories; a housewife— 1,800–2,300 calories; an active teen-age school boy—2,500–3,800 calories. If a person eats much more of the fuel foods than his body requires daily, the extra material may be changed into fat tissue. This is ordinarily undesirable, since the added fat serves no useful purpose and is a burden for the body to carry around. Insurance statistics show that people who are 10 percent or more overweight for their particular build shorten their lives measurably. Since most cases of overweight are the result of overeating, the prevention and remedy are obvious.

THE BASIC FOUR

A well balanced diet is one planned to meet the body's needs for energy, for building all tissues and for the manufacture of the many regulatory substances. In order to make it possible for the general public to select a good diet, simple guides to good nutrition have been developed by nutrition committees of governmental agencies. One of these guides is known as "The Basic Four" (formerly "the Basic Seven"). The groups and the recommended amounts in this diet follow:

(1) *Breads and Cereals* (4 or more servings daily)
Enriched bread and whole grain bread
Flour
Cereals
Potatoes
(2) *Meat* (2 or more servings daily)
Meat, poultry, fish
Eggs, legumes
(3) *Vegetables and Fruits* (2 fruits and 2 vegetables daily)
Fruits, including citrus
Vegetables, including green, leafy, and yellow
(4) *Milk* (adults—2 or more cups of milk or its equivalent daily; children—2 to 4 cups of milk or its equivalent daily)
Milk, cheese, ice cream

The Basic Four provides a foundation for a day's meals and includes choices which allow for variations for seasons, regions, and economy.

DIGESTION—PREPARING FOOD FOR THE USE OF THE BODY

We would starve, despite all of the food that we eat, if it were not for the digestion of this food. Most of what we eat is not in proper form to pass into the blood or to be used by the cells of the body. The digestive system is composed essentially of a long tube and the digestive glands that secrete chemicals which act on food in the tube. The entire tube is known as the alimentary canal. It is surprisingly long—about 30 feet in adults. Most of this length is made up of the coiled small intestine, which is about 22 feet long.

THROUGH THE ALIMENTARY CANAL

Let us observe the changes in food as it travels through the alimentary canal. Before we do, we might look at a preview of what is going to happen. The food mass is going to be chopped, ground, and finally reduced to a kind of liquid mush. At the same time, the molecules of the proteins, carbohydrates, and fats in the foods are going to be split into smaller molecules. This molecule-splitting will be accomplished by the action of enzymes in the various digestive fluids. It will serve two purposes. First, it will permit the molecules to pass through the membranes of the small intestine into the blood stream, thus becoming available to the entire body. Second, it will transform the complex molecules into a form in which they can be used by the cells of the body for building new protoplasm or for burning.

SEE
PA●
32●

The food enters the body via the mouth. The jaws hold the teeth, some 32 in the adult. The front teeth are chisel-shaped and are used for cutting the food. The four sharply pointed canine teeth, at the corners of the mouth, are used for ripping and tearing. These are seen in fully developed form in the cat and dog families. The rest of the teeth are grinders. Breaking up the food into tiny particles makes the chemical action of digestion more effective. While the food is being chewed, the tongue moves it about, thereby helping to mix it with the saliva. Saliva is made in six salivary glands whose secretion is brought into the mouth by tubes or ducts. Enzymes in saliva start the digestion of cooked starches, splitting the large molecules into the smaller ones of sugar. After a few moments in the mouth, the food is swallowed and passes through the food pipe or *esophagus* into the stomach.

Food may remain in the stomach up to four hours, depending upon the kind of food. While there, it is churned about and mixed with the gastric juice from the gastric glands. This juice contains, among other substances, an enzyme that helps to digest proteins. Astonishingly, some of the stomach glands manufacture hydrochloric acid. The minute amount of this acid that is made helps the enzymes to work and also helps dissolve minerals in the food. After it leaves the stomach, the food is pushed into the small intestine.

The small intestine is the main center of digestion in the body. And, as we will see, it is the place where digested food leaves the food tube and enters the blood. Into the small intestine pour the juices of three digestive glands—intestinal juices given off by the glands in the walls of the small intestine itself, bile from the liver, and pancreatic juice from the pancreas. The enzymes in the juices of the intestinal glands and the pancreas, as well as certain salts in bile, complete the process of breaking down carbohydrates, proteins, and fats into simpler substances.

OUT OF THE CANAL.   Digested food is able to pass through the thin membranes of the small intestine into the blood. This process is known as absorption. The small intestine is admirably fitted for the job of absorption. Its 22-foot length, its thin walls abundantly supplied with capillaries, its millions of microscopic, fingerlike projections called *villi*—all serve to make it an effective "blotter" for carrying out the function of absorbing the digested foods and then transferring them to the circulatory system.

WASTE DISPOSAL.   The indigestible part of the food goes into the large intestine. This is large in diameter as compared to the small intestine, but it is much shorter in length, being only about 5 feet long. The material in the large intestine is mainly composed of cellulose from plant foods, and bacteria. Water is removed from this mass as

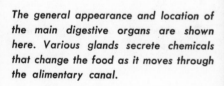

The general appearance and location of the main digestive organs are shown here. Various glands secrete chemicals that change the food as it moves through the alimentary canal.

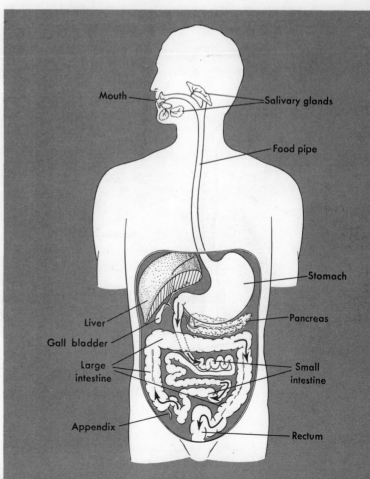

Mouth — Salivary glands — Food pipe — Stomach — Pancreas — Liver — Gall bladder — Large intestine — Small intestine — Appendix — Rectum

it moves along. The waste products form semisolid feces that are eliminated from the body through the rectum.

RESPIRATION—HOW THE BODY BREATHES

A person may be able to survive without food for a week or more. Without oxygen, however, the human being cannot live for more than a few minutes. Oxygen is required by every cell for the oxidation of food to produce energy. It is the job of the respiratory system to supply this vital oxygen and also rid the body of the carbon dioxide wastes resulting from cellular oxidation.

MECHANICS OF BREATHING. If you place your hand on your chest, you will notice that it rises and falls as you breathe.

Not so readily noticed is the movement of the diaphragm, an arched muscular partition between the chest and the abdomen. Air is not "breathed in," but is forced in by atmospheric pressure (see chapter 9A) through the action of the diaphragm and of the chest muscles. During inhalation, the diaphragm contracts and is thus pulled downwards. At the same time, the muscles of the ribs contract and pull them up and out. These movements enlarge the chest cavity and reduce its pressure on the lungs. The outside air is thus pushed into the nose, windpipe, and lungs because of its greater pressure.

During exhalation, the diaphragm moves up and the ribs move down and in. These movements decrease the size of the chest cavity, squeezing the air out of the lungs. When at ease, this cycle takes place about 12 to 15 times a minute. During exer-

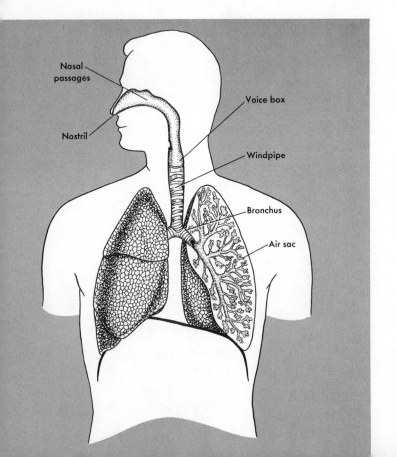

Nasal passages

Voice box

Nostril

Windpipe

Bronchus

Air sac

The pathway for air from the nostrils to the air sacs is shown in this diagram.

cise, or other strenuous activity, we breathe more rapidly and more deeply. This is necessary in order to obtain the added oxygen needed for the increased energy required by such activity. When a person sleeps, the breathing rate lessens.

PATHWAY FOR AIR. The inhaled air passes through the nostrils, where small hairs strain out large dust particles. It then traverses the nasal passages. The labyrinthine arrangement of the bones in the nasal passages enormously increases the area of mucous membrane over which the air must pass. This is desirable because the mucous membrane moistens, cleans, and warms the air to body temperature. If these actions did not take place, the air entering the lungs might damage the lung membranes and thus not only cause irritation but also provide an entry for harmful mircroorganisms. This is the reason why it is more healthful to breathe through the nose than through the mouth.

The air now enters the throat cavity and then passes by the trapdoor guarding the entrance to the windpipe. This trapdoor, the *epiglottis,* closes when we swallow food, to prevent food particles from entering the windpipe. The windpipe branches into two pipes, the bronchi. These lead the air by means of smaller and smaller tubes ultimately into the air sacs of the lungs.

EXCHANGES IN THE AIR SACS. The air sacs are microscopic chambers in the lung tissue. The lungs have nearly a billion of these balloon-like structures. This provides an enormous area for the absorption of oxygen from the air. The air sacs have very thin walls, richly supplied with capillaries. The oxygen passes through the thin walls of the air sacs and capillaries and into the blood, and eventually is carried to every cell in the body. Moving in the opposite direction, carbon dioxide and water vapor leave the blood capillaries and pass into the air sacs. When we exhale, these gases pass out of the body as part of the exhaled air.

CARE OF THE RESPIRATORY SYSTEM. We have discussed the value of breathing through the nose. Since enlarged *adenoids* (tissues in the nasal passages near their junction with the throat cavity) may prevent breathing through the nose, it is wise to seek competent medical advice when these are present. Chronic mouth-breathing, particularly in children, warrants medical observation to find the reason and possible correction.

SEE PAGES 326 TO 327

Cigarette smoking has recently taken the forefront as a cause of respiratory-system damage, notably cancer of the lungs. To quote the American Cancer Society[1]

> *The fact that cigarette smoking is the major cause of lung cancer has been proved beyond a reasonable doubt. Twenty-eight studies have shown that a history of cigarette smoking is much more common among the lung cancer patients than among those without the disease. Five follow-up studies have demonstrated that the death rate from lung cancer among cigarette smokers is about ten times that of nonsmokers.*

> *Studies also indicate that cigarette smoking is associated with about 75 to 80% of all lung cancer. The incidence of the disease increases with the number of cigarettes smoked and the length of time the smoker has smoked. Conversely, lung cancer death rates decrease among those who discontinue smoking, and the decrease is roughly proportionate to the length of time since last smoking.*

> *Microscopic examination of the lung tissue of cigarette smokers shows progressive cell changes of the type that precede cancer. The degree of such changes increases with the amount of cigarette smoking, and diminishes as smoking is discontinued before the development of invasive cancer of the lungs.*

[1] *Answering the Most Often Asked Questions About Cigarette Smoking and Lung Cancer.* (American Cancer Society, New York City, 1962.)

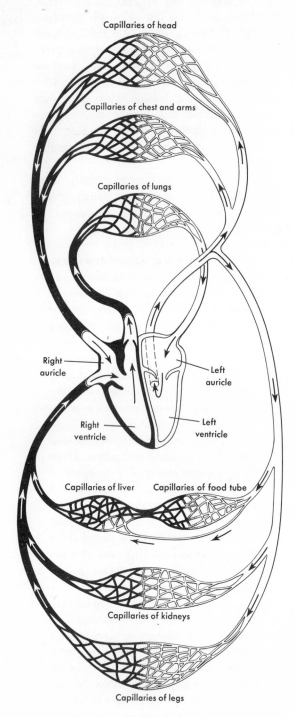

Capillaries of head

Capillaries of chest and arms

Capillaries of lungs

Right auricle

Left auricle

Right ventricle

Left ventricle

Capillaries of liver   Capillaries of food tube

Capillaries of kidneys

Capillaries of legs

Blood moves around the body in a continuous closed circuit of arteries, veins, and capillaries, with the heart serving as a pump.

Intelligent people will follow the medical research in this field carefully and be guided by the recommendations of scientists who are investigating lung cancer. In this connection, we should point out the importance of periodic chest x-rays. This is one of the most valuable health measures for early detection of tuberculosis and of lung cancer. In most communities, such x-rays are provided without cost.

CIRCULATION—HOW MATERIAL IS TRANSPORTED AROUND THE BODY

THE HEART. More than three hundred years ago, William Harvey demonstrated that blood flows in a continuous, closed circuit through the body. This was the first time in history that an accurate concept of circulation was formed. Even now, when knowledge of circulation is widespread, we are awed at the marvels of the heart mechanism. Here is a living pump that pushes blood through 70,000 miles of blood vessels, and beats 100,000 times a day, every day of our lives.

The heart is a muscular pump about the size of your fist. It is made of four compartments. The upper two are known as *auricles*, and the lower two as *ventricles*. The left ventricle is the largest chamber, making up three-quarters of the whole heart in size. Its muscle wall is three times as thick as that of the right ventricle. This difference is related to the job performed by each of these parts: the left ventricle must push the blood completely around the body, but the right ventricle pushes the blood only to the nearby lungs.

AROUND THE CIRCULATORY SYSTEM. With the help of the illustration (left) let us join the blood entering the right auricle and journey with it throughout the body until it makes a complete circuit. But before we do, let us take a quick look at our itinerary. Blood enters the right side of the heart from all parts of the body, goes to the lungs, returns to the left side of the heart and then goes to all parts of the body. It is then returned to the right side of the heart and the trip starts all over again. Stated more briefly —blood travels from the body to the right heart to the lungs to the left heart to the body. Notice that to make a complete round trip, blood has to go through the heart twice. Now for the details.

Blood is brought to the right auricle by two veins, the *venae cavae*. This blood has come from every part of the body except the lungs. When the right auricle is filled with blood, the trap door or *valve*, as it is called, between it and the right ventricle opens, and the blood flows into the ventricle. The valve closes as the right ventricle contracts and sends the blood through *arteries* (blood vessels that carry blood away from the heart) to the lungs. In the *capillaries* which envelop the air sacs of the lungs, the blood picks up oxygen and gets rid of carbon dioxide and some water. The blood now goes back to the left side of the heart by means of *veins* (blood vessels that return blood to the heart).

The oxygenated blood from the lungs enters the left auricle. When this chamber fills, the valve between it and the ventricle opens and the blood flows into the left ventricle. The valve then closes, which prevents a backflow of the blood as the large muscles of the left ventricle contract. This sends the blood coursing throughout the body by way of the *aorta*, the largest blood vessel in the body. In the adult it is slightly thicker than a man's thumb. The aorta sends branches into the head and arms, and the main line continues down through the chest and abdomen and sends off a number of branches. It finally divides into two arteries that supply the legs.

The blood from the arteries is widely dispersed through a branching network that divides first into *arterioles,* and then into millions of thin-walled capillaries to reach all the cells of the body. Here, oxygen, food, and other needed substances are transferred from the blood to the cells. In turn, the tissues give up to the blood their waste products. The capillary network reunites to form the veins, which then return the blood to the heart again by way of the venae cavae, the largest veins in the body. The cycle then starts over again. It has been estimated that it takes about fifteen seconds for the blood to make one complete circuit of the body.

Of the 4,000 gallons of blood that are pumped through the heart daily, none is absorbed through the walls of the chambers. The muscles of the heart receive blood containing oxygen and food in the same way as all other tissues. For this purpose, a special set of arteries branch off from the aorta and go immediately into the heart structure. These are the coronary arteries. The coronary veins bring the blood back from the heart tissues to rejoin the main circulation.

BLOOD. The blood stream is the distribution system of the body. This surging fluid carries food and oxygen to all the cells of the body. It receives and delivers many chemical products, such as the hormones. It collects wastes and brings them to the organs that remove them from the body. The blood also contains chemicals and cells that protect the body from disease. In addition, the blood has its own built-in system for plugging leaks in any of its pipes.

Blood is composed of cells and a liquid in which the cells are immersed. The cells are the red and white blood cells and the platelets. The liquid is the plasma.

The red cells (also known as red corpuscles), as we noted previously in our study of tissues, are the oxygen carriers. These cells contain hemoglobin, which is made of an iron compound combined with protein. Hemoglobin is responsible for the red color of blood. It is the substance that enables the red cells to carry oxygen. The hemoglobin molecule contains four atoms of iron. Lack of iron in the diet may lead to one type of *anemia*, a blood condition in which there is an insufficiency of hemoglobin. In the lungs, the hemoglobin combines with oxygen. When the blood reaches the tissues of the body, the oxygen is released.

There are about 25 trillion red cells in the body. Each cell lives only about four months. New red cells are manufactured in the red marrow of bone.

The white corpuscles may be regarded as the standing army of the body. One of their primary jobs is to fight off invading bacteria and other harmful microorganisms. This they do by engulfing the harmful organisms, digesting them, and thus destroying them. White corpuscles are able to squeeze through tiny openings in the capillary walls and leave the blood stream. They move, much like an ameba, to any part of the body where danger threatens. This has earned them the name of "wandering cells." Normally, there are about 6,000 to 10,000 white corpuscles in every cubic millimeter of blood. A cubic millimeter is a tiny drop. In this same drop there will be about five million red corpuscles.

The plasma is about 90% water, in which many substances are dissolved. These include fats, sugars, proteins, antibodies (protective substances against disease), hormones, enzymes, minerals, and wastes. The adult human has about 5 quarts of blood. The donation of one pint of this precious fluid to the Red Cross, for building up the nation's stockpile of plasma for emergencies, will not harm a healthy adult. The body replaces such losses quickly.

One of the protective mechanisms of the blood is clotting. Everyone has had the experience of cutting himself. Small cuts or scratches bleed for a few minutes and then, without any outside assistance, stop, and a hard clot forms. This prevents excessive loss of blood. In clotting, a plasma protein called *fibrinogen* coagulates into threadlike fibers that slow the outflow of blood, entrap the corpuscles, and thus form a clot.

The circulatory system is a *closed* system of arteries, veins, and capillaries. The capillaries, however, are thin-walled enough for some of the liquid part of the blood to pass through them and to bathe the tissues of the body. This escaped liquid, together with the white blood cells that have forced their way out of the capillaries, make up the fluid called *lymph*.

CARE OF THE CIRCULATORY SYSTEM. Care of the circulatory system is attracting increasing attention at the present time. Health statistics show that in the United States heart disease is the number one cause of death. Of course, part of this is the inevitable result of those measures that have enabled people to live longer. Circulatory ailments are particularly the problem of middle and old age, so in an aging population it is to be expected that these will become prominent health concerns. Although the toll is exacted in later life, it is during our younger years that we pave the way for an ailing or a healthy old age. The normal rules of healthy living apply with equal force to the heart and its blood vessels. These include a moderate, balanced diet, exercise in the fresh air and sunshine, sufficient sleep, freedom from excessive worry, and a periodic medical checkup. Cigarette smoking, referred to earlier in connection with lung cancer, is also related to heart disease. The death rate of cigarette smokers from coronary heart disease is at least double that of nonsmokers.

EXCRETION—GETTING RID OF BODY WASTES

During normal activity of the body, waste products are formed. The chief wastes of the body are carbon dioxide, water, urea, and salts. Water and carbon dioxide are formed in every cell as a result of the oxidation of food to produce energy. We have already described how carbon dioxide is eliminated through the lungs. Water is disposed of in three places—the lungs, the skin, and the kidneys. The water exhaled from the lungs can be seen readily on a cold winter day. Sweat coming from the sweat glands of the skin is mostly water, together with some salt. This is brought to the sweat glands by the blood circulating in the skin. Evaporation of the sweat not only rids the body of excess water, but is a valuable way of cooling the body.

Urea is a product resulting from the breakdown of protein foods and of protoplasm. It is excreted chiefly by the kidneys. Each of the two kidneys has about a million microscopic filters. The blood flows through these filters, and the urea, salts, and water are removed. These flow into the bladder as urine, which is eliminated from the body periodically. The kidneys also perform the essential job of controlling the concentration of practically every chemical in the blood. They eliminate excess substances and retain valuable ones. As a result, the fluids which eventually leave the capillaries to bathe the cells of the body provide the cells with a uniformly favorable environment.

Urine gives valuable clues to body health. Among the substances for which urine is analyzed are sugar and albumen. Sugar in the urine may be indicative of diabetes. Albumen may signify that the kidneys are not functioning properly.

GROWTH

Food supplies the primary building material of the body. Proteins and water, together with other food substances, are changed by the body cells into new living protoplasm. This change of food to protoplasm is called *assimilation*. As more protoplasm is formed, cells become larger and then divide to form more cells. This increase in the number of cells takes place by a process called *mitosis*. In mitosis, the hereditary units in the nucleus, the *genes*, are doubled and then equally divided between the two new cells. The cytoplasm (the protoplasm outside the nucleus) also divides, and thus two new cells are formed that are identical to the original cell. In this way, an epithelial cell in the skin, splitting by mitosis, produces two new identical epithelial cells.

Some of the vitamins play an important part in regulating growth. Vitamin D, for instance, is needed for proper growth of the bones. Some of the hormones, the secretions of the endocrine glands, also have a role in growth regulation. We discuss these in another section of this chapter.

THE BODY FRAMEWORK AND HOW IT IS MOVED

The human body is built on the same plan as a modern skyscraper. There is a rigid internal arrangement of beams and girders, the skeleton, to which the rest of the structure is attached. The human framework has the added feature of flexibility: its parts can be moved. The long bones are designed as levers that are moved by the muscles attached to the bone framework. The bones of the skull are different. They are plates that form a box to hold and protect the brain. A typical long bone, such as the upper arm bone, is not solid bone. It is a cylinder, with the space within occupied by marrow. This hollow formation gives great strength combined with lightness. The bone tissue itself, as we have seen, is composed of scattered bone cells around which have been deposited mineral salts, chiefly calcium phosphate. The minerals give the hard quality to bone.

All muscles exert power by shortening or contracting; relaxation of muscles following contraction cannot produce bodily

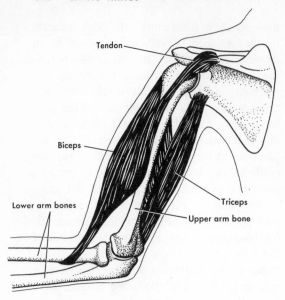

Tendon

Biceps

Lower arm bones

Triceps

Upper arm bone

One muscle bends the arm and another muscle straightens it.

BODY CONTROL

The human body is under the dual control of the nervous system and the endocrine glands. The primary control is exerted through the nervous system, whose branching nerves penetrate the entire body. Chemical control is effected by the endocrine glands, through the hormones they secrete into the blood stream. Let us look first at the nervous system.

THE NERVOUS SYSTEM. The headquarters of the nervous system is the brain. Messages from most parts of the body enter and leave the brain by way of the main trunk line—the spinal cord. The exact nature of a nerve message is not known, but a combination of electrical and chemical changes pass along the nerve cells when a nerve impulse is transmitted. The eyes, ears, and sense organs in the skin, tongue, and nose are specialized for receiving sensations. (See chapter 22A for a description of the ears and chapter 23A for a description of the eyes.) The unit of structure and function of the nervous system is the nerve cell, or neuron. We saw, in the section of this chapter called "Blueprint of the Body," how a neuron is fitted for its job.

The brain's main parts are the cerebrum, the cerebellum, and the medulla, as shown in the illustration. The *cerebrum* is the part of the brain where the centers that control consciousness, intelligence, reasoning, memory, imagination, and learning are located. Also in the cerebrum are centers that receive and interpret sensations, such as sight, hearing, smell, taste, pain, pressure, and others. Here also are the centers for initiating and directing voluntary activities. Lift your arm to wave to a friend. The impulse for this action originates in the cerebrum, speeds from there down a nerve pathway in the spinal cord, and then along a nerve to muscles in your arm, causing them to contract.

movement. Therefore, when you move any part of your body in one direction, you are using a different muscle from the one you use to move that same part in the opposite direction. A convenient place to see how this operates is in the arm. (*As you read the following, consult the illustration on this page.*) On the upper surface of the upper arm is the bulging biceps muscle. This is attached firmly at the shoulder. The other end of the muscle is attached to the bone of the forearm by a tendon. Underneath the upper arm is the smaller triceps muscle, similarly connected. If you place your left hand around the right upper arm so that the fingers encircle the arm, you will be able to discover the movements of the two muscles. When you flex the arm, you will feel the biceps contract and harden, while at the same time the triceps relaxes and loosens. When the forearm is lowered, the biceps relaxes and the triceps contracts. Complex motions, such as handwriting, may involve many pairs of muscles.

The *cerebellum* is a coordinating center for muscular movements. Any action, such as walking, requires the coordinated functioning of many muscles. The precise timing of muscular contraction and relaxation is ensured by the cerebellum. Another job of the cerebellum is the control of balance. In the mastoid bone of the skull, which also contains the inner ear mechanism, are three canals oriented in the three directions of space. A fluid moves in these canals and the position of the body in space is communicated to the cerebellum by the effect of this fluid on the sensitive nerve tissue lining the canals. The cerebellum automatically interprets these messages and sends impulses to the proper muscles to maintain the body in balance.

The *medulla* controls what might be termed the housekeeping functions of the body. Heart rate, breathing, and body temperature are some of the activities regulated by the medulla. It is obvious that this is a vital center. Any damage to the medulla may cause instant death. The medulla is just within the skull at the base of the brain. Nerve pathways in it continue downward without interruption into the spinal cord.

The *spinal cord* is the main pathway between the brain and the rest of the body. Through the spinal cord go many of the nerves that bring impulses to the brain from the body receptors, the sense organs. In the opposite direction, impulses from the brain to many parts of the body pass through nerves in the spinal cord. In addition, the spinal cord is the center for many reflex actions.

A reflex action is the simplest type of action of the nervous system. If, unthinkingly, you touch a hot object with your finger, what happens? You pull your hand away before you are aware that it is hot. Awareness comes later. The action starts with stimulation of receptors in the finger by the hot object. The nerve impulse generated in the heat receptors of the skin is carried

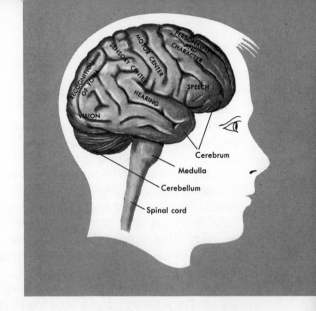

The three parts of the brain control different levels of activity. The cerebrum is the center for voluntary movement, for the reception of sensations, for reasoning and memory. The cerebellum controls balance and the co-ordination of muscles, as in walking. The medulla controls such automatic functions as breathing, digestion, and heartbeat.

along by sensory nerve cells to the spinal cord. Here, connections are made to motor nerve cells. The motor nerve cells carry a message out to the muscle and the muscle contracts, pulling the arm away. All of this takes but a few thousandths of a second. Meantime, a second series of connections are made in the spinal cord, and a message starts up to the brain to advise the brain that the object was hot. This message, however, does not arrive in the brain until some thousandths of a second after the hand has been pulled away. We can appreciate the protective advantage of reflex actions when we realize that hundreds of these inborn, automatic actions are built into the workings of the human body.

CHEMICAL CONTROL. The endocrine glands constitute the other controlling system of the body. The action of these organs was first discovered in the middle of the nineteenth century. Scientists found that certain glands poured chemicals into the blood stream that affected various parts of the body. Such chemical messengers were named *hormones*, which is a Greek word meaning "I excite." Hormones are produced in minute amounts. They enter the blood directly from the gland where they are made. Thus they are quickly carried to all parts of the body. This explains the rapid action of some hormones. The main endocrine glands of the body are the pituitary, thyroid, islands of Langerhans, adrenals, thymus, and gonads.

The *pituitary* gland is attached to the base of the brain. It produces a number of

Chemical control of the body is exercised by the endocrine glands, whose secretions are carried by the blood to all parts of the body.

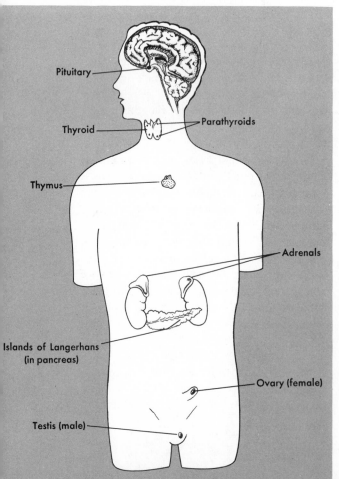

Pituitary

Thyroid

Parathyroids

Thymus

Adrenals

Islands of Langerhans
(in pancreas)

Ovary (female)

Testis (male)

different hormones. One of these regulates bone and body growth. Excessive secretion during childhood may produce a giant. Undersecretion, on the other hand, may make an individual a dwarf. Other hormones of the pituitary gland regulate blood pressure and many phases of the reproductive cycle. The pituitary gland is often called the "master gland" because it produces hormones that control many other ductless glands.

The *thyroid* gland is in the neck in front of the voice box. Its secretion, *thyroxin,* regulates the speed at which the body works, or body metabolism, and body development. The *islands of Langerhans,* located in the pancreas, secrete *insulin*, needed by the cells for the burning of sugar. Insulin extract, first used in January, 1922, for the treatment of diabetes, has saved the lives of thousands of persons.

The *adrenal* glands lie on top of the kidney. One of its secretions, *adrenin,* is important in regulating blood pressure. It causes the heart to beat faster and more strongly and has been used as a lifesaving drug when the heart falters. Other secretions of the adrenal gland are involved in regulating cellular oxidation.

The *thymus* gland, located just below the neck and behind the top of the breastbone, has recently been found to have some important functions. The thymus increases in size until puberty and then begins shrinking until it is reduced to its size at birth. Studies on animals indicate that thymus activity is significant in body defense against bacteria, viruses, and other foreign substances, and that the thymus may hold the key to a number of baffling diseases such as rheumatoid arthritis, and to the growth of cancerous tissue.

The *gonads,* the testes and ovaries, not only make the reproductive cells, but also manufacture hormones. These influence the so-called secondary sex characteristics such as the deep voice and broad shoulders of the male, and the breasts and broad hips of the female. In the female, they also are involved in the cycle of egg production and menstruation.

HEREDITY

The passing of traits from parents to children has engaged human interest for many centuries. However, it was not until 1865, when Gregor Mendel, an Austrian monk, performed his classic experiments on thousands of pea plants, that the science of heredity was launched.

Heredity has its basis in reproduction. The sperm contributed by the male and the egg by the female contain all the hereditary material that the new individual is going to receive from his parents. The hereditary material is concentrated in the nucleus of each of these cells. There it is organized into structures called *chromosomes,* which are visible under the microscope.

Every cell in the human body contains 23 pairs of chromosomes, or 46 chromosomes—with one exception. The exception

is the sperm or egg cell that the mature individual produces. These contain only 23 chromosomes, one from each of the pairs. When the sperm and egg unite to form the fertilized egg, this cell contains 46 chromosomes, or 23 pairs of chromosomes. Therefore the new individual arising from the fertilized egg has the same number of chromosomes as each of his parents, having received half from each.

Within the chromosomes are thousands of the basic determiners of the body's traits—the *genes*. It is beyond the scope of this book to go into the ways in which the genes operate or to discuss in detail the principles of heredity. However, we cannot overlook the spectacular discoveries of the last decade which have led us close to the unraveling of the chemical nature of gene activity. It appears that the gene material is a complex molecule known as DNA, which is a convenient way of referring to deoxyribonucleic acid. The DNA molecule may be considered a kind of code, or template, which sets patterns for the making of the vital substances within a cell. From the

Each body cell in a human contains 46 chromosomes. The chromosomes shown here are those of white blood cells, enlarged 1400 diameters. Those on the left are from a man, those on the right from a woman. (The symmetrical appearance of each chromosome is due to the fact that each of the 46 has replicated itself in preparation for cell division.)

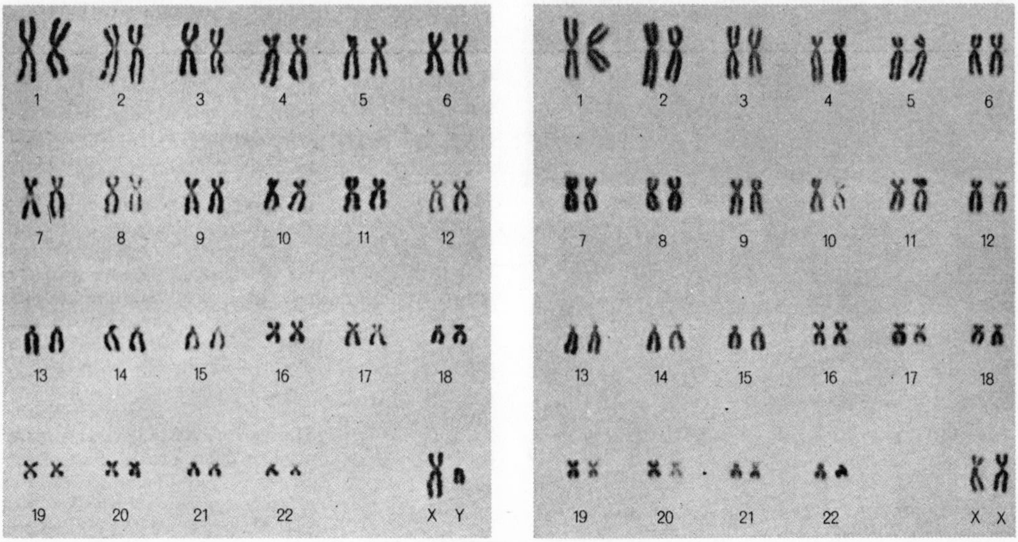

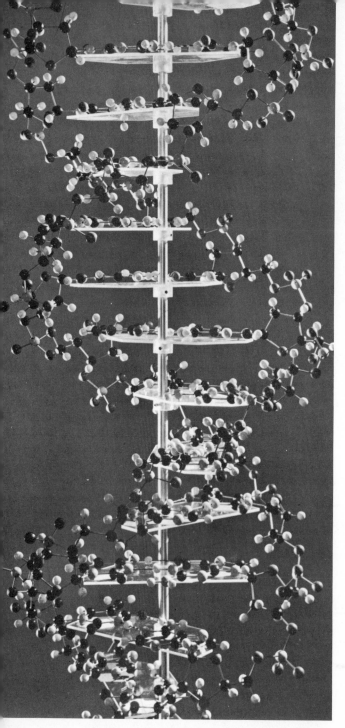

Model of DNA (deoxyribonucleic acid) molecule. Often called "the code of life," DNA is the chemical found in the nucleus which stores, codes, and sends chemical "information" to the rest of the cell. Watson, an American, and Crick, a Briton, took all the available chemical and x-ray information and postulated that the parts of the DNA molecule were arranged in this double helix fashion.

viewpoint of the entire body, DNA may be compared with the architect whose plans eventually result in the construction of a building from a heap of steel, concrete, and wood. The particular kind of DNA an individual has determines his characteristics. In reproduction, the basic "information" encoded in the parental DNA is meticulously reproduced (replicated) and passed on to the offspring via the sperm and eggs.

A new phrase has come into being to characterize the discovery of these molecules of life—*molecular biology*. It is hoped that further research in molecular biology will lead to many medical triumphs, including, hopefully, the solution of the mystery of cancer.

Before leaving this discussion of heredity we should understand that the characteristics of an individual are determined both by the particular package of genes he has inherited from his parents *and* by the environment in which he grows up. Heredity and environment work together to produce the individual.

HEALTH AND DISEASE

Many people think of health only when they do not have it—when they are ill. They regard health as the absence of illness. On the contrary, health is a positive phenomenon. It is the normal condition of the body with all of its parts working efficiently together. The old Greek concept of "a sound mind in a sound body" is still a good definition of health. SEE PAG 326 TO 327

The body has natural lines of defense that ordinarily keep it safe from infectious diseases. The skin that surrounds the entire body is the first line against invasion. As long as the skin remains intact, it serves as a strong wall to ward off harmful disease agents. Just beneath the outer skin is a layer of fat tissue that serves as an insulator to help maintain the body heat. Fat tissue also serves as padding material, cushioning our bodies from the shocks of a "hard world." We have already mentioned the standing army of the body, the white blood corpuscles. The blood also carries the chemical warfare service of the body. In the blood plasma, a variety of chemical substances, called *antibodies*, help to overcome microbes and their poisonous products.

Illness may result from various causes. Some diseases develop from nutritional lacks. These are the deficiency diseases, such as scurvy and rickets. Some diseases result from a breakdown of one of the body organs. An example of this is diabetes, a disease caused by a breakdown of cells of the islands of Langerhans in the pancreas. When they stop secreting sufficient insulin, the body cannot effectively oxidize the sugar taken in with food.

DISEASES CAUSED BY GERMS. Probably the most widespread diseases are those caused by other living things invading the body. The chief of these are the *microorganisms, or microbes*—microscopic one-celled organisms. Both plant and animal micro-

organisms can cause disease. The chief plant offenders are the microscopic *bacteria*. Tuberculosis, diphtheria, scarlet fever, meningitis, typhoid fever, and one type of pneumonia are examples of diseases caused by bacteria. Some one-celled animals, or *protozoa*, are disease producers. Probably the most widespread disease of the world is malaria, caused by a protozoan. The parasite is injected into the blood by an Anopheles mosquito carrying the organism. Another protozoan disease is amebic dysentery, common in the tropical regions. A third group of microbes is the *viruses*. Viruses are extremely minute particles having characteristics of both living and nonliving material. Smallpox, measles, poliomyelitis (infantile paralysis), yellow fever, and influenza are some of the virus-caused diseases.

HOW GERMS INVADE. Prevention of diseases caused by germs requires that we know how the microbes are spread. Some enter the body with the air breathed in, usually near an infected person. Measles, diphtheria, scarlet fever, whooping cough,

This is a photomicrograph of one strain of the poliomyelitis virus. These viruses are magnified 77,000 times by the electron microscope.

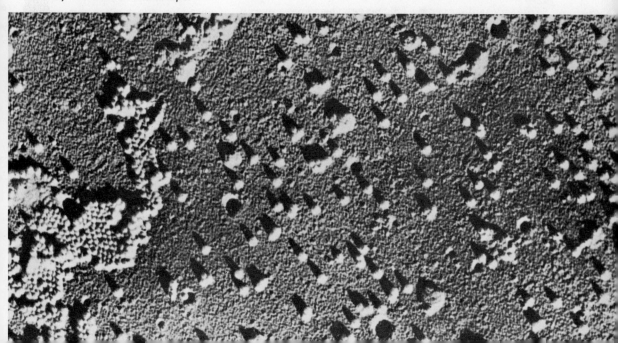

the common cold, and smallpox are examples of diseases spread in this way. Some microbes, such as those causing typhoid fever and amebic dysentery, enter the body with food or water. Some microorganisms enter the body through breaks in the skin. Boils and skin infections may be caused by microorganisms that come in through this channel. In other cases, the infective organism must be introduced by the bite of a carrier, as is the case with malaria. Yellow fever is likewise transmitted through the bite of a mosquito carrying the yellow fever virus. Rabies is acquired through the bite of a dog sick with rabies. The saliva of the rabid animal contains the rabies virus.

VACCINES. Protective substances that enable the body to resist disease have been a goal of medicine since earliest times. Only within the last century and a half has this aim been partly realized. In 1790, Edward Jenner, an English country doctor, discovered that individuals infected with cowpox, a mild disease resembling smallpox, acquired immunity against smallpox, a dangerous disease. Today, vaccination is recognized in all civilized communities as a preventive against this dread scourge. After Jenner's work, almost a century passed before another immunizing agent for human beings was discovered. This was the vaccine against rabies produced by Pasteur.

A *vaccine* is a preparation of killed or weakened germs. When a vaccine is injected or placed on a scrape in the skin, it causes the blood to start chemical warfare against the particular type of germ in that vaccine. The blood produces antibodies to combat the weakened or killed germ. These antibodies remain in the blood stream for many years, and will be effective against an invasion by the active, living germs of the specific disease. Vaccines are used against typhoid fever, smallpox, rabies, whooping cough, and yellow fever.

A great victory in medicine were the vaccines developed by Dr. Jonas Salk and Dr. Albert Sabin against infantile paralysis. The Salk polio vaccine consists of dead viruses while the newer Sabin oral polio vaccine consists of live, but weakened, viruses. Each vaccine has the ability to stimulate the body to produce antibodies which are active against the virulent forms of polio virus. They have markedly reduced the incidence of polio with its toll of paralysis and death.

Two measles vaccines—one a live-virus preparation and the other an inactivated virus—are now licensed for use in the United States. At the present writing, the United States Public Health Service has recommended immunization for all children over nine months old without a history of measles.

A vaccine may also consist of poisonous substances, called *toxins*, produced by disease-causing microorganisms. Toxins are used in developing immunity to diphtheria, lockjaw, and whooping cough. The toxin causes the body to produce its own antibodies.

SERUMS. Sometimes we use the antibodies produced in an animal to treat a human disease. Blood extracted from such animals and prepared for injection constitutes a *serum*. Serum injections are used for diphtheria and lockjaw. The type of immunity acquired in this way is temporary, and is frequently used as a cure rather than as a preventive measure.

DRUGS AGAINST DISEASE. For thousands of years, man has searched for drugs to fight disease. We are indebted to primitive man for quinine, from the bark of the cinchona tree, so effective against malaria. Many other valuable drugs have been extracted from plants. It was not until 1932, however, that a drug that would destroy many kinds of bacteria in the body was discovered. This was sulfanilamide. Since then a chemical family of *sulfa drugs* have been synthesized by scientists to fight different bacteria effectively. Between 1936 and 1940,

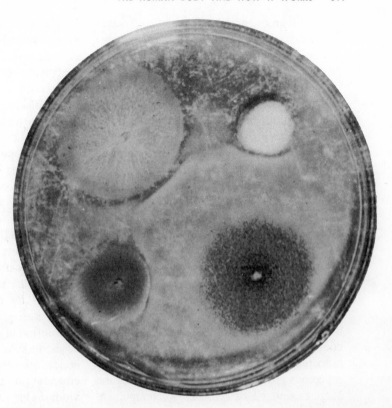

Growing in this petri dish are four different molds. Scientists grow thousands of mold cultures such as these in hopes of finding a new mold that can be used to produce antibiotics.

the number of deaths from pneumonia decreased by 50 percent as a result of the use of sulfa drugs.

Sir Alexander Fleming discovered the antibacterial action of penicillin in 1927. He was awarded the Nobel Prize for his work.

ANTIBIOTICS.   In 1927, Alexander Fleming, an English scientist, noted the peculiar behavior of some bacteria cultures that he had left untouched for some time. They had been contaminated with some mold growth, and oddly enough, where the mold was growing the bacterial colonies seemed to dissolve. This was the beginning of the golden age of antibotics in modern medicine. An *antibiotic* is a substance produced by a living organism that can kill microbes or stop their growth. The bacteria in Fleming's culture had been destroyed by an antibiotic produced by the mold. It was named *penicillin*, after the mold *Penicillium*. The availability of penicillin in World War II undoubtedly reduced the number of deaths. Fleming was awarded the Nobel prize for his work. Since the finding of penicillin, many

other antbiotics, derived from other species of mold, have been used successfully against various diseases.

CANCER. Cancer has been known from ancient times, but it has only become a paramount health problem in this country in this century. It is now the second largest cause of death in the United States. This has come about, in part, because we are now living long enough to be stricken by cancer, which is mainly a disease of middle and old age. A *cancer* is an abnormal growth of cells. For reasons yet obscure, the cells seem to become outlaw. They multiply out of control of the normal body limits. They invade neighboring tissue, crowd it, rob it of its nourishment, and destroy it. The greatest danger occurs when cells break away from the original growth and move through the body to colonize elsewhere. The aim of cancer fighting is to detect and remove the cancerous growth before colonization occurs. Most cancers, if detected early enough, are curable. One method of achieving this is to see a doctor if you detect any of the following signs of *possible* cancer, described by the American Cancer Society:

1. *A sore that does not heal.*
2. *A lump or thickening in the breast or elsewhere.*
3. *Unusual bleeding or discharge.*
4. *Change in a wart or mole.*
5. *Persistent indigestion or difficulty in swallowing.*
6. *Persistent hoarseness or cough.*
7. *Persistent change in bowel or bladder habits.*

In addition, periodic medical examinations are recommended for the detection of early signs of cancer.

How can cancer be fought when it is detected? At present, the only known methods are surgery and radiation. Surgery is still the primary treatment. The entire growth must be removed without leaving one cell behind. The second method involves destruction by means of x-rays, radium, and other radioactive substances. It is fortunate that cancerous cells are more easily killed by these radiations than are normal cells. A more recent source of radiation are the radioactive isotopes (see chapter 19A). Science holds out the hope that one day we may find the specific cause or causes of cancer and learn how to prevent this disease.

HEALTH AND SOCIETY. Over the years, society has found that some health problems can be helped by legal methods. Today every state has laws relating to health. Some of these are: compulsory vaccination as a prerequisite to entrance into school, quarantine in cases of certain contagious diseases, medical licensing, sanitary and health codes, and many others. We also rely upon education to improve the health of each individual. One of the cardinal objectives of all education is the promotion of robust health. When hygiene and health are effectively taught, they will result in action by each individual to attain and maintain sturdy health, a basic asset for him and for our nation.

Some of the important generalizations developed in this chapter are:

Man studies his body in many ways.

The unit of structure and work of the body is the cell.

Similar cells are organized into tissues for efficient performance of their job.

Groups of tissue cooperate to form organs that perform the major work of the body.

We require food for energy, for growth and repair, and for proper functioning of our bodies.

Food is prepared for the use of the body by the process of digestion.

A continuous supply of oxygen is needed to obtain energy from food.

The body has a number of automatic mechanisms that maintain a constantly favorable internal environment.

The respiratory system supplies oxygen to the body and gets rid of carbon dioxide.

Materials are transported around the body by the circulatory system.

Blood flows in a closed system of tubes around the body, pumped by the heart.

The skin, the kidneys, and the lungs rid the body of liquid and gaseous wastes.

Growth is the result of cell multiplication.

All movement in the body is powered by muscles.

The bony skeleton serves as a framework for the body.

The body is under the dual control of the nervous system and the endocrine glands.

The genes in the nucleus of the cell carry the hereditary traits.

The gene material is a complex molecule known as DNA.

The DNA molecule may be regarded as a kind of code which sets patterns for the making of vital cell substances.

Heredity and environment work together to produce the individual.

Reasonable adherence to the rules of hygiene will go far toward keeping the body in good health.

Application of medical discoveries has greatly prolonged life.

Man has developed powerful weapons in fighting disease.

Education is of prime importance in keeping our nation in good health.

DISCOVERING FOR YOURSELF

1. Acquaint yourself with the latest research findings concerning the relationship of lung cancer and smoking.
2. Use the Red Cross Handbook or some other similar source and learn to attend to simple injuries.
3. Examine bones, muscles, tendons, and other body parts of animals from a meat market to learn about body structure and function.
4. Look through a microscope at slides of body tissues, blood cells, bacteria, or other slide material related to the human body to see details of structure.
5. Conduct, with the assistance of your local Board of Health, a study of the communicable diseases that have been prevalent in your community during the past two years. Find out how they are spread and what the public health service does about control.
6. Visit a research laboratory where experiments in nutrition or other related areas are being carried out. Learn as much as you can about the methods employed.
7. Take your body temperature and pulse and your rate of breathing. Exercise and note the change in pulse and respiration.
8. Try to find out more about molecular biology and DNA.
9. Find out how the electron microscope has contributed to our new knowledge of cells.

CHAPTER 13B

Teaching "The Human Body and How It Works"

With the material on the human body, we come to the living thing closest to children themselves. The child's body, because it is alive, eats, breathes, grows, and responds to stimuli, should be observed and used as a firsthand source for developing concepts of how it is built, how it works, what it needs, and how it keeps well. Through this, children add to their understanding of all living things.

Pupils are naturally curious about their bodies and how they work. Probably we have not capitalized sufficiently on this natural curiosity to teach about the general structure, function, and care of the human body. It is expected that study about their bodies will develop these attitudes: that the human body is a wonderful machine, that its development is natural, that with reasonable care the body can remain healthy.

The subject matter may be organized around solving such problems as:

How do our senses help us?
Why do we need different kinds of food?
How much should we weigh?
How do we keep food from spoiling?
How does our community safeguard our health?
What can we do in our homes to prevent accidents?
How does the body protect itself from germs?

Later chapters (22A, 23A, and 23B) give further information as well as suggestions for teaching about the eye and ear in connection with the material on light and sound.

Some of the things younger children may profitably do are listed below:

1. Find out where the food we eat comes from (plants, animals, and so forth).
2. Learn how our senses help us to make discoveries, by using eyes, ears, nose, and others to find answers to questions.
3. Observe how we change in weight and height as the months go by.
4. Learn what constitutes a good breakfast, lunch, and dinner.
5. Find pictures that show different kinds of foods and put them in groups that show such things as: "meat that we eat"; "vegetables that we eat"; "animal products that we eat"; "fruits that we eat"; "plant products that we eat."
6. Make pictures that show good health practices, such as: "getting plenty of sleep"; "exercising"; "eating the right foods."
7. Visit a grocery and meat market to observe the different kinds of foods and discuss such problems as: "Where did the foods grow?" "How are they kept from spoiling?" "What must be done to them before we eat them?"

LEARNING WHAT THE BODY CAN DO

To develop an appreciation of the many intricate things the body can do, suggest that pupils make a list of twenty-five kinds of things that their bodies have done since they got out of bed. (Examples: chewed food, ran, breathed in air, remembered things, and so forth.) This list may be used later to see how many of the items are understood better at the end of the study than they were before and whether there are ways of helping the body to do some of these things better.

BREATHING

Before a recess or outdoor activity period, ask the children to count the number of times they breathe out in a minute (about 18–20 times), while sitting quietly. Make a record of the findings. After the outdoor activity, have the children make a new count. They will

A graphic experience such as this serves to make the scientific principles real and understandable. Arithmetical computations also add to the comprehension.

find a significant difference. Discussion should bring out the idea that the body requires air for its activities, and that the more active the body is, the more air is needed.

A simple way of *seeing* the amount of air breathed out is to breathe into a tube connected to a jug of water, as shown in the illustration. As the air goes in, water is pushed out of the jug. Using this device (which is called a *spirometer*) pupils may compare quiet and rapid breathing by seeing how many normal exhalations are necessary to empty the jug in each case.

By *dividing* one gallon by the number of exhalations needed to empty the jug, pupils can estimate the amount of air in *one* breath. By *multiplying* the amount of air in one breath by the number of breaths in a minute, pupils can estimate the amount of air breathed in in one minute. Here again, pupils will see mathematics used meaningfully.

HEARTBEAT

Pupils are probably aware that exercise increases their heartbeat as well as their breathing rate. One way of measuring heartbeat is to measure the pulse, which is caused by the surge of blood through an artery. Two fingers (not the thumb) of one hand should be placed on the wrist of the other hand. Experiment, as in the breathing study, to determine the effect of exercise on the number of heartbeats per minute. The pupils should understand that the increased rate of heartbeat brings blood, containing food and oxygen, more rapidly to all parts of the body.

MOVEMENT

Children can develop some general ideas of how muscles and bones move the body by observing their own motions. How, for example, is the forearm moved? Ask the pupils to allow one arm to hang loosely, with the palm forward. Have them feel the muscle in front that goes from the shoulder almost down to the elbow. A tendon connects this muscle, called the biceps, to the forearm bone. If they lift the forearm by bending the arm at the elbow, they will feel the biceps muscle becoming shorter and thicker. The shortening of the biceps actually pulls on the forearm bones, causing the arm to rise.

How is the arm straightened out? Have the pupils make a fist and with the other hand feel the muscles along the back of the arm tighten as they straighten the arm. This muscle pulls the arm straight. With these simple observations on their own body, children begin to understand that movement of large body parts is accomplished by the shortening of muscles, which work in pairs and pull on the bones.

They can also look for muscles, tendons, and bones in a chicken leg or in a shank of lamb (meat is usually muscle). They can list the ways in which their own muscles have helped them in the course of a day.

LEARNING ABOUT FOODS

It is easy to find information about kinds of foods. The following assignment is appropriate: "Bring to class a list of all the sources we may use to find information about the kinds of foods and how they help us. Think of places, books, magazines, newspapers,

A survey of the eating habits of pupils makes the learning more interesting and functional. Such an activity involves gathering, analyzing, organizing data as well as devising a graphic way to show the results. It can also result in improved eating habits.

and people." This activity of locating material will not only supply much useful informational material but will give pupils an opportunity to use their originality and resourcefulness in finding it.

The school cafeteria is a practical place to learn about foods. The manager or someone else on the staff may explain how she decides on a menu, and show how it provides a balanced diet.

The teacher will, with some planning, accumulate much material about foods that pupils may use. He may help to point out to pupils the importance of seeing that the material, if it is commercially prepared, is honest in its presentation. There is much good material published by various manufacturers. Such material should be evaluated for accuracy before it is used by pupils. It is important to remember that no one factor is completely responsible for good health. The U. S. Department of Agriculture publishes material for teachers on school lunches and on nutrition.

In connection with the study of foods, radio and television advertising may come in for consideration. For example, the fantastic claims that are made about some kinds of bread may be discussed. The fact that you eat a certain kind of bread is no assurance at all that you will be healthy. Bread is only one of the important foods. The fact that your favorite radio personality. advertises a certain brand of breakfast food is not sufficient reason for using it to the exclusion of all others. It may be interesting for pupils to copy down some of these advertising claims and analyze them. A scientific approach is essential in trying to interpret advertising, and certainly, a science class is an appropriate place to be introduced to such an approach. Obviously, young pupils cannot scientifically test these foods, but once they can see, for example, that every kind of bread cannot be the best, they may become more alert in interpreting advertising. This same attitude, of course, holds true for patent-medicine advertising.

A very practical application of the principles learned about foods and a balanced diet may be made if children plan refreshments for a party; plan, prepare, and serve a meal at school; or plan the menu for a picnic. The selection and preparation of foods involve many of the ideas that pupils have learned. (In connection with the study of food and how it supplies the needs of the body, the practice of selling candy and soft drinks in school should be evaluated and made to conform to what are considered good health practices.)

The sources of foods are sometimes surprising to children, especially those who live in large cities. It may be interesting to list the foods served in the school lunch room or at home on one typical day and let each pupil choose one kind of food and report as much as he can discover about its source. The following are typical: sugar, cereal, bread, milk, fruit juice, honey, vinegar, spices, butter, and cooking oils. Labels on packages may help supply information.

LEARNING ABOUT TEETH

The periodic dental inspection in the school provides an opportunity to ask the dentist to talk with pupils about the care of the teeth. Such a discussion may be very helpful to pupils because it comes from an authoritative source. Individual pupils who are having dental work done may ask their dentists to explain causes of tooth decay and similar things to them. Dentists often can provide charts that show tooth structure and tooth care, and they usually have the latest information about the use of fluorine and other new discoveries to prevent tooth decay. As we have said before, the best results in the use of such a resource person come about if he is given a list of specific questions and is in other ways prepared for his school visit or for an interview.

DEVELOPING GOOD HEALTH PRACTICES
IN THE HOME, SCHOOL, AND COMMUNITY

As pupils learn more about the human body and what is needed to keep it well, they begin to find out for themselves what health practices are and how their own practices and habits can be improved. This activity may well be carried out through three or more committees or small groups, each with a chairman. The three groups may make a survey of health practices in their own homes, in the school, and in the community, respectively.

To begin, the teacher may ask pupils to suggest ways of carrying out the investigation, and the group may make a list of questions they want to answer and of specific places to look for the answers. For example, at home they may find out how food is kept and prepared to avoid the effects of harmful bacteria, how dishes are washed, how milk and water are made safe, how the house is kept clean, and what safety measures are observed. In the school, pupils may investigate such things as how the drinking fountains are kept in sanitary condition, how the building is kept clean, and what the health authorities do to prevent the spread of diseases in school. In the community, they may study the work of the health department to see what health practices are required in restaurants, food stores, and public buildings and how garbage and sewage disposal and water purification are carried on. This committee may arrange for a member of the health department to come to the school to

The methods of water purification are better understood if children do some experimenting themselves. They should understand that processes vary with needs and that several steps may be necessary before some water sources are safe to drink.

answer questions and explain the work of the department. This is another example of the close overlapping of science and social studies. The most successful teachers and administrators are concerned that pupils learn about health, develop good health habits, and grow in ability to find and organize information.

Pupils should become acquainted with the purpose and methods of inoculation against smallpox, diphtheria, polio, measles, and other diseases—a practice often carried out in school under the direction of health authorities. If tuberculosis tests or any similar medical tests are being made, pupils will often ask questions about them. This is an example of a so-called "incidental" experience that may produce very important learning and result in a thorough study of health problems. A visit to a dairy or to a local food-processing plant or cannery may yield considerable practical information about sanitary practices in preserving and handling foods.

PRACTICING SAFETY EDUCATION

A great deal of useful material has been prepared to help in the teaching of safety.[1] The activities of the school safety patrols are important and useful to the general study of safety.

---

[1] National Commission on Safety Education, National Education Association, 1201 Sixteenth St. N. W., Washington 6, D. C. Write for catalogue of safety publications. These publications include material on general safety education, bicycle safety, fire safety, safety patrols, etc.

National Safety Council, 425 North Michigan Ave., Chicago 11, Ill. Write for information about current publications.

American Automobile Association, Traffic Engineering and Safety Department, Pennsylvania Ave., at Seventeenth St. N. W., Washington 6, D. C., or your local branch. Write for information about publications.

American Red Cross, Washington 6, D. C., or your local Red Cross chapter. Write for first-aid material.

It's Smart to be Safe - to Stay Safe you have to Stay Smart

ALL DAY LONG—FROM THE MOMENT YOU START OUT TO SCHOOL

YES NO   IF YOU'RE WALKING, DO YOU
Cross streets at CORNERS?
WAIT for GREEN LIGHT?
Look — look both ways?
W-A-L-K, not RUN?
OBEY the safety patrol?

YES NO   IF YOU'RE BICYCLING, DO YOU
Drive CLOSE to CURB?
OBEY TRAFFIC RULES?
REFUSE HANDLEBAR rides?
Keep from HITCHING to AUTOS,
BUSES, STREETCARS?

YES NO   IF YOU'RE SKATING, DO YOU
Tie on skates FIRMLY?
Skate ONLY on SIDEWALKS?

SKATING is only WALKING ON WHEELS, so
Cover the WALKING RULES with your
HAND and see if you're SMART enough
to SKATE to school SAFELY.

SCHOOL BUS

YES NO   IF YOU'RE RIDING IN A BUS, DO YOU
Quietly TAKE your SEAT?
KEEP from sticking your ARMS and
HEAD out the window?
KEEP FROM talking to driver?
Look — look both ways when get-
ting off?

YES NO   DURING SCHOOL DO YOU
W-A-L-K, not RUN, in HALLS?
W-A-L-K, not RUN, on STAIRS?
WAIT your turn, not PUSH?
Know your FIRE DRILL?
Know the NEAREST EXIT?
Keep PENCILS, CRAYONS, out of
MOUTH?

YES NO   WHEN CLASS IS DISMISSED, DO YOU
Go home RIGHT AWAY?
Know the SMART and SAFE way to
WALK, SKATE, BICYCLE, or RIDE a BUS
home?
COVER these RULES with your HAND
and see if you are SMART enough to
get home SAFELY.

YES NO   WHEN YOU PLAY DO YOU
PLAY on SIDEWALK or PLAY AREA?
WAIT your turn, not PUSH?
Swim in a SUPERVISED place?
KEEP FROM playing with fire?
Know ALL the WALKING, BICYCLING,
and SKATING rules?

PLAY AREA

**YES NO   ANIMALS ARE NOT AS SMART AS
YOU ARE, SO DO YOU**
KEEP from TEASING them?
AVOID strange animals?

YES NO   AND WHEN YOU GET HOME, DO YOU
Put your SKATES on a nail or hook?
Put your BICYCLE on the porch or in
the garage or cellar . . . OFF THE
SIDEWALK?
W-A-L-K, not RUN, on STAIRS?
KEEP FROM playing with matches?
PUT all TOYS in box or on SHELF?
Put matches in METAL BOX?
KEEP FROM playing with firearms?
KEEP FROM reaching for handles of
pots on STOVE?
KEEP FROM touching electrical fix-
tures with wet hands?
PICK UP pins from FLOOR?

Science classes may study pupils' use of bicycles and, with the help of the safety patrol, devise some regulations to ensure safe practices in and around school. With the school custodian, pupils may make up a similar set of suggestions for safety within the school building. Pupils may investigate places in and around school and at home that are possible hazards and make suggestions about avoiding or correcting these hazards. There are many instances of excellent results from such work by pupils.

Safety education should be touched on in many of the school activities and should be made a regular part of the curriculum. The study should not be academic; it should be practical, sensible, and understandable. It should begin with very young children and continue throughout the school experience.

The *Check List for Child Safety*[2] at the top of the opposite page is reproduced by permission of the American Red Cross.

RESOURCES TO INVESTIGATE

1. Local doctors, dentists, and nurses for information about the human body and health.
2. Life insurance companies for bulletins, charts, and other information.

---

[2] *Accident Prevention Check List for Child Safety*. Write to the American Red Cross, Washington 13, D. C., or to your local Red Cross chapter for information about this check list and about other safety-education publications.

3. Meat markets for bones and other animal body parts to examine to see structure.
4. Local Red Cross for printed information about health and safety matters.
5. National Dairy Council, 111 N. Canal St., Chicago 6; National Live Stock and Meat Board, 36 South Wabash Ave., Room 700, Chicago 3; Wheat Flour Institute, 309 W. Jackson Blvd., Chicago 6; Cereal Institute, Inc., 135 S. La Salle St., Chicago 3; United Fresh Fruit and Vegetable Association, 777 14th St., Washington 5, D. C.—for catalogues of teaching material.
6. High school biology teacher to show blood sample under microscope, and for other aids.
7. Local health and sanitation officers to discuss health practices and rules and to obtain information about symptoms of child diseases.
8. Local museums containing displays of models of the human body.

CHAPTER 14A

Ancient Animals and Plants

One of the most important achievements of science in the past hundred years has been the discovery of *change*—the discovery that everything in the universe, from the scenery outside our window to the clusters of stars in the heavens, has always been changing.

Hills are worn down into plains; rocks crumble into soil. New mountains rise from the earth; sea bottoms become dry land. The face of the earth changes and with it the kinds of animals and plants that live on it.

So slowly do these changes occur that man's memory, even when aided by written records, can scarcely be expected to encompass them. The few thousand years of civilization are but a fleeting moment in the giant calendar of earth events. Indeed, only in the last century have we understood the meaning of the evidences that lie around us, evidences

that say: The earth is very old, the earth is ever changing.

Animals and plants of the past have recorded their own history in a number of different ways. Let us consider some of these.

RECORDS OF PAST LIFE

ACTUAL REMAINS. The remains of the woolly mammoth, an elephant with long thick hair that became extinct thousands of years ago, have been found in the ice and frozen soil of Alaska and Siberia. Arctic explorers report that the animals were in an excellent stage of preservation; their sled dogs even enjoyed eating the flesh. Ancient man must have known living mammoths, for he made paintings and carvings of these creatures on the walls of his caves.

SEE PA 354 TO 355

Natural asphalt is also an excellent preserver of animals. At the La Brea tar pits, in Los Angeles, California, there is an ancient pool of hardened asphalt from which the bones and teeth of thousands of animals have been dug. Among these are the remains of birds, wolves, horses, and bison that lived about 15,000 years ago. Many animals were probably trapped while attempting to prey on creatures struggling in the sticky mass. The tar sealed the bones of these creatures, and preserved them perfectly from decay. Best known of the entombed animals is the extinct saber-tooth, a member of the cat family.

The remains of the woolly mammoth and the saber-toothed cat are both examples of *fossils*, which may be defined simply as the records of ancient life. Of course, when most organisms die, they are not preserved. They usually decompose into chemicals that enrich the soil and the waters of the earth. Only under special conditions do animals and plants leave some kind of a permanent record of themselves.

We have seen how ice and asphalt provide a means for preserving the remains of animals. These, however, are unusual ways of fossil formation. Much more common are those in which plants and animals are submerged in water and covered with sand and mud.

STONY RELICS.   In the Petrified Forest in Arizona are the stony relics of great pine trees that once grew there. At some time in the past, about 190 million years ago, these trees were submerged in water that flooded these ancient forests. How was the wood in these trees replaced by stone? The first stage in this transformation was the filling of the pores or cells with minerals carried in solution in the water. Silica was the common mineral deposited in the pores by the waters percolating through the trees. Later the silica hardened into rocky quartz. Finally the woody cell walls were changed chemically into hard materials.

This method of fossil formation, called *petrifaction*, is unique in that it preserves the finest details of organisms. Thus we can still see in the stony pine trees at the Petrified Forest and other similar places the annual growth rings, knots, and even the microscopic cellular structure of these ancient plants. The bones of animals,

Here the three lobes of the tri-lobite are clearly visible. Fossil records show that there were many kinds of trilobites living in the shallow waters of ancient seas. Those pictured here were found near Lockport, N. Y.

An ancient relative of the modern scallop has left its record in rock.

being porous, may also be petrified by the infiltration of minerals such as silica, or, in some cases, lime.

PRINTS IN STONE.   We have all seen footprints of children or dogs in concrete sidewalks. These, obviously, were made while the concrete was moist and soft. Many plants and animals of the past have made records of themselves in a similar way.

Certain types of rocks, notably the *sedimentary* rocks, were once soft muds and sands and therefore impressionable, like the soft concrete just referred to. Most sedimentary rocks are formed by the gradual settling of materials to the bottoms of bodies of water. (These rocks are discussed more fully in chapter 6A.) Plants and animals that happened to be buried in this soft material, called sediment, left an impression that became permanent when the sediments hardened into stone. The shell of a clam, for example, may have fallen into the soft mud and sand at the bottom of a lake. Later the mud and sand slowly hardened into rock. The shell disintegrated and disappeared, but

SEE PAGE 355

a permanent impression was left in the surrounding rock.

Prints of plants and of animals in rock are plentiful, and are the most common type of fossils. One example is the footprint of an animal. Dinosaurs wandering in the Connecticut valley about 150 million years ago left their tracks in the sand of that time, which later hardened into red sandstone rock. (See photograph on page 347.)

FINDING FOSSILS.   Fossils are not rare, as some people think they are. In many localities in the United States, fossil hunts are practicable for amateurs. Local geological societies, museums, and the state Geological Surveys will often be glad to furnish fossil prospectors with the essential information. You may not find dinosaurs, but you may be able to discover fossils of seashells, fish, and leaves. Amateurs should cooperate with the organizations just named to avoid indiscriminate collecting and possible destruction of valuable specimens.

Fossils may occur in any region where there are layers of sedimentary rock. Fortunately for fossil hunters, these underlie most of the United States. Rocks exposed in cliffs, along the sides of ravines, in stream beds, in quarries, and in excavations along railroads and highways may yield fossils. In many cases, good specimens may be found in loose fragments of rock in these places. Sometimes the fossil must be broken from the rock. For this a hammer and a stone chisel or a mason's hammer are useful. Permission of property owners should be sought before entering private areas and prospecting for fossils.

IMPORTANCE OF FOSSILS.   Fossils tells us many things. Some, like those of the dinosaur and the saber-toothed cat, tell us of strange animals of the past that are now extinct. Some fossils, like those of ferns (plants that usually live in warm places) found in the Arctic regions, suggest that the climate there has changed. Fossil seashells found high in the Catskill Mountains and fossil coral reefs in Chicago indicate that these areas were once covered by seas. But most important of all, fossils, when studied in relation to the rock formations in which they are found, reveal the *sequence* of life down through the ages.

Ancient life has left us a monumental library inscribed in stone, in which the rocky books are stacked one on top of the other. The oldest volumes in this picture-book library are on the bottom of the pile and the most recent acquisitions are on top.

Of course, the library of stacked volumes is the layers of sedimentary rocks that have accumulated down through the ages. We recall from our previous consideration of "Prints in Stone" that these rocks and the fossils in them were formed under water after the soft bed of mud and sand had hardened into stone. Layer upon layer of rock was built in this way. In some later period, the whole mass may have been elevated by a great earth movement, or the sea may have receded, thus making the rock a part of man's landscape.

The Grand Canyon of Colorado furnishes us with such a sample of ancient history. There, layers of rock a mile high have been exposed to man's view by the slow but relentless cutting action of the Colorado River and by weathering. A climb up the walls of the Canyon is a trip through time, for the building of its rocks required hundreds of millions of years. At the lowest or oldest rock formations, we search in vain for fossils. As we proceed upward we find our first evidence of life, the remains of simple water plants, the group known as algae. Climbing higher, we find fossils of simple animals without backbones. The trilobites, which we shall describe later, are a notable and characteristic example of these. Seaweed is also represented here. A few hundred feet higher we detect the first evidence of vertebrate life in the fossilized remains of fish scales, along with contemporaneous relics of shells and corals. Much further up the canyon walls we discover the first evidences of land plants and animals. Primitive "evergreens" and fern-like plants are seen here; insect fossils are in evidence

SEE PAGE 355

A climb up the Grand Canyon of Colorado is a trip through time, for the building of these layers of rock required hundreds of millions of years.

for the first time; tracks of crawling amphibians and reptiles are found in the sandstones. We notice also that some invertebrates, like the trilobites, are no longer seen.

The Grand Canyon is but one of thousands of places where the earth has written its own history. From a study of these, and from other evidences, scientists have come to the following conclusions:

1. *Life has existed on the earth for at least 2 billion years.*
2. *The kinds of living things on the earth have been different in different periods.*
3. *Some types of life have become extinct.*
4. *Simple forms of life appeared first; more complex forms appeared later.*
5. *The more complex forms arose originally as modified descendants of simpler forms.*

Taken together, these conclusions constitute our understanding of the history of life on our planet.

THE ERAS OF THE EARTH

Current estimates of the age of the earth vary, but all agree in counting it in billions of years. Recent studies indicate that the earth is about 5 billion years old. The evidences for this were discussed in chapter 6A.

Geologists, the scientists who study the changing earth, divide the history of our planet into long periods called eras. Each era is separated from the next one by some great disturbance in the crust of the earth and by some marked changes in living things. The chart on the facing page identifies the four eras of geological history and gives some of their outstanding characteristics.

In thinking about the vast span of geological time it is helpful to remember that:

1. *For about half of its long history, the earth was apparently barren of life.*
2. *Man is a newcomer. If all earth time were compressed into one year, then man would come on the scene on December 31, just a few hours before midnight.*

The four eras, in order, are Cryptozoic ("obscure life"), Paleozoic ("ancient life"), Mesozoic ("middle life"), and Cenozoic ("recent life").

EARLY LIFE

THE CRYPTOZOIC (OBSCURE LIFE) ERA. The way in which the earth, its sister planets, and the sun were formed is still an open question. (See chapter 7A for a discussion of various theories of the origin of the solar system.) According to a currently popular theory the earth began as a cloud of cold dust and gas, which in time contracted to form the body of the earth. The primeval earth heated up slowly, taking perhaps a billion years to reach a molten state. It may be imagined that during the early Cryptozoic era the entire earth was a huge chemical laboratory in which the future materials of this planet were put together. In this liquid stage the heaviest substances sank to the center of earth, the lighter floated to the surface, and the others found their place in between. Huge bubbles of various gases, including water vapor, erupted from the molten mass to form the first atmosphere.

A thin crust of cooled rock formed on the surface of the earth. The churning molten mass underneath constantly burst through weak points in this skimpy covering, bringing outpourings of lava (molten rock) accompanied by smoke and flame. Wave upon wave of lava spread across the original crust and congealed into the rock that may have formed the platforms for the continents as we know them today. There was no water

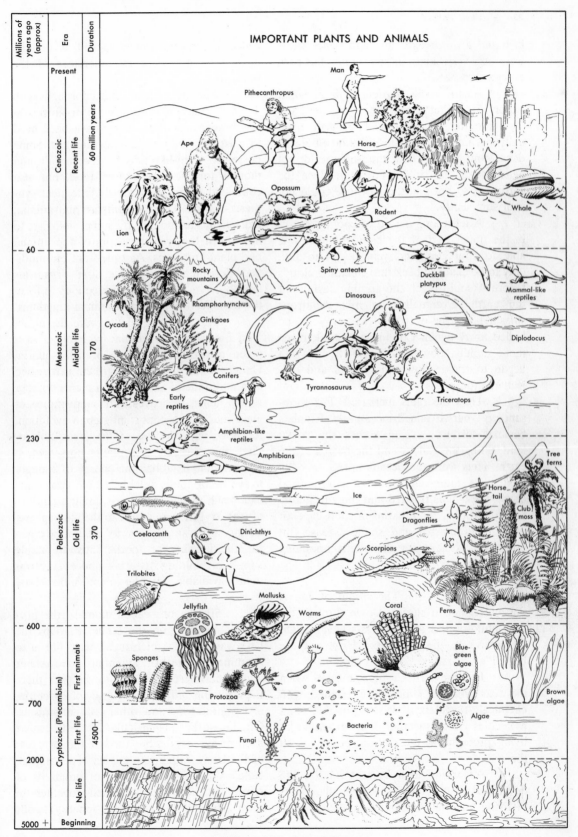

Millions of years ago (approx)	Era	Duration	IMPORTANT PLANTS AND ANIMALS
Present			
60	Cenozoic — Recent life	60 million years	
230	Mesozoic — Middle life	170	
600	Paleozoic — Old life	370	
700	Cryptozoic (Precambrian) — First life — First animals	4500+	
2000			No life
5000+			Beginning

Progress of life through the eras.

in liquid form at that time and hence there were no rivers, lakes, or seas—only hot rock everywhere.

As the rocks hardened, more water vapor and other gases were released and rose into the atmosphere. The earth gradually became wrapped in an atmosphere so dense and cloudy that the sun could not penetrate it. Still it did not rain, since the earth was so hot that the moisture could not cool sufficiently.

After a long period of cooling, water in the upper part of the cloud blanket was able to condense, and rain began to fall, only to be changed back into steaming clouds before it could reach the sizzling surface of the earth. Eventually the first raindrops splashed on the warm rocks, only to be boiled away again. Cooling now took place more rapidly, however, so that at last rain began to trickle down the slopes and collect in little pools.

Then the rains increased. For thousands of years it rained incessantly. Rivulets became torrents, raging across the rocky land, filling the valleys and the basins of the earth. Thus were the oceans born.

As more and more water poured down, the clouds thinned and the sun finally broke through, illuminating a landscape of rocky land masses and shallow seas. But upon the whole earth there was no living thing.

LIFE BEGINS.   The origin of life is the mystery of mysteries. Down through the ages philosophers and scientists have sought an answer to the question, "How did life begin?"

In those early Cryptozoic times when the seas and the atmosphere seethed with chemical turbulence, it is possible that molecules joined together to form specks of living protoplasm, the starting points of all life.

According to a current theory, life developed in two directions from these bits of living material. One branch became one-celled organisms which lacked a definite nucleus. These were the ancestors of the bacteria.

The main branch started as cells with a definite nucleus. The original organisms in this branch would probably have been hard to classify as either plants or animals. Some possessed whip-like tails for locomotion and mouths for the ingestion of food, but also contained chlorophyll for the chemical synthesis of food. These organisms, half-animal, half-plant, are thought by some biologists to have been the true ancestors of the animal and plant kingdoms. As time went on, modified descendants of these first organisms developed in two different directions to form the basis for the plant and animal kingdoms.

The first true plants were the algae. You probably are familiar with algae as a green growth on the side of fish aquaria. Under the microscope this growth is revealed as a multitude of simple green plants without roots, stems, or leaves. The appearance of algae marked an important step in evolution, for now, with the aid of the green chlorophyll that these simple plants possessed, it was possible to utilize the energy of sunlight to synthesize foods quickly. At the same time, as a result of photosynthesis, great quantities of free oxygen were added to the atmosphere. Living organisms began to use this oxygen for the burning of food. Thus an ample supply of building materials and energy was made available for the plant and animal world.

Simple, one-celled animals, the protozoa, appeared on the scene. Perhaps the best way to get a picture of early life is to examine a drop of stagnant pond water under the microscope and to discover there the teeming lilliputian world of bacteria, algae, protozoa, and other tiny organisms. One creature is of particular interest because it furnishes a possible link in the progress of life from simple to complex. This animal, called Volvox, is composed of hundreds of semi-independent cells joined together to form a beautiful, translucent sphere. It rolls

SEE PAGE 356

Several groups of invertebrate animals are shown in this restoration of an ancient sea. Some were soft-bodied, some had hard body parts. Some, such as the trilobite, have become extinct.

through the water by the cooperative beating of whip-like flagella, a pair of which extends from each of the cells. Volvox, or creatures like it, may have provided a transition between the one-celled and the many-celled animals.

During the closing stages of the Cryptozoic, a few groups of animals without backbones (the invertebrates) made their appearance in the sea. These included the protozoa, the sponges, jellyfish and their relatives, the sea pens, and various types of worm-like animals. Others were so unlike animals living today that they are hard to classify. Animal life, at least, was limited to the oceans in Cryptozoic times. Even the most advanced of the invertebrates, the arthropods—jointed-foot animals that were later to include crustaceans, spiders, and insects—had their beginnings in Cryptozoic times.

On the other hand, plants had not progressed very far by the close of this era. Those that had made their appearance included bacteria, blue-green algae, the brown algae or seaweeds, and mold plants.

The Cryptozoic era did not leave many fossil remains. After years of search in the rocks of this era, we have only a few specimens of the simplest plants—algae and fungi—and low forms of marine invertebrates. Why fossils are so rare is not yet understood. One theory is that organisms of this era had not yet developed hard, easily preservable parts. Another is that the rocks formed during this era were later subjected to so many stresses and pressures that any fossils they may have contained originally have been destroyed. The former theory seems to be preferable because the late Cryptozoic rocks of many areas are quite fresh and unaltered in appearance, yet they generally do not contain fossils.

One indirect evidence of ancient plant life is represented in the "lead" of your pencil. This is not the metal lead, but a carbon material known as graphite. We have good reason to believe that graphite is derived in large part from primitive seaweeds and simple animals. Graphite has been found in Cryptozoic rock, thus furnishing strong but indirect evidence that life was present when some of the oldest rocks were forming, some 2 billion years ago.

More direct evidence of earlier life was found in 1954 by the scientists Tyler and Baghorn. Turning their microscope on rock determined to be 2 billion years old, these scientists discovered fossils of filaments and threads of fungi (mold-like plants). This find was made in Ontario, north of Lake Superior.

ANCIENT LIFE

THE PALEOZOIC (ANCIENT LIFE) ERA.
The next 370 million years of earth history, which began about 600 million years ago, were filled with important events. Plant and animal forms emerged from the seas and tenanted the land. Invertebrate animals multiplied and were kings of the earth, only to be dethroned by the first evolving vertebrates, the fish and amphibia. Reptiles had their beginnings.

The plant world flourished, clothing the barren land with green. The first forests appeared, including those that gave rise to

This restoration of Dinichthys is based on fossil bones found in shale rock near Cleveland, Ohio.

the world's present supply of coal. The major groups of plants took root before the end of the Paleozoic.

The physical events of this era were marked by widespread changes. Seas covered wide areas of the earth—at one time more than three-fifths of North America. Huge mountain ranges, the Appalachian and the Ural, were thrust up by gargantuan folds in the crust of the earth.

THE RISE AND FALL OF THE TRILOBITES.
In early Paleozoic times, life was confined to the water. In the shallow seas covering large parts of the continents, and in the surface water of the deeper oceans lived protozoa, sponges, corals, worms, snails, starfish, crabs, and shrimps. Except for fish, which had not yet appeared, these are the types of animals we find in the sea today. But most of these ancient forms would look strange to our eyes, because they were quite unlike their modern descendants. And these ancient seas would appear strange also because they were the home of the trilobites. These ancient relatives of lobsters and crabs have since disappeared from the earth. Trilobite means "three-lobed" and the trilobite is so named because it was divided longitudinally into three clearly distinguishable parts. (See pictures, pages 331, 337.)

Predominant on the earth for 100 million years, the trilobites averaged only 2 or 3 inches in length. These former kings of the earth dined on decaying plants and animals and microscopic organisms. Later the trilobites fell to a position of insignificance, possibly because of the rise of fish. By the close of the Paleozoic, the trilobites became extinct. We know them today only as stony fossils.

FISH COME TO THE EARTH.
The animals living in the early Paleozoic era did not have backbones. Whatever supporting structures they possessed were external, consisting of shells or plates. The emergence of fish from these lower forms was a most significant event, marking the origin of animals

Giant ferns, club-moss trees (lycopods), and horsetail rushes are some of the plants shown in this restoration of an ancient landscape. It is from such plants as these that coal was formed.

with backbones, the vertebrates, a group that includes the fish, amphibia, the reptiles, the birds, and the mammals, including man himself.

Fish, then, were the first animals with backbones. The earliest forms, however, were quite different from the fish we know today. One of these was the 20-foot-long Dinichthys, the "terrible fish" of the Paleozoic era. Remains of this animal have been found in black shale rock near Cleveland, Ohio.

Dinichthys was well protected by hinged armor plates over the head, neck, and the front of the trunk. It was unique in being the only animal that used its jaw-bones for eating, since its teeth-like structures were nothing but sharp projections of its upper and lower jaws. These fearful jaws were capable of slicing in two any of its contemporaries.

Before the close of the Paleozoic era, sharks appeared, and then the fish with hard bones, which are the ancestors of today's forms.

PLANTS INVADE THE LAND. The scorpions and insects apparently were the first animals to emerge from the waters of lakes and seas, but this event did not occur until late Paleozoic time; they had been preceded by the plants in the invasion of the land. For a billion years the plant kingdom had been confined to water and had not advanced beyond a simple seaweed level of development. Then, in a relatively short period, plants overran the land, carpeting it with green mosses, ferns, and seed plants.

Naturally, the transition from water to land was made at the edges of seas and lakes. On the seashore any of the new water plants that could withstand partial exposure to air might survive on the moist beach when ocean tides retreated. Similarly, lake plants that could withstand seasonal receding of lake waters in dry seasons might survive.

SEE PAGE 356

Having established a foothold on the rocky land, plants advanced steadily. Soil formed for the first time from the organic matter furnished by the decay of many generations of the first plant invaders and from the crumbling rock underneath.

The mosses may have been the first land plants to evolve from aquatic plants. Their conquest of the land was limited because they lacked the internal "pipes" which were needed to carry watery sap any great distance from roots through stems to leaves. As a result the representatives of this group were small and were confined to moist areas.

The ferns, however, did evolve the pipes through which water could be elevated many feet above the ground. Plants now were able to extend their invasion of the ground to the conquest of the air above it. Ferns towered over the Paleozoic landscape.

THE COAL FORESTS. Most of the world's present supply of coal had its origin in Paleozoic forests. For a period of about 50 million years, the prevailing moist climate and swampy terrain provided conditions favorable for the luxurious growth of a group of flowerless plants, many of which were destined for conversion into coal. Included in this group were the club mosses, horsetails and scouring rushes, and the true ferns.

Horsetails, which today are small plants characterized by unbranched, hollow, jointed stems were then trees 75 feet tall and 3 feet in diameter.

Club mosses, which today include the small, inconspicuous plants used as Christmas decorations, were the real giants of the coal forests. One of these, Lepidodendron, had large, needle-like leaves and a branched, expanded crown. A fossil trunk of this plant found in an English coal mine was 114 feet long.

There were also many kinds of true ferns, some of which reached heights of 50 feet.

The conversion of the wood of these swamp plants into coal is not difficult to understand from a chemical viewpoint. Wood is essentially a chemical compound of carbon, hydrogen, and oxygen. Coal is essentially carbon. To change wood into coal, it was only necessary to drive off the hydrogen and oxygen, and then subject the remaining black carbon to pressure.

Two peculiar conditions in the Paleozoic swamp forests favored the formation of coal. First, as generation after generation of trees died, they were protected against rapid rotting by their immersion in the waters of the swamp. Thus bacterial action, instead of decomposing the whole mass of wood, worked slowly on it, removing the hydrogen and oxygen and leaving a substance that had a high percentage of carbon in it.

The second condition responsible for coal formation was the sinking of the land. The resulting floods from nearby seas and rivers dumped thick layers of mud and sand over the accumulated vegetation. The coal forest's existence was thus terminated. In time, the pressure of the mud and sand, and possibly some earth-heating accompanying the pressure, changed the buried vegetation into coal. The mud and sand eventually changed into rock.

The process just described would account for one layer or *seam* of coal. Later, as the flood waters receded and the land rose again, the entire cycle was repeated, on top of the previous formation. Each swamp forest provided another layer of coal. In parts of present-day Illinois, fifty such cycles have resulted in the deposition of fifty seams of coal.

MEMBERS OF THE COAL FAMILY. Different kinds of coal are classified roughly on the basis of how far they have progressed from a plant-like to a coal state, varying from the peaty vegetation of the original swamp to brown coal, then to soft and finally to hard coal.

Peat-making, the first stage in coal formation, is occurring today in such places as the Great Dismal Swamp of Virginia and

The Coelacanth, a cast of which is shown here, was known only as an extinct fish until a living one was caught by fishermen in 1938. Coelacanths are related to the type of fish that probably were the first to crawl out of the water.

North Carolina. Here the partial decay of plants results in a brown, matted mass of peat. When taken from such swamps, peat is cut into blocks, allowed to dry and then used as fuel.

If considerable sand and mud is deposited over the peat, a compact, crumbly mass of brown coal, or lignite, is formed. Large quantities of lignite are found in North Dakota, Montana, and Texas.

Great pressures transform the buried material into bituminous, or soft coal, by far the most important member of the coal family, both as a fuel for industry and as a rich source of many chemical materials.

In the Appalachian regions, particularly in northeast Pennsylvania, the pressure of mountain building squeezed the bituminous coal into hard anthracite, a coal that is ideal for heating dwellings, since it burns with very little smoke, soot, or odor.

The plant origin of coal is apparent because fossil impressions of fern fronds are frequently found in coal beds, and sometimes whole tree trunks that have been transformed into coal.

ANIMALS GO ASHORE. The luxuriant plant cover of Paleozoic times provided a home and a supply of food for the animals that were emerging from the crowded seas. Air-breathing scorpions and spiders, descendants of the sea scorpions, made their appearance. These eight-legged creatures were followed by the six-legged insects. Notable among these for a time were eight hundred different kinds of cockroaches, some of them four or five inches long. No wonder this period is sometimes called the "Age of Cockroaches."

Primitive dragonflies with a wingspread of two and one-half feet flitted around the giant horsetails and club mosses in ancient coal forests. Evidence of these largest insects of all times was found in certain coal fields in Belgium. The richest occurrence of Paleozoic insect fossils yet discovered is in rock a few miles south of Abilene, Kansas, where more than 12,000 specimens have been collected.

The development of the insect group from Paleozoic times on is a fantastic success story, having its climax in the more than 700,000 different kinds of insects inhabiting the world today.

LAND VERTEBRATES. In 1938, a curious fish was dredged up by fishermen working along the coast opposite East London, South Africa. This strange fish was well known to scientists—but only as a fossil! In fact, hundreds of fossil species of these ancient fish, called Coelacanths (seal'a-canths), had been found during the excavation for a new library at Princeton University, New Jersey. The scientific world bubbled with excitement as this "living fossil" was studied and compared with its fossil counterpart. Coelacanths are of particular interest because they are descendants of the primitive lobe-finned fish, which are believed to have given rise to land vertebrates. We will find out more about the lobe-fins presently.

The emergence of one group of vertebrate animals from their aquatic environment depended on the acquisition of two important organs—lungs and legs. The breathing structures of fish are gills. These are essentially flaps of tissue, richly supplied with blood vessels. In the water which must constantly flow over the gills there is dissolved oxygen, some of which passes through the thin gill membranes into the circulating blood. In air-breathing vertebrates, on the other hand, oxygen passes from the *air sacs* of the lungs through moist membranes into the blood stream.

How did lungs arise? Clues are provided by a close look at modern fish. Most fish have sac-like air bladders, a kind of "float" which helps them maintain a stationary position at different depths in the water without muscular effort.

In the curious lungfish that live today in Africa, South America, and Australia, the sac takes on another function during the dry seasons these fish experience. The African lungfish, instead of trying to follow the receding waters into the river, burrows into the mud and forms a hardened mud capsule around itself. The capsule has a tube that permits air from the outside to pass into the mouth of the fish and thence to its air bladders, which function as lungs. The fish lives in the mud capsule for nearly half of the year, breathing with its lungs and living on the fat that it stores up during the wet season.

There is evidence that seasonal dryness, with the receding and even drying up of large areas, occurred during some periods of the Paleozoic. Thus the environmental conditions were favorable for the emergence of air-breathing animals. Those fish whose air bladders could serve as lungs even to a small degree, would have an enormous advantage over others. These fish may have provided the link between water and land vertebrates.

As indicated previously, legs were also essential for the liberation of the vertebrates from an aquatic existence. In fish, the principal locomotor structure is the muscular tail. The paired fins are used for changing direction, for staying in one place, or for moving slowly. But the ancient lobe-finned fish were different. They had paired fins with a basic bone pattern remarkably like that of four-legged animals. It is probable that the forerunner of land animals were lobe-finned fish who were able to crawl out of the water and move about to some extent on land.

Descendants of walking lobe-fins spent more and more time on land. From these were probably derived the amphibians, which today are represented by frogs, toads, and salamanders.

The life history of modern frogs provides a good parallel to the evolution of life from water to land. Frogs begin life as fish-like tadpoles, propelling themselves through the water with their tails and breathing through gills. Before our eyes they transform themselves into land creatures, growing first hind and then front legs, losing their fishy tail, and developing air-breathing lungs. However, their exodus from the aquatic environment is only partial, since most species must return to the water to mate and to lay their gelatinous masses of eggs.

Complete liberation from the water was achieved by the reptiles, who made their appearance in the late Paleozoic era, probably as descendants of primitive amphibia. These reptiles had developed an egg with a tough covering that protected the embryo

SEE PAG 356 TO 357

from drying up on land and yet was porous enough to permit it to breathe.

It must not be thought that *all* animals became terrestrial. Corals, clams, snails, fish, and many other forms continued to live and flourish in the sea.

END OF THE PALEOZOIC. The distance between Altoona and Philadelphia, both in Pennsylvania, was once 100 miles greater than it is today! Such is the estimate of the State Geological Survey of Pennsylvania. How is this possible?

Geologists tell us that the closing period of the Paleozoic was marked by revolutionary earth changes. Terrific pressures on the rocks of the earth's crust caused them to buckle up, just as a rug might if it were pushed together. As a result, mountain ranges, including the Appalachian, were thrust up, reaching majestic heights of 20,000–30,000 feet. Hence a shortening of lateral distances between places occurred.

This period of mountain building, which also produced the Alps in Europe, was followed by the receding of inland waters and the advance of sheets of ice across what is now Brazil, South Africa, and peninsular India. Great extremes of climate marked these late Paleozoic times.

Naturally, these revolutionary upheavals caused great destruction of life. Many marine invertebrates were hard hit by the draining of their homes at the edge of the sea. The warmth-loving, swamp-living plants of the coal forests were replaced by hardy, seed-bearing plants like the conifers, sago palms, and cycads.

MIDDLE LIFE

THE MESOZOIC (MIDDLE LIFE) ERA. The Mesozoic is truly the age of reptiles. During these times, reptilian dinosaurs ruled the land, reptilian "sea serpents" invaded and conquered the ocean, and reptilian "flying dragons" dominated the air. For over 100 million years, the reptiles, modestly represented today by turtles, crocodiles, alligators, lizards, chameleons, and snakes, were the masters of all the habitats of the earth. Our

Tyrannosaurus Rex, the "king" of the dinosaurs. This skeleton gives us some notion of the fierceness of this ancient reptile.

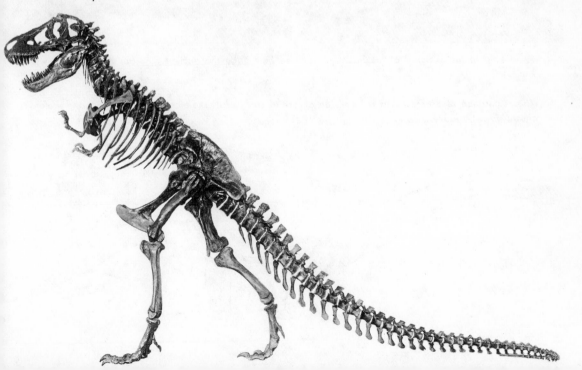

museums are filled with the massive bones left by this mighty group in their Mesozoic graveyards.

THE DINOSAURS. The stars of the ancient reptilian world were the dinosaurs. King of them all was Tyrannosaurus Rex (tī-răn′-à-sô′rŭs), 50 feet long from nose to tail and 18 feet tall when it stood erect on its hind legs. The head of this meat-devouring creature was 4 feet long and was armed with sharp teeth projecting 5 or 6 inches from the jaw. Tyrannosaurus's huge mouth, probably the most savage one of all time, provided this animal with a mighty weapon against less powerful dinosaurs.

Brontosaurus (brŏn′tô-sô′rŭs), the "thunder lizard," another huge dinosaur, was 60 to 70 feet long and weighed about 30 tons. In contrast to Tyrannosaurus, this creature walked on all fours and had a long slim neck ending in a small head adapted for its vegetarian habits. Diplodocus (dĭ-plŏd′à-kŭs), a close relative of Brontosaurus, was the longest creature ever to walk the earth. The best skeleton of this animal, now in the Carnegie Museum, in Pittsburgh, is 87 feet long.

Stegosaurus (stĕg′ô-sô′rŭs), perhaps the queerest-looking of all the dinosaurs, was equipped with a double row of long triangular plates carried erect along its body and extending from its relatively tiny skull along the whole length of its back, almost to the end of its tail. Near the end of its short tail were 2 pairs of heavy spikes, each 2 feet

SEE PAGES 357 TO 358

By looking at the skeleton of the man, we can see how huge the ancient dinosaur Brontosaurus was.

This restoration of Brontosaurus is based on a careful study of its skeleton. Compare it with the skeleton shown directly above.

long, which must have been an effective weapon against the meat-eating dinosaurs. Despite this, Stegosaurus was vulnerable to a flank attack from an enemy.

Protected in a different way was Triceratops (trī-sĕr′à-tŏps), with its 3 horns and a curious bony frill that extended backward from its 7-foot head over its neck.

REPTILES RETURN TO THE SEA.
The reptiles were the first vertebrates to achieve complete liberation from the water; they were also the first to return. The marine reptiles became the largest and most powerful creatures of the Mesozoic seas while their dinosaur cousins ruled the land. The aquatic ichthyosaurus, for example, reached lengths up to 60 feet. Instead of legs, it had relatively small paddle-like limbs; a well-developed fish-like tail was its main organ of locomotion. Instead of going back to shore to lay eggs, it gave birth to its young alive. The ichthyosaurs retained, however, the reptilian characteristic of breathing with lungs.

Another group of marine reptiles were the mosasaurs (mõs-à-sôrs), long slender creatures, some 50 feet long, looking very much like the legendary "sea serpents"

Fossil dinosaur eggs were first discovered in the Gobi Desert of Mongolia in 1923. Distinct bones of embryo dinosaurs were found in some of the eggs.

supposedly "seen" every few years by impressionable mariners.

REPTILES INVADE THE AIR.
The insects, as we have seen, were the first creatures to extend their domain to the regions of the air. The first *vertebrates* to leave the ground and the trees were the reptiles, represented by a group called the Pterodactyls (tĕr′ŏ-dăk′tĭls). These pioneer gliders derived their flight power from a wing membrane made of skin, stretched from the greatly elongated joints of the fourth finger of the forelimb and attached to the body as far back as the hip. The first three fingers were of ordinary length, each terminating in a claw which was probably useful for climbing and for clinging to branches of trees.

Some of the pterodactyls were no larger than a sparrow; others had a wingspread of 20 to 25 feet. Pteranodon, one of the largest of the flying reptiles, must have been a common sight in the Mesozoic air over what is now western Kansas, gliding with its 25-foot wing span over the ancient seas that once covered this area and catching fish with its sharp bill. Despite its large

Pterodactyl, a flying reptile, was a flesh-eater with sharp teeth and long wings, with fingers on the wing bones.

wing span, Pteranodon did not weigh much more than 20 or 30 pounds because its body was small and its bones were hollow.

THE FIRST BIRDS. Another branch of the reptiles took to the air at the same time as the pterodactyls. In this group was the first known true bird, called Archaeopteryx (ar-kĭ-ŏp′tĕr-ĭks). This creature was about the size of a domestic pigeon but was only partly covered with feathers. The short rounded wings were probably not powerful enough for real flight, the animal being more of a glider than a flier.

Archaeopteryx had three fingers at the end of each wing, which were equipped with claws and used for grasping and tearing. These early birds had strong jaws without bills; they also had teeth—something no modern bird has. Also unique was their long bony tail. Thus the only strictly bird-like characteristic of Archaeopteryx was its feathers.

In the next era, from Archaeopteryx and its relatives, there developed birds without teeth and claws, similar to the birds we know today. Modern birds, however, still reveal their reptilian ancestry in the scales that cover their legs.

An egg-laying mammal, the duckbill or platypus, a rarity in the animal world. (See page 348).

MAMMALS GET THEIR START. During most of the Mesozoic era, small inconspicuous animals, most of them no larger than rats, were scurrying around, preserving their lives by their quickness of foot and agility in dodging dinosaurs. This was a new class of animals, which in the next era would become the rulers of the earth. These were the mammals—the warm-blooded creatures that were covered with hair, and suckled their young by means of mammary glands.

The mammals, themselves descendants of reptiles, played second fiddle to the dinosaurs and their cousins throughout the Mesozoic. Toward the end of this era hard times came upon the earth. The coldness and dryness during this period made some of the mammalian characteristics very valuable. Being warm-blooded and covered with fur, mammals could maintain a constant body temperature against freezing weather. Being fleet of foot, they could change their habitat more readily than could many of the sluggish dinosaurs. The fact that they took more care of their young also contributed to their survival. Another virtue may have been significant—their apparently superior intelligence, which we infer from the structure of their fossil brain cases.

OTHER MESOZOIC EVENTS. The rise of reptiles, birds, and mammals in the Mesozoic era should not obscure the fact that changes were taking place in the other and older major groups of animals. In the invertebrate world of protozoa, mollusks, starfishes, lobsters, and insects, and also in the fish world, significant changes were occurring.

Notable advances were also being made in the plant kingdom. The cycads, palm-like seed plants without true flowers, were so abundant that the early Mesozoic is sometimes referred to as the Age of Cycads. Conifers, spruces, pines, junipers, cypresses, and cedars, were abundant in the Mesozoic. Some of these probably reached a height of 200 feet, judging from the logs in the Petrified Forest of Arizona, described earlier in this chapter. A third group that flourished during the Mesozoic was the ginkgoes, now represented by only one species, the ginkgo tree. This species was probably protected from extinction by cultivation in China and and is now common as an imported tree all over the world.

The cycads, conifers, and ginkgoes are part of a group of seed-bearing yet flowerless plants. Another group, the plants with true flowers, also got its start in the Mesozoic, expanding rapidly near the end of this era to become the dominant plant form. The flowering plants include those which are best known and most valuable to man—hardwood trees like oaks, maples, and elms, and the grasses and grains.

Plant evolution affected animal evolution. Thus we find that bees and butterflies put in their appearance with the advent of flowering plants. Hardwood trees furnished shelter and the cereal grains furnished food for many of the evolving mammals.

By the end of the Mesozoic and the beginning of the next era, all of the common types of familiar plants had made their appearance. The animal kingdom, on the other hand, was still to expand enormously, admitting many new members to its ranks.

END OF MESOZOIC. The 170 million years of the Mesozoic ended in the Rocky Mountain Revolution. This was a period marked by the general raising of the land and by mountain-building activities. Tremendous stresses in the crust of the earth, pushing from the west, folded rocks into the great system of the Rocky Mountains, extending 3,000 miles from Alaska to Mexico.

With the raising of land masses, marshes dried up and inland seas retreated. The continental masses grew bigger. The earlier mild climate, which had permitted palms and fig trees to grow in western Greenland, gave way to colder temperatures. Climatic zones became more marked.

The closing of the Mesozoic brought

These large holes were recognized as dinosaur-footprints by paleontologist Roland T. Bird. One hundred and thirty-five million years ago, Brontosaurus, or Thunder Lizard, left these prints in mud flats in a region now called Texas.

the curtain down on the dinosaurs. What caused the total extinction of this mighty group of animals? We can only present the speculations of scientists who have sought for an answer.

One theory has it that the low intelligence of this group was responsible for its downfall. Scientists point to Stegosaurus as the most stupid of all animals, with a brain weighing only 2½ ounces in a body that weighed a few tons. Brontosaurus had a brain of 1 or 2 pounds in a body of 30 to 35 tons. By contrast man has about 2 pounds of brain for every 100 pounds of body weight.

Starvation may have played an important role. A reduction in plant life might have caused widespread starvation among the herbivorous dinosaurs, followed in turn by the starvation of the carnivorous dinosaurs who preyed upon them.

The increasing number of mammals appearing on the earth, some of whom may have had a fondness for dinosaur eggs, may have been a factor in the extinction of these ancient reptiles.

World-wide reduction in temperature could have been fatal to cold-blooded reptiles. With their bodies chilled to the same temperature of their environment for long periods, their activities would be slowed to the point where the maintenance of normal functions would break down.

Some scientists say that the large size of many of the dinosaurs made it difficult for them to adjust to change.

How did the jolly dinosaur
Improve each shining era?
By getting large and specialized
Extinction drawing nearer.
RADCLIFFE "BLUE BOOK"
JUNE 1926

Some scientists think that the extinction of the dinosaurs is linked to the geologic changes in the late Mesozoic, previously described. The drying up of swamps, the disappearance of food, the general coolness of climates all resulted from the basic changes in the earth at the time of the Rocky Mountain Revolution.

Rulers of the earth for 100 million years, about 100 times as long as man's

time on earth, the dinosaurs disappeared completely, giving way at the close of the Mesozoic to those successful latecomers, the mammals.

RECENT LIFE

THE CENOZOIC (RECENT LIFE) ERA. The Rocky Mountain Revolution terminated the reign of reptiles and opened the Cenozoic era, the Age of Mammals. This most recent era, the one in which we live today, goes back about 60 million years. During these years, the earth's surface was given the form familiar to us today. Rivers in the western United States cut deep channels in rock to form magnificent gorges like that of the Grand Canyon. During the last million years of the Cenozoic, glaciers have advanced and retreated over the continents, putting their finishing touches to the face of the land.

Ranging from the surface waters of the seas to the highest mountain peaks, from dense forests to open plains, from the torrid tropics to the freezing arctic, mammals made the whole earth their home. Showing remarkable adaptations in their teeth, their limbs, and their sense organs, mammals found food and safety in an amazing variety of habitats, including even the air, as demonstrated by the bats.

THE PARADE OF MAMMALS. The diversity of mammalian life is reflected in the many groups that are familiar to us today. These had their origin in basic types that appeared early in the Cenozoic. An early stage in mammalian development is represented by two animals of Australia that are still with us, the duckbill and the spiny anteater. Both of these creatures have fur and nurse their young. But both retain the ancient reptilian characteristic of laying eggs! These egg-layers, however, are not considered to be the ancestors of today's mammals. Rather they are thought of as a side branch of the main evolutionary line of development.

More truly ancestral were the primitive mammals of the Mesozoic, mentioned previously, which were on the average no bigger than a rat or a mouse. They resembled these rodents in their general appearance (but not in their basic structure). Two lines of evolution developed from these early forms. One led to the marsupials, the pouched mammals, of which the American opossum of today is an example. The tiny young of this species are raised in a kind of incubator or pouch where they find shelter and warmth, and where nourishment is provided by the inclosed teats. Marsupials are found almost exclusively in Australia. There all of the native mammals are pouched.

Another line of evolution led to the placentals, those animals that nourish their developing young internally through a common membrane, the placenta. In the placenta, food and oxygen are passed from the blood stream of the mother to the separate but adjacent blood stream of the embryo. The placentals include the carnivores, the rodents, the hoofed mammals, the whales, the primates, and some other groups.

The carnivores or flesh-eating mammals have claws and sharp teeth that fit them for their way of life. Included in this group are the popular animals of the zoo: cats (including the lions, tigers, leopards, lynxes, and jaguars), dogs, wolves, foxes, weasels, badgers, minks, ermines, ferrets, skunks, and otters.

One group of mammals returned to the seas. This group includes the whales, porpoises, and dolphins, whose forelimbs have been modified to become fin-like paddles. The hindlimbs are absent, and the tail is fish-like. The young are born alive and are nourished by milk from mammary glands, like other mammals. The sulphur-bottom whale is distinguished by being the largest animal known, living or extinct, reaching a length of nearly 100 feet and a weight of 150 tons.

The rodents are gnawing animals with two long chisel-like front teeth in each jaw. This group includes mice, rats, chipmunks, squirrels, woodchucks, muskrats, beavers, and porcupines.

The hoofed mammals include pigs, hippopotamuses, camels, sheep, goats, cattle, bison, giraffes, deer, and horses. They are vegetarians.

THE HORSE GETS BIG. The horse is worthy of special mention in this chapter about ancient life because many splendid fossils of this animal have been found in North America. Eohippus, dawn horse, appeared early in the Cenozoic. No higher than a fox terrier, this diminutive horse had slender legs and a long slender face. It had four toes on its front feet and three on the hind feet. Eohippus browsed on shrubs, rather than on grass, as modern horses do. The subsequent evolution of the horse saw an increase in the size of its body and the development of specialized teeth for cropping and grinding grain. The toes were reduced in size, except for the middle one, which was enlarged to form the hoof. (See page 350.)

Buried in the flesh of the legs of modern horses are two inconspicuous bones. These are the vestiges of the second and fourth toes, evidence of the kinship of today's horses to their many-toed forebears.

Although horses originated and developed in North America, they became extinct on this continent, surviving only in Europe and Asia. They were reintroduced to their ancient home here by the early settlers.

MAN APPEARS. The primates, which include monkeys, apes, and human beings, are distinguished by having a large brain. Our knowledge of human evolution is inadequate because relatively few fossils of

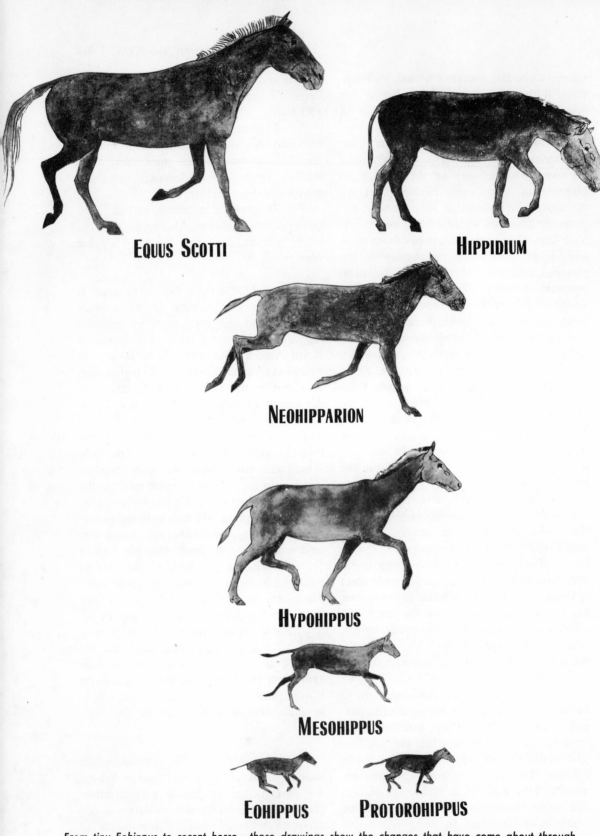

Equus Scotti

Hippidium

Neohipparion

Hypohippus

Mesohippus

Eohippus   **Protorohippus**

From tiny Eohippus to recent horse—these drawings show the changes that have come about through the ages. Fossils furnish the evidences of these changes. Our knowledge of past life on the earth grows as additional fossils are discovered, studied, and classified.

man's forerunners have been unearthed, and most of these are only fragments of skulls and limb bones. However, our knowledge is constantly increasing. This we do know: that modern man appears to have been present on earth 50,000 years ago, and his prehuman ancestors perhaps 2 million years ago; that today only one species of man, designated *Homo sapiens* by scientists, exists.

Notable in the small collection of fossils are Pithecanthropus erectus ("erect ape-man"), Peking man, Neanderthal man, and Cro-Magnon man. Recent finds of some significance have been made in Africa. Deposits there have yielded skulls and bones that prove the existence of a primitive near-human being, capable of making and using stone implements. All of these finds indicate that Africa was a place of major importance for human evolution. To quote Dr. L. S. B. Leakey, who was responsible for some of these discoveries, the searches "give promise of throwing more and more light upon the critical stage when the prehuman primates were 'crossing the Rubicon' to become true men." In 1963 Dr. Leakey reported the discovery in Kenya, East Africa, of the remains of a creature that radioactive dating had determined to have lived 14 million years ago. This creature, according to Dr. Leakey, seems "to lie midway between the early apes and man."

The ancestry of man has been subject to some misunderstanding. No *living* member of the apes is the ancestor of man. Apes (as well as other primates) and man had common ancestors, but the two lines separated millions of years ago.

CHANGE GOES ON. From our knowledge of the past, there is every reason to believe that change will go on. The geologic forces that have been shaping the earth for billions of years will continue their activities. New forms of life will emerge.

With the coming of man to the earth a new force has been added—man's intelligence. With this intelligence, he has the power to change the earth in many ways. For the first time a species exists that can deliberately and consciously influence its own future evolution—or its own extinction.

In looking back over the development of living things on the earth, certain ideas stand out that help us grasp the meaning of change through the ages. Some of the important ideas are:

The development of living things upon the earth has been from the very simple organisms to the complex ones. Modern life developed from ancient life.

The changes have been extremely slow.

Great changes have taken place in the physical appearance and conditions of the earth during its long history.

These physical changes have influenced the development of plant and animal forms.

Many plants and animals that once lived on the earth have entirely disappeared.

Fossils tell us many things about ancient animals and plants and about conditions on the earth in past ages. Fossils in rock formations reveal the sequence of life through the ages.

There were living things in the seas long before they existed on the land.

The earth is very old—perhaps more than 5 billion years old.

For more than half of its long history, the earth was barren of life.

Man is a newcomer; modern man appeared only about 50,000 years ago.

Man's intelligence is a new factor in evolution today.

Scientists continue their investigations to unravel the many mysteries of the earth's past.

DISCOVERING FOR YOURSELF

1. Make a "time line" chart and arrange in order the important changes that occurred to the earth and life on it, through the ages.
2. Visit a museum, select three or four fossils, and try to discover what kind of environment the animal or plant may have lived in, how it may have become fossilized, and what present living thing it may be related to. Then read the museum description and see how nearly right you are.
3. Try to make a collection of fossils.
4. Watch newspapers for accounts of fossil discoveries. Read the accounts and apply the principles you have learned in this chapter to understanding the various implications of the brief newspaper account.
5. Try to make a cast of an animal track.
6. Find out what fossil animals and plants have been found in your state. What do these fossils tell you about changes that have taken place in your state through the ages?
7. Investigate the theories which try to explain *how* evolution is caused.
8. Investigate theories which try to account for the beginning of life on earth.

CHAPTER 14B

Teaching "Ancient Animals and Plants"

The study of fossils and the earth's story can be lively and interesting to both children and teachers. Dinosaurs fire the imagination of children. A museum trip to see fossils, for example, will provoke discussion and raise some very searching questions from children. They often bring fossils to school from gravel pits, quarries, and rock ledges. Sometimes they bring pictures of fossils from magazines, newspapers, and advertisements. Frequently, local newspapers tell about fossils that have been accidentally discovered in the nearby country-side. Petrified wood is often brought to school. Excavations of various kinds that show soil and rock layers raise questions about the age of the earth, the formation of soil, and the changes in the earth's surface. Children have, for some reason or other, considerable curiosity about the world of long ago.

Although in the study of fossils there are not so many opportunities to experiment with materials as, for example, in the study of sound or electricity, there are many occasions to stress the kinds of problems which scientists tackle. For example: How do scientists know that the earth has changed? How do they know that the climate has changed, and how do they know how the oceans were made? How can a plant or animal leave a print in hard rock?

There are also many opportunities for the use of scientific attitude. For example, why must scientists use such words or phrases as "It seems evident that," "Many people believe," "Evidence seems to show," "It may be," or "It is generally believed," in telling about the earth's past? There are scores of opportunities to stress the importance of holding conclusions tentatively, of searching for reliable evidence, of not jumping to conclusions, and of the other elements of scientific attitude mentioned in part one.

There are many opportunities for reading and reporting by children as they try to answer such questions as:

How has life on the earth changed?
What can we learn by studying early life on the earth?
What did living things look like in the Age of Dinosaurs?

The broad problems in this area may be stated in this way:

How have living things changed through the ages?

Or,

What do fossils tell us about past life?

Or, if it seems preferable to break this into smaller unit problems:

What were early animals like?
What were early plants like?
How has the earth's surface changed?
What are dinosaurs like?

Unlike many of the other chapters on living things, this one on ancient animals and plants does not fit easily into the primary program. Time sequence and slow change are difficult for very young children to understand. Here, however, are some study and activity suggestions that have been tried out successfully in the primary grades. They can, of course, be used at any level.

1. Examine fossils to see what can be discovered by looking carefully at them. Touch the fossils to learn that they are hard, like stone.
2. Look at pictures of dinosaurs and tell what these animals were like.
3. Go to a museum to see different kinds of fossils, ask about them, tell about them, draw pictures of them.
4. Watch water animals to see how they move, get food, and protect themselves.

VISITING A MUSEUM TO SEE FOSSILS

Children will want to see any fossils that have come from their own community or state and to learn about how they happened to be discovered. They will want to know what these fossils show about the ancient history of their region. Ask the museum guide whether there is any published material about fossils and early geology in your state. If pupils have collected fossils, they may take them along to the museum for examination. The resource person at the museum may tell the pupils how he can identify the specimens, and will answer other questions. The museum or your local library may have a file of newspaper clippings that describe local or state fossil discoveries. Frequently the museum's curator is willing to give the school some common fossils or duplicates of his collection. These may form the beginning of a fossil collection.

TAKING A FIELD TRIP TO FIND FOSSILS

A nearby stone quarry, gravel pit, or ocean shore may be a good place to find fossils. A local science teacher may know about the possibilities if you are not sure that a trip would be advisable. Try to discover a person who knows something about the place, ask him to accompany you and the class to help answer questions. Let pupils plan the trip by putting down questions they think they might be able to answer and by listing things they think they might find. If it does not seem advisable for all pupils to go, certain interested pupils may wish to take the trip and report to the class. (For other suggestions for field trips, refer to chapter 3.)

To make the trip more purposeful the pupils may try to answer the following questions: How do you think this place has changed through the ages? What has made these changes? How do you think these changes affected the animal and plant life? How do you think the place is changing now?

MAKING A CAST OR A PRINT

Making a cast or a print of a fossil or shell may help some pupils better understand how fossils are formed. Place a layer of clay in the bottom of a cardboard box. Press a clam shell into the clay to make a deep print. Carefully lift the shell out so that a clear print is left. Make a thick paste of plaster of Paris, add a little salt or vinegar to keep it from hardening too quickly, and pour the mixture into the shell print. When the paste hardens, you have a cast of the shell. It is not necessary for every child to participate in this activity. Some pupils will like to do it. It is important for them to understand that the experience shows how a fossil cast was made when the animal or plant made a print of itself and decayed, and the space was subsequently filled with material that later hardened somewhat as the plaster of Paris did. Pupils may like to make a cast of the footprint of a pet dog or cat.

A print will help to develop the idea of how fossils are formed. Make a thick paste of plaster of Paris. Cover some shells with a thin film of vaseline to keep them from sticking and cover them with the plaster. Let the plaster harden, then break it open to find the prints of the shells. A milk carton may be used to hold the plaster. It is important to compare this method of print making with the way in which real prints were made. Unless this is done, such activities are mostly busy work.

OBSERVING THE EARTH'S LAYERS

Pupils can more easily understand that part of the solid outer crust of the earth is built up in layers if they can actually see the layers. Pupils may be asked to observe the layers of rock and of soil in a cut in a road nearby and to tell which layers they think might be the oldest and why they think so. In addition to seeing such layers, they may be able to find in geography books, in the *National Geographic Magazine*, in travel folders, and elsewhere, pictures of mountains and canyons, that will help them to get an understanding of what the earth under their feet is like. If their school is not located where such layers are observable, children may recall having seen rock layers in mountains when they have been traveling. This is an example of helping children to tie up their past experiences with their present problem in order to help them understand science more clearly.

OBSERVING WATER LIFE

Let pupils observe a plant growing under water (perhaps in your aquarium) and one growing in soil (a geranium or coleus, for example) to find answers to these questions: "What do you think the land plant needs that water plants do not need?" "How do you think the water plant would have to change to live on the land?" "Do you think this water plant could change so that it could live on land?" Take a piece of the water plant out of the water and expose it to the air for a time. By observing what happens and discussing it, pupils will realize more clearly that land plants need some means of getting water from the soil, supporting themselves in an erect position, and keeping the water inside them from escaping. This water plant soon dries up when it is exposed to the air, and it could not, of course, adapt itself to living on land. At one time in the history of the earth's living things, there were only water plants. Land plants developed from them. Such a change as this involves a very long time.

Pupils may also observe a fish carefully to learn as much as they can about how it moves through the water, how it breathes, how it gets food, and how its shape adapts it to life in water. After careful observation they may discuss the following problems: What changes would the fish have to make before it could live on land? How do you think water animals changed through the ages to become land animals? How is this fish different from ancient fish you have been learning about and how is it like the ancient fish?

LOOKING THROUGH A MICROSCOPE

Place under the microscope some pond scum from your aquarium or some water from a stagnant pool for your pupils to see. If possible, the pupils should obtain the stagnant water themselves and watch as it is placed under the microscope. It is not necessary that pupils know the names of the plants they see, but a look through the microscope at them may be very revealing, for it is from such simple plants as these that our plant kingdom developed. Tiny animals may also be observed in this water. They are examples of the kind of life from which more complex forms come. Such an experience as this give more meaning to the development of life on the earth. It is not necessary to purchase an expensive compound microscope for use in the elementary school. It may be borrowed, as we have suggested here, or a relatively inexpensive one can be purchased.[1] A high school biology teacher will probably be glad to help in the use of the microscope if this is desirable or necessary.

RAISING FROGS' EGGS AND
MOSQUITO LARVAE

If it is spring, and frogs and toads are croaking in the ponds, you can probably find their eggs. Watching the eggs hatch and seeing the tadpoles develop will help pupils to see how animals change as they grow. This can lead to an understanding of how animals changed as they went from water habitat to land habitat. Frogs' eggs are laid in bunches; toads' eggs in strings. Scoop them out of the water into a pail of pond water. Place them in a glass con-

---

[1] *Microscope Outfit,* Educational Materials and Equipment Co., P. O. Box 63, Bronxville, N. Y. Other science supply companies also sell microscopes.

Here teachers are learning to make models of prehistoric animals in order to help pupils plan an exhibit to show life in past ages. They too are learning the importance of accurate details.

tainer of pond water so that they can be easily observed. Don't keep more than 10 or 20 eggs for each gallon of water. Use magnifying glasses to see them better. Pupils can see them hatch and watch the animals change. The young tadpoles feed on the tiny water plants in the water. The children may make drawings of the animals as they appear on different dates and write sentences to point out the developmental changes. (See pages 229–230 in chapter 10A.) *Frog Eggs*[2] is a very useful reference to help you raise tadpoles.

If there is a stagnant pool nearby, you may be able to find mosquito larvae, commonly called "wigglers." Put some in a jar nearly full of water and keep the jar covered with a piece of glass or a piece of fine wire netting. Use a magnifying glass to observe the larvae as they change. The experience of watching this development and seeing the adult mosquito emerge above the water helps pupils to understand something of what is involved in an animal's change from water to land habitat.

MAKING MODELS OF DINOSAURS

Dinosaurs are wonderful subjects for modeling, and pupils seem to like to model them in clay or in papier-mâché. If the models are to be successful from a science point of view, they should be as nearly accurate as possible in details of structure and proportion. If they are to be placed in the natural habitat in which they were found, further study of text and pictures is necessary to insure an accurate result. This is a sensible situation in which art and science may well make use of each other. The models make a good art activity and also tell a scientific story. If various models are made to the same scale (including one of modern man), children will be able to compare their sizes more easily. The dimensions of some ancient animals seem either unbelievable or incomprehensible to children. Many children have no very clear idea of how high, for example, thirty feet is. Try measuring some of these proportions and try to decide whether the animal could fit into the schoolroom, see over the schoolhouse, stretch the length of the corridor, or fit into the principal's office.[3]

In addition to model-making, pupils may enjoy drawing large pictures of ancient birds, amphibians, mammals, and plants, and organizing a picture side show patterned after

[2] Turtox Service Leaflet, No. 3, *Frog Eggs,* General Biological Supply House, 8200 South Hoyne Ave., Chicago 20, Ill. (4¢ per copy).

[3] G. O. Blough, *Discovering Dinosaurs* (New York, Whittlesey House, 1960).

a circus. One sixth grade produced such a show and named it "Astonishing Authenic Ancestors." They included drawings of several of the most interesting and unusual ancient
living things and prepared talks such as a side-show barker might give telling startling things
about these ancient animals. They selected Archaeopteryx, Eohippus, a trilobite, a ginkgo
tree, the early elephant, and several other examples. The side show was produced as an assembly program. There are many variations of this plan that pupils can work out.

It is essential to remember that there are other purposes for such an activity besides
what is commonly considered learning science. The activity should help pupils learn how
to locate material, organize it, plan for a good audience situation, and many other things.
They learn to give the source of their information, to exercise caution in reporting as facts
only those statements that are supported by reliable evidence, and to indicate material that
was based upon theory or imagination alone.

FINDING FOSSILS IN BUILDINGS

Fossils are often found in the limestone which is commonly used in the exterior construction of buildings. Limestone is gray, often cement-like in appearance. Have the children
look at limestone carefully to find fossils of little animals, such as shells, and make drawings
of what they see. Consult books, talk with museum people to help identify the fossils which
are found.

Limestone is formed under water from materials derived from the shells of marine
animals. Sometimes their fossil remains are left in the rock.

RESOURCES TO INVESTIGATE

1. The local, state, college, or university museums to look at fossils collected nearby
   and to see rock collections. Sometimes such institutions lend collections to
   schools.
2. Newspapers and magazines for pictures and accounts of recent fossil discoveries.
3. A place where the highway cuts through a hill to observe layers of soil and
   various rock formations.
4. The State Geologist and publications from his office and from local geological
   societies, to learn about local land forms, rocks, fossils, and mineral deposits.
5. A local individual who makes a hobby of rock or fossil collecting.
6. A high school science department for information about local earth resources.
7. Gravel pits, beaches, and other places that often yield fossils of different kinds.
8. Local environment to find club mosses and horsetails that are examples of
   present-day plants that are very small but were once of huge proportions.

CHAPTER 15A

Conservation of Our Resources

There are two Americas. There is the America of the song:

Oh, beautiful for spacious skies
For amber waves of grain
For purple mountain majesties
Above the fruited plain. . . .

This is the America we sing of. This is America the beautiful, America the bountiful. *This is the America we inherited.*

But there is another America too. There is the America whose "spacious skies" are filled with factory soot, with noxious chemicals and poisonous gases. There is the America whose "amber waves of grain" have been replaced by clouds of dust. There is the America whose "purple mountain majesties" stand amid the stumps of cut trees or the charred ruins of burnt forests. There is the America whose "fruited plains" are now gullied by erosion and washed away into rivers. *This is the America we made.*

These are the two Americas. It is late, very late, but not too late to save much of the America we inherited. It is not too late to save the precious 9 inches of topsoil that lies between us and extinction. It is not too late to save much of our forests, our clear waters, and our wildlife. It is not too late to pass on to our children their rightful heritage of the recreation, the beauty, the peace, and the spiritual values of an unspoiled out-of-doors.

OUR VANISHING
NATURAL RESOURCES

When the white man first settled here, North America was an unspoiled land. Vast forests and thickly sodded prairie covered most of the continent. Animals of many kinds were found everywhere. The lakes and streams had many fish. Vast mineral wealth lay undiscovered in the ground. Nearly everywhere water was abundant and safe to drink.

The Indians were the only inhabitants of our vast country. They seldom wasted natural resources. Animals were killed only when food was needed. Trees were cut down only when there was need for fuel or when small clearings for simple crops were required. And the soil, of course, was used scarcely at all.

With the coming of the white man, all was changed. Being agriculturists, the early settlers cut down the trees as rapidly as possible. They did this because they needed land on which to grow crops. Trees also provided lumber for homes and for furniture. It is quite understandable that they were not thinking about the preservation of timber resources. The early settlers often girdled the trees so that they died. The dead trunks and branches were then burned. Animals were shot in huge numbers, often only for their skins or choice parts of the meat.

As the white man spread over the continent and settled in many places, further changes were made. Hilly land was plowed up and down the slope. As a consequence, gullies formed easily. Land was cropped year after year, with no effort to restore any of the soil constituents being used up. When the soil was depleted, the farmers moved to new areas of virgin, unspoiled soil. Petroleum, coal, iron ore, and other mineral wealth were removed without sufficient thought for the careful and efficient use of these resources.

Gradually, much of our natural wealth has been lost. Of course it was necessary to cut trees to clear the land for farming, but we were not always farsighted in our lumbering methods. For example, lumber companies cut only the best trees and were not careful to protect young saplings. Much valuable timber was left on the ground to rot or to be destroyed by forest fires.

Animals such as the bison (buffalo) were killed for their skins, or just for sport. Passenger pigeons and turkeys were slaughtered merely for pleasure. As a result of such wanton attacks by man, wild animal life was greatly depleted or, in some cases, virtually wiped out. Passenger pigeons are now extinct and wild turkeys almost so. Bison were almost extinct when a few were rounded up for preservation in zoos and private game preserves. Many other kinds of animals are now very scarce.

Authorities say that one-third of our original topsoil has been washed away. Every year, erosion by water alone carries away enough topsoil to make 10,000 one-hundred-acre farms in the United States. The Mississippi River alone carries 7,000 of these potential farms into the Gulf of Mexico. These figures do not include erosion by wind. Faulty farming practices and the removal of the forests have been factors in our frequent floods, for trees provide a mulch of leaves that serves as a sort of sponge to hold water and retain it long enough to keep it from running off all at once and causing floods.

Water, once abundant in most parts of the United States and safe to drink everywhere, has been polluted with sewage and industrial wastes and used so carelessly that cities are periodically threatened by water famine. We use an enormous amount of water annually in manufacturing plants alone. For example, one paper mill in Texas uses 22 million gallons every day. It takes 65,000 gallons of water to cool a ton of molten steel. To make one ton of coke requires 3,600 gallons. If the polluted or overheated water is returned to a stream, it can destroy life for a considerable distance downstream and render the water unfit for drinking or recreational purposes.

The explosive increase in the world's population makes the resource problem even more serious. Today's world population is about three billion. It is growing by fifty-one million a year. If the present rate continues, the population in the year 2000—which is only 36 years from the date of publication of this edition of *Elementary School Science*—will be double what it is now, or six billion! All these people must live on the earth's natural resources.

Moreover, the capacity for the consumption of natural resources has increased even faster than the population. In the last fifty years, while the population of the United States has *doubled*, the consumption of power has increased *eleven* times, of fuel *thirteen* times, and of paper (from wood pulp) *fourteen* times.

Another factor must be added to complete the balance sheets of people and resources. For the first time in history there is a *universal* aspiration for a rapid improvement in the standard of living. Millions in Asia, Africa, and Latin America are demanding the opportunity to attain the same standard enjoyed by Europeans and North Americans.

WHAT IS CONSERVATION?

The goal of conservation is to keep our earth as rich and productive as we found it. William Dean Howells said: "A nation is great not because it mines coal, cuts timber, or builds railways, but rather because it has learned how to produce, build, and grow without destroying the bases of its future existence."

Conservation does not mean merely saving. Only misers hoard for mere savings sake, and they reap no rewards from their hoarding. Conservation means wise use. What does this concept imply? It means, for example, that our forests should be protected from excessive destruction—not that we must never cut trees. Trees must be cut, because we need wood products. But when trees are removed, they should be replaced by replanting whenever it is possible to do so.

Conservation does not mean that soil should lie fallow, but it does mean that it must be protected against erosion and excessive cropping. Coal and iron ore in the ground are of no use to anyone, but our concept of conservation means that they should be removed without undue waste. Water supplies must be used, but they must not be consumed wastefully and they must have an opportunity to replenish themselves.

Certainly conservation does not mean that flowers must never be picked, but it does mean that the picking of flowers should be done discriminately and sparingly. It does not mean that wild animals, edible and fur-bearing, and birds and fish must never be killed. If excess numbers were not removed, many would starve, or they would become so numerous as to destroy crops. Wild animals should be used sensibly, like any other resource.

A recent definition of conservation[1] reflects the growing disparity between what we know we should do and what we are (and are not) doing. "Conservation . . . means the protection and preservation of our vital natural environment. This includes the air we breathe, the water we drink, and the land we live on."

INTERRELATIONSHIPS: KEY TO CONSERVATION

The understanding of interrelationships is the key to sound conservation practice. We refer both to the interrelationships of living things with each other and of living things with their physical environment.

Consider the diet of an Eskimo, consisting largely of seal meat, fish, and birds. All of these food sources are ultimately dependent on tiny plants that live in the sea. Let us see how. The seals and birds feed on fish. The fish feed on smaller fish.

---

[1] Hal Borland, "To Keep This Earth Habitable," *Teachers College Record*, Columbia University, January 1963.

An animal such as a gray squirrel may have hidden a cache of pine seeds here and then left them. Nine seedlings, as shown above (with their seed coats still in place), are the result.

Little fish feed on copepods, tiny relatives of the lobster. Copepods feed on microscopic one-celled plants, called diatoms, which live near the surface of the sea. Diatoms are green plants which are able to make their own food by the process of photosynthesis (see chapter 10A). Hence, the diet of an Eskimo depends on diatoms.

This is a long chain. The elimination of any link in it would mean the elimination of the Eskimo. If, for example, some act of man, such as the pouring of a chemical into the sea, were to destroy the diatoms, it would inevitably mean the destruction of the Eskimo in his natural environment.

There are thousands of such relationships in nature. Before we decide to SEE PAGE 393 enact measures that would eliminate a plant or animal, before we decide to stock a territory with a new plant or animal, before we decide to drain a swamp, before we decide to spray a wide area with an insecticide, before we decide to build a dam, we must ask ourselves: What are the consequences? What is our act doing to the chain of plants and animals and their environment? For the altering of this chain may affect, for better or for worse, man's existence itself.

SILENT SPRING. In the fall of 1962 a book was published that was destined to awaken the American people to the danger of pesticides, the chemicals used to kill insects, weeds, fungi, herbs, and rodents. This book *Silent Spring* by Rachel Carson,[2] an author already famous for her moving book *The Sea Around Us,* was a grim, eloquent, and heavily documented warning about the harm that modern man is doing to his world and to himself by the ignorant and indiscriminate use of pesticides.

The spring of 1963 was not silent—at least not for those who could hear the warning of the President's Science Advisory Committee. Responding to Rachel Carson's message, the committee told the nation of the dangers in the use of pesticides, and recommended changes in laws and regulatory practices to guard against the hazards in the widespread use of chemicals. The Department of Agriculture was advised to stop its mass spraying to eradicate certain insects. The Food and Drug Administration was asked to review "as rapidly as possible" the tolerance of the human body to the various pesticide chemicals that remain in the food that is eaten. The Department of Health, Education, and Welfare was urged to gather data on pesticide residues in air, water, soil, wildlife, and fish.

It is true that pesticides have enabled man to make spectacular increases in agricultural production, and have freed him from communicable diseases to an unprecedented extent. In less developed areas of the world, malaria, typhus, and yellow fever, which caused the death and disability of millions, are now limited and in some locations eradicated.

The Science Advisory Committee was concerned with the fact that many of the pesticides turned up in many food items, in some clothing, in man himself, in animals, and in the natural surroundings. While be-

---

[2] Houghton Mifflin, New York.

lieving that pesticides properly used and controlled are necessary, the committee warned that "precisely because pesticide chemicals are designed to kill or metabolically upset some living target organism, they are potentially dangerous to other living organisms. Most of them are highly toxic in concentrated amounts, and in unfortunate instances have caused illness and death of people and wildlife."

Pesticides may set off a chain reaction. Elm trees are often heavily sprayed with DDT to kill the bark beetles that spread the Dutch Elm disease. If this is done in summer, the poison clings to the leaves until they fall in autumn. Later, as earthworms feed on these decaying leaves, the DDT accumulates in these bodies. These worms, though not killed themselves, can be deadly to robins who eat them the following spring.

The committee's report pointed out that mortality among birds approached 80 percent in areas heavily treated with DDT.

THE ENDURANCE
OF RESOURCES

INEXHAUSTIBLE RESOURCES. The resources of the earth are of four kinds—inexhaustible, renewable, nonrenewable, and new and to-be-developed. Some resources we will have always. These are air, sunlight, water, and rocks. They are unique in that, much as man may use them, they continue in abundance. Water is such a resource. As long as the oceans cover the earth we will have water. Lifted (with the help of the sun's warming rays) from the ocean as vapor that eventually falls as rain, it is available for agriculture, for industry, and for our personal needs. Dropping from falls, water can be used as a source of power. Limitless though it is, water presents some of our most pressing problems of conservation. These are mainly problems of distribution and use, as we shall see later in this chapter.

Sunlight is the source of all our energy, except for atomic energy. Water power results, as we have just seen, from the lifting of water with the help of the sun's energy; fossil fuels, such as coal and oil, are the products of the sun's radiant energy stored by plants in past times; solar energy is used directly in solar engines. Astronomers reassure us that the sun will continue to be our powerhouse for at least a few billion years more.

RENEWABLE RESOURCES. Renewable resources are our soils, vegetation, animal life, and fresh water supplies. These are the resources that may be maintained indefinitely, under wise management. It is to these resources that the efforts of conservation are mainly directed. The renewable resources are dependent one on the other. Crops will not grow in soil without water. Animals play an important role in the life cycle of many plants. We need mention here only the pollinating work of the bee (see chapter 12A). Forests and grasslands prevent harmful rain runoff and also store water. Plant cover provides essential protection of the soil against erosion by water and wind. Weaken one link and the whole life supporting chain is imperiled.

Man is in a key position to keep this chain in working balance. The fields can continue to produce healthy crops each year if he maintains and improves the fertility of the soil. Forests can be managed so as to assure a perpetual yield of wood, a steady flow of water, and a constant source of pleasure. Game and other animal life can be helped to renew itself and to continue its role in the web of life.

NONRENEWABLE RESOURCES. The nonrenewable resources are those that can be used up. Such materials as coal, oil, natural gas, metals, and most minerals are of this nature. When copper is mined, new copper will not "grow" in its place. When a lump of coal is burned, it is gone forever. All of our conventional fuels, except wood, fall into the category of resources that become unavailable once they are used.

Government and industry are meeting the problem of the conservation of our mineral and fuel resources in a number of ways: by finding new sources of material; by seeking new materials; by minimizing waste; and by learning how to use materials more effectively. Geologists are prospecting in every corner of the globe for new supplies. When deposits near the surface of the earth are depleted, men dig deeper into the earth. Wells have been drilled under the ocean to tap the petroleum and sulfur found there. Chemists have found how to extract magnesium and bromine from ocean waters in commercial quantity and at a marketable price. Scientists are learning how to utilize low grade ores (such as takonite with its relatively small percentage of iron) as higher grades become scarcer. New ways are being discovered of preventing rusting and corrosion, thus extending the life of the finished products.

NEW AND TO-BE-DEVELOPED RESOURCES. Less than a century ago crude oil was considered a useless substance. Less than 50 years ago some scientists were saying that the atom could never be split. Yet what enormous sources of energy have we been able to release from the molecules of gasoline and from the nucleus of atoms! New resources will be added as the skill and creativity of scientists and engineers discover uses for materials that may be of little or of no value today, or may presently be inaccessible. Perhaps, also, we will be able to add to our resources those of the moon, or of Earth's sister planets.

THE LOSS OF SOIL

A GROWING DEFICIT. Productive soil is the basis of our existence. Almost all of our food and fiber, except that derived from the sea, comes from the soil. Soil also provides almost all of the food required by domestic and wild animal life. History records what happened to Greece, Italy, and Spain with the loss of much of their productive soil. Yet many people today in America feel that "it can't happen here." They point to the huge yields of our farms and to the improvements in technology. Our main problem seems to be to dispose of our surplus. The federal government, to support

SEE PA 38!

The straight, cultivated rows are natural ditches to carry away the water and valuable topsoil downhill after a sudden downpour. Contrast this with the photograph on page 366.

the economy, has bought up billions of dollars worth of such crops. Where is the crisis?

Let us look at statistics. It is expected that the population of the United States by 1975 will be 235 million, an increase of about 55 million over the 1960 population. We will need millions of additional acres of cropland to produce what we will consume in 1975.

But needed acres will not be available. We shall have to make up the deficit by increasing the productivity of the land we now have. In fact, science and technology have been doing just that. But the population is increasing faster than the increase in productivity.

In the United States erosion has destroyed an estimated more than 50 million acres of farm land since colonial times. (This is an area larger than Nebraska.) Erosion has partly destroyed another 50 million and threatens another 100 million acres. The damage is primarily due to man and his practices of farming, grazing, and lumbering.

EROSION.   Much of the land from which the forests were removed should never have been cleared. From hilly land with rather thin topsoil, the good soil is removed very easily by erosion. Farmers helped the erosion along by plowing straight up and down hills. This practice made it easy for water to run down the slopes, carrying with it the valuable topsoil.

You may often have noticed the brown color of creeks and rivers after a rainstorm. The color is due, of course, to soil—the topsoil of the nearby fields being carried away, to be deposited in the bottom of the lake, sea, or ocean into which the stream flows. Obviously, it is lost to use. The Ohio and Mississippi rivers, as well as many smaller rivers and streams, have already carried away untold agricultural wealth.

The infamous "dust bowl" of the middle west was caused by cultivation of a rather arid area. This area should never have been plowed in the first place, but should have been left as grasslands. Natural grasses bind the soil and prevent the wind from blowing it away. They also retard the action of erosion by water. When such grasslands were plowed and planted with grain crops with little soil binding power, conditions for disaster were set up.

Erosion has been going on for millions of years. Soil is picked up from one place and deposited in another, As long as there is soil and wind and water, some erosion is inevitable. Soil erosion is a natural process. Ordinarily it takes place slowly, so that the new soil constantly being created balances the loss. Man, however, by his unwise practices, can speed up erosion to the point where land becomes unproductive in one generation. We have realized why erosion is becoming a problem, and we have learned how to slow it down. The job that remains to be done is to convince people of the importance of action and to help them see how best to work at conservation.

Another aspect of soil conservation is concerned with the loss of soil minerals essential for plant life. Our forefathers often exhausted the soil of a farm by planting the same crop over and over, and then moving westward to other farm lands. This migration is no longer possible, because all the good land, with the exception of small areas still to be brought into production through drainage and irrigation projects, is now under cultivation. Hereafter we shall have to get along with what we have and learn to use it to best advantage.

PREVENTION OF EROSION

As we said at the beginning of this chapter, 9 inches of topsoil lie between us and extinction. This is the upper layer of soil in productive farmland. In that top 9 inches are the vital materials necessary for plant growth. Remove them, and we come to earth that can barely support vegetation.

This photograph illustrates contour farming and strip farming, both used to trap water and hold the soil. See text for details.

One of the ways of preventing excessive erosion on hilly farm land is *contour farming*, in which the land is plowed around the contours of the hill instead of up and down. This prevents the water from running downhill (see picture above). As you drive through the country, you may see examples of contour farming. There is a great difference in the productivity of farms that use this method and comparable farms that do not. Another way of preventing wasteful erosion is *strip farming*, in which alternate strips of grass or similar cover crop are left to check the downhill runoff of water. Water that begins to run downhill in the cultivated strip is stopped when it reaches the cover crop. Still another method—perhaps a better one—is not to plow steep hillsides at all but to leave them for pasture, orchard, or forest.

Another way of preventing the erosion of hilly land is the use of terraces. On ground that has been terraced, water has time to soak into the soil during and after a rain instead of running directly down the hillside. Older nations have terraced their hilly land for centuries, but we have never had to follow such a practice to any extent because of our abundance of good land. Terracing, as older nations have practiced it,

requires considerable hand labor and hence is usually expensive, but modern terracing in the United States is done by machinery. With an ever-increasing need for soil, we may someday be forced to terrace land that would ordinarily not be worked.

Forests are of great assistance in preventing erosion. If you have ever been in the woods during a rain, you have seen that the drops of water do not hit the ground with great force. Instead, they strike the leaves and branches and gradually drop to the ground or run down the trunk. The ground under the trees is covered with leaves. It is soft and spongy and full of the roots of trees and other plants. The roots bind the soil together and hold it in place. The humus on the surface serves as a sort of sponge to hold some of the water that falls during a period of rainfall. This water then drains very gradually into the earth during dry periods.

MAINTAINING SOIL FERTILITY

If soil is to be satisfactory for plant growth, it must contain the essential mineral compounds. The most important—compounds of nitrogen, phosphorus, and potassium—seem to be the most easily removed from the soil by plants. Let us consider nitrogen first. In nature, the soil is replenished with this important mineral by the decay of plant and animal material. When man, however, harvests crops, he is, in a sense, mining the soil of this valuable nitrogen. His crops will become poorer and poorer, unless he does something to make up for the loss. He can replace the lost nitrogen by adding animal manure or commercial fertilizers to the soil.

Nitrogen, to be available for plant use, must be in the form of soluble nitrates. The air contains limitless amounts of nitrogen, since about four-fifths of the atmosphere is nitrogen. But few plants can make use of nitrogen in the free form in which it is present in the air. The nitrogen-fixing bacteria that live on the roots of clover, peas, beans, and alfalfa, and in the soil, are among the few living things that can utilize atmospheric nitrogen. They convert the free nitrogen of the air into nitrates, which are thus supplied to the soil. When a farmer grows the same crop on the same land year after year, the soil is depleted. He can help replenish the soil with nitrates by growing a crop of plants such as clover and then plowing it back into the soil.

Phosphorus and potassium must be provided through commercial fertilizers. Lack of phosphorus not only slows growing, it also results in crops that are deficient in this substance. People depending upon such crops for their phosphorus supply may have their health endangered by its lack. Farm animals suffer similarly from lack of this element. Potassium compounds are also needed for sturdy plant growth. Calcium, sulfur, magnesium are also essential to plant life, as well as minute amounts of some other elements.

Today, farming is a scientific occupation that requires considerable technical knowledge and skill. For example, soil should be analyzed so that the lacking con-

Nodules such as these are found on the roots of clover, alfalfa, and other legumes. Bacteria associated with these growths enrich the soil by taking free nitrogen from the air and using it to make nitrates.

stituents may be added. Methods of preventing erosion must be studied and applied to the particular farm. Rotation of crops should be practiced so that the same minerals are not being removed constantly. Crops such as corn, cotton, and tobacco use up large amounts of mineral material and should be rotated with hay or with pasture crops. At one time, tobacco, corn, and cotton were grown on some lands for such long periods that eventually the harvest did not amount to enough to pay for the seed. Increased knowledge has diminished this practice.

The present-day farmer has available many sources of information and assistance in efficient farm management. Every state in the union maintains an agricultural college where the future farmers of the state can learn sound, scientific ways of using the soil to best advantage. Extension courses are a feature of these colleges. These bring the college right to the farmer, so that he need not take time away from his work to learn better ways of farm management. Agricultural experiment stations are supported by the states and the nation to study farm problems, both locally and on a country-wide basis. Here, men who are a combination of scientist and practical farmer try to find solutions to the farmers' problems. The development of new insecticides, for example, has been one outcome of such studies by the agricultural experiment stations. The breeding of newer and better varieties of plants and animals is another achievement of agricultural scientists.

In most communities, the man who is in large measure responsible for bringing this assistance to the farmer is the county agricultural agent. These hardworking men have been particularly successful because they are the farmer's own neighbors. The farmer respects these men for their practical experience. The agricultural agent is the key figure in communicating scientific discoveries to the grass roots where they must then be applied by the farmers.

THE ENEMIES OF FORESTS

Forests not only provide wood products, which make up an important part of our national economy, but they also assist greatly, as we have seen, in preventing floods, in reducing soil erosion, and in conserving water. Forests provide a home for birds and other wild animals and recreation for millions of people.

We have already noted that trees were once regarded by the pioneers as something that had to be eliminated before the land could be farmed. Fortunately, the American public is finally taking action to protect its forest resources. Several national private organizations, as well as our state and federal governments, are engaged in planning conservation programs. Many schools have reforestation projects and are actively engaged in other ways in helping with conservation problems.

Let us consider some of the enemies of forests.

MAN. More than three-fourths of the original forests of the United States have been cut down. Every year far more trees are cut down than are replaced. Either the rate of cutting must be reduced or the rate of replacement must be stepped up.

Wasteful practices in the past have been responsible for much timber loss. Trees suitable for lumbering were cut down and allowed to fall on young trees and break them. Branches and other waste materials were allowed to remain on the ground, there to furnish ready fuel for forest fires. No attempt at reforestation was made. When an area had been denuded of all marketable trees, the lumberman moved on to a new area. Carelessness caused many forest fires.

FIRE. Fire still destroys more trees than are cut by man. In the decade 1948–1957, forest fires consumed over 109 million acres in the United States. Some forest fires are started by natural causes, mainly lightning. In 1957, lightning accounted for 8 per cent of the forest fires; 69 per cent were started accidentally by man, 23 per cent were of incendiary origin. Campfires, smokers, and railroads start many of them. Debris left on the forest floor is a contributing factor, since it furnishes the tinder that a stray spark may set ablaze. Though these causes of forest fires are well known, we still continue to throw burning cigarettes from our cars as we drive through the country, drop smoldering matches when we are walking through the woods, and neglect to put out campfires.

INSECTS, AND DISEASE. The chief enemies of the forest are insects and disease. They destroy nearly seven times the amount of timber that fire does. An example of the inroads of disease on trees is the case of the chestnut blight. This is a fungus disease of the American chestnut tree. It first received serious attention in 1904. Thirty years later there were no marketable chestnut trees east of the Ohio River. The blight had killed off almost all of the native chestnut trees in the

Two smoke-jumpers are parachuting to a small forest fire to prevent it from becoming a big one.

northeast. Resistant strains of this valuable tree are now being developed but it will be many decades before it is restored to its former abundance, if it ever is.

Another current problem concerns the destruction of the graceful elm tree by Dutch elm disease. Since its introduction into the United States in 1930, Dutch elm disease has wiped out nearly 50 million elm trees. The disease is found in at least 21 states of the union, mainly east of the Mississippi River. It is caused by a fungus organism, but the fungus is spread only by tiny bark beetles. The disease can be checked by getting rid of the beetles. Communities that have carried out consistent control programs have proved that the elms can be saved. Scientists have also been seeking a kind of elm that is resistant to the disease.

Many insects that are harmful to trees and plants come here from other countries. Their immigration is accidental, occurring in shipments of fruits or vegetables from other shores. The modern airplane can be a source of entry. Because of this, planes arriving from other lands are sprayed with insecticides as soon as they land at American airports. Quarantine and inspection are ways of stopping the entrance of some harmful

insects, but even with the most stringent care the problem will continue to exist.

The Japanese beetle is a well-known example of an insect that came from abroad and wreaked havoc on our crops and trees. Birds are of some help in controlling the pest. The prime reason why foreign insects become a problem in other countries is that they leave their natural enemies behind them when they are brought to new territory. In combating such insects, we often study them in their native habitat to find their natural enemies there. Such was the case with the Japanese beetle. It was found that a particular Japanese wasp was its chief enemy. This wasp was imported and raised in quantity and then released in areas where the beetle was out of control. The wasp lays its egg in the beetle larva. When the wasp young hatches out, it feeds on the larva and destroys it. In spite of this and other measures, we have not conquered Japanese beetles. They do an immense amount of damage each year. Importation of natural enemies of insect pests must be preceded by careful study, for it is possible that the insect brought in to control one pest may itself prove to be a nuisance.

Insects can frequently be controlled on a small scale, such as on a small vegetable farm, by spraying plants with chemicals that kill the insects but do not harm the plants. It is obvious that the cost and difficulty of application on large areas would be prohibitive. Therefore, to protect our forests against harmful insects by chemical spraying is out of the question. Moreover, widespread spraying might destroy insects and other forms of life that are essential in the chain of interrelationships described earlier in this chapter, and could lead to incalculable damage. That is why there must be unremitting study to discover natural enemies of insects. One field that has been investigated in this connection is the diseases of insects. If such diseases can be found and used, they may help to lessen the insect menace. Here again, care must be exercised before such measures can be put into practice, to make certain that the disseminated disease is not harmful to other living things.

REPLACEMENT OF FORESTS

SEE PAG 388

The early settlers in American never dreamed that we might ever be short of timber. The concept that timber should be

A so-called natural forest is here contrasted with a forest from which some of the trees have been carefully removed. Tall, straight trees are necessary to produce good lumber. Study the upper drawing and you will see why many of the trees are useless for lumber. The lower drawing shows the result of carefully planned cutting.

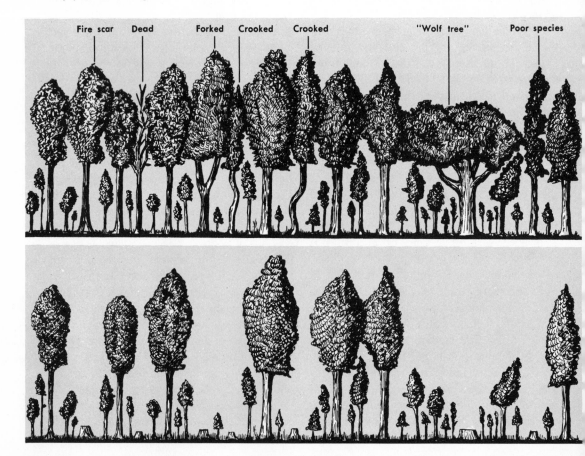

Fire scar Dead Forked Crooked Crooked "Wolf tree" Poor species

cultivated and harvested as a crop, instead of being "mined" out of the soil like ore, is a comparatively recent one. Theodore Roosevelt created a Bureau of Forestry in the early years of this century to protect our rapidly shrinking forest reserves. Gifford Pinchot, its first chief, had the task of changing the prevailing attitude toward forests. According to Pinchot, people believed that forests were "inexhaustible and in the way." Corrective measures were intiated, including the setting aside of forest reserves and national parks. Forest-owners slowly came to treat forests as a crop, instead of as a mineral to be mined. As a result of these and other measures mentioned in the previous section, the forest situation has improved markedly in many respects. However, the nation's future forest requirements are still not assured.

It is surprising to learn that today more than half of our remaining forest land in the United States are small holdings. All too often in the past, small owners have permitted wholesale cutting of their trees for cash. More and more owners are discovering that small wood lots can become important sources of yearly income by the practice of "tree farming."

The spearhead in demonstrating the profit in harvesting wood lots was the forestry college. This type of institution proved that a small wooded tract, carefully managed in accordance with good forestry practice, can continue to yield a harvest year after year. One of the leaders in this movement was the New York State College of Forestry. A small tract of land in the Adirondacks had been donated to them. The area was named the Pack Demonstration Forest. Here, approved forestry methods were used, and the Pack Forest became a living primer of the tree-farming idea. Groups of people were invited to the forest and shown how such land could be a profitable source of timber or wood pulp. The idea caught on, and today an increasing number of small wood lots are being brought into productive use.

Progressive owners of private forest lands are becoming more and more concerned with reforestation, and they are being encouraged in their programs of scientific forestry by the United States Forest Service. Expert advice is free for the asking, and seedlings are furnished at cost or below through federally subsidized nurseries operated by governmental agencies.

The federal government has set aside 186 million acres of public lands for national forest purposes and has engaged in a program of purchasing more land. Trees in such areas may be cut only if they are carefully replaced. Many state governments are engaged in similar projects. Some of this is made possible by reforesting land that has reverted to the state because of nonpayment of taxes.

Although not very important in supplying our national wood-products needs, SEE PAGE 388 school forests are doing a great deal to show children the need for conservation and how it may be carried out. Under this plan, schools acquire run-down land by purchase or gift. Young trees are planted and cared for as far as possible by the children themselves. School forests are valuable for recreation and for the teaching of science, and they also afford an opportunity for a firsthand study of conservation practices. The study in this case includes not only forest conservation but also conservation of birds, other wild animal life, and soil.

PROTECTION OF WILD FLOWERS

Wild flowers can give enjoyment to SEE PAGE 387 more people if they are left growing than if they are picked. The conservation "rule" here is "Look and leave it, so that others may enjoy it too."

Wild flowers can be picked without destroying the plants. The flowers of plants that are easily pulled out by the roots should be cut with a knife or shears rather than picked.

The wild flowers in one spot should never all be removed. Only the commonest should be picked at all. If some blossoms are not left to produce seed, the plants in that place will soon vanish.

Many states have designated certain flowers as "protected." That means that the protected species is in danger of extinction and may not be picked without violating the law. The most success is achieved by education. Most people, when they realize why the flower must be protected, will refrain from destroying their inheritance of beauty.

OUR VANISHING ANIMAL LIFE

Early explorers told stories of animal abundance that gave them reputations as spinners of tall tales. But the tales were true. The number of animals in colonial days was prodigious. At one time, 100 million bison roamed the western prairies. These animals were slaughtered for their hides and fur. Birds were exterminated for their decorative feathers. Enormous numbers of game and wild fowl were killed for sale as food. What saved our wild life was the birth of a con-

servation movement in the final quarter of the nineteenth century. For some animals, this came too late. The passenger pigeon was one of those that never recovered. There has not been a live passenger pigeon in America in fifty years; the bird is as extinct as the dinosaurs.

It was, of course, inevitable that the number of wild animals should diminish as the United States became more thickly settled. Wild animals find it difficult to live in a land from which many of the forests have been eliminated. Animals also find it difficult to live where they are hunted ruthlessly. Many of them have been killed even though they had little value as food or skins.

Animals whose skins were valuable were hit the hardest in the early days. Skins of such animals as the beaver, otter, mink, fisher, seal, lynx, wolf, bear, skunk, and muskrat had value in the markets of Europe. As a result of the ruthless exploitation of animals whose skins were valuable, the United States was largely denuded of its fur bearers. This is particularly true of bison and seals. Had we not protected the seals by law, they would have vanished entirely. Beaver, mink, and other fur bearers have had

The heath hen has joined the ranks of other vanished American birds. The last living specimen was seen in 1932.

to be protected by closed or limited seasons, by limitations on numbers allowed to be taken, and other means.

WHY CONSERVE ANIMALS?

The economic value of wildlife is tremendous. Fisheries, for example, supply important food worth many millions of dollars annually. However, the value of wildlife cannot be counted only in dollars and cents. Our national parks, with their fearless animal populations, are a source of pleasure to many people.

Certainly we should expect some animals to retreat from the haunts of man. Such animals as the deer, elk, wolf, bear, and lynx cannot well live in cleared sections. Muskrats, beavers, otters, minks, and other water dwellers cannot remain when swamps and lakes are drained and when streams and rivers are used for water supply and irrigation.

We should not, however, drive these animals into extinction. We should protect them in the natural habitats that remain for them. And we should also be intelligent enough to leave enough desirable space for them. There is ample land that should not be cleared for agricultural or industrial purposes. In such spots the animals can live—if they are protected.

Why protect wild animals? In their natural habitat they are a pleasure to watch, and they provide enjoyment for large numbers of people. They are as much a part of forests, lakes, ponds, streams, and meadows as the trees and flowers.

Each wild animal, as we have seen, is part of a life chain. This chain may lead directly to man. The destruction of coyotes in certain areas permitted a ruinous increase in the number of rodents. The killing off of Swainson's hawk in the west was followed by grasshopper plagues that destroyed millions of dollars worth of crops.

There is much that we do not know about interrelationships in nature. Even the simplest creature may be important in our existence. Let us remember this when someone asks, "What good is this animal?"

The person who asks such a question often implies also that unless the creature serves man's immediate needs, its continued existence is unimportant. Besides being shortsighted, from man's selfish viewpoint, this attitude may also be challenged on an ethical or philosophical basis.

BIRD CONSERVATION. Without birds, we would certainly suffer more damage from insects to farm crops, trees, and shrubs than we do now. Many birds feed on insects and thus help to control the large numbers of insects. Some of the harmful insects that birds eat are potato bugs, cutworms, chinch bugs, leaf beetles, and boll weevils.

The stomachs of many kinds of birds have been examined in an attempt to determine just how helpful they are. Examination of the stomachs of ruby-crowned kinglets, for example, revealed that 94 percent of their food was animal matter consisting of plant lice, mealy bugs, scale insects, caterpillars, and other insects. A young red-eyed vireo is known to have eaten 100 grasshoppers a day in addition to many other harmful insects. The diet of meadow larks is 99 percent insects—nearly all of them harmful to crops. The stomach of one flicker contained 5,000 ants. A nighthawk's stomach contained 500 mosquitoes.

Sometimes birds are accused of doing harm to man. Hawks are often alleged to be harmful because they kill chickens. Some kinds of hawks do kill a few chickens, but they also kill mice, which dig out freshly planted corn and are destructive to other seeds and to crops. Many kinds of hawks live mainly on mice rather than on chickens. There is little doubt that they do more good than harm.

WILDLIFE SANCTUARIES. The need for wildlife management and protection has been recognized for a long time. As far back as the beginning of the eighteenth century, practically all of the original colonies had established closed seasons on deer. But it was not until after the Civil War that protective legislation was established on a wide scale. The need for wildlife sanctuaries has been recognized, and many state and national areas have been set aside where wild animals and wild fowl can live and breed without interference. Scientific study of wildlife problems has increased. We know more about the interrelationships of living things than we did fifty years ago, but there are still vast unexplored realms that need investigation.

Nature preserves or sanctuaries, where all wild plants and animals are protected with as little disturbance by man as possible, are valuable as outdoor schoolrooms and scientific laboratories. Here the interrelationships discussed in this chapter can be studied. This is the purpose of the "Nature Centers" now being established in many communities with the guidance of the National Audubon Society.

CONSERVATION OF WATER

DROUGHT AND FLOOD.   In December 1949, the following message was sent to the teachers of New York City by its Superintendent of Schools, Dr. William Jansen.

WE MUST SAVE WATER

For the first time in the history of our city, we face the complete exhaustion of our water supply. In numerical strength and in area of coverage, the public schools are New York's greatest and most far-flung public service agency. We must therefore use every resource at our command to bring home to the people of our city the full implications of this crisis.

Mud and wreckage are piled in front of stores along desolate Main Street of North Topeka, Kansas, after the Kaw River waters receded.

We must join forces with the Department of Water Supply, Gas and Electricity, and with all other city departments, in publicizing every known method of preventing this unthinkable catastrophe. In our own buildings and in our homes, we must do everything in our power to cut down the consumption of water. We must do all this now, and we must go on doing it until the emergency has passed.

. . . I call upon every member of our staff to . . . enlist all our children in this crucial drive to save water.

Nor does the responsibility end here. Through our children, and through our position in the community, we must make every effort to convey this vital information to all the homes in our areas.

The schools will work actively and willingly with the entire community at this greatest and most serious job that faces us all today—the conservation of our precious, fast-dwindling water supply.

On July 30, 1951, *Life* magazine pictured a story of a flood in photographs and in these words:

RUIN ROLLS DOWN THE WIDE MISSOURI

Last week the great flood poured a wave of disaster down the wide Missouri. The rank, swirling waters, fed by all the rivers of Kansas, swept through the twin Kansas Citys and across the fertile farm lands toward St. Louis. Traveling with awesome majesty at about 35 miles a day, it surged forward, in places five miles wide, into Lexington, Jefferson City and on to St. Charles, near the Missouri's junction with the already flooding Mississippi. All along its stricken path it lapped inexorably higher, topping or crumbling levees sometimes 25 feet high, inundating farms, shops and homes and cutting off power facilities and bridges.

Ahead of the crest thousands worked desperately to thwart the foul, mud-laden tide. The flood's toll was staggering—41 lives lost, 165,000 persons left homeless, two million acres of farm land under water. Property losses came to more than $1 billion, making it the worst natural catastrophe in the history of the U.S.!!

Too little water, too much water— these are the two sides of the one problem of water conservation. Let us examine the nature of this problem to determine the cause of our water difficulties and some possible cures.

THE WATER SUPPLY OF THE EARTH. Water, one of our most precious resources, is also our commonest and cheapest. Unlike copper or coal, water is indestructible; it will not wear out. Its supply is inexhaustible. The sea covers three-quarters of the earth and holds 300 million cubic miles of water. Locked in glaciers, ice caps, and ice sheets are 11 million more.

In the course of the water cycle, water on the surface of the ocean and other bodies of water evaporates into the atmosphere. It is held there as invisible water vapor, and under certain conditions forms clouds. The water in the clouds falls back to the surface of the earth as rain or snow. Eventually, the water works its way back to lakes, seas, and oceans, thus completing the cycle. This process goes on without end. (See chapter 9A for a full discussion of the water cycle.)

The supply of water on our planet is ample; the problem is to obtain the right amount of fresh water in the right place at the right time. Water is a resource that moves; conserving it for use means controlling its movement.

WATER SHORTAGES. The basic cause of water shortages in big cities in recent years is the increased consumption of water. The average city in 1960 required 150 gallons a day per person. This figure includes

SEE PAGES 387 TO 388

water for domestic, commercial, industrial, and municipal uses. It is expected that our demand for water will continue to increase, because of the expected increase in the population and in the ways in which we will use water. A new problem of water usage will arise in connection with new atomic energy plants already under construction, since these require enormous quantities of water for their operation.

The supply of available water has not kept pace with the demand. Cities have not enlarged their water resources sufficiently to meet the new requirements of individuals and industries. Therefore, a dry winter and spring brings a shortage, because the reservoir system supporting the city does not have enough capacity to carry it over this dry spell.

The water shortage in cities has had at least one good effect: it has made city dwellers aware of their dependence on the land. It has made them realize, as one Washington official put it, that "water doesn't grow in faucets." The city dwellers learned a new word "watershed," an area of hundreds of square miles that acts as a basin to catch rainfall and to let it flow and seep slowly into the streams that feed reservoirs.

WATERSHEDS.   As stated previously, the problem of water conservation is one of having sufficient fresh water when and where it is needed. The watershed is of key importance in solving this problem. Let us look at watersheds more carefully.

Sooner or later, much of the water from rain or snow appears as streams. Small at first, these upland water courses become wider and deeper as they approach valleys, where they combine to form larger streams and rivers. The area that produces the water that appears as a stream or river is a *watershed*. Watersheds are of many shapes and sizes. Some cover millions of acres, like the Columbia and Missouri river drainages.

Under natural conditions, the soil, the plants in the soil (the "cover"), and the moisture of a watershed tend to be in bal-ance. When man ignorantly or carelessly upsets the balance by destroying much of the plant cover, perils arise, often resulting in dust bowls, spreading deserts and ruined valleys, water shortages, polluted rivers, and ravaging floods.

Forest land has enormous value as a regulator of water flow. Not only do forest soils retain and store water, they also control water movement on and beneath the surface. This control spells the difference between clear, steady streams and erratic flows of muddy water, rising rapidly after rains and shrinking as rapidly, leaving only dry river beds.

An old Chinese proverb says, "To rule the mountain is to rule the river." A healthy forest cover on the slopes of hills and mountains restrains floods and provides a steady flow of clear water. When the cover is removed by fire or overcultivation, an imbalance is set up that permits less and less water to be taken in and stored in the soil, to the detriment of farms, towns, and cities.

WATER TABLE.   We depend not only on the surface water that we can see and measure in streams, lakes, rivers, and reservoirs, but on underground water, that is, water that is some distance below the ground level. Underground water begins as rain that sinks into the ground and then soaks into porous rock. As rain continues, the bottom rock layers become filled or saturated with water. The upper level of this underground water is called the *water table*. Above this, rock particles may be coated with a film of water but air fills most of the pore space.

The underground rocks of the United States hold more water than all its surface reservoirs. The depth of the water table below the surface depends on many factors. In desert regions, for example, there may be so little rainfall that a water table never forms. Whenever the water table is high enough to reach the surface, we may have a spring or swamp, or we may dig a well to tap this source. Such springs and wells are a direct source of water for millions of people in the United States, in farm areas and in many urban areas as well.

A great concern of the United States government in recent years has been the falling water table in many areas, caused in part by the increasing amount of water being pumped out of the ground and in part by drought. In 1947, the water tables were the lowest on record in parts of Colorado, Nebraska, Kansas, Missouri, and Iowa. Record water-table drops brought on a brackish water problem. Overpumping and drought made this a serious matter in Kansas towns. Water levels in Wichita dropped nearly 30 feet between 1940 and 1957, a period in which the city's water use tripled.

THE ANSWER TO SHORTAGES AND FLOODS. What is the answer to water shortages and floods? Most important is the protection and extension of watershed areas, discussed previously. Concurrently, storage facilities—dams and reservoirs—must be constructed so that billions of gallons of water do not flow unused into the sea or cause destructive floods. There must be improved industrial practices, including the treatment of water after its use to help prevent the pollution of streams. Industry can help by reusing water, and home dwellers by eliminating the waste caused by dripping faucets and leaking pipes.

It has been proposed that sea water be processed for industrial, agricultural, and

Before a dam is built, the question must be asked—what effect will building this dam on this site have on the soil, the water, the plant and animal life, the people? Advice must be secured not only from the engineer, but also from the biologist, the chemist, the economist, the sociologist, and the anthropologist. Pictured here is the Fontana Dam, towering 480 feet, the highest dam east of the Rockies. Built by the Tennessee Valley Authority, Fontana is on the Little Tennessee River in North Carolina. The electric power installation generates 202,500 kilowatts.

home use. A network of pipe lines is en-
visioned, carrying desalted water from the
seacoasts to places where it is needed. The
power to pump the water would be supplied
by atomic energy plants. The government has
sponsored experimentation to produce a
cheap method of removing salt from water.
A plant in Freeport, Texas, began operation
in 1961 and was the first to supply the water
needs of a United States municipality—one
million gallons of desalted water a day.

CONSERVATION OF AIR

Air, like water, is an inexhaustible
resource, but pure air—air fit to breathe, air
that does not irritate our eyes, air that does
not damage plant life, air that does not soil
and corrode the materials that we use—is
becoming scarcer. The seriousness of this
problem is recognized in a government report[3] from which we quote.

Unpolluted air is a mixture of nitrogen, oxygen, water vapor, carbon dioxide and a few rare gases. Fortunately,
nature has provided a huge reservoir of
this mixture of gases and the temperature
changes on earth necessary to insure constant mixing of man's contaminants by air
currents. However, these natural processes
sometimes proceed at a slow rate. Whenever man's activities discharge to the air
noxious or troublesome substances at
rates faster than those forces operating to
disperse or destroy them, a build-up in
pollution concentration occurs and persists until natural forces can again cope
with the situation. . . .

Today, the concern with air pollution in urban areas relates to the emission of a variety of gases, fumes, and
solids, followed by chemical reactions and

physical combinations among them in the
open air. The pollutants potentially come
from incomplete combustion of various
fuels and wastes in home and factory,
from automobiles and other vehicles, from
evaporation from many volatile substances
in common use, and from processes resulting in evolution of dust, fume, or gases. . . .

Air pollution adversely affects man
in many ways; at times under certain circumstances the effects have been serious.
Outstanding among the several recorded
episodes when air pollution was the immediate cause of illness and death are the
Muse Valley, Belgium, episode where one
hundred were made ill and sixty-three
died in 1930; the Donora, Pennsylvania,
episode of 1948 when over a thousand
persons were severely affected and twenty
died; and the London, England, episode
of 1952 when four thousand excess
deaths were recorded during a two week
period in December.

Just as important, and perhaps
more difficult to deal with than the occurrence of a few episodes, is the possibility
that air pollution may be responsible for
chronic health impairment in our population. Statistical studies of mortality and
morbidity of human populations, and laboratory studies of animals suggest relationships between air pollution and
incidence of lung cancer. Similar relationships are seen with regard to cancer of
the stomach and esophagus, heart disease,
and several respiratory ailments, such as
emphysema and chronic bronchitis. In
addition, air pollution can act upon exposed mucous membranes, causing eye,
throat, and nasal irritation. Such irritation, combined with the general nuisance
effects of air pollution, produces an as
yet unmeasured but perhaps significant
amount of psychological harm to the
people in our urban areas.

Air pollution affects man in many
other important ways. It is estimated to
cost America billions of dollars annually

[3] *National Goals in Air Pollution Research,*
U. S. Department of Health, Education, and Welfare, 1960.

in soiling and corrosion alone. It damages vegetation and livestock and, by reducing visibility, creates hazards for ground and air traffic. It interferes with man's enjoyment of his surroundings, contributes greatly to the physical deterioration of communities, constitutes a variety of annoyances, and is frequently offensive to the senses.

Some cities have improved their air somewhat by turning from the burning of soft coal to natural gas. By ordinance and by self-imposed regulation, industries are increasingly putting in smoke-abatement installations. Auto manufacturers have been working on devices which cut down the amount of poisonous exhaust resulting from the incomplete burning of gasoline. By 1965, it is expected that these devices will become compulsory for all of California's cars.

Despite these efforts, it seems likely that the personal, community, and industrial activities responsible for today's community air pollution will experience accelerated growth in the future. By 1970 it is expected that two-thirds of our national population of 214 million will live in urbanized areas. Data from the National Air Sampling Network demonstrate generally a progressive increase in air pollution concentration with increase in city size. Thus, as our metropolitan areas grow larger, the air pollution potential grows greater. That is why greater efforts by industry and government are essential to meet the growing threat to the air we breathe.

CONSERVATION OF WILDERNESS

Wilderness was once thought of as something to be subdued and conquered, something to be fought and destroyed. There is growing recognition today that wilderness itself is a most precious heritage. In 1959, General Omar Bradley said, "Year after year

our scenic treasures are being plundered by what we call our advancing civilization. If we are not careful, we shall leave our children a legacy of billion dollar roads leading nowhere except to other congested places like those they left behind. We are building ourselves an asphalt treadmill and allowing the green areas of our nation to disappear."

As each mile of asphalt is built, the defense of our unspoiled wilderness becomes increasingly important. In a recent controversy over the proposed building of an automobile highway along the length of Fire Island, a barrier beach lying south of Long Island, New York, Stewart L. Udall, Secretary of the Interior, said:

Natural shore-line areas, both on our ocean coast and inland waters, have been developed at such a rate in recent years that there are very few such areas left. . . . But as our population grows, we need diversity of recreational opportunities. And, in particular, we need to provide for the preservation of natural open spaces free of automobile traffic, parking lots, and hot dog stands.

Fire Island offers just such an opportunity. We must use our ingenuity to do our public work so thoughtfully that this generation and the succeeding generations who come to the public park at the east and west end will see the magnificent sand dunes, natural vegetation, bird life, and the splendid beach untouched, much as they are now.

The chief purpose of the national park system is to preserve scenic treasures and wilderness for human recreation and esthetic appreciation. The task of maintaining a friendlier human environment through the conservation of a pleasing landscape and open spaces for recreation and the restful long view, has fallen with increasing emphasis on municipal and regional planning authorities.

Our generation in the coming years has, in the words of President Kennedy, a "last-chance opportunity." We can still save from 15 to 20 million acres for national parks, another 2½ million acres for national recreational areas, more than one million acres for national parkways and scenic roads, and 4½ million acres for wildlife refuge areas.

This land acquisition is costly today, but will be even more costly tomorrow. Yet, if we delay too long there may be little land to acquire at any price.

Here are some of the important generalizations growing out of the material on conservation:

In the long run, man's welfare depends on the natural world around him. His well-being depends on other living creatures, on water, on air, on soil, and on mineral resources.

Two reasons for concern about the world's resources are:
(1) The world's human population is increasing at an almost explosive rate.
(2) Industrialization has resulted in an enormous increase in the consumption of resources.

Conservation means the protection and preservation of our vital natural environment. This includes the air we breathe, the water we drink, and the land we live on. It means the wise use of our resources, for our present and future existence.

The understanding of interrelationships of living things with each other and with their physical environment is the key to sound conservation practice.

Pesticide chemicals should be used with caution because they may end up in plants and animals other than those for which they were intended, and because they may disturb a chain of interrelationships in such a way as to harm other forms of life.

Some resources, such as air, sunlight, water, and rock, are inexhaustible.

Some resources, such as soil, vegetation, animal life, and fresh water are renewable.

Some resources, such as coal, oil, natural gas, and metals, are nonrenewable. Their supply cannot be replenished.

New resources may be discovered and developed in the future by scientists and engineers.

All plant and animal life, including man's, is dependent directly or indirectly on the soil.

One-third of the valuable topsoil in the United States has been lost since the coming of white man, largely because of his unwise practices.

The erosion of soil can be checked by contour plowing, strip farming, and terracing.

Forests are very important in preventing soil erosion and floods.

To maintain soil fertility it is necessary to return to the soil what the crops remove.

Rotation of crops, the planting of legumes, and the addition of fertilizers help maintain soil fertility.

Fire, insects, disease, and wind are responsible for much forest destruction.

Man has been an enemy of the forest.

Timber should be cultivated and harvested as a crop.

Forest conservation measures include combating fire, harmful insects, and tree diseases; practicing careful lumbering methods; reforestation; and the establishing of national and state forests.

Wildlife should be protected because of its economic value, both immediate and long range, its recreational value, and its right to exist.

Wilderness is a precious heritage.

The problem of water conservation is that of having the right amount of fresh water in the right place at the right time.

The basic cause of water shortages in cities in recent years is the increased consumption of water.

A matter of concern in recent years has been the falling water table in many areas.

Water conservation involves the protection and extension of watershed areas, construction of dams and reservoirs, improved industrial practices in relation to water usage, and elimination of waste.

The desalting of sea water may provide a possible solution of the fresh-water problem.

With growing urbanization and industrialization, the seriousness of the air pollution problem increases.

DISCOVERING FOR YOURSELF

1. Examine carefully a wood lot or other area that has been burned. Find out how animal and plant life has been changed. Observe the area over a period of a month or more to see what happens to the living things that remain.
2. Observe various hillsides after a heavy rain. Describe them and compare the results of the rain on the surface of each. Explain what happened.
3. Keep a record of the things that come from the earth that you use in one day. Indicate those that are in danger of becoming depleted, those that are being replaced in sufficient quantity, and those that appear to be in plentiful supply.
4. Interview a county agriculture agent or some other individual who is concerned with soil, water, and wild-life conservation in your area. Find out what the most pressing conservation problems are, why they have become critical, what is being done about them.
5. Visit an experimental farm or station and find out how research is being carried out to solve conservation problems.
6. Find out, either through direct observation or by other means, how soilless gardening is carried out.
7. Plan and carry out an experiment that will show the results of using and not using a commercial fertilizer in soil.
8. Get copies of the game laws of your state for the past five or ten years. Examine the laws. What changes have been made? Why have they been made?
9. Find out what the problems of forest conservation are in your state. Locate the tree nurseries. Visit one and report your findings.
10. Gather seeds of various kinds of forest trees and try to germinate them.
11. Talk with a forest ranger, forest lookout observer, or other individual who has firsthand information about forest conservation.
12. Find out where the Christmas trees in your community come from and how they are grown and transported.
13. Read *Silent Spring* by Rachel Carson. What pesticides are in common use in the area where you live?

CHAPTER 15B

Teaching "Conservation of Our Resources"

Since conservation is based on an understanding of the interrelationships of man with his natural and physical environment, it is sound practice to study conservation *in* the environment. Any neighborhood can serve as a laboratory for the study of these interrelationships. Almost any neighborhood has plants, animals, rocks, soil, hills, and valleys. The school building, with its natural and man-made stone reveals how we use some of nature's resources. The school grounds are constantly changing under the influence of the sun, rain, and wind. The trees on the street are rooted in soil. They provide shade and beauty for human beings, protection for birds, food for insects. Nearby parks, fields, streams, and rivers provide further opportunities for discovering interrelationships in nature.

Each school can make an inventory of the outdoor resources which are available to it. Children, teachers, parents and other interested individuals may cooperate in making such an inventory. The outcome of this survey may be an exhibit, a fair, a mimeographed guide, a nature trail, a project to improve the school grounds, a campaign to clear up an area, or any other project which involves children in constructive community activity. When children see that what they do makes a difference, they have learned one of the prime concepts of conservation.

The time spent in teaching conservation is practically useless unless the knowledge gained is translated into action. It makes little difference that children can, for example, identify the wild flowers that they should not pick—if they go out with adults on Sunday and tear them up by the roots. It is unimportant for children to know which birds are helpful and which are harmful—if they destroy birds' eggs nevertheless. Conservation teaching must be so skillfully done that it makes lasting impressions which inspire continued intelligent action on the part of the learners.

Conservation cannot be learned by sermons, except for the sermons that nature itself preaches. Conservation education should be based on *things to do*, here and now, so that children will start moving in the right direction with their muscles as well as their brains. Conservation education should be based on enjoyment of the out-of-doors. We should make every effort to heighten that enjoyment so that our children, now and later as adult citizens, will be motivated to save and protect that which gave them pleasure, peace, and beauty.

The concepts involved in conservation may in some ways seem more appropriate for older than for younger pupils, but there are many experiences for young children that will help prepare them for better understanding of conservation practices. Some of these activities—for example, keeping an animal pet, raising a garden, observing the places where animals live, and seeing how animals take care of their young—have been described in earlier chapters. Here are other such activities.

1. Observe and tell about all of the things we eat and wear that come from plants and animals.
2. Look for different places where animals and plants are useful to us.
3. Find pictures that show how we use animals and plants and tell about the pictures. (What does the picture show? Have you ever used plants and animals this way?)
4. Take a walk to see: plants that we use for food; plants that we use for making houses, furniture, and other useful things; animals that give us food; how people take care of plants and animals.
5. Learn about "Smokey the Bear." Discuss how forest fires start and why they are harmful.

Planting a tree may be a rewarding experience. Observing the growth from year to year, supplying the needs for growth, and realizing how long it takes for a tree to grow, contribute to children's appreciation and interest. Selecting an appropriate kind of tree and its location are important experiences.

6. Take a walk after a heavy rain to see what happens to the water and to the soil. Discuss: "How does water carry soil away? Why is this harmful?"
7. Plant seeds or plants in good topsoil and in subsoil to note difference in growth.
8. Plant a tree on the school grounds. Observe roots of the tree, see how the tree is planted, learn what the tree needs so that it can grow, observe the changes in the tree as it grows.
9. Plant grass seed in good soil to see how it grows. Use a reading glass to examine the seeds as they sprout. Sow grass seed on a section of the school grounds to see how it grows.

The term *conservation* and what it implies begins to be more thoroughly comprehensible at the fourth- and fifth-grade level. Obviously, much of the material on conservation is taken up in the teaching of social studies courses. The scientific and social aspects of the problem are, of course, related. This is one of the places where the two areas of the curriculum should certainly be considered together.

FINDING OUT WHERE THINGS COME FROM

It is important for pupils to realize how much we depend on the earth's storehouse for our everyday existence. One interesting way to emphasize this is to make a list, for a period of two or three days, of the things pupils do, such as: eat breakfast, come to school, work in the garden, deliver newspapers, help repair the garage door, help prepare dinner, buy groceries, play baseball, listen to the radio, look at television. After they have listed several such activities, pupils may list for each one of them the things they used (1) that came from the earth; (2) that grew in soil; (3) that came from animals which depend on plants; (4) that needed water to grow. Their list would, of course, include food from plants and animals, gasoline for transportation, coal or oil for warmth, iron and other metals for tools and machines, and wood for making paper and other necessities. We have named only a few. Through such an activity as this, pupils begin to see how thoroughly we depend on our natural resources.

"Where does it come from?" is always an interesting question, and an extension of this idea as it was suggested in the previous chapter about food might be enlarged to include clothing and shelter. As in the case of foods, various materials used for clothing (cotton, linen, leather, and others) and shelter (bricks, glass, lumber, and others) may be assigned for investigation.

Following these activities, the discussion might center around the fact that the supply of many of these materials is diminishing year by year. Pupils may find figures in pamphlets and bulletins and elsewhere to show the decrease in coal, petroleum, and other vital resources. There is considerable opportunity for older pupils to use arithmetic[1] in interpreting these figures by calculating the fractions and percentages of the amounts consumed in relation to the estimated remaining supply. Experience with these figures will begin to make pupils realize the seriousness of the problem of using our resources wisely.

---

[1] *Ranger 'Rithmetic,* U. S. Department of Agriculture, Washington 25, D. C. Some examples in arithmetic using forest data. Free to teachers.

EXPERIMENTING WITH SOIL

Several of the concepts about soil and its conservation may be learned from simple experiments. Pupils can see that soil is composed of materials of different kinds and char-acteristics by taking a two-quart or gallon jar, placing several handfuls of garden soil and some water into it, shaking it up thoroughly, and allowing it to settle for a few hours or longer. The heavier materials settle to the bottom, and the lighter materials form in layers above. Soil from the woods will show even more plainly the different materials. Much of the lightest material contains the important nourishment for plants and is carried away by water as it runs over land which is not protected by a cover of vegetation.

After a heavy rainfall, pupils may take samples of the water from a nearby stream and examine it to see what makes it look muddy. They can see the particles of soil in the water. If the water is left standing in jars for several hours, the soil will settle to the bottom, and the water may be poured off and the sediment examined so that pupils can see that it really is soil. The banks of the stream from which the water is taken should be examined to see the small gullies that the running water has worn away. If sections of the bank are sodded or covered with plants, these may be compared with barren parts of the bank to see how plants keep the soil from being washed away.

Set up some experiments to show the effects of good and poor soil on growing things. Get samples of several different kinds of soil from a fertile flower or truck garden, from the woods, from a place in the schoolyard where nothing seems to grow very well, and from a place where a cellar for a house is being dug. Place identical amounts of each soil into identical flowerpots with identical drainage and plant several bean or corn seeds in the pots. Observe the difference in the growth of the plants.

OBSERVING THE EFFECTS OF
RUNNING WATER

After a heavy rain, pupils may explore the school grounds or other nearby places to see effects of the rain. They may notice places where soil has been washed over the side-walks and find the gullies from which the soil has been removed. They may look for similar places on their way to and from school. In many schools, pupils have planned ways by which to stop such runoff erosion and have successfully carried out their plans.

The next drawing shows an experiment planned to compare the effect of water running over bare soil with that of water running over soil covered with grass. The arrange-ment was built of boards from packing boxes. Both slanting surfaces are covered with the same kind of garden soil; one surface is left bare, and the other is covered with grass sod. Children may substitute grass seed, barley, or rye for the sod. A measured amount of water is poured over each surface and caught again after it has run through the soil. The amounts and color of the two runoffs are then compared. From this experiment, pupils can see that the soil covered with sod takes up more water than the bare soil. They can use these findings later, in their outdoor observations.

Observations and experiments can provide pupils with some background for com-prehending the seriousness of soil erosion when they see it in fields. It is important for them actually to see places where land has been eroded as well as places where steps have been taken to stop erosion. We shall later describe in some detail a suggested conservation trip that will include observing soil erosion as well as other conservation problems.

How Can We Save
Our Soil?

PLOT # 1				PLOT # 2		
No Grass or Dams				With Grass and Dams		
Date	Water on	Water off	Soil off	Date	Water on	Water off	Soil off

Experimenting to solve a problem that involves setting up careful controls, collecting and recording data, and drawing conclusions is an important science learning experience. The charts indicate the date, the amount of water poured on, the amount that runs off, and the amount of soil washed off in each case.

INVESTIGATING SPECIAL CONSERVATION PROBLEMS

Several problems in the study of conservation lend themselves to investigating—especially in the local or state area—and reporting by individuals or by small groups. For example: (1) Does our state set up any plant quarantines? The report would indicate why the quarantines are established and how they operate. (2) Are there any special plant diseases or insect pests in our state that may become very dangerous? (Dutch elm disease and Japanese beetles.) (3) What animals and plants in our state are in danger of becoming extinct? What is being done about this? (4) Are air and water pollution a problem in our community? If so, what is being done about it? (5) How is conservation practiced in our school? (Efficient use of fuel for heating, painting iron to prevent rusting, turning off lights when they are not in use, and so on.) The report might include suggestions for improving conservation practices.

Subjects for other reports will suggest themselves—for example, animals and plants that have become extinct; whether starlings are helpful or harmful; how the English sparrow came to be imported to this country; a swamp I like to visit and what lives there; vegetable gardens in our neighborhood; natural stones used in the buildings on my street; what lives in an "empty" lot.

STUDYING WILD FLOWERS

Learning about wild flowers in order to know which of them should be preserved is an important part of conservation. It involves learning not merely their names but also how the flowers reproduce, because this, of course, has a direct bearing on whether or not they may be picked. Pictures of wild flowers may be mounted on a large cardboard and used with an electric questioner (see page 538). The circuits may be arranged so that the light goes on for the flowers that need special conservation efforts.

A committee of pupils may arrange exhibits of single flower specimens, indicating which may and which may not be gathered in quantity. This should be done at times of the year when the various plants blossom. The display may be set up in cooperation with members of the biology class of a nearby high school, and the exhibit maintained in a place where many persons may see it. Several of the books on identification listed in the bibliography will be helpful in the study of wild flowers.

LEARNING ABOUT THE WATER SUPPLY

The problem of an adequate water supply has become acute in certain sections of the country. No matter in what regions pupils live, they may investigate to find the answers to the following problems: "Where does our water supply come from?" "How is it made pure?" "Is there any danger that the supply may be depleted?" "Should anything be done to increase it?" If water comes from deep wells, pupils may be able to find a place where a well is being driven, talk to the well-drillers, get samples of the soil that is brought up in

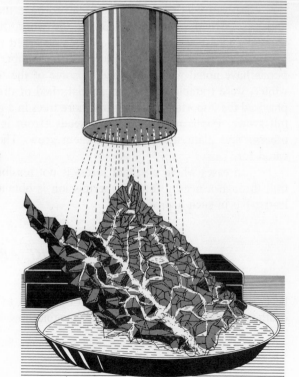

This demonstration helps to make the idea of the watershed more meaningful. Children may be asked to compare what is illustrated here with a real watershed.

the drilling, and learn something about the nature of the layers through which the drilling is being done.

If water comes from lakes, streams, or similar sources, pupils may visit the water works to learn what the source of the water is, whether or not it is adequate, and whether there are plans for enlarging the supply. While they are on the visit, they will want also to see how the supply is purified. They can see the filtering beds and the other methods used for purifying water.[2]

Children may not realize that direct rainfall produces only a small part of the supply of water in a collecting reservoir. Most of the water in a reservoir flows into it from the sloping land surrounding it. This land, called a watershed, receives the water originally as rain. Brooks and streams from the watershed feed the reservoir.

To demonstrate how a watershed area collects water, crumple a large piece of aluminum foil, then open it up and crease it lengthwise. Place it as shown in the illustration and sprinkle water on it from a sprinkling can. Children will see how the water runs together from the wide area into the collecting "reservoir."

STARTING A SCHOOL FOREST

There are a large number of school forests in the United States. Most of them are operated by high school pupils, but there are places where elementary school pupils have taken an active part in assisting with reforestation of a tract of land. There are, in the vicinity of many elementary schools, small tracts of uncultivated land that should be planted with trees because the land is unsuitable for other use. Often arrangements may be made to plant young trees on a small area of such land. The state conservation department will furnish the trees, along with directions for planting them. In many cases, the owner of the land has been very cooperative in paying a small sum to have the trees planted, has furnished the tools, and has assisted with supervision of the work. Individual pupils marked the trees they planted and for several years thereafter observed them to see how they were growing. In some places, records have been kept of the number of trees planted, and from year to year pupils have noted what happened to some of the trees that died (did not survive the cold winter, were trampled on by an animal, died of drought or of unknown causes). This emphasized the importance of planting more trees in a given space than could possibly live when full grown. Pupils may collect tree seeds (from maple, elm, oak, cone-bearing trees, and others) and plant them to watch them grow. The small trees may be transplanted and cared for.

In cases where a school forest is not feasible, it may be possible to make a nature trail through a nearby forest if permission is obtained. Interested parents have often taken leadership in such a project.

TELLING ABOUT THE LIFE OF A TREE

The story of the life of a tree from the time the seed sprouts until it is big enough to be cut for use is an interesting one for children to work out. They may choose some tree on the roadside near the school and imagine how it began, how it obtained the material it

---

[2] *The Ground Water Table,* Audubon Nature Bulletin, National Audubon Society, 1130 Fifth Ave., New York 28, N. Y. (15¢).

needed to grow, how a dry summer nearly killed it, how a grass fire around it nearly killed it when it was three years old, how a rabbit nearly girdled it one day but was frightened away by a passing automobile, how it finally grew to its present size, perhaps how it was cut and made into all sorts of useful things, how it had spread seeds, how young trees are growing up to take its place. In such a story as this there is opportunity to use imagination as well as facts. The general outline may be worked out by the class as a whole, and then various groups may write sections of the story. It lends itself very well to illustration.[3] A tree stump section, when examined, tells an interesting story of the life of a tree—its age, its years of great and of thwarted growth, etc.

MAKING A CONSERVATION MAP

After pupils have made an extensive study of conservation, they may make a map of their country or state to organize and summarize what they have learned. The general problem may be: "What kind of map can we make to help us share what we have learned about conservation with other people who should also know about conservation?" They will then have to decide on the size of the map, what materials to use in making it, what to show on it, and how to show it.

The map should be large and may be made on white wrapping paper. It should show parts of the adjacent states or counties, and pupils may decide to indicate the important rivers, streams, and other bodies of water, and the capital city or county seat and other major cities in order to locate more easily the conservation feature they wish to show. Following are examples of the kinds of things they may show on the map: state parks, game refuges, and fish hatcheries; significant forest areas; areas where reforestation is in progress; coal, mineral, and petroleum deposits; areas where flood-control projects are in operation, being built, or contemplated; areas where there have been recent forest fires; and areas where erosion is most serious. The information included on the map will vary with counties and states and with data that are available. Information for the map will come from the many sources—books, pamphlets, and people—used during the study.

If the pupils plan and make it themselves, such a map involves considerable group work and problem-solving. In order to approach accuracy of scale, considerable arithmetical computation is necessary. (Elementary pupils can hardly be expected to be exact in every instance, because some of the problems will be rather involved.) It requires considerable geography and map study to determine locations and distances. (Many highway maps contain information of considerable value in constructing such a map.) When the map is finished, individual pupils may prepare informal talks to describe what the map shows. These talks should not be memorized but "talked."

A map of this kind made by a group of sixth-graders turned out successfully enough to be shown at a parent-teacher association meeting along with a film on conservation that was sent by the state conservation department. The conservation department also sent a representative to present the problem of conservation to parents and pupils at the meeting.

---

[3] "How a Tree Grows" (W-3) and "What We Get From Trees" (D-5) are posters available from U. S. Forest Service, Washington 25, D. C. Single copies free to teachers. Write for information about other materials available from the Forest Service.

G. O. Blough, *The Tree On the Road to Turntown* (New York, Whittlesey House, 1953). The story of the life of a tree.

Trees Are History Books; How Trees Live; Our Brothers, the Trees; Audubon Nature Bulletins, National Audubon Society, 1130 Fifth Ave., New York 28, N. Y. (15¢ each).

What can we learn about topsoil by observing it? This class has the opportunity to compare soils, see the depth of the topsoil, collect samples for examination and use in experiments, and see the effects of erosion. There is no substitute for such firsthand observation to develop understanding.

Pupils described the map to the parents, saw the film, and listened to the speaker. The activity was successful because of the pupils' growth in science information and in the ability to express themselves in oral and visual form. It was a good public-relations event for the school and an example of using available resources for adult education both in knowledge of how their school operates and in conservation practices.

TAKING A CONSERVATION FIELD TRIP

During the study of conservation, pupils may take field trips to observe as many as possible of the things they have learned. Such trips may, of course, be taken at any time during the conservation study as a motivating activity, to raise problems and stimulate observation and thinking. Trips are important enough to deserve some attention from the county agricultural agent or from some of his assistants. They can help to plan the trip by suggesting places to visit and persons to talk to. There are many instances in which parents have provided the needed transportation for trips because the school could not provide it. These parents have been most helpful when they were informed beforehand about the purpose and general plan of the trip.

Trips are extremely valuable to pupils in helping to make conservation problems real to them but, if extensive trips are not possible, many things may be observed by individuals and reported to the group, and some may be seen on short field trips from the schoolhouse The class discussion to summarize the findings of such trips as these is very important.

Here are suggestions for a one-day trip. Not all the things mentioned can be seen in any one place and certainly not all could be studied on any one-day trip, but they have all been observed at various times by elementary pupils on conservation trips.

1. Observe how the highway department has taken steps to stop erosion of the roadside, especially where there are steep grades (planting, seeding, terracing, covering with straw and brush, and so on).

2. Observe fields that are idle and try to decide why the land is not being used (county agricultural agent will help here). Observe what happens to unused fields if they are not covered with grass or other plants.

3. Observe the difference in erosion between pasture fields and bare fields.

4. Observe how streams cut through the land; look at the banks of the streams; examine the water to see whether it is muddy or clear.

5. Go into a woods and dig down to see how the floor of the woods can absorb water more readily than hard ground can. Notice how the roots hold the soil together and how the leaves decay to make soil. Bring back a sample of the soil to examine more closely. Notice how the trees in a woods are different from those in an open field and see why they are better for lumber. Try to find out how many acres of land the woods covers and if possible find out the value of the timber.

The concept of plants adapting to their environments becomes real when children go to see examples and note the effects of light, moisture, soil, and temperature. It is important to remember that identification is only a means to an end; the other science learnings after identifying are most important.

6. Look for a place—either a forest or a roadside—that has recently been burned over. Walk over the burned area and see what has happened to plants and animals. In order to see what damage has been done, compare it with a nearby place that has not been burned over.

7. Observe the effects of insects on the leaves of trees and on other vegetation. Try to find out whether the damage is serious and whether anything can be done to stop it.

8. Visit a farm where conservation practices are in operation. Try to find out how much the conservation activities have cost, how they were accomplished, and why the farmer decided to invest in them. Find out whether the government gave financial assistance to the project. Find out how deep the well is, whether or not there are springs on the farm, and how the farmer supplies water for his livestock.

9. Make and put out a campfire. If pupils take their lunch on the trip, they may choose a location in which to build a fire, learn how to build a fire out-of-doors, and take especial care in extinguishing it, using sand and water. One committee may be appointed beforehand to be responsible for making the fire, and another one to extinguish it. After the latter committee has done its work, the group may evaluate the job by deciding whether the fire has actually been extinguished. Ashes should be spread out to make sure. The discussion should be held "on the spot" to make the idea real. Before leaving, pupils may observe the surroundings to answer the question "What harm could this campfire have done if it had not been properly extinguished and had been allowed to spread?"

10. Look for places that provide good shelter for birds and see whether there are birds there. Try to observe the birds closely enough to see what they are eating.

11. Find places where young trees are coming up and try to decide how they came to grow there. Were they planted? Did they grow from the seeds of other trees nearby? Are they on highway property or on privately owned land? Why are they important?

12. Look for "No Hunting" and "No Fishing" signs and try to decide why they were put up in these places.

13. Look for hawks or other preying birds and try to decide whether they should be shot. Discuss what facts should be known before a decision is made.

14. Take two samples of soil from a cut in the highway—one from just under the sod, the other from farther down. Measure the depth of the layer of dark soil at the top and note how far the roots of different kinds of plants go into this soil. Take the sample of topsoil and the sample of subsoil back to the school-room for further examination and for use in experimenting.

15. Visit a sawmill to watch trees being sawed and see how trees are selected, cut, and trimmed for use. One group visited a sawmill and listened to the county agent explain the conservation practices that were involved. He then asked pupils to estimate the value of one of the large trees that was about to be cut. After the pupils had given their estimates, the mill-owner told them his estimate. When the class had returned and was discussing the trip, each pupil was asked what things he could buy with the money which the tree represented. This helped pupils to see the value of trees and to realize more clearly what happens when trees burn in a forest fire.

USING A CITY ENVIRONMENT

Operation New York[4] is an example of a project designed to explore the use of a city outdoor environment for enriching teaching. The report suggests ways in which rocks, water, soil, plants, and animals may be used to provide meaningful and enjoyable experiences for girls and boys. It is a guide to the study of many interesting earth forms: hills, plains, rock outcrops, lakes, rivers, harbors and beaches. Use is made of the locale of the school—the schoolyard, nearby buildings, excavations, sidewalks and curbs—for an understanding of man's use of earth resources. Attention is directed to the forces of nature at work: erosion of soil in a vacant lot or nearby park, formation of "flood areas" following a storm, the wearing away of stone, the decay of leaves into soil. The interrelationships of living things—including man—with their physical surroundings are understood as boys and girls explore the many 'little environments' which are found within the city.

A study of this report will provide many suggestions to other city groups for using their environments more effectively.

STUDYING FOOD CHAINS

The interdependence of living things with each other and with their physical environment is best understood by studying it in small samples called food chains. A food chain might be defined simply as "who eats who?" A school lawn is a good place to look for food chains. Grass, spiders, insects, slugs, earthworms, robins, starlings, Japanese beetles, aphids, ants, caterpillars, honeybees, squirrels, are involved in a number of food chains. Pupils will enjoy the detective work involved in tracking down some of these chains. For example, pupils find that robins eat earthworms which eat soil. Leaves decay to form soil. The leaves of some plants are sucked of their juices by aphids which in turn are "milked" by ants. There are countless numbers of such chains to be discovered through careful observation and reading to verify.[5]

RESOURCES TO INVESTIGATE

1. Leaders in a 4-H Club for information about what the young people of the state are doing to promote conservation.
2. State soil conservation department for information on erosion problems of local area and conservation practices in action.
3. The state conservation department for printed matter, films, and other resources useful in teaching conservation.
4. National Parks Service for conservation regulations regarding the collection of materials in national forests and for other conservation information.
5. The Wilderness Society, 2144 P St., N.W. Washington 7, D. C.; Wildlife Management Institute, 709 Wire Building, Washington 5, D. C.; National Wildlife

---

[4] *Operation New York*. Using the Natural Environment of the City as a Curriculum Resource. Board of Education of the City of New York, Publication Sales Office, 110 Livingston St., Brooklyn 1, N. Y. ($1.00).

[5] *Food Chains*, Cornell Science Leaflet, Vol. 55, No. 4, 1962. Ithaca, New York, State College of Agriculture (25¢).

Federation, Servicing Division, 1412 Sixteenth St., N.W., Washington 6, D. C.; The Conservation Foundation, 30 East 40 St., New York 16, N. Y.; National Audubon Society, 1130 Fifth Ave., New York 28, N. Y., for information about printed material available to teachers.

6. Surrounding farm and forest area to observe conservation or need for conservation practices.

7. County agriculture agent, high school biology teacher, for materials, suggestions, and information on local and state conservation problems.

8. State Geologist for information about mineral deposits and other similar resources.

9. The local water-purification and sewage-disposal plants to observe sources of water and conservation practices.

10. Game warden for information about hunting and fishing regulations.

Energy and Matter

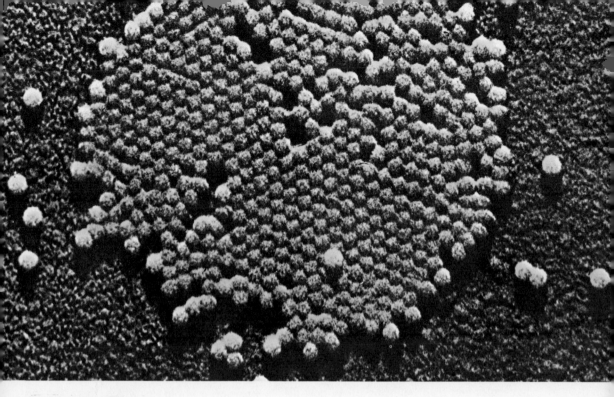

PART FOUR

What Things Are Made of

... the little things are infinitely the most important.

SHERLOCK HOLMES

One of the most fundamental generalizations of science is that large-scale events have their causes in the behavior of minute particles. We have seen how the functioning of plants and animals is dependent on the activities of their component cells. Let us probe more deeply for the more fundamental particles whose activities account for happenings in living and nonliving things—from the turning of a plant toward the light to the formation of a universe.

Consider a small amount of a common substance—a glassful of water. What do we know about the minute make-up of the water in this glass?

If we pour out half of it, we still have the same substance left—water. Pour out half of the remainder and keep repeating this process. Would we ever reach a speck so small that to split it again would be to produce something other than water? Or is there no limit?

MOLECULES

There is a limit, and that limit is reached when only a single *molecule* of water is left in the glass. We can split such molecules easily (with the aid of an electric current), but if we do, we no longer have water; what we do have we will discuss presently.

SEE PAGES 407 TO 408

To our sight, to our touch, to our taste, water appears to be a *continuous* substance; it is hard for us to imagine that it is made of tiny molecules. It seems to be quite different, for example, from a glass of beads. Actually, water is made of separate, distinct particles: molecules. In a glass of water there are billions and billions of water molecules with a lot of empty space between them.

The theory that all substances are made of molecules is fundamental in all of science. It holds true for liquids, gases, or solids. A gas such as air, for example, is made of molecules separated by wide spaces. Even an object as solid as a bar of iron is made of separate molecules, with much emptiness between the molecules.

Molecules differ from each other in a number of ways, as we shall see, but they have one thing in common: they are in constant motion at high speeds, striking other molecules and then bouncing off in new directions. Sometimes molecules "escape" from their surroundings. A street puddle "dries up" because its water molecules have bounced into the air and disappeared from view, adding to the water vapor content of the atmosphere. If the air containing these molecules is chilled somewhat, as it might be as it rises to higher altitudes, the molecules of water lose some of their energy and join together, condensing into the small droplets that make up a cloud.

When a lump of sugar dissolves in a cup of coffee, the molecules of sugar fly away from the lump and move in among the molecules of the liquid. Soon, if you taste the coffee, you taste the sugar.

A question that may arise when we consider the molecular nature of things is this: if all matter is composed of separate particles (which means that all matter is full of holes) what holds things together? What makes an iron bar so tough, so solid, so impenetrable? The answer lies in the powerful attractive force that exists between molecules. This attractive force holds molecules together without any material coupling, much the same as a magnet can exert a force on a nail from a distance.

Thus, to our picture of molecules as separate, ever-moving entities, we add one more characteristic: their mutual attraction for each other. In a solid, this attraction is sufficient to prevent the object from changing shape easily. The motion of the molecules is restricted to a small space. In a liquid, such as the glass of water we were investigating, molecular movement is not quite as restricted as in a solid; bouncing water molecules occasionally escape from their particular neighborhood and wander a bit. This greater molecular freedom makes it possible for liquids to assume the shape of the container into which they have been placed. In a gas, the energy of motion of the molecules is great enough to permit their rapid and free scattering. Open a bottle of ammonia in one corner of a room in which there are no drafts of air. Gradually the odor of ammonia will permeate every corner of the room as the ammonia molecules, escaping from the bottle, fly freely through the great spaces between the other molecules that comprise the air.

One more point should be stressed. The molecules of ammonia are different from the molecules of water and both of these are different from the molecules of other substances. But any water molecule is identical with any other water molecule, and any ammonia molecule is identical with any other ammonia molecule, and so on.

To sum up, the molecular theory of matter makes four basic assumptions:

1. *Matter is composed of exceedingly small separate particles called molecules.*
2. *Each different kind of matter is made up of its own particular kind of molecules.*
3. *Molecules are in rapid and ceaseless motion.*
4. *Molecules attract each other.*

What proofs do scientists offer to back the molecular theory of matter? There are many, but to describe them all would involve too detailed a presentation for this chapter. Let us mention just two:

1. *Stir some dry, fine, oil pigment (carmine red will do) in a little water. Place a drop of this on a microscope slide and cover with a cover slip. Observe at a magnification of 440 power or higher. Observe the pigment carefully, and you will see that individual specks of it move short distances in a zigzag fashion, never stopping. What causes this jiggling in a nonliving substance? We believe that it is due to the bombardment of these pigment particles by the smaller invisible molecules of water in which they are immersed. This, of course, is indirect evidence.*

2. *With the electron microscope, which magnifies up to 100,000 times, we have recently been able to actually photograph the individual molecules of many substances, such as the very large molecules of polio virus shown in the frontispiece of this chapter.*

ATOMS

All matter, then, is made of separate, ever-moving molecules. Let us return now to the glass of water to see what would happen if we were to split its molecules.

In a common experiment performed in high school science classes, an electric current is passed through some water. In this process, known as the electrolysis of water, two gases are produced, which on testing prove to be hydrogen and oxygen. Careful measurements would show that the weight of water that is lost is matched exactly by the combined weight of the two new gases which have been envolved. If this experiment is

continued (with appropriate apparatus) to its very end, all the water will disappear and in its place there will be hydrogen and oxygen gas.

Evidently, water can be "taken apart" to form two new substances. This is possible because each molecule of water is made of two kinds of smaller particles—*atoms*. Specifically, each molecule of water is made of 2 atoms of hydrogen and 1 atom of oxygen, and nothing else. The word "splitting" used in reference to molecules is somewhat misleading; it conjures up a picture of breaking open a sphere and finding some new things inside. The water molecule is *nothing more* than a close partnership of 2 hydrogen atoms and 1 oxygen atom. The chemist's formula H_2O gives the exact name to this partnership.

We note also that the new substances produced bear little relationship in their properties to the original substance of which they were a part. Hydrogen is highly burnable gas; oxygen is a gas that supports burning. The water from which they were derived

An electric current splits water into oxygen and hydrogen gases. This is possible because water molecules are composed of oxygen and hydrogen atoms.

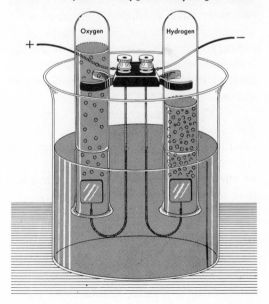

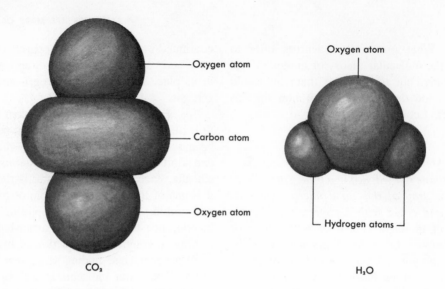

The carbon dioxide molecule (left) is composed of one carbon atom and two oxygen atoms. The water atom (right) is composed of two hydrogen atoms and one oxygen atom.

is a liquid (at room temperature) that does not burn. In other words, when hydrogen and oxygen atoms are linked in a water molecule, the properties they display as unattached atoms are not in evidence. Their union results, not in a compromise or a blending, but in an entirely different substance. Indeed, the very essence of chemistry is to be found in such mysterious unions. Thus, an atom of a silver-colored, waxy, poisonous metal combined with an atom of a green, poisonous gas forms a molecule of ordinary table salt. The chemist would say here that an atom of sodium (Na) plus an atom of chlorine (Cl) forms a molecule of sodium chloride (NaCl).

Unions between atoms can be broken. The salt molecule, for example, can be separated into its component sodium and chlorine atoms. These atoms, moreover, show no effects from their former union. They are pure sodium and chlorine atoms again.

Molecules are generally made of linked atoms. In some cases, as in the helium found in the atmosphere, only one atom may comprise the molecule, in which case the molecule and the atom are identical. In other cases, as in a protein, thousands of atoms may be linked together to form a giant molecule.

Let us look at some molecules to become acquainted with their atomic make-up. Molecules of carbon dioxide, the gas that makes soda water bubbly, are made of one carbon and two oxygen atoms and have the formula CO_2. The free oxygen in the air we breathe is made of molecules having two atoms in them, both of them oxygen atoms. Its formula is O_2. The kind of alchohol found in some beverages is made of molecules containing carbon, hydrogen, and oxygen atoms, with the formula C_2H_6O. The sugar in grape juice has the formula $C_6H_{12}O_6$. Thus we see that some molecules contain the same atoms, but in different quantities, so the substances that the molecules compose are quite different.

In the various substances named thus far in the chapter, we have come across five different kinds of atoms. These were carbon, hydrogen, chlorine, oxygen, and sodium. An investigation of all substances found on earth thus far has revealed 92 different kinds of atoms found in nature. (There are also some man-made atoms, which will be discussed in chapter 19A.) These basic particles are called *elements* by the chemists. Since there are 92 different kinds of atoms, there are 92 different elements. Some familiar elements include the following.

aluminum	iodine	platinum
argon	iron	radium
carbon	lead	silver
chlorine	mercury	sodium
copper	neon	sulfur
gold	nickel	tungsten
helium	nitrogen	uranium
hydrogen	oxygen	zinc
	phosphorus	

These elementary substances, unlike water, salt, and sugar, cannot be broken down into other simpler substances. (We will qualify this statement somewhat when we take up atomic structure in chapter 19A.) Thus, the metal silver is made up only of silver atoms; the gas helium is made only of helium atoms. Water, sugar, and salt, all made of molecules built of more than one kind of atom, are examples of what the chemist designates as *compounds*. The known compounds identified thus far number more than 700,000, but all of these are composed of various combinations of only 92 elements.

The different elements are not equally abundant in nature. The most abundant element on the earth's surface is oxygen, the next being silicon. The two most abundant elements in the entire universe are hydrogen and helium. The ten most common elements make up 99 percent of the earth, as shown in the following chart.

PERCENTAGE OF ELEMENTS IN THE EARTH
(CRUST, OCEANS, AND ATMOSPHERE)
BY WEIGHT

	Percent
oxygen	49.5
silicon	25.8
aluminum	7.5
iron	4.7
calcium	3.4
sodium	2.6
potassium	2.4
magnesium	1.9
hydrogen	0.9
titanium	0.6
all others	0.7
TOTAL	100.0%

CHANGES IN MOLECULES

SEE PAGE 406

Let us see what happens to molecules in some of the changes which take place around us. When water evaporates from a puddle into the air, no new substance is made. Water vapor is still made of water, that is, it is still made of molecules containing 2 hydrogen atoms and 1 oxygen atom. It is still H_2O, The same is true when water freezes into ice. Such a change is referred to as a *physical* change. We have noted, in chapter 9A, some physical changes, and we will see other kinds in the chapters to come, dealing with heat, machines, magnetism and electricity, sound and light.

Many changes, however, result in the formation of new substances that have characteristics very different from those of the original materials. The breaking of water into hydrogen and oxygen gases, previously described, is an example of this kind of change. Changes in which new substances are formed are called *chemical* changes.

COMMON CHEMICAL CHANGES. We drop a nail outside and forget about it for a few weeks. When we pick it up, we find that it has changed markedly. Instead of a smooth, shiny, hard exterior, it has a crumbly, red coating. The iron in the nail has undergone a chemical change. We call the new substance produced *rust*. The chemist calls it *iron oxide*. Iron atoms in the nail have joined with oxygen atoms in the air to form molecules of iron oxide or rust.

SEE PAGES 408 TO 411

Another everyday event which involves the joining of atoms is the tarnishing of silver. If a silver spoon is used for eating an egg, a black layer of tarnish forms on the spoon. The silver combines with sulfur (always in an egg) to make the black material, which is silver sulfide. The chemist describes this event in the following equation:

$$2Ag + S \rightarrow Ag_2S$$

In words, he says: 2 atoms of silver combine with 1 atom of sulfur to form one molecule of silver sulfide.

Chemical changes occur during the burning of fuels. The atoms of the fuel combine with oxygen to produce a new substance. In this process, energy is released in the form of heat and light. When coal burns, for example, the carbon in it combines with oxygen to form the gas, carbon dioxide.

$$C + O_2 \rightarrow CO_2$$

The common candle has two kinds of atoms in its chemical make-up, carbon and hydrogen. When a candle burns, the carbon atoms of the candle combine with oxygen atoms of the air to form carbon dioxide, while the hydrogen atoms of the candle combine with oxygen atoms to form water.

$$(1)\ C + O_2 \rightarrow CO_2$$
$$(2)\ 2H + O \rightarrow H_2O$$

However, since oxygen molecules in the air contain 2 atoms, the second equation must be written:

$$(2)\ 2H_2 + O_2 \rightarrow 2H_2O$$

Both the carbon dioxide and the water escape invisibly into the air. The soot that is formed on the bottom of any object heated by a candle is composed of unburned

When a candle burns, its atoms combine with oxygen to form new substances. At the same time, energy in the form of heat and light is released.

carbon atoms, that is, carbon atoms that have not combined with oxygen atoms.

The fact that the candle is finally "used up" might lead one to conclude that in burning there is destruction of matter. This is not so. *Every atom is accounted for.* Every carbon and hydrogen atom of the candle is now part of a new substance—in a different place and in a different state—but not one atom has been destroyed.

The process of digestion, as we saw in chapter 13A, involves chemical changes. The large starch molecules, for example, with their many atoms, are broken into sugar molecules, which are smaller. The sugar molecules are small enough to pass through the intestinal membranes into the blood stream.

In the making of bread, chemical changes play an important role. Yeast (one-celled plants) acts on the sugar in the dough to produce carbon dioxide gas and alcohol.

$$C_6H_{12}O_6 \rightarrow 2C_2H_5OH + 2CO_2$$

dextrose	ethyl	carbon
sugar	alcohol	dioxide

One molecule of sugar is converted into 2 molecules of alcohol and 2 molecules of carbon dioxide. The carbon dioxide helps "blow up" the dough. This makes the bread light and spongy. The small amount of alcohol produced evaporates in the baking. A similar change occurs in the process of wine-making, except that in this case the carbon dioxide escapes while the alcohol is retained in the final product. In both bread-making and wine-making, the yeast cells cause a chemical change in sugar called *fermentation.* (The yeast cells also profit from this transaction: the splitting of sugar molecules liberates energy essential for their life processes.)

A chemical change which makes life possible on earth has been referred to in a number of different places in this book. It is the process of photosynthesis, in which green plants unite atoms from carbon dioxide and water to form sugar and oxygen. The following equation represents a summary of what actually requires a series of complex steps in a living plant cell:

$$6\ CO_2 + 12H_2O \rightarrow$$
$$C_6H_{12}O_6 + 6H_2O + 6O_2$$

Changing these symbols to words, a chemist says: 6 molecules of carbon dioxide plus 12 molecules of water yield 1 molecule of sugar plus 6 molecules of water plus 6 molecules of oxygen. Incidentally, if you count the number of atoms on the right and left sides of this equation, you will see that they are equal. Looked at from a global viewpoint, this chemical process of photosynthesis provides food and oxygen for the use of the plant and animal kingdoms and removes carbon dioxide from the earth's atmosphere.

We have seen how chemical changes are involved in rusting, tarnishing, burning, photosynthesis, digestion, and fermentation. Chemical changes are found in thousands of other everyday phenomena: the souring of milk, the spoiling of meat, the repairing and building of tissues of living things, the manufacture of soap and plastics. The understanding of these chemical changes becomes increasingly important each year in agriculture, industry, and medicine.

CHEMICAL CHANGES AND ENERGY

Chemical changes involve not only the forming of new substances, but the transfer of energy also. When a candle burns, energy in the form of heat and light is released. When a green plant makes glucose sugar molecules from atoms in water and carbon dioxide, it packs energy into the molecules. If the glucose is ignited in an oven or burned in the human body, it releases the energy which was originally stored in it.

Just how can a molecule store energy? Where is it hidden? Energy is used to form the *bonds* that hold together the atoms in a

molecule. In a glucose molecule, for example, there are bonds which hold together the 6 carbon, 12 hydrogen, and 6 oxygen atoms. We do not know what a bond is, but we may compare it to the spring in a jack-in-the-box. In this child's toy, energy must be expended to squeeze "jack" into the box. When the lid is opened, "jack" releases about the same amount of energy as he pops out. (Bond energy—chemical energy—is not the same as the energy in the nucleus of the atom, discussed in chapter 19A.)

THE ATOMIC THEORY. It is evident from the examples we have considered that atoms are involved in all chemical changes. The true character of atoms was first conceived in 1808 by John Dalton, an English schoolmaster. In modern form, the fundamental ideas of Dalton's atomic theory might be stated as follows:

1. *All matter is composed of a limited number of kinds of fundamental particles called atoms.*
2. *All atoms of any one kind are identical, indivisible, and unalterable. (We will modify this statement in chapter 19A.) to bring it in line with modern atomic theory.)*
3. *Molecules consist of definite combinations of atoms. The atomic construction of all the molecules of one kind is identical.*
4. *Chemical changes involve the making of new combinations of atoms to produce new molecules and hence new substances.*

THE GREEKS AND US

Man has long been curious about the basic composition of matter. The Greek philosopher Aristotle said that all matter was made of four fundamental "elements": earth, air, fire, water. By mixing these in various proportions, according to Aristotle, all kinds of substances could be formed. Bones, for example, were made of two parts of fire and one part each of earth and water; flesh consisted of equal parts of the four "elements."

Although we know today that not one of these four are truly basic elements, that indeed there are at least one hundred different ones, we are indebted to Aristotle and other Greek philosophers for their spirit of inquiry that led them to ask: What are the fundamental particles of matter? As we will see later, in the chapter on atomic energy, we are still searching for the answer to that question.

This brief exploration of molecules and atoms has emphasized certain basic generalizations. Some of these are:

All matter is structured of exceedingly small separate particles—called molecules—which are in ceaseless motion.

Molecules attract each other.

Molecules are made of atoms linked together in definite combinations.

There are about 100 different kinds of atoms, called elements.

Chemists have identified about 700,000 kinds of compounds.

In a physical change, the composition of molecules is not changed.

In chemical changes, the composition of molecules is altered. New materials are formed by the assembling of new combinations of atoms.

Compounds differ markedly in their properties from the elements of which they are composed.

Chemical changes involve a transfer of energy.

Chemical changes play an important part in our lives.

DISCOVERING FOR YOURSELF

1. Make a list of destructive chemical changes that you observe, and indicate what is done to try to prevent each of the changes.
2. Use litmus paper to test the liquids and fruits in a kitchen to see if they are acids, bases, or neither.
3. Visit a local manufacturing plant to discover how chemical changes are used in production of goods.
4. Choose some chemical change that is important to you and learn as much as you can about it. (What raw materials are used, what energy is involved, what waste products are there, how the characteristics of the finished product differ from those of the raw material used.)
5. Demonstrate the difference between a chemical and a physical change by using some common materials.
6. Find out about some of the newest elements listed in Chapter 16A. Find out where they were discovered, by whom, when, and any other information you can. Keep a list of the sources you used, and describe your method of discovery.
7. List as many as you can of the *elements* (in a free state) in your house—copper in wire and in a penny, oxygen in the air, tin on the cover of cans, etc.
8. List some of the simple chemical compounds you encounter during a day and give their atomic makeup: water, H_2O—hydrogen and oxygen; sugar, $C_6H_{12}O_6$—carbon, hydrogen and oxygen; table salt, $NaCl$—sodium and chlorine; bubbles in carbonated water, CO_2—carbon and oxygen; etc.

CHAPTER 16B

Teaching "What Things Are Made of"

Children introduce themselves to the world of substances through many and varied experiences as they begin to explore their environment by the use of their senses. For example, they test the qualities and characteristics of things through tasting, feeling, lifting, listening, smelling, scratching, breaking, twisting, wetting, crushing, biting, pushing, spilling, etc. These are, in a way, tests that they devise without instructions from adults. We encourage them to continue to discover through the use of their senses. We help this process by providing them with experiences that raise problems in their minds, and then by giving them opportunity for experimentation. This latter we do when we encourage them to work with clay, sand, water, soil, and other similar materials. We encourage them to show what they can do by changing the materials. Their understandings of chemical and physical change may be deepened by firsthand experiences in the preparation, cooking, and preserving of foods, i.e., observing the changes in color, shape, and texture that accompany processes such as the making of applesauce, cranberry sauce, popcorn, candles, butter, and jello. In all of these experiences, the wise teacher emphasizes the changes as they occur. "How did it change?" "Why do you think it changed?" "Could we change it back again?" are some typical questions to give more meaning to the experiences. In later elementary grades, the phenomena of contraction and expansion of materials, burning, food manufacture in plants, and other changes are studied to see how changes in matter occur and why they are important.

Let us not be too concerned at the primary level with the lack of scientific terminology. Science is a method of discovery. When questions about "what happened?" are being answered through observation and discussion, the study of science is beginning. As the study proceeds, more complicated examples will involve more technical terms.

The following activities for primary grades will contribute toward understanding of what things are made of and how they change.

Put a lump of soil into a jar of water to see if there is air in soil. (Watch it bubble.)
Melt ice, freeze water, and evaporate water.
Observe the changes inside a jack-o'-lantern pumpkin as mold develops.
Mix sugar, salt, sand, and other substances in water to see what happens.
Make plaster of Paris and concrete molds.
Make lemonade or cocoa.
Watch "dry ice" disappear.
Watch the liquid in a thermometer rise and fall.
Separate rocks from sand with a strainer.
Make soap bubbles.
Color water with vegetable dyes, ink, and water colors.

CHANGING MATTER FROM ONE FORM TO ANOTHER

To see what is meant by changing matter from one form to another, pupils may perform simple experiments showing how this happens. Melt an ice cube by heating it in a dish over a candle or hot plate. (Solid to liquid.) Heat the water until it evaporates. (Liquid to gas.) Melt some paraffin (in upper part of double boiler for safety sake). Let the paraffin cool. (Solid to liquid—liquid to solid.) Note that in these examples no new material is produced. The substance has merely changed its form. Pupils may look for other changes from one form to another—especially in the kitchen, where the refrigerator and the stove are. They may investigate to see some very important changes in the form of matter—for example, iron and other metals from liquid to solid, glass from liquid to solid. They may make a picture collection to show how everyday things are made by man's skill in changing the form of matter (glass, metal objects, and so on).

COLLECTING ELEMENTS

Once pupils know what the elements are, they can find many examples. Elements in addition to those indicated in chapter 16A are listed in many books.[1] (See bibliography.) Pupils can find common objects containing such elements as: iron (nails), copper (electric wiring, pennies), mercury (in thermometers), tin (covering of cans), zinc (in galvanized iron), silver (money), and many others, and display them on a table. They may find out more about some of these elements by reading in encyclopedias and elsewhere, and report their findings to the class. Before they begin reading, they may make a list of questions they wish to answer about each element, such as: Where is it found? For what is it used? Is it scarce? If pupils have questions such as these to guide their reading, they are not so

---

[1] B. M. Parker, *What Things Are Made Of* (New York, Harper & Row, 1959), 36 pp.

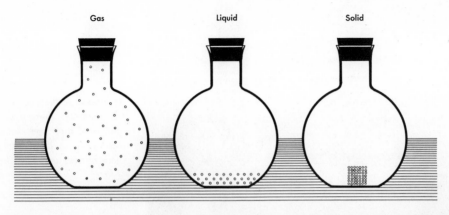

Gas   Liquid   Solid

The concepts related to molecules and atoms, their structures and behavior, are indeed difficult for children to grasp; any representation that illustrates the ideas is helpful. Children may be encouraged to search in encyclopedias and other books for illustrations such as this that will be helpful.

likely to copy from sources and tell uninteresting things that neither they nor their classmates understand.

Pupils enjoy discovering the number of ways in which elements are used. Chlorine, iodine, mercury, neon, sulfur, lead, nickel, oxygen, phosphorus, silver, platinum, silicon, and chromium have especially interesting uses. Each pupil may keep track of how he went about finding information—people he asked, books and other sources he consulted, places he went to observe. If we believe that learning how to locate information is often as important as the information itself, we ought to make the most of activities such as this. Pupils may go to drug stores, garages, paint shops, factories, hardware stores, and similar places. To find information, they may look through books and encyclopedias and talk to dentists, jewelers, merchants, and many other persons.

Discuss why water, sugar, and salt are compounds. Pupils may make a similar exhibit of such compounds and report on some of the sources and uses of some common ones. This may be tied up with discovering how local industries make use of various elements and compounds in their manufacturing process. An interesting and instructive experience in geography may result when pupils attempt to discover where these elements and compounds come from and how they·are transported.

ILLUSTRATING INFORMATION ABOUT ATOMS AND MOLECULES

The idea of what atoms and molecules are and how they behave is an example of science information that pupils can talk about quite glibly, yet understand only vaguely. One way to help them understand more clearly some of the things they learn about atoms and molecules and how they behave is to help them illustrate what they have read. In addition to the textbooks and encyclopedias that pupils are using, several of the books in the bibliography will help to supply ideas.[2] Pupils may make some of the following, either on

[2] B. M. Parker, *Matter and Molecules and Atoms* (New York, Harper & Row, 1957), 36 pp.; *The Everyday Atom* (New York, Harper & Row, 1959), 36 pp.

the chalkboard or on a large sheet of white paper: a drawing of molecules in a solid, in a liquid, and in a gas; a drawing to show what happens to molecules of water when the water is boiling; a drawing of a molecule of hydrogen to show the number of atoms in it; a drawing to show what happens to the molecules in a piece of iron when it is heated. They will think of other ideas to illustrate.

PRODUCING SOME CHEMICAL CHANGES

Chemical changes function continually in the lives of children, producing many of the things they use every day. There are many simple experiments that show chemical changes. Following are a few. Textbooks and supplementary books give many more. Remember that the important idea for pupils to understand is that as a result of chemical changes, new materials are made that may have characteristics entirely different from those of the elements or compounds that went into the process. Children will be interested in the symbols for elements, the formulae of compounds, and the chemical equations that describe chemical changes. Introduce them to the simple ones, some of which are illustrated in the following examples. General source books and those in the bibliography have many examples.

PRODUCING RUST

Get two identical large iron nails, and paint one with any kind of house paint that is at hand. Do not paint the other one. Stand both nails in a jar containing a little water and cover the jar, so that the air in it will remain moist. When, after a few days, you examine both nails, you will find that the unpainted nail has rusted but the painted one has not. Oxygen from the air has united with the iron in the unpainted nail to make the rust. Rust is a compound formed from the combining of iron and oxygen. Scrape off some of the rust and you will see that it no longer looks like the iron. It is brown, crumbly material.

The painted nail did not rust because the paint formed a protective layer that kept the oxygen from uniting with the iron. Ask children to find examples in their environment that illustrate how we keep oxygen from uniting with materials.

BREAKING DOWN SUGAR MOLECULES

Place some sugar in a spoon, heat it, and watch what happens. After the white sugar has turned black, let it cool and taste it. It will no longer taste sweet. A chemical change has taken place and a new material has been formed. When sugar is heated, its molecules break down into water and carbon. The water bubbles off leaving the black carbon in the spoon.

PRODUCING CARBON DIOXIDE

Pour vinegar on some baking soda and observe what happens. Hold a match over the bubbles. (See page 430 for more details.)

TARNISHING SILVER

Put some cooked egg yolk on a polished silver spoon and leave it for an hour or so. Ask pupils to try to decide what happened. There is silver in the spoon, sulfur in the egg yolk. The black material on the spoon is made when these two elements unite. It is a compound called silver sulfide.

CHANGING STARCH TO SUGAR

Let children thoroughly chew soda crackers before swallowing them, being especially careful to note changes in taste. The sweet taste is due to a chemical action (enzyme-caused) which changes starch to sugar.

LOOKING FOR CHEMICAL CHANGES

The foregoing experiments are examples of what happens when a chemical change takes place. Such changes are going on all around pupils and even inside of them. From what pupils have seen and read, they will now be able to answer such questions as "What happens to a bridge when it rusts, and why is it frequently repainted?" "Why do we coat cans with tin?" "What happens when a fire burns?" "What happens to milk if it is left in a warm place for a few days?" "What happens when the soda-and-acid fire extinguisher is turned upside down?" "Why is baking powder used in cake-making?"

Let pupils do some reading and observing to find out: "How is window glass made?" "What happens when silver tarnishes?" "How can sodium (an element that would burn your tongue) and chlorine (a poisonous gas) be part of the common salt that is used every day?" "What must happen to oxygen and hydrogen to make them combine to form water?" "What happens in green leaves that helps to feed us?" "What must happen to the food we eat before it becomes a part of us?" "How are chemical changes used in making photographs?" "Why are chemical changes important?"

Blueprints are a result of chemical change. These pupils are demonstrating the change and will explain to their classmates what happens.

Testing to identify materials can be developed into a very informative activity, i.e., the test for sugar, starch, etc., can be done by many children. The bibliography will be helpful in this regard.

STOPPING CHEMICAL CHANGES

Obviously not all chemical changes are desirable. Some we go to great pains and expense to stop or retard. A little investigating will turn up many examples of this. Each pupil may try to discover for himself and report to the class one example of a harmful chemical change and a way to stop it. The following suggestion to pupils will help to make such an investigation more interesting: "Try to find an example that no one else will find, and tell us where you found the example and how you happened to find it." Pupils will find such things as painting, refrigeration, the use of dark or airtight containers, and keeping certain things dry.

USING HELPFUL CHEMICAL CHANGES

Each pupil may be asked to report the two chemical changes that he things are most helpful to him. Examples may be: oxidation of food in the body, making of starch and sugar in plants, explosion of gasoline to drive an automobile.

An instructive and interesting exhibit may be made of pictures that show important use of chemical changes. The pictures may be found in magazines and newspapers, and may be mounted and placed on the bulletin board.[3] Examples are: making pottery and glass, making cement, making paper, baking bread, making blueprints (see page 581).

RESOURCES TO INVESTIGATE

1. A professional or amateur photographer to illustrate how chemical changes are useful in picture-making.
2. A chemistry set to illustrate chemical change.
3. A high school chemistry teacher for an exchange of ideas about teaching the material in this unit.
4. Local industries (soap factory, rubber factory, bakery) to see and learn about the use of elements and compounds as raw materials, chemical changes, and other phases of chemistry involved in industry.
5. Printed material describing manufacturing processes that involve chemical changes and demonstrate science principles: Aluminum Company of America, Pittsburgh 19, Pa. (limited supply); Crown Zellerback Corp., Rincon Annex, Box 3475, San Francisco 19, Calif.; Goodyear Tire and Rubber Co., 1144 E. Market St., Akron, Ohio. These are but a few of the manufacturers supplying such information about their products.

---

[3] J. Schwartz, *It's Fun to Know Why: Experiments with Things Around Us* (New York, Whittlesey House, 1952). Gives many simple experiments that children can perform with iron, coal, glass, bread, paper, cement, and other materials.

CHAPTER 17A

Fire and Its Prevention

For thousands of years, fire has been a subject of mystery, fear, superstition, and adoration. Earliest man must has associated fire only with catastrophe. How he must have trembled when lightning bolts set forests aflame or when fiery volcanoes erupted and converted the landscape into a molten inferno. Even today, as we sit around a campfire, our imaginations conjure up strange visions in the flickering flames.

At some time in his development, man learned how to capture fire and how to tame it. Evidences of the use of fire by Neanderthal man of 50,000 years ago and Peking man of 250,000 years ago have been found in their caves. These and other primitive men found out how to use fire for warmth, for cooking food, for protection against wild animals, and as a torch against the dark of night.

KINDLING FIRES

RUBBING STICKS AND STRIKING STONES. Through the ages, man has searched for easier ways to make a fire. Until comparatively recent times the work required for the starting of a fire was so difficult that he would travel miles to obtain a flame from a fire already burning rather than start his own. To start a fire, primitive man rubbed two sticks together, either by hand or the use of a bow, or he struck a piece of flint in such a way that a spark fell into some kindling. In the bow and drill method, a stick was twirled rapidly in a hole in a flat piece of soft wood. The work done overcoming friction (see chapter 20A for a discussion of friction) produced fine, flammable, wood dust as well as the heat to ignite the dust. The tiny fire started in this way was used to flame some tinder—shredded bits of bark, dried grass or moss, or the down or floss of seeds. The flaming tinder was then applied to prepared branches and logs. The bow and drill method is not particularly easy, as any Boy Scout knows.

Cave men stumbling in the dark and kicking some stones may have noticed that sparks were produced when the stones struck each other. Experience may have taught them that these sparks were hot—hot enough to set tinder afire. Trial and error may have shown them that certain kinds of rocks were better than others for this purpose.

The mythology of many peoples has references to the striking of iron against stone as a way of starting fires. Ancient priests kept the "secret of the stones" and regarded the starting of fires as their special privilege. Our American forefathers carried a tinder box with them in which there was a piece of flint and a piece of steel. The steel was struck against the flint, producing sparks of good size and heat. These fell into the tinder box, which was filled with easily flammable charred cloth. Even today, explorers still carry the old-fashioned flint and steel around with them, for matches may be spoiled. The cigarette lighter is a modern adaptation of the flint and steel method of fire-making.

In these early experiences, two science ideas were implicit, although only dimly realized by primitive man. These were:

1. *Rubbing or striking one object against another produces heat.*
2. *Certain materials catch fire more easily than others.*

MATCHES.   In all of the primitive frictional methods, the two great difficulties were to create a spark and then to bring it immediately into contact with easily burnable tinder. The modern match obviates both of these difficulties by applying some of the chemical discoveries of the past two centuries. Indeed, the match is essentially a small chemical laboratory. Consider what happens when you light a strike-anywhere match:

1. *Rubbing heats a chemical in the tip of the match (a phosphorus compound) that ignites at a very low temperature.*
2. *The tiny flame causes another chemical in the bulb of the match (potassium chlorate) to liberate large quantities of oxygen.*
3. *The heat and the large supply of oxygen cause a third chemical (sulfur) to ignite and burn vigorously.*
4. *The fire spreads rapidly over the wood, aided by a fourth chemical (paraffin) in which the original wood splint was dipped.*
5. *A fifth chemical (ammonium phosphate) in the wood of the match prevents an afterglow.*

In the safety match, the easily ignitable phosphorus compound is placed on the box or folder, rather than on the stick. In order to be lit, the match must be rubbed against this phosphorus surface. In this way all the chemicals necessary for the chain of reactions are brought together.

ESSENTIALS FOR BURNING.   Three things are essential for any fire. First, of course, there must be something to burn, a fuel of some kind; then this fuel must be made hot enough to burn; and lastly there must be a continuous supply of oxygen to support the burning. Let us see how each of these three factors contributes to the making of a fire.

A FIRE NEEDS OXYGEN

WHAT IS "BURNING"?   Reduced to its simplest terms, it is the process in which a fuel unites chemically with the oxygen of

SEE PAGES 426 TO 427

the air, a process that the chemist calls *oxidation*. It might be wise at this point to reread the description of burning in chapter 16A, page 402. We learned there that atoms of fuel combine chemically with atoms of oxygen to form new substances. This is quite a different view of burning from the commonplace one, which regards burning as destruction. The chemist sees burning as the union of atoms. Carbon and hydrogen are the common atoms in the fuels we use. Their partnerships with oxygen are set down by the chemist in this way:

1. $C + O_2 \rightarrow CO_2$, or
   carbon plus oxygen yields carbon dioxide,
2. $H_2 + O \rightarrow H_2O$, or
   hydrogen plus oxygen yields water.

Since the carbon dioxide and water pass off invisibly in the smoke, we are not usually aware of these new products of burning. When we watch a campfire, we do see the smoke, because it contains unburned carbon particles. We also see the ash that remains, but this is the mineral content of the wood, which does not burn. We see light and feel the heat. These represent forms of energy that are released as a result of chemical union of the atoms.

We should not say that oxygen burns. Rather, it *supports* the burning of fuels. A spark applied to a bottle of oxygen will *not* set it afire; oxygen is not a fuel and it cannot burn.

HOTTER FIRES. The intensity of fire can be increased, up to a point, by supplying more oxygen to it. When we fan a campfire, we are bringing a greater quantity of oxygen to the burning fuel. In the coal furnace, the rate of burning is controlled by regulating the amount of air that comes in contact with the coal. This is done by adjusting the furnace doors and turning the damper, which is a kind of door in the chimney. You may have seen men cutting through steel beams with sparkling torches. These are oxy-acetylene torches, and they are fed by a tank of the fuel acetylene and a tank of oxygen. The intense heat produced is over 5,000° F.

Oxidation is also hastened by reducing the fuel to small particles. When we break a piece of wood into small pieces, we expose more of its surface to the air and consequently make more oxygen available. Similarly, in a kerosene lamp or a candle, the fuels are dispersed through the wick in such a way as to help them evaporate easily. The evaporated fuels around the wick are exposed to more of the oxygen of the air, and hence burn more rapidly. Again, when the carburetor of an automobile sprays a mixture of gasoline and air into the cylinders of the motor, it breaks the liquid gasoline into a fine vapor so that each of its molecules is surrounded by oxygen atoms. The gasoline burns so rapidly that an explosion is produced, pushing with a force of thousands of pounds against each piston.

Explosions, of course, can be destructive. On March 29, 1956, the *New York Times* reported:

Philadelphia. . . . The ʻbustling midtown section of this city, crowded with theater-goers and shoppers, was rocked last night by a terrific explosion. Four persons were feared to have died; scores were injured.

The blast demolished a big grain warehouse in the busy Thirtieth and Market Street area, shattered windows in buildings for miles around.

. . . The intense heat of the flames kept firemen from getting near enough to search the debris for bodies.

On a hospital bed, Samuel Purdy, acting superintendent of the granary, reported that the blast had occurred while he was trying to ignite a pilot light in a drying bin.

. . . Fire department officials attributed the explosion to a heavy accumulation of dust in a grain elevator.

The earth-shaking explosion, with the sound and blast force of a bomb was felt as far away as Bryn Mawr on the west and the Delaware River on the east.

What caused the violent explosion? The accumulation of sufficient dust (from the stored grain) in the air of the warehouse provided the fuel. Each speck of dust, suspended in the air, was amply supplied with oxygen. All that was needed was a match to set a few of these specks aflame. These in turn ignited those around them. Thus the fire spread in a chain reaction until all of the suspended particles burned. Because this rapid burning occurred in a few seconds, the terrific heat and the ensuing expansion of the hot gases blew the warehouse apart.

Gaseous fuels, like the gas in a kitchen stove, burn vigorously and smoothly because the fuel particles are of the smallest possible size—molecules—and because pressure forces the gas to flow steadily. In the gas stove, moreover, the gas is mixed with air before it leaves the tiny openings on top of the stove, thus providing a good burnable mixture.

KINDLING TEMPERATURE

The lowest temperture at which a substance will catch fire is called its *kindling temperature*. Kindling temperatures are different for different substances. Phosphorus, as we have seen, is used in the tips of matches because it has a very low kindling temperature; the small amount of heat produced by rubbing is sufficient to ignite it. Carbon disulfide (a chemical used in some insecticides) will catch fire if it is poured on a hot steam radiator. Of course, as we have seen from the previous discussion of oxygen, the ease with which a substance catches fire depends not only on the nature of the substance but on other conditions, such as the size of its particles and the supply of oxygen.

The kindling temperature of wood is over 500° F. That of kerosene is somewhat lower; because of this it is often poured on wood (a dangerous practice) to ignite the wood. Gasoline also has a low kindling temperature. It is more dangerous than kerosene because it gives off vapors more rapidly. These vapors catch fire so easily that gasoline must never be used in starting fires, nor should it be stored in a place where its vapors can accumulate. Every year people are severely burned by using gasoline to start fires. Frequently they use it in stoves designed to burn kerosene.

Home dry cleaning with gasoline is very dangerous; gasoline fumes have been known to travel 15 or 20 feet across a kitchen and then to be ignited by the pilot light of a gas stove. Even when no flame is nearby, rubbing may produce a tiny spark sufficient to ignite the gasoline vapor. Ether is another dangerous fluid. Like gasoline, it vaporizes easily, and its fumes are easily ignited.

SPONTANEOUS COMBUSTION

In a classic demonstration sometimes performed in college chemistry classes, a piece of filter paper is mysteriously dipped into an unidentified solution. The paper is then lifted (with tongs) to a safe place on a metal ringstand. The lecturer goes on talking until the class is startled by the sudden bursting into flame of the paper. What has happened?

The solution contained yellow phosphorus. When the liquid evaporated from the filter paper, dry phosphorus remained. For a time, before the phosphorus burst into flame, a process called *slow oxidation* was occurring. In this process, as in the rapid oxidation of burning, the fuel combines chemically with oxygen. However, although heat is liberated, there are no flames. Finally, enough heat accumulates to ignite the phosphorus, which, as we recall, has a low kindling point.

Slow oxidation is a common phenomenon. When the iron in steel wool rusts, it combines slowly with oxygen to form iron oxide or rust. In this process heat is released but escapes rapidly to the surrounding air. Oily rags exposed to the air also undergo slow oxidation, producing a small amount of heat as the oil oxidizes. Green, new-mown hay, also undergoes slow oxidation. If substances such as these are in the open, so that currents of air can carry away the heat that is produced, there is no danger that they will catch fire. But if oily rags are placed in a closet or box, or piled up on the floor, and if green hay is heaped up in an unventilated barn, heat produced by slow oxidation may begin to accumulate steadily in the interior of the pile. Finally, the kindling temperature is reached and fire breaks out.

Newspapers frequently report incidents involving the spontaneous combustion of hay in barns. Houses that have just been painted also have fires because rags full of paint and oil have been carelessly left in a pile. They should, of course, be destroyed or placed in a metal container.

KINDS OF FUELS

SEE
PAGES
427
TO
428
Wood, charcoal, coal, coke, the various petroleum products, and gas are among our common fuels. They make the wheels of modern civilization go round, supplying the energy for the production of electricity, for transportation, for smelting of ores and thousands of other industrial processes, for heating and cooking purposes in homes. In all of the fuels just named, carbon and hydrogen atoms, in varying proportions, are the basic fuel ingredients.

SOLID FUELS.   For many thousands of years wood was the chief heating fuel available to man. Wood is not as efficient as other fuels because it contains a good many impurities that do not burn. Charcoal is made by roasting wood in the absence of air so that it cannot catch fire. The liquid and gaseous impurities are driven off, leaving, essentially, only burnable carbon. Although charcoal is not used extensively for heating, it is a clean fuel that produces a steady heat. It is popularly used for the roasting of peanuts and the broiling of steaks.

Coal has been a basic fuel in the United States since the early 1800s. Today coal furnishes us with about one-third of our total fuel energy. Coal burned to boil water and produce steam provides the energy for more than half of the electricity produced in this country. In chapter 14A there is an account of the origin of coal as well as a description of the various forms of coal.

Coke is made by heating coal in ovens, without access to air. In this process, various gases are driven off. The coke that remains is about 90 percent carbon. It is a grayish, brittle porous substance that burns rapidly, producing the hot fires needed for the smelting of ores.

LIQUID AND GASEOUS FUELS.   The solid fuels—coal, wood, and their derivatives—are being replaced more and more by "fuels that flow," that is by fuels in the liquid and gaseous state. These fuels are easily conveyed to homes and factories. They are convenient and clean to use, leaving no ash and producing little smoke.

Petroleum and natural gas are believed to originate from the decomposition of plants and animals that died millions of years ago. Most petroleum is located deep under the surface of the earth in certain kinds of rock formations. Although petroleum has been known for many centuries, the first oil wells were drilled in 1859, at Titusville, Pennsylvania. These early wells were shallow ones, not more than 100 feet deep, and produced only 25 barrels of oil a day. With our present facilities for well-drilling, we some-

This natural-gas pipeline, shown just before it is laid underground, is carrying the fuel a total distance of 1875 miles, from its source in Texas to New York and points north.

times force pipes almost 5 miles down and get yields of thousands of barrels a day. We have oil wells in about twenty states today, the most productive of which are in Oklahoma, California, and Texas. There are also a considerable number of offshore wells along the Gulf Coast and the Pacific Coast.

The raw petroleum as it comes from the earth is known as "crude oil." From it many valuable fuels are produced, including fuel oil, gasoline, benzine, and kerosene.

Gases that burn are especially convenient for towns and cities, because they can be piped directly into homes and factories. Natural gas is found together with petroleum in oil deposits and also in the neighborhood of coal fields. At one time it was burned off or allowed to escape carelessly into the air; now it is piped hundreds of miles from oil and coal fields to the consumers. Pipelines from Texas now carry natural gas to New York and to the New England states.

Natural gas consists mostly of methane (marsh gas), which has the chemical formula CH_4. It is the best of the fuel gases, producing the most heat. The gas fields most used today are in Texas, California, Oklahoma, Louisiana, and West Virginia.

Artificial fuel gases are manufactured from coal, coke, and petroleum. These contain chiefly hydrogen, carbon monoxide, and hydrocarbons (chemical compounds of carbon and hydrogen) in various proportions.

FIRE AS A DESTRUCTIVE AGENT

Fire, a great servant of man, is also one of his greatest enemies. There are in this country an average of 5,400 destructive fires a day, or one every 20 seconds. During a typical year, 11,000 Americans lose their lives as a result of fires! Each year, the direct financial loss from fire averages about a billion dollars.

CAUSES OF FIRES. From a scientific viewpoint, fires occur when three factors are present: fuel, oxygen, and enough heat to raise the fuel to its kindling point. Behind these three factors is man himself, responsible through carelessness and oversight for three-quarters of all destructive fires. The other

SEE PAGE 428

Whatever life existed in this valuable forest in Montana is now gone. Much time, money, and work is involved in attempting to reforest such areas.

fourth are of uncertain causes, probably largely preventable. Forest fires, as you read in chapter 15A, are nearly all started by careless smokers or campers. About forty home fires a day are caused by electric irons connected and then forgotten. The careless use of matches, together with careless smoking habits, are the chief causes of all fires in the United States. Other common causes are poor electric wiring, automobile ignition defects, forgetfulness about turning off gas or electric stoves, faulty furnaces, carelessness with gasoline and other readily flammable liquids, and spontaneous combustion. We know that these are the cause of fires—hence the advice "the best time to fight fires is before they start."

The following are the specific instructions for an end-of-the-year fire-prevention inspection by the principal and the custodian of each school in a large city. Although these instructions were drawn up for custodians, teachers may also find them a useful check list.

1. *Storage of any oil paint, turpentine, acids, etc., in classroom wardrobes or closets is to be avoided.*
2. *Metal storage cabinets for hazardous items [should be] securely fastened to wall or floor, and proper locking devices are to be used.*
3. *Raffia used in kindergartens is highly flammable, and must be stored in metal containers at all times.*
4. *Surplus and nonessential homemade furniture such as orange and egg crates, old tables, etc., should be removed and destroyed.*
5. *All passages and aisles must be cleared and remain in this condition during the school year.*
6. *Clear all rubbish, junk, and waste from custodial work spaces.*
7. *Check date on all flameproofed curtains and drapes on stage and over windows.*
8. *Check and provide signs for sprinkler control valve.*
9. *Check and remove all furniture from moving picture booth.*
10. *Oil rags and mops must not be stored in unventilated closets or rooms. Metal containers must be provided for these at all times.*
11. *At the proper time, recharge all fire extinguishers and date same.*
12. *Rooms or other spaces when not in use must be locked.*
13. *In the event that no proper space for storage of paint and any other flam-*

mable materials now in classrooms, etc., exists, ask your principal for permission and remove same from classrooms, shops, and laboratories, and store in your own paint storage closet.

WHAT TO DO IN CASE OF FIRE

SEE PAGE 29

All of us need briefing about what to do in case of fire. Do you, for example, know what you should do right now if you smell smoke that may come from a fire out of control?

If it is possible to do so without danger to oneself or others, one should try to extinguish a small fire. Probably about one-third of the fires extinguished by municipal fire departments could have been put out with sand, pails of water, or hand fire extinguishers. But certainly it is better to call the fire department if there is the slightest doubt about the extent of the fire or the availability of means with which to extinguish it.

Fire department assistance is necessary to extinguish all fires caused by high-voltage wires (recognizable by sparks that are given off) and all fires started by any sort of faulty electric wiring. One can easily suffer serious injury from turning a stream of water on a faulty electrical connection or a high-voltage wire, because the stream of water may conduct electricity to the person holding the hose.

Children should be urged to report any fire to an adult immediately and should be taught how to call a fire department by means of a call box or telephone. They should be taught how to give clear, accurate information over the telephone. The number of the fire department should be common knowledge and should be posted at all telephones.

In the school, children and teachers should be familiar with all the fire rules for the particular school. They should know these well because they have had frequent and regular fire drills. The safety of pupils is, of course, the major consideration in planning for drills, and the fighting of fire is considered only after everything is done that will insure the safety of all persons. It is essential that pupils be trained to leave the building in a quiet and orderly manner. Speed is important, but secondary to order and quiet. Pupils should be trained to leave the building no matter in which part of it they may be and whether they are with their teacher or not. Drills should be conducted using alternate exits, so that pupils will know what to do in the event that the customary one is obstructed by smoke or flame.

EXTINGUISHING FIRE

SEE PAGE 427

The extinguishing of fires is based on the elimination of one or more of the three factors essential for burning. Thus, to put out a fire we cut off the supply of oxygen, we remove the fuel, and we lower the temperature of the burning material below its kindling point. The exclusion of oxygen and the lowering of the temperature are the most widely used methods of extinguishing fires. The removal of flammable material is effective for small fires, such as those in coal bins, wood piles, or waste baskets.

Among the readily available ways of excluding oxygen are covering the fire with dirt or other material that will not burn or throwing a heavy blanket or coat over the fire. The latter is particularly effective in putting out fire on a person's clothing. If a blanket or coat is not available, the flames on a person's clothing can sometimes be smothered by rolling the person on the ground.

SEE PAGES 429 TO 430

Fire extinguishers achieve their effect by cooling and by smothering (which actually means keeping the oxygen away from the fire). There are a number of different kinds

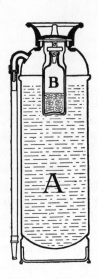

The soda-acid fire extinguisher is one of the most common types. The bottle (B) contains sulfuric acid, which, when the extinguisher is inverted, mixes with the baking soda solution (A). Carbon dioxide gas is formed as a result. The gas forces the water out in a strong stream.

of chemical extinguishers, each with certain virtues and certain limitations.

The *soda-acid* type of fire extinguisher is usually rather large and is found hanging in corridors of public buildings. The main part of the receptacle is filled with water in which baking soda (sodium bicarbonate) is dissolved (see drawing). In the top of the extinguisher there is a small bottle of sulfuric acid, with a loose-fitting stopper. When the extinguisher is turned upside down, the stopper falls out and lets the acid mix with the solution of baking soda. As a result of chemical action, a large amount of carbon dioxide gas is rapidly formed. The pressure of this gas forces the water out of the hose with enough force to send it 30–40 feet. The water extinguishes the fire chiefly by cooling the fuel, partly by wetting it, thereby excluding the oxygen. The carbon dioxide formed in this extinguisher is used primarily to pro-

duce the pressure necessary to force the water out; its value in extinguishing the fire is small compared to that of the water.

Soda-acid extinguishers are rather cumbersome, and must be kept in an upright position until they are used. Before inverting them, one must gasp the nozzle and direct it so that the stream will not strike any person. This is important because the stream contains some destructive chemicals, including acid which has not yet reacted with the soda. It is not safe to use this type of extinguisher on an electrical fire, because the solution is a good conductor of electricity. Water is also generally not a good extinguisher of oil fires, because it is heavier than oil. Thus, it may carry the flaming oil and spread the fire. In order to operate reliably when needed, the soda-acid extinguisher must be discharged and refilled about once a year.

For oil or for electrical fires, *carbon tetrachloride* extinguishers, like the one shown here, are recommended. These are frequently referred to as "Pyrene" extinguishers. To operate this extinguisher, remove it from the bracket that holds it and twist the handle until the plunger can be pulled out. The handle is worked in and out like a pump, and the stream is directed at the base of the flames. Carbon tetrachloride,

This extinguisher sprays a stream of liquid carbon tetrachloride. The liquid forms a vapor that smothers the fire. It is safe to use on electrical fires.

when heated, vaporizes rapidly, forming a dense blanket of gas that is heavier than air. Thus the air is pushed away from the fire and the fire is smothered.

Pyrene extinguishers are usually small and can easily be carried in automobiles and boats or hung on walls of entryways and kitchens. The fluid does not injure upholstery or fabrics. This type of extinguisher is particularly valuable against electrical fires, since the fluid will not carry electricity, as will a stream of water. It should be remembered, however, that carbon tetrachloride vapor is poisonous when released in closed rooms, buildings, or even automobiles. Doors or windows should be opened at once after a pyrene extinguisher has been discharged in a confined space. Incidentally, certain kinds of cleaning fluids for clothing and upholstery contain carbon tetrachloride. Although not flammable, these fluids must be used with caution because their fumes, if allowed to collect in an unventilated room, may be poisonous.

For combating oil and gasoline fires and fires in live electrical equipment, the *foam-type* extinguisher is now frequently used. A common type is similar in size and appearance to the soda-acid extinguisher. When it is turned upside down, chemicals mix, producing carbon dioxide. However, the solution also contains some foam-making material, like licorice root extract. This traps the carbon dioxide and forms a tough, thick coat on the oil, thereby shutting off the supply of oxygen.

The *carbon dioxide* extinguisher is used for electrical fires and confined fires on oil. Carbon dioxide extinguishers consist of cylinders of varying sizes containing compressed liquefied carbon dioxide gas. When the gas is released from the cylinder, it expands to about 500 times its stored volume to form a cloud of cold, heavy gas. It extinguishes the fire both by absorbing heat from the fuel and by excluding the air.

Small home fires in broilers or skillets are effectively put out with carbon dioxide extinguishers. Another method is to sprinkle the burning fat with baking soda or table salt.

RECENT ADVANCES IN EXTINGUISHING FIRES

Research and experimental programs costing 20 million dollars a year in the United States are developing new ways of fighting fires.

One of the latest chemicals for fighting flammable liquids is potassium bicarbonate, used in a dry powder known as Purple-K for its identifying color. Purple-K can put out airplane crash fires effectively, and is now on reserve at Cape Kennedy launching pads, and at several large airports.

Another new fire-extinguishing agent is silicone-treated monoammonium phosphate. This chemical not only puts out the flames but it sticks to the surface of the burning material, forming a coating that retards subsequent burning. It is safe for all kinds of fires and is recommended for the replacement of the potentially dangerous carbon tetrachloride.

Detergent-like chemicals which make water wetter by decreasing its surface tension are now in use. These agents increase the speed with which water can penetrate into such porous materials as kapok, cotton, hay, decayed leaves, and pine needles. These chemicals are effective in keeping a fire "knocked down" after fire fighters have moved on to other burning spots.

This chapter supplies information that provides the basis for the intelligent use of fire and for protection against uncontrolled fire. Here are some of the essential generalizations:

Burning is oxidation: it is the chemical union of a fuel with oxygen.

Three factors essential for burning are:

1. *A supply of oxygen*
2. *A supply of fuel*
3. *Enough heat to raise the fuel to its kindling point.*

The intensity of burning can be increased by exposing more surface of the fuel to the oxygen in the air or by increasing the supply of oxygen.

Oxygen supports burning, but it does not burn.

The rapid burning of fuels may produce an explosion.

Fuels differ in their kindling temperatures.

In slow oxidation, a small amount of heat is produced, but no flames.

Spontaneous combustion may occur when slow oxidation raises a material to its kindling point.

Fire is essential in our homes, in industry, and for transportation.

Fire out of control is a very destructive force.

The prevention and the fighting of fires is based on the elimination of one or more of the three factors essential for burning.

Most fires are preventable.

DISCOVERING FOR YOURSELF

1. Find out what your city or community fire inspector and local fire departments do to prevent fires.
2. Find the fire-alarm box nearest to your house, the number of your department, and how to report a fire.
3. Examine the hook-and-ladder truck, the pumper engine, fire-tower wagon, and any other equipment at your local fire station. Learn how they are used.
4. Read accounts of destructive fires as reported in your local newspaper for a two-week period. Make a list of the reported causes and try to find out how the fires could have been prevented.
5. Learn how to use the fire extinguisher in your home, school, and automobile.
6. Work out a functional program for an elementary schoolroom for Fire Prevention Week.
7. Use the Self-Inspection Blank for schools and the Fire Safety Check List. (See p. 428.)
8. Find out how fireproofing is done in your school and in other buildings that you use.
9. Find out what the latest methods for fighting forest fires are.

CHAPTER 17B

Teaching "Fire and Its Prevention"

The study of fire is of a very practical nature, for it is directly related to the safety of the home, the school, and the community. In the experiments suggested here, it is essential to exercise the utmost caution. Fire safety should be practiced whenever matches or other fire is used. The activities should conform to the school regulations if there are such. In some cases, with younger children, the experiments will best be performed by the teacher to demonstrate safety precautions. This chapter is closely related to the chapter on teaching chemical change, for it deals with the safe use of one of our most important chemical changes. Because of the importance of fire and because of the need for special emphasis on safety, the subject is treated separately here, as it is in many courses of study. It is a good idea, however, to be aware of the material in both chapters while teaching either one.

A teacher who wishes to know if he is placing proper emphasis on the various phases of the teaching of fire and its uses should read the following objectives carefully and weigh his teaching methods to see if they conform to these intentions or objectives.[1] Where the development of attitudes is concerned, it is considered good practice to stress things to do rather than things not to do. The objectives are therefore stated in terms of positive knowledges, skills, and attitudes. Development of such positive attitudes in coping with fire or its prevention should be strived for in the teaching of children.

---

[1] *Fire Prevention Education,* New York State Education Department, Albany, 1958, 63 pp.

SUGGESTED LEARNINGS FOR THE CHILD IN KINDERGARTEN, GRADE ONE, AND GRADE TWO

IN THE SCHOOL, THE CHILD SHOULD:

a. Know, follow, and respond to the signals and rules for a fire drill.
b. Follow the rules in case of fire.
c. Respond skillfully without unwarranted fear in times of emergency.
d. Know places used in an emergency and the need for keeping them clear.

IN THE SCHOOL AND HOME, THE CHILD SHOULD:

a. Know that careful habits prevent fires.
b. Know that a clean, orderly school or home is less apt to catch fire and he will help to keep his orderly; know that rubbish, especially oily rubbish, catches fire easily.
c. Enjoy an orderly environment, make plans for, and be cooperative in keeping school and home in order.

IN THE HOME AND NEIGHBORHOOD, THE CHILD SHOULD:

a. Know the danger connected with matches, an open fire, scalding liquids, or any hot materials.
b. Understand that matches, electrical outlets and cords, firecrackers, stoves, lanterns, or lighted candles may be a source of danger.
c. Keep away from hot stoves, bonfires, and other open fires.
d. Keep away from containers of hot liquids and willingly refrain from handling anything that can burn or scald him or cause a fire.
e. Know the importance of obtaining the help of an older person and call one at once in case of fire.
f. Know what to do in case his or another person's clothing catches fire, and practice correct procedure.
g. Realize the importance of keeping level-headed, dependable, and reasonably unafraid in a fire emergency.
h. Understand the benefits of fire when properly used.
i. Understand the functions and benefits of the local fire department.

SUGGESTED LEARNINGS FOR THE CHILD IN GRADE THREE AND GRADE FOUR

IN THE COMMUNITY, THIS CHILD SHOULD:

a. Be alert to the fire hazards in his everyday living and be cooperative in observing fire-prevention measures.
b. Know the commonly used materials which are flammable; understand the danger of using kerosene to start a fire, or "cleaners," such as gasoline and the like.
c. Know how to give a fire alarm by telephone or at the alarm box, asking an adult to give an alarm in case of fire or giving it himself if an adult is not available.
d. Know he should wait at the fire alarm box for firemen to come to the scene in order to tell them the exact location of a fire if he gives the alarm.

e. Be reasonably calm and level-headed in a fire emergency.
f. Have an appreciation for the part firemen play in serving the community. (Have visited the nearest fire department or have talked with a local fireman who has visited his school.)
g. Understand his responsibility toward the fire protection services provided by the community.
h. Have a strong appreciation of the role that fire protection has played in the history of the community.
i. Understand the scope of his responsibility in promoting fire safety.
j. Understand the danger of false alarms.
k. Help reduce the incidence of false alarms.
l. Know the danger of objects being struck by lightning, how to avoid this danger, and be unafraid during an electrical storm.
m. Appreciate and understand the beneficial uses of fire and electricity in the community.

THE CHILD IN GRADE FIVE AND GRADE SIX

IN THE COMMUNITY, HE SHOULD:

a. Know advantages of electricity and the dangers from carelessness in its use.
b. Know the danger of touching a live electric wire or of handling electrical equipment with wet hands.
c. Be familiar with incidence of fires and their causes, as well as danger and expense involved in false fire alarms.
d. Know the proper way to use matches, bonfires, and campfires.
e. Recognize social significance of fire safety.
f. Recognize the interdependence of individuals and groups in fire prevention.
g. Realize that a safe community makes possible more and more interesting work and play.
h. Know precautions insofar as fire is concerned that should be taken during and following an atomic attack.
i. Know how to care for individuals in the case of fire, air raid, or other emergency.
j. Understand benefits of fire used properly and dangers resulting from its misuse.
k. Accept his role as a member of his community and country in preventing fires.

In accordance with the objectives and suggested learnings for kindergarten and grades one and two just cited, the following activities seem appropriate for younger children.

1. Help parents or other adults to extinguish picnic fires.
2. Discuss ways that fire helps us and ways in which it can harm us.
3. Help to make the home and school safe from fire hazards by participating in campaigns to discover such hazards and correcting them.
4. Listen to exactly what to do during school fire drills and feel personally responsible for the success of such drills.

5. Perform simple experiments to see that fire needs air to burn and that smothering a flame means keeping the air away from it. Discuss how this knowledge is used in controlling fires.
6. Collect pictures that show how fire destroys things and tell how such fires might have been prevented.
7. Visit the fire department to: see the equipment, listen to the firemen tell about their work, and ask questions. (See details in later discussion.)
8. Rub hands together to feel the resulting heat in order to understand how friction lights matches and starts other fires.
9. Observe a Halloween or birthday candle to see that it needs a supply of air to burn.

USEFUL FIRES IN OUR COMMUNITY

A small group of interested pupils or the whole class may plan a trip to see how fire is used for heating, production of power, building construction, street construction, factories, and businesses. A story of "life without fire" written by a committee of interested pupils, is an interesting language-arts activity.

FINDING OUT WHAT A FIRE
NEEDS FOR BURNING

In the photograph here, a pupil is making use of a convection box with smoke to experiment to show that a fire needs air. The Halloween candle in a pumpkin also provides an excellent opportunity for children to see the importance of providing fire with a supply of fresh air.

The apparatus which Charles made for his demonstration is called onvection box.

ke appointments with Charles for monstration and explanations mall work groups will be most

How does a fire get the air it needs? Unequal heating in the convection box causes the air to move. Children watch a child demonstrate.

Another simple experiment which shows that fresh air is necessary is performed with a lamp chimney, two pencils, and a candle. Light the candle and set the lamp chimney over it on a smooth surface so that air cannot enter at the bottom of the chimney. Watch the candle. Now set the chimney on two flat-sided pencils so as to permit air to enter at the bottom. The candle now burns brightly. Cover the top of the chimney with a piece of glass. Note that the flame soon goes out. Remove the glass cover from the chimney and light the candle again. If a smoking splinter is held near the bottom of the chimney, the smoke enters the chimney and moves up past the flame. The smoke shows which way the air is moving. The pupils will suggest that air must *enter* and *leave* if the candle flame is to continue to burn. The convection box used in the chapter on weather illustrated this same principle.

After the lamp-chimney experiment has been performed, pupils may be asked to tell where they have seen this same thing happen. (Draft through a stove or furnace, draft toward an outdoor campfire, draft toward a burning building.) This idea will be used again if there is discussion about the importance of keeping windows and doors closed when part of a house is on fire.

FINDING OUT HOW FIRES ARE PUT OUT

Having discovered what a fire needs to burn, pupils will be ready to discover how we keep these essentials away from a flame. There are several simple ways of showing some of the means by which we keep air away from fire in order to extinguish the fire. These experiments should be performed on an asbestos pad as a safety measure. Set a short candle in a bowl or a wide-mouthed jar. Light the candle and then cover the container with a large piece of crumpled-up cloth (a small piece might catch fire). A piece of asbestos may be substituted for the cloth. The candle goes out, because the cloth has shut off the supply of air. Light the candle again. This time pour sand into the container to cover the candle. Again it goes out. Try the same thing with water. This puts out the fire mostly by reducing the temperature of the fuel. These simple demonstrations show why we suggest wrapping in a blanket persons whose clothes are afire, why we cover a campfire with earth, and why we use water to put out fires. Another method of putting out fires is by removing the fuel. This may be demonstrated by putting several pieces of crumpled paper on a pie plate. Light one. We can prevent the spread of fire to the other pieces by removing them. Use a tongs to remove them. These experiments with fire should be performed by the teacher or under the supervision of the teacher.

MAKING AN EXHIBIT OF FUELS

An exhibit of some of the common materials used as fuels in the community may be made—including wood, charcoal, hard and soft coal, coke, crude oil, kerosene, and a container of manufactured or natural gas. There probably are several pupils who have never seen oil of the type that is burned in furnaces; some may never have seen coke; or compared soft coal with hard coal. The kerosene bottle should be plainly marked, as should any other liquid and gas fuel, in order to prevent accident. Special precautions should be taken to dispose of such fuels after the exhibit is over. Some pupils may make reports on how charcoal is made, how coke is made, how gas is produced and transported, how crude oil is obtained from the earth and transported, how coal was formed. Again, here is opportunity to stress how inventions and discoveries of new processes have changed our way of living.

KEEPING TRACK OF CURRENT FIRES

One way to make fire hazards assume real significance is to have a committee of pupils keep track of newspaper accounts of fires, noting especially their causes and the estimated amount of damage. It is amazing how many such accounts there are in newspapers within a month and how varied the causes are. The accounts may be clipped from the newspapers and placed on the bulletin board or pasted in a scrapbook, with the important sentences underlined in red. A list of the causes may be made so that pupils may become more aware of how fires start. They will probably report instances of spontaneous combustion (see previous chapter). Pupils may make a report of these causes in connection with the use of the Inspection Blank described in the next paragraph.

CHECKING THE SCHOOL FOR FIRE SAFETY

One way to bring to the attention of children the various ways in which fires start and the essential safety precautions is to help them make a thorough check of their school. The *Self-Inspection Blank For Schools*[2] may be used in your school. The school custodian may be of help in interpreting some of the items on the blank. It is the responsibility of the school administration to see that the building is safe; the purpose of the children's use of the blank is to emphasize to them the various places that require inspection, to show them how the school is kept safe, and to make them see that they themselves can help to keep their school safe from fire. The school custodian may explain to the children some of the steps that have recently been taken to make the school safe.

Whenever children put up a Christmas tree, scenery for a play, or any similar temporary thing, they should consider the aspects of safety involved. Christmas trees stay green longer and are consequently less hazardous if kept standing in a pail of water. The fire department will give further advice about special safety precautions.

CHECKING THE HOME FOR FIRE SAFETY

Home inspection is of great importance, and, with the help of the blank *Fire Safety Check List* which is available from the National Board of Fire Underwriters (see footnote 2 below), pupils can be of real help in seeing that home fire hazards are eliminated. The family should help to fill out the blank. This is an occasion when the school and home can cooperate in a very practical way. Use of these blanks has been welcomed by parents in many communities. This is a type of homework assignment that makes sense to most parents. Pupils should be given opportunity to report to the class anything done at home as a result of using the blank.

---

[2] Prepared by the National Board of Fire Underwriters, approved and adopted by the National Association of Public School Business Officials, and available from the National Board of Fire Underwriters, 85 John Street, New York 7, N. Y. Write for information regarding other materials on the subject of fire safety.

PRACTICING FIRE DRILLS

In connection with the study of fire safety and with the use of the Self-Inspection Blank for Schools, there is opportunity for pupil discussion of "How can we improve our fire and air raid drills?" Children will pay more attention to drills if they themselves work out rules for conduct. Often they will contribute good ideas. If only one class in the school is studying the material on fire, this class may share its suggestions with other groups, either by sending a representative to tell the other groups about the suggestions or by sending a carefully worked-out chart presenting the suggestions. The school will probably give special attention to drills during Fire Prevention Week, but the emphasis should be continued throughout the year. During drills, emphasis should be placed on following directions promptly. An evaluation session after a drill is important to discuss its effectiveness.

VISITING THE FIRE STATION

Every year children in the United States make an enormous number of trips to fire stations. Some are very useful. Some waste time because they are poorly planned. Children go without much notion of what they will see or why they are going. For such procedure there is no excuse. Children should go to the fire station only because there they can learn some things firsthand in an interesting way. They should go armed with questions and have clearly in mind certain observations that they wish to make. They should understand that they are not on a picnic, that firemen are engaged in the serious business of protecting the community from fire loss. They should remember that they asked the fire department for permission to come, and consequently they have the responsibility of giving the personnel courteous attention. It is also important for children to know that members of the fire department are not teachers and are not expected to be. Firemen's explanations may not always be clear, and they may not always express themselves well. This matter should be discussed before the trip, and pupils should recognize their responsibilities toward the persons who are helping them, especially since they have asked for the help. Many fire departments designate specific individuals on their staff to work with school children. This is a helpful practice.

Children have many questions to ask the fire department about how the fire apparatus works, how the alarm system works, and so on. These questions should, if possible, be sent to the fire station before the visit. It is good language-arts experience to state the questions clearly, and it is helpful to the fire-station personnel to learn in advance what the pupils wish to know. The problem of where the funds to support the fire department come from is one that pupils will be curious about. This again illustrates a close connection between social studies and science.

LEARNING ABOUT FIRE EXTINGUISHERS

The picture on this page illustrates the use of the fire department in helping pupils to see how a fire extinguisher works. After this demonstration, the pupils with the custodian returned to the school with the refilled fire extinguisher and hung it in its place outside their room.

For a simple experiment that demonstrates the action of one type of fire extinguisher, use baking soda and vinegar. Place a tablespoonful of baking soda in a drinking glass and slowly pour the vinegar on it. The bubbles that are formed are carbon dioxide. A burning match held over the bubbles will be extinguished. This should be a teacher-demonstrated experiment. The general rule in the elementary school should always be, "Do not light a match unless some adult is with you."

Fire extinguishers of the type shown in the picture are commonly used in schools. If pupils do not see such an extinguisher at the fire station, the school custodian may be asked to show one to the pupils and explain to them how it works and how it should be cared for.

RESOURCES TO INVESTIGATE

1. Local fire department for learning its operation and for a source of information about the causes of fire and its prevention.
2. Local fuel distributors for fuel samples to examine.
3. Newspaper accounts of fires to learn their cause and to determine how they might have been prevented.
4. Pennsylvania Crude Oil Association, Oil City, Pa.; Standard Oil Co. (New Jersey), 30 Rockefeller Plaza, New York 20, N. Y.; National Coal Association, Coal Building, Washington 6, D. C., for printed material describing fuel products.
5. The school custodian to show a school fire extinguisher.
6. The schoolhouse, pupils' homes, public buildings to see how places are fireproofed and how caution should be exercised in order to prevent fires.

CHAPTER 18A

Heat and How We Use It

We rub our hands on a cold day, and they feel warmer. We burn gas under a kettle of water, the kettle gets hot, and the water boils. Electricity runs through the coils of wire in a toaster, and they get red hot. In the glare of the summer sun, a sandy beach heats up.

Thus, heat is produced in a number of different ways. The mechanical work done in the process of rubbing our hands, the chemical energy released in burning, the electrical energy charging through the wire, and the radiant energy winging 93 million miles from the sun—all of these forms of energy have raised the temperature of something. They have actually made something warmer.

Before discussing the nature of heat further, we should understand the meaning of the word "energy" as the physicist uses it. Let us discuss energy.

ENERGY

We live in a universe of matter and energy. In chapter 16A we investigated matter and found that it is made of molecules and atoms. Matter is all around us. So, too, is energy. Energy is defined as the capacity to do work. A baseball flying through the air has energy. If it hits a window it can do work against it, as a houseowner knows only too well. The baseball's energy was derived from a chemical process in the batter's muscles— the burning of molecules of sugar, resulting in the release of the energy stored in them. If we go back further, we find that the energy in the sugar was obtained from sunlight during the process of photosynthesis (see chapter 10A).

All forms of energy are interchangeable. Radiant energy in sunlight is transformed into chemical energy stored in sugar.

431

When the sugar is burned, the stored chemical energy in it is changed to the energy of motion of the batter's muscles, and by way of his swinging bat to the motion of the ball.

A speeding baseball, a molecule of sugar—both possess energy, both can do work. Energy appears in many forms. Water held high in a mountain lake can do work when it falls and turns a waterwheel. It possesses energy by virtue of its position. A wound spring has energy stored in it that may be released slowly to run a clock or rapidly to make a toy scoot across a floor. Radiant energy from the sun is delivered to the earth in the form of waves. In the next chapter we will consider still another form of energy—atomic energy.

THE NATURE OF HEAT

What is heat? What actually happens when something gets warmer? At one time, some scientists, such as Lavoisier, believed that heat was a real *substance*, a fluid. They thought that when something got warmer, more of this fluid, which was named "caloric," flowed into it. Losing some of this caloric, it became colder.

At the beginning of the nineteenth century, Count Rumford of Bavaria challenged the caloric theory. He became interested in this subject when he observed the vast quantities of heat produced by working against friction during the boring of a cannon. He found it hard to believe that the apparently inexhaustible heat produced during the boring could be a material substance. He proposed the idea that nothing was "capable of being excited and communicated in the manner heat was excited and communicated in these experiments, except it be *motion*." According to this theory, heat, the result of mechanical energy being expended, was energy itself, not a substance; it was the energy of motion, not a fluid.

But how can "motion" be contained in a substance? When we finish with the rubbing of our hands, visible motion has ceased. What has happened to the energy that has been expended? The molecular theory furnishes the answer. As we learned in chapter 16A, all matter is composed of exceedingly small separate particles called molecules. These molecules are in ceaseless motion. We have experimental evidence that when a substance is heated its molecules move with more speed or with more energy. Evidently heat energy is the energy of the motion of molecules. When you rub your hands, you bump the molecules in the outermost layer of your skin and cause them to move faster. Those in turn bump against those just beneath them, and so on. In this way, the entire thickness of your skin is heated.

In all the materials cited before—the metal of the kettle and the water in it, the wire in the toaster, the sand on the beach— molecules have been activated into faster motion. This, then, is the meaning of heat: it is energy, the energy of moving molecules.

In these terms, "cold" has a new meaning. It is simply a subjective way we have of characterizing less heat, less molecular activity.

An important effect of the increased molecular activity that results from heating should be mentioned here. As the molecules bounce more vigorously and more freely, the substance they comprise expands. Although it is hard to see it, your skin gets bigger as you rub it. The metal in the kettle, the water, the coil, the sand, all get larger as they get warmer. Conversely, they contract as they cool. We will discuss this more fully later.

TEMPERATURE

The common thermometer used to measure temperature is essentially a sealed glass tube containing a liquid like mercury or colored alcohol. The principle involved in the functioning of a thermometer is that fluids generally expand when heated and contract when cooled. (Solids expand and SEE PAGE 449 TO 450 contract too, of course, but the glass in a thermometer does not expand enough to affect the reading materially.) The hollow inside of the thermometer, the *bore*, is very narrow; in some thermometers it is finer than a human hair. Thus, a small change in temperature causes enough expansion or contraction in the liquid to force it a noticeable distance up or down the bore. Since the tube is calibrated—that is, marked in degrees—the expansion or contraction of the fluid can be measured in exact units.

SCALES. There are two common temperature scales in use, the Fahrenheit and the centigrade (also called the Celsius scale). The Fahrenheit thermometer is so calibrated that it registers 32 degrees when the temperature is at the melting point of ice and 212 degrees at the boiling point of water. These are written 32° F. and 212° F. respectively. Thus there are 180 degrees between the melting point of ice and boiling point of water. Of course, the scale may be extended below and above these points.

Incidentally, the zero of the Fahrenheit thermometer does not mean "no degrees." This zero point was somewhat arbitrarily selected by its originator, Fahrenheit, who, on mixing some salt and ice, achieved a low temperature which he decided to call zero. Since, in the making of a scale, two points are needed to determine the calibration, a second point of 100 was selected, which Fahrenheit believed was the temperature of the human body. It is said that this error (body temperature is actually 98.6° on this scale) was made because Fahrenheit based his figure on the temperature of a cow rather than a human. The Fahrenheit scale, although arbitrarily arrived at, is still in use in many English-speaking countries. The people there are accustomed to this scale and have resisted attempts to change it. The rest of the world, and scientists everywhere, use the centigrade scale.

On the centigrade scale, zero marks the melting point of ice and 100 the boiling

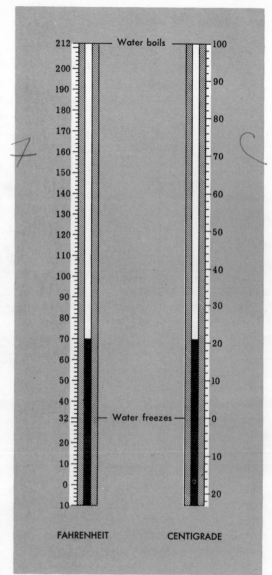

The Fahrenheit and centigrade scales. To convert from centigrade to Fahrenheit, multiply by 9/5 and add 32. To convert from Fahrenheit to centigrade, subtract 32 and then multiply by 5/9. Or, simply place a straight edge across the two scales—and read!

point of water. These are written 0° C. and 100° C., respectively.

Absolute zero, −460° F., represents the lowest point that matter can theoretically reach. Scientists have produced temperatures only one millionth of a degree above absolute zero.

Some interesting temperatures (approximate) are shown in the following table:

	Degrees Fahrenheit	Degrees Centigrade
Surface of the sun	10,000	5,500
Electric arc light	7,232	4,000
Tungsten lamp filament	4,500	2,482
Kitchen-range flame	3,092	1,700
Iron melts	2,795	1,535
Mercury boils	675	357
Lead melts	620	327
Water boils	212	100
Ethyl alcohol boils	172	78
Highest official temperature record (Azizia, North Africa, Sept. 13, 1922)	136	58
Paraffin melts	128	52
Songbird's temperature	113	45
Body temperature	98.6	37
"Room temperature"	70	21
Ice melts	32	0
Freon boils	–2	–19
Mercury freezes	–40	–40
Lowest official temperature record (Vostock, Antarctica, 1958)	–125.3	–87.4
Ethyl alcohol freezes	–202	–130
Air boils (changes from liquid to gas)	–310	–190
Absolute zero	–460	–273

THERMOMETER FLUIDS. To be useful, a thermometer fluid must remain a liquid at the temperatures which the thermometer is intended to measure. If the fluid freezes solid, it cannot flow; if it boils, it will break the thermometer. The boiling point of mercury, 675° F., is high enough to permit its use in thermometers used at moderately high temperatures. It's freezing point, –40° F. (that is, 40° below zero, F.) is low enough for its use in an average winter in temperate climates. Moreover, mercury expands uniformly throughout a wide temperature range, another essential in a thermometer fluid.

Alcohol boils at a much lower point (172° F.) than water and hence cannot be used in thermometers that are to be exposed to high temperatures. Its low freezing point

(–202° F.), however, makes it useful in polar and arctic regions. Alcohol is used also because it is cheaper than mercury and because it expands six times as much for a given rise in temperature, and is therefore more sensitive to temperature variations. Alcohol is colored with a red or blue dye for visibility.

THERMOMETERS FOR DIFFERENT PURPOSES. Thermometers come in different shapes and sizes for different purposes. The clinical thermometer has a very narrow bore so that a difference of one-tenth of a degree is easily read. It is calibrated to read only from 92° F. to 110° F. Heat forces the mercury out of the bulb and up the bore, but a constriction in the bore keeps the mercury up in the stem when the thermometer is removed from the patient, even though the surrounding temperature is lower. In this way, the thermometer registers the highest point to which the mercury goes. A quick jerk of the wrist forces the mercury back into the bulb.

Expansion and contraction is the principle behind metal thermometers such as those used in ovens, but here it is a solid rather than a liquid that changes size. In one common metal thermometer, the basic unit is a coil made of two strips of metal welded together along their lengths. Brass is commonly used for the inside strip and steel for the outside. Brass expands more for a given rise in temperature than steel does. As a result, the expansion or contraction due to heating or cooling causes the coil to loosen or tighten. This motion is conveyed to a pointer that sweeps over a scale calibrated in degrees.

MEASUREMENT OF HEAT

Which has more heat in it—a cupful of water at 212° F. (its boiling point) or a potful of water at 212° F.? Both have the same temperature, which, as we learned, means that the *activity* of the molecules in each is the same. But the potful of water has *more* of these active molecules, hence we say that it has more heat in it. It takes much more burning of gas to produce a potful of boiling water than a cupful; in turn, the pot has more heat to give up to something else. That is why you can take the chill off a bottle holding baby's milk formula more quickly by putting it into a potful of hot water than into a cupful, other things being equal.

The unit used in measuring the *quantity* of heat is the calorie. The calorie is defined as the amount of heat necessary to raise one gram of pure water (about half a thimbleful) one degree centigrade. (This calorie is known as the small calorie; the large calorie that biologists use to measure the heat values of foods is equal to 1,000 of these small calories.) Heat, then, is measured in units called calories; temperature is measured in units called degrees.

EFFECTS OF HEATING

The expansion and contraction of substances that is occasioned by their heating and cooling is important in everyday life. Railroad rails are laid with a small space between each section, because summer temperatures cause them to expand considerably. One mile of railroad track may be four feet longer on the hottest day of summer than on the coldest day of winter. The space between the sections of rail allows for expansion of steel; otherwise the expanding rails would buckle. Sidewalks must be laid in sections with expansion joints between them for the same reason. Otherwise the sidewalk would buckle up and break.

The steel tires on wagon wheels are put on hot so that they will contract and hold fast around the wooden wheel. Hot liquid poured into a cold glass sometimes causes it to crack because the heated inside surface expands suddenly, pushing out the unheated outside surface. Pyrex glass is useful because

it contains substances that reduce the amount of contraction and expansion that can be induced by heat.

Liquids as well as solids, as we have found in our study of thermometers, expand when they are heated and contract when they are cooled. For this reason we do not fill automobile radiators to the top with cool water.

Water, however, is unique in that at certain temperatures it reverses the rule of contracting with cooling and expanding with heating. From 39° F. to 32° F., its usual freezing point, water expands slightly as it is cooled. As a result, ice is slightly lighter than water and floats on it. This peculiar behavior of water has important consequences for life on this planet. When ice forms on a lake or pond, its lower density (it is only nine-tenths as heavy as liquid water) keeps it on top. Thus, it acts as an insulating blanket, preventing the rapid loss of heat of the water below it. This is why ponds and lakes do not freeze solid to the bottom but leave a liquid zone under the ice for the survival of aquatic life.

The fact that water expands as it changes into ice accounts for the bursting of unprotected water pipes in the winter. Similarly, if water is allowed to freeze in an automobile, it may break the metal block of the engine. Consequently, in cold weather we add antifreeze, a substance which has a low freezing point, to the water in our automobile cooling system. Milk, which consists mainly of water, pushes up out of the bottle when frozen. If it did not, the bottle would break. In chapter 6A, we saw how the freezing of water is one of the forces responsible for the splitting of rocks.

We have seen how solids and liquids change in volume with temperature. Gases expand and contract even more. Air expands when heated and becomes lighter than an equal volume of cooler air. In chapter 9A, we saw how the unequal heating of the air is one of the driving forces in the weather "machine" of our planet. We make use of this principle in the heating systems and in the ventilation of our homes.

CHANGE OF STATE

SEE
PAGE
452

Matter can exist in a solid, liquid, or gaseous state. We can cause a change of state of any substance by adding or subtracting heat. Butter taken out of the refrigerator on a hot day gains heat and melts into a liquid. Water placed in the ice-cube compartment solidifies as it loses heat. Gaseous water vapor in the air condenses into a liquid as it loses heat.

When we say that a substance is a solid, liquid, or gas, we really mean that it is commonly found in one of these three states at ordinary temperatures found on our planet. Thus mercury is usually regarded as a liquid, but it will solidify into a solid at −40° F. or boil off as a gas at 675° F. Iron, copper, and other metals change from solids to liquids if they are heated sufficiently. Air is always thought of as gaseous; yet, with sufficient chilling, air can be converted into a liquid, known as *liquid air*. Sufficient chilling of one of the gases of the air, carbon dioxide, changes it into a solid; we know it as *dry ice* and use it when we wish to keep food at very low temperatures. (See diagram, p. 407.)

The temperature at which a substance changes from solid to liquid is known as its *melting point*. We make use of the fact that different substances have different melting points. Tungsten, the metal used for the filaments in electric lamps, can withstand temperatures of thousands of degrees without melting. On the other hand, an alloy of metals with a low melting point is useful in electric fuses, because a rise of temperature caused by a short circuit or an overloading of the electric line will cause it to melt and break the circuit (see chapter 21A). Automatic sprinkling systems also use such metals for plugs; the heat produced in a fire causes the plugs to melt, thereby releasing water from the pipes.

We also make use of the fact that different substances have different *freezing points*. Alcohol, for example, freezes only when it has been chilled to −202° F., but water freezes at 32° F. For this reason, alcohol (or some other antifreeze) is mixed with the water in the radiator of automobiles to prevent freezing. The alchohol-water mixture has a lower freezing point than the water alone. Salt-water mixtures freeze only at temperatures lower than the freezing point of water. The practice of scattering salt on icy sidewalks results in a mixture which has a freezing point lower than the temperature of the air; hence, the ice melts.

PRESSURE COOKERS. As previously stated, water normally boils at 100° C. or 212° F. By "normally" we mean at sea level altitude and in an open vessel. No matter how rapidly it is boiling under these conditions, the temperature remains the same. If you keep the gas high once water is already boiling, you are merely wasting gas. Whatever is in the water will take just as long to cook once the water is boiling; a high flame does not speed the process. The excess heat energy simply changes the water into water vapor more rapidly. But it is possible to make water hotter than 212° F. by increasing the pressure on it. This is what pressure cookers do. Since they are closed vessels, the steam is kept in and the pressure rises. In these cookers, instead of boiling at 212° F. the water (and the steam) reaches a higher temperature, perhaps 250° F. in the common pressure cooker. Naturally, meat, potatoes, string beans, or any other food is cooked more quickly. Since the steam exerts considerable pressure, safety valves or blowout plugs are provided. They function if the pressure reaches a danger point.

In one of the early flights across the Atlantic in a nonpressurized plane, a radio message was sent from the plane to Washington with this question, "How long does it take to cook a three-minute egg at our altitude?" A quick computation was made by a physicist and the answer was radioed back. The time given was several minutes more than three, and the egg was cooked to the satisfaction of its eater. Why was more than three minutes required? Since air pressure decreases with increasing altitude from sea level, water will boil at a lower temperature than 212° F. For this reason, it takes a longer time to cook eggs or any other kind of food in boiling water. This is essentially the opposite of the pressure-cooker effect.

HEAT MOVES

An iron poker is left in a camp fire. In a few minutes, its handle gets hot. In a tree branch forty feet above the fire, a bird feels the fire's warmth. Boy Scouts sitting around the fire feel a warm glow on their faces.

In each of these instances heat was transferred—from the fire to the poker, bird, and boys, respectively. But the principle *method* of heat transfer involved in each was different. Let us consider each of these ways—called *conduction*, *convection* and *radiation*—to see how objects gain or lose heat.

CONDUCTION. Heat traveled from the end of the poker in the fire to the handle by conduction. It is simple to understand conduction when we recall that the poker, like all other substances, is made of molecules, in this case mostly iron molecules, and that the heat in the poker is due to the vibration of its molecules. The molecules in the end of the poker in the fire vibrate rapidly. These, in turn, strike adjacent molecules in the cooler part, just outside of the flames, and cause them to vibrate more rapidly. This continues inch after inch up the poker until the handle becomes hot.

Conduction, then, is a method of heat movement in which energy is transferred from molecule to molecule by colli-

sion or bombardment. You burn your fingers on the handle of a hot skillet because the heat from the flame has started molecular activity which reaches your skin by conduction. Even the molecules in your skin vibrate vigorously as they are heated. Sense organs in your skin detect this vibration and send a special nerve message (*not* by heat conduction) to your brain. You thus become aware of the heat.

Not all objects conduct heat equally well. Because wood is a poor conductor of heat we use it for the handles of pots and pans. In general, metals are better conductors than nonmetals. Liquids, gases, and nonmetallic solids, all poor conductors of heat, are designated as heat *insulators*, and are used to shield our bodies or objects from heat, or to prevent the loss of heat. When we use a potholder to pick up hot pans and kettles we are making use of the insulating qualities of both the material and the air that is trapped in it to protect our hands from the heat.

CONVECTION. How was the bird high in the tree warmed by the campfire? A layer of air directly over the fire was heated. The heat caused it to expand and thus made it lighter than the surrounding colder air. The heavier, colder air around the base of the fire swept into the fire and pushed the warmer, lighter air up to the bird. We saw in chapter 9A how convection currents like these, caused by the unequal heating of the earth, were responsible for the large scale movement of air and therefore of weather around the earth.

SEE PAGES 453 TO 454

Convection currents are responsible for the heating of a room by a radiator. (A better name for this type of heater would be "convector.") Warm air heated by the radiator is pushed up and sweeps across to cooler parts of the room. Cold air falls and moves toward the radiator, where it is heated. Fireplaces are poor room heaters because most of the heat is convected up the chimney rather than out into the room.

SEE
PAGE
454

RADIATION. In conduction, heat is transferred as molecules kick adjacent molecules. In convection a whole volume of heated material—gaseous or liquid—circulates. The transfer of heat by radiation is quite different from both of these. The transfer of heat from campfire to face is effected not by vibrating molecules or circulating air but by an energy wave called *infrared radiation* (see chapter 23A).

This is a most important method, since it accounts for the heating of the earth by the sun. Obviously, conduction and convection could not carry heat from the sun to the earth, since most of the 93 million miles between them is empty space, almost devoid of molecules.

Infrared rays themselves should not be thought of as heat. The space between the sun and the earth is not heated by these waves, since there is practically nothing there to be heated. The rays might be compared to television waves emanating from a broadcasting station. These waves, as you know, must be picked up by your television set and converted into light for you to see a picture. Similarly, the infrared rays broadcast by the sun produce heat only when they strike and excite the molecules of substances.

Infrared rays are invisible to the human eye, lying just beyond the visible red rays in the spectrum of the sun's colors (see chapter 23A). All substances give off infrared radiation. If you hold your hand under an electric iron (to avoid heat by air convection) it is heated by radiation. You can detect your own radiations by holding your open hand very close to the side of your face, without touching it.

EVAPORATION COOLS

SEE
PAGE
452

Dip your finger into water which is at about body temperature and hold it up to the air. It feels cool as the water evaporates. Evaporation is a cooling process, or to put it in other words, a heat-removing process. Why? The molecular theory comes to our help again. We have found that the heat of a substance is due to the energy of all of its moving molecules. Not all of the molecules have the same speed. Some of the faster moving (higher-temperature) molecules escape from the surface of the water on your skin, leaving the slower moving (lower-temperature) ones behind. The moment that evaporation begins, heat leaves the water that remains momentarily on your finger. The water is being chilled and so removes heat from your skin, making it feel cool. We hasten cooling of a feverish patient by sponging him with alcohol, which evaporates quickly and thus cools more effectively than water.

The evaporation of perspiration from our skin serves to regulate body temperature. Our bodies are heat machines; the skin serves as a cooling system; perspiration is the cooling fluid, its evaporation providing the means by which excess heat is disposed of.

You may recall that in chapter 9A we saw how the cooling effect of evaporation could be used to measure the humidity of the air, because evaporation and hence cooling take place more rapidly in dry air than in moist air.

INSULATION

SEE
PAG
455

Stated simply, the purpose of insulation is to prevent heat from going where we do not want it to go. This is true whether we are considering our bodies or our homes. In all instances, the flow of heat is regulated by controlling conduction, convection, and radiation, since these are the three methods by which heat travels.

CLOTHING. As stated previously, our bodies are heat machines, burning fuel and maintaining a temperature of 98.6° F. The purpose of clothing is to keep the wearer comfortable in the particular environment in which he happens to be. In cold weather, clothing prevents the rapid loss of heat from the body. It does this by providing layers of air cells, that is, still air trapped in the fine meshes of the fabric. Trapped in this way, air cannot transmit heat by convection; it prevents your body from losing heat. Birds protect themselves from cold by fluffing their feathers, thereby trapping more air. Woolen clothing is generally warmer than other materials because it can hold more cells of trapped air. Thicker fabrics are generally warmer than thinner ones because they hold more of this "dead air."

In designing clothing for warmth, provision must also be made for the evaporation of perspiration. If the moisture is permitted to accumulate in the inner layers of the cloth, it will fill some of the tiny air cells that would otherwise provide insulation. Thus heat would be conducted away from the body more rapidly. To provide for the evaporation of perspiration several layers of fabric are better than a single layer.

Wind is also a source of danger and discomfort in cold weather, since the currents of air carry heat away from the clothing. That is why it is wise to have tightly woven cloth, such as Byrd cloth, in the outermost layer of clothing to serve as a windbreaker.

In warm weather, the problem is still insulation—insulation against the blistering heat of the sun. Clothing must be thick enough to prevent the sun's rays from penetrating and yet porous enough to permit evaporation, which as we recall, is the body's natural cooling process.

Dark-colored materials *absorb* more radiant heat than light-colored materials. Place a piece of dark fabric and a piece of light fabric of the same size and material in the sunlight. Feel each after a few minutes SEE PAGES 452 TO 453

If a house is not insulated (left), the heat provided by the heating system is lost rapidly through the walls. Heat is transferred by conduction through the walls and by convection currents in the air spaces between the walls. In the insulated house (right), the heat is retained within the living space. Because insulation material is a poor conductor, heat is lost slowly by conduction, and since insulation fills the air spaces, it prevents convection currents from being set up.

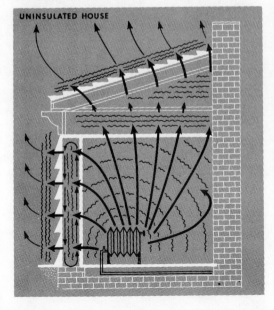

UNINSULATED HOUSE

INSULATED HOUSE

and you will find that the dark cloth is much warmer. For this reason light-colored clothing is cooler than dark clothing of similar material, when worn in sunlight, and is recommended for summer wear.

HOMES. The prevention of heat loss from homes makes them healthier and more comfortable to live in and serves to lower fuel bills at the same time. The principles involved are similar to those employed in clothing. Buildings are insulated in a number of ways. One method is to fill the spaces between the inner and outer walls with poor conductors, such as asbestos or spun glass. Insulation is thus improved, because these materials prevent air currents from convecting heat away; they provide a way of trapping air, which, as we know, is a poor heat conductor. (See illustration, page 439.)

Wood, brick, cement, and cinder block are used in building construction partly because they too are poor conductors of heat and hence will retard the flow of heat out of the building. Inside the building, hot-air pipes and steam pipes are often covered with asbestos, spun glass, or other material to prevent loss of heat from the pipes in the cellar or in other parts of the building where warmth is not needed. Refrigerators have a thick fibrous packing between the inner and outer walls to prevent the heat of the room from getting inside them. Weather stripping around windows and storm doors prevents considerable loss of warm air through these openings.

HEATING OF HOMES

SEE PAGES 455 TO 456 At one time, fireplaces were the only means of heating homes. But the fireplace was never a very effective heating device. The pioneers often had to spend winter evenings in bed to keep warm. Even if they came close to a roaring fire to receive heat by radiation, cold air chilled their backs. Commonly our ancestors heated a soapstone on the fire and then hurried off with it to warm a cold bedroom and an icy bed. No wonder they used feather beds and thick comforters.

THE FRANKLIN STOVE. In 1744, Benjamin Franklin invented a stove that marked a real improvement in heating. This stove was placed within the fireplace. Since it was partly enclosed, the fire's heat was not wasted as much. Although the Franklin stove heated the room mainly by radiation, it did set up some convection currents, so that warm air was carried to those not directly in the path of the heat waves. Other men improved on Franklin's invention. They brought the stove into the room, closed it completely around the fire and provided it with a stovepipe chimney. This type was more effective, both as a heat radiator and a heat convector.

In today's homes, the fire has been moved into the basement or a special utility room. Its heat is conveyed to the rest of the house by means of circulating air or water.

HOT-AIR HEATING. In the hot-air furnace, the stove is enclosed in a brick or iron jacket. Air within this jacket is heated and is pushed upward by inflowing cold air through a pipe to a grating in the floor of the room above. Hot-air pipes frequently branch to provide warm air to the different rooms of a house.

HOT-WATER HEATING. Hot-water heating systems depend on the convection currents that are started when water is heated, as shown in the diagram on page 441. As water is heated in the boiler, it expands, becomes less dense, and is pushed upward by the heavier cold water entering the bottom of the boiler. The warm water travels through the radiators. Here heat is conducted to the metal of the radiator walls causing them to become warm. The radiator, in turn, heats the air in contact with its surface. The heated air then circulates because of the convection

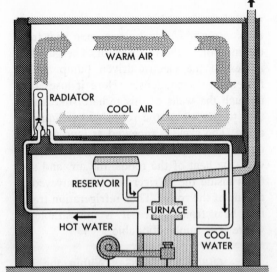

This oil-burning hot-water heating system illustrates the ways in which heat is transferred from one place to another. The flame from the oil burner heats the water by conduction through the walls of the boiler. The hot water flows upward by convection, being pushed up by the cool water returning from the radiator for reheating. The radiator warms the air of the room partly by radiation but mostly by the convection currents of air, indicated by arrows.

radiators. Here it condenses against the cooler radiator walls and gives up its heat.

As in the hot-water heating system, the same water circulates in a continuous cycle, not unlike the water cycle in nature described in chapter 9A, in which water changes to water vapor and then back to water again.

RADIANT HEATING. A form of heating known as "radiant heating" or "panel heating" is being used in many new homes and buildings. In this system, hot water is circulated through iron pipes concealed in floors, walls, or ceilings. These pipes, replacing exposed, space-consuming radiators, heat the floors and walls, causing them to radiate heat. When these radiations (like those from the sun) reach people or furniture, they cause them to warm up. Thus people are heated directly by floors or walls by radiant heat, whereas in conventional systems of heating, the air has to be heated first. Engineers claim that this method of heating is more economical and more pleasant than air-heating systems.

REFRIGERATION

A discussion of refrigeration belongs in a chapter on heat because to cool something means to subtract heat from it. A refrigerator is a heat subtractor, at least as far as the food stored in it is concerned.

Mechanical (iceless) refrigerators have revolutionized the care of food. Such refrigeration is not confined to homes. Refrigerated railroad cars, trucks, and planes bring fruit, dairy products, fresh vegetables, meat, and fish hundreds and thousands of miles to our tables. We are able to keep food from one year to the next in deep-freeze units. They make out-of-season foods become in-season any time we choose. Let us see how refrigerators work.

Basically, refrigeration depends on the principle that evaporation is a cooling or

currents that are then set up. Meanwhile, the water inside the radiator, after giving up its heat and thus becoming cool, descends to the furnace through the return pipe and is heated again. Thus, the same water is used over and over again in a closed system, being heated in the furnace and giving up its heat in the radiators.

STEAM HEATING. In steam heating systems, the boiler is partly filled with water. As the furnace gets hot, some of the water is changed into water vapor (commonly called "live steam"). The water vapor occupies much more space than water (one quart of water can make about 1,600 quarts of water vapor) so that the pressure generated forces the water vapor up into the

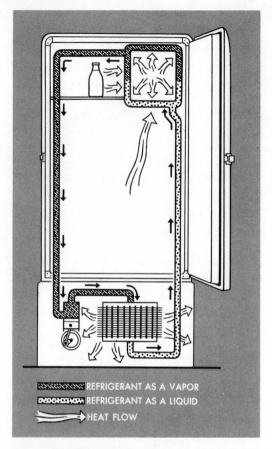

REFRIGERANT AS A VAPOR
REFRIGERANT AS A LIQUID
→ HEAT FLOW

The mechanical refrigerator keeps its contents cold by transferring heat from the cooling compartment to the outside air.

heat-removing process. Dab some alcohol on your wrist. It feels cool as the alcohol evaporates. The evaporating alcohol carries heat away from your hand; the alcohol vapor then disperses in the air of your room. If you had a way of collecting the alcohol vapor, and could compress it back into a liquid, you could repeat the original operation and thus keep your wrist cool. This kind of a cycle is possible in a refrigerator.

Instead of alcohol, *refrigerants* like ammonia, methyl chloride, or Freon are used as the evaporating fluids. The refrigerant travels through pipes in a closed system, as indicated in the diagram. As the refrigerant (in a liquid state) passes through the coils

around the ice-cube compartment, it evaporates into a gas, thereby removing heat from the interior of the refrigerator. The gas then moves to the electric-driven pump and is forced into a condenser. Here it loses heat through the walls of this radiator-like structure to the air of the room and is liquefied again. The cycle is repeated as long as cooling is required in the refrigerator. In this way, the heat of the foods, the air, and surfaces inside the refrigerator are conveyed to the air of the room. Thus refrigeration transfers heat from where it is undesirable to where it is unobjectionable.

QUICK FREEZING. Within the last few decades, it has been found that if various foods are quick-frozen and then kept at a temperature below freezing, they will keep almost indefinitely. (Recall the deep-frozen mammoths described in chapter 14A.) Quick freezing requires specially designed refrigerating machines that subject the foods to the intense cold of 10° to 20° below zero F. Used hitherto mostly in commercial plants, quick freezing has come into many private homes.

Why must the freezing be *quick?* When food is frozen, the water in it freezes into crystals. If the water freezes slowly, large ice crystals form. These rupture the cells of the food and destroy their consistency and flavor. This is particularly true for fruits and vegetables. When foods are frozen quickly, on the other hand, numerous but small ice crystals are formed, which do not break through the cell walls.

Quick deep-freezing of foods is rapidly replacing older methods of processing and preserving foods, as is evident from a casual inspection of the assortment of frozen foods available in any food market.

AIR CONDITIONING

In its broadest sense, air conditioning is a term that applies to any man-made improvement over prevailing atmospheric conditions. Civilized man, demanding more precise control of his environment, finds that the temperature is too high or too low, the air too moist or too dry, the air dirty, or the odor unpleasant. Air conditioning remedies these deficiencies.

In a more specific sense, we apply the term air conditioning to the equipment that is finding increasing use in theaters, office buildings, and private homes.

Self-contained room air conditioners, made to be installed in the windows of homes, have become very popular. A cooling coil is connected to a refrigeration machine housed in the conditioner; the outdoor air carries away the heat of the room. A fan causes the room air to be forced into the conditioner through filters, which remove dust and pollen. The air is then passed through the cooling and dehumidifying apparatus. The conditioned air is then blown into the room at high speed. A fresh-air connection is usually provided so that fresh, outdoor air may be forced into the conditioner.

A recent development in the conditioning of air is known as the *heat pump*. This type of apparatus provides fully automatic, year-round air conditioning, cooling in summer and heating in winter. It uses electricity exclusively and does not require any fuel.

The heat pump is like a two-way refrigerator. In the summer, the inside of the house becomes like the inside of a refrigerator. Heat is "pumped" from the house to the outside by having the heat-absorbing evaporator coils operate in the conditioned space while the heat-losing condenser is on the outside of the house. For winter heating, the process is reversed: the heat-absorbing evaporator is outdoors (air even at low temperatures, as you recall, has heat in it) and heat is "pumped" to the heat-losing condenser in the house. Thus, there is year-round air conditioning.

SOLAR ENERGY

All heat on the earth, save that obtained from the interior of atoms (see chapter 19A) comes, in the last analysis, from the sun. Not only does the sun warm the earth, but energy from sunlight makes it possible for plants to synthesize the food that provides fuel for their own needs and for the animals that eat them. The heat of the sun causes water to be evaporated from oceans into clouds. Falling as rain on the mountains, the water from the clouds rushes down to the sea in streams and rivers. In the path of the falling water, engineers place turbines hitched to generators which convert its wild energy into useful electricity. The common fuels we use, whether gas, oil, coal, or wood, are the remains of products of organisms that derived their original energy from the sun.

Coal, natural gas, and oil, the so-called "fossil fuels," are limited in their supply. In the long run, these fuels will be exhausted; natural gas first, then oil, and finally coal.

That is why all over the world there is an intense search for new sources of heat energy. Atomic energy is now being developed for that purpose. However, even atomic energy at present is limited by our supplies of uranium and thorium. If we could harness the H-bomb, nuclear fusion (discussed in chapter 19A) could supply us with an endless supply of energy, since our supply of hydrogen is practically limitless. But we have not been able to do this as yet.

Perhaps the solution to the problem is staring us in the face when we look up at the sky—in the sun itself, which for millions of years has poured its essentially perpetual energy on us. The energy the United States receives from the sun in about two hours is equivalent to the energy produced by our present fuel consumption in a whole year.

Why don't we use some of this vast supply? Various attempts have been made to

This solar oven utilizes four flat mirrors that reflect sunlight into the interior of the stove. Dr. Maria Telkes, its inventor, is sampling some sun-cooked hamburger.

utilize the heat of the sun directly. So-called sun machines, by concentrating the sun's rays upon a small area by means of a number of mirrors or lenses, have been able to change water into steam and thus furnish power. Some of these devices have been used experimentally to melt metals; temperatures up to 6,000° F. have been obtained in this way. A great deal of experimentation is now going on in a number of countries to develop efficient solar engines. Thus far, however, the cost of solar machines has made their use uneconomical in competition with conventional methods. One possible exception may be the small solar cooker that is being tested in torrid areas where fuel is scarce, as in parts of India.

The sun's rays have been used in another way, in subtropical and even temperate climates, to furnish part of the heat needed in homes. You may be familiar with the fact that the inside of an automobile becomes quite warm, even in cool weather, if the sun is shining in and if the windows are closed. Glass admits much of the radiant energy from the sun. This is changed to heat energy when it strikes the upholstery in the interior of the car. The heat accumulates, and the car warms up.

The principle underlying this is often called the "hothouse effect" because it accounts for the warmth that builds up in a gardener's hothouse in the winter. Here, again, the large expanse of glass permits the sun's rays to penetrate and to warm the soil and other materials in the hothouse. Of course, these heated substances also broadcast heat waves, but these are different from the original solar waves, so that instead of passing out through the glass roofs and walls they bounce back. Ordinary window glass, then, has the unique property of being transparent to 90 percent of the *sun's* radiant heat energy, but opaque to the heat reradiated by objects under the glass. A hothouse is thus an energy trap.

This principle has been used in "solar houses," which have been developed by engineers and architects. In these houses, much of the walls consists of glass. Such houses require little artificial heat even on winter days in as cold a climate as that of

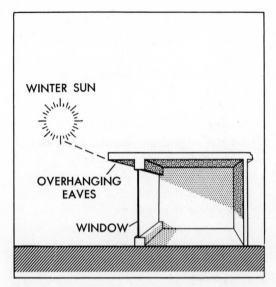

This schematic diagram shows how a solar house is warmed by the sun in winter and yet not overheated during the summer. Remember that the sun is much lower in the sky in winter than it is in summer.

Chicago—provided that the sun is shining. Fuel bills, of course, have been materially reduced as a result. Overhanging eaves prevent the summer sun's rays from entering the house, as shown in the drawing on this page.

The sun's radiation may be used to heat water. Solar water-heaters have been used for many years in California and Florida. One type has blackened coils of pipe under a glass cover that is placed on roofs of houses and tilted in a southerly direction to receive as much radiation as possible. When the sun is shining, the water becomes warm and circulates to radiators, or it may be used for washing.

Solar energy is now being converted directly into electrical energy by *solar batteries*. The principle is not new; the photoelectric meter, used in photography and the "seeing eye" for opening doors, converts light into electricity. These, however, are not very efficient; only one-half of 1 percent of the sun's light energy is changed into electricity. The solar battery is about 20 times as effi-

cient. However, it is still not economically feasible to produce electricity on a large scale in this way. Solar batteries are used to supply electrical energy for equipment in many of the artificial satellites, such as the spacecraft Syncom depicted in the frontispiece of this chapter. The many cells shown on its cylindrical surface convert sunlight into electrical energy needed by this communication satellite.

HEAT AND SPACE

Astronauts must cope with extremes in temperature in order to survive in space. Above the protective layer of the insulating atmosphere, the side of a space vehicle facing the sun is red hot, while the side in the shade is freezing. To equalize the difference in temperature, some kind of an air-conditioning system inside the spaceship is required.

On long trips, it might be practicable to regulate the internal temperature by having the ship rotate so that all sides have equal exposure to the sun's radiation. Another way of moderating the temperature could be achieved by painting the space vehicle in a pattern of black stripes (to absorb radiation) and silvery, polished stripes (to reflect radiation).

The first astronauts to land on the moon will arrive during the two-week lunar day. The temperature of the surface onto which they first step will be close to 214° F., about the boiling point of water. A pair of thick, well-insulated shoes should take care of the heat conducted directly from the ground. However, the radiation from the sun, together with the reradiated energy from the moon's surface impinging on the astronaut's space suit will be searing. Consequently, a lunar astronaut will have to carry a back-pack cooling system. If the astronaut moves into the shadow of a lunar cave, he will experience a sudden drop in temperature, since there is no air on the moon to conduct and convect surface heat into sunless places. He might have to turn off his cooling equipment and turn on his heating system!

When spaceships leave or enter the earth's atmosphere they, like meteors, experience great heating because of the frictional resistance of the air. High temperatures may develop, ranging from 10,000° F. to 18,000° F., which can be damaging to the vehicle and lethal for its occupants. Spaceships are designed to minimize this danger. They are shaped to avert the building up of heat. In addition, special materials are used that can withstand high temperatures. In spaceships such as the Mercury, special heat shields absorb most of the heat and protect the part which houses the astronaut.

Spaceships entering or leaving the moon would have no frictional heat problems, because, as we have seen, the moon has no atmosphere. For each of the planets we wish to explore, we must plan to meet the special heat problems related to landing, living, and leaving.

Some of the important generalizations in the foregoing material are:

A body has energy if it can do work.

Heat is a form of energy—the energy of moving molecules.

As a substance gets warmer, its molecules move more rapidly; as it cools, less rapidly.

Cooling is the removal of heat.

Substances generally expand when heated and contract when cooled.

Water is unique in that it expands just before it freezes; this explains why ice is lighter than water.

The temperature or heat intensity of a body is measured in degrees; the total quantity of heat in a body is measured in calories.

Substances exist in three states—gaseous, liquid, and solid.

The addition or removal of heat from a substance may cause it to change from one state into another.

Heat is transferred by conduction, convection, or radiation.

Different materials vary in their ability to conduct heat; those that conduct heat slowly are called insulators.

Clothing keeps us warm because it prevents the body from losing its heat too rapidly.

Clothing, blankets, and some home insulating materials are effective in preventing the loss of heat because they contain trapped air, which is a poor heat conductor.

Dark-colored materials absorb more radiant heat than light-colored materials.

Heating systems make use of all three methods of heat transfer.

Modern refrigerators utilize the cooling effects of evaporation in their operation.

Scientists and engineers are trying to trap some of the abundant energy of the sun for man's use.

To explore space successfully, it is necessary to cope with extremes of temperature.

DISCOVERING FOR YOURSELF

1. Find out as much as you can about the heat problems that must be solved in space travel.
2. Locate as many different kinds of thermometers in your environment as you can. Compare their construction, purpose, and operation.
3. Make a list of as many ways as you can observe in which heat is controlled in a kitchen.
4. Observe as many as possible of the sources of heat in your environment. List these sources.
5. Observe examples of heat causing materials (solids, liquids, gases) to expand.
6. Find examples of heat traveling by conduction, convection, and radiation.
7. Find examples of the use of insulation (against conduction, convection, and radiation) in your home and school.
8. Examine a refrigerator and a furnace to see how they use the principles of conduction, radiation, and convection.
9. Locate, observe, and describe different types of heating plants used in houses to find out the differences between them and the advantages of each.
10. Plan and perform an original experiment to show the advantage of wearing light-colored clothes in warm weather and dark clothes in cold weather.
11. Find out how man has experimented with the use of sunlight to heat water and to help heat houses.
12. Scientific supply companies sell radiometers (solar "meters") and solar energy "furnaces," both of which use the energy of the sun. Obtain and observe one of these devices and explain how it works.

We saw that
Heat Expanded
the air in the balloon
the water in the flask.
the mercury in the thermometer
the paint jar with the tight lid
the iron screw in the d...
the pavement in fro...
the surface of ...
the railroad tracks ...
bridge

oven

indoor
outdoor

CHAPTER 18B

Teaching "Heat and How We Use It"

Concepts about heat and heating have many applications in pupils' lives. The experiments that are performed lead to understandings that function in the room where they are learned as well as at home and elsewhere. Pupils can see how we use what we know about heat in making our homes and other buildings more comfortable to live in.

Heat may be, and often is, taught as a separate unit; or, some of the concepts may be learned as part of a weather unit (see chapter 9B) or studied in connection with a unit on molecules, electricity, space, atomic energy, and needs of living things. Heat is associated with many phenomena. The material has been assembled here as a unit but it may be used by the teacher in any of the ways that suit her needs.

The experiments are not ends in themselves; they are used as a means of making ideas clearer and their applications are important. Some of the experiences particularly suitable for primary grades are listed below. Of course, many of the other activities suggested throughout this chapter can also be used for younger children.

1. Look for different sources of heat and tell how heat is helpful in each case.
2. Keep a chart of the temperature as it changes from day to day. Some of the older pupils can learn to read the thermometer.
3. See the relationship between the position of the fluid in a thermometer and the children's feeling of warmness or coolness.

4. Put water in places of different temperatures to see how heat affects the rate of evaporation.
5. Look for different places where thermometers are used and find out why it is important to know the temperatures in these places.
6. Find out how rapidly wet doll clothes and other wet things dry under varying conditions—heat, wind, spreading clothes versus bunching up, etc.
7. See what happens to dew on the grass as the sun gets higher in the sky. Feel the warmth of the sun on the window sill and on faces.
8. Use heat to bake cookies, boil water, or for other activities in the schoolroom.
9. Feel heat at its source (radiator or hot air register) in the room.
10. See the importance of refrigeration by keeping milk or other food in and out of a refrigerator and observing the results.
11. Set a pan of water outdoors on a freezing day to observe that ice forms at the top, and that ice floats. Put a glass jar full of water (with screwed-on top) outside in freezing weather to see that it cracks. (A refrigerator may be used for both experiences.)
12. Place hands in shoes that pupils have just taken off and compare the "feel" with shoes that have not been worn for some time to see that their feet warm their shoes and not vice versa.
13. Feel soil, sidewalk, pan of water, in the sun and in the shade to discover that the sun heats things on the earth.

FINDING SOURCES OF HEAT

Pupils may make a list of as many different sources of heat as possible—for example, friction, electricity, fires, atomic energy—and tell some of the things that heat from each of these sources does for them. Then they may try to trace each of the sources back to the sun. This activity may raise several questions about heat and is therefore useful in introducing the study of how we use heat. These questions may form the beginning of a list of problems to solve, to which more will be added both by the pupils and by the teacher as the study continues.

STUDYING THERMOMETERS

The principle of the thermometer is not difficult to understand, and it is easy to demonstrate (see drawing page 451). Use a Pyrex flask, a one-holed rubber stopper to fit, and a 1½-foot piece of glass tubing that will fit into the hole of the stopper. Fill the flask with water that has been colored with a few drops of red ink or vegetable coloring to make it easier to watch. Fit the glass tubing into the stopper so that a little of the tubing extends through the stopper. Fit the stopper into the flask firmly. A little of the water should extend up into the tube. Tie a piece of thread around the tube at the level of the water. Now heat the flask and watch the water level in the tube. (It rises as heat expands the water.) Mark the level with another piece of thread. Now cool the water by setting the flask in cold water or by rubbing it with ice. Watch the level of the water fall. Cooling contracts the water. A Pyrex baby bottle may be used if a flask is not available.

To introduce the idea of *measurement* and the unit of measurement—the degree—fasten an index card to the tube with scotch tape. Place the flask up to its neck in a jar of hot water. Let it stand for about half an hour, or until the water stops rising in the tube. Then with a thermometer, take the temperature of the water in the jar. Mark the card at the level of the water in the tube and next to it write the temperature just read. Now place the flask in a jar of cold water and let it stay there for about half an hour, or until the water stops falling in the tube. Again take the water temperature, and mark it on the card.

With these two points you have a basis for making a *scale* of degrees. Mark off the degrees between the two points, and then below and above them.

In order to use this crude thermometer over a period of time it will be necessary to place a drop of oil on top of the water in the tube to prevent evaporation. Also, if it is to be used outdoors in cold weather it will have to be remade, using about ¾ water and ¼ alcohol to prevent freezing. Your pupils may want to make their own thermometers, using any bottles which are available, a clear plastic "pea-shooter" tube, and a makeshift bottle top with an appropriate hole for the tube.

OBSERVING THE EFFECTS OF HEATING

There are many ways for pupils to see for themselves that heating makes solids, liquids, and gases expand and that cooling makes these materials contract. Following are examples:

TO SEE WHAT HEATING DOES TO A PIECE OF
COPPER WIRE AND TO OTHER SOLIDS

The screw and screw eye pictured are substitutes for the commercially available ball and ring often used to show that solids expand when they are heated and contract when they are cooled. The handles are made of 1½-inch dowel about a foot long. With a nail make a hole in one end of each stick. The large screw eye is screwed into the end of one stick and the large screw head (just too large to go into the eye) is screwed into the other. When the screw eye is heated, it expands so that the screw will go through it.

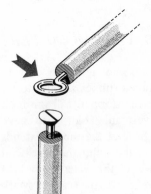

This screw and eye may be used to show that a solid expands when heated and contracts when cooled.

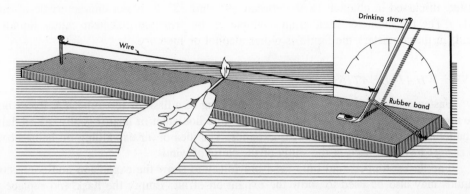

This improvised scale helps the experimenters see how much expansion takes place as the wire is heated. Use a candle as the source of heat if the heat from a match is not sufficient.

Although these experiments do not show that *all* solids expand when they are heated and contract when they are cooled, pupils should perform other experiments, which they will find in books and elsewhere, and should read to substantiate this idea. Pupils should be urged to find other solids which are expanded by heat and contracted by cold. Examples are telephone and telegraph wires, pavements, sections of railroad tracks, and iron bridges. In some cases pupils can also observe how allowance is made for this expansion and contraction—for example, leaving spaces between sections of concrete sidewalks.

TO SEE WHAT HEATING DOES TO WATER

Use the same apparatus as was used to demonstrate the principle of the thermometer. Applications of the principle that heat expands water are evident in automobile radiators,

This flask filled with colored water can be used to show how heat causes a liquid to expand. The string tied around the tube marks the level of the water before it has been heated.

in our hot-water heaters, and in other places where liquids are heated. (The unusual behavior of water, discussed in chapter 18A, between 39° and 32° F. is not characteristic of other liquids.) The thermometer itself is an example of the principle that heat causes liquids to expand; in thermometers the liquid is either alcohol or mercury.

TO SEE WHAT HEATING DOES TO AIR

Fasten a toy rubber balloon over the opening of a flask or test tube. (A Pyrex baby bottle may also be used.) Set the glass container into hot water or heat it gently over a flame. The balloon begins to fill up as the gas expands. The idea of air expanding on being heated (and rising) has been used in the study of the cause of winds.

The flask, stopper, and tube used previously to show the expansion and contraction of liquids may also be used to show the expansion of air. Empty the flask and replace the stopper with the tube. Invert it so that the end of the tube is in a glass of water. Warming the flask, even by holding both hands around it, will be sufficient to cause air bubbles to escape from the tube into the water. When the air cools, it contracts, and water will go up the tube into the flask.

TO SEE THAT HEATING AND COOLING CHANGE THE FORM OF MATTER

To show that temperature changes affect the form of matter, use variations of the experiments performed to show this principle in connection with the study of molecules and atoms. (See page 479.)

TO SEE THAT EVAPORATION COOLS

There are many simple experiences that help pupils realize that evaporation of a liquid from a surface causes the surface to become cool. Let a child wet one of his hands and fan it briskly. He will note that his hand becomes dry and cool. It is important for pupils to realize that when heat is taken away from anything it becomes cool. Heat is absorbed in the evaporation of water. (As pupils will remember from earlier experiments, heat helps evaporation.) The heat to evaporate the water comes from the surface of the skin; consequently the pupil's hand becomes cool.

An easy way to tell the direction of the wind is to go outdoors, wet the index finger, and hold it up as high as you can. The side of the finger that faces the wind feels cool. Pupils will recall having been sponged with alcohol when ill. Alcohol evaporates rapidly and the cooling is rapid.

TO SEE THE EFFECT OF HEAT ON LIGHT AND DARK OBJECTS[1]

There are many ways to show that dark objects absorb heat more readily than light ones. The tin cans shown in the drawing have lids that fit tightly. One is painted black, or it may be darkened by holding it over a lighted candle so that carbon will form on it, and

---

[1] G. O. Blough and M. H. Campbell, *Making and Using Classroom Science Materials in the Elementary School* (New York, Holt, Rinehart and Winston, 1954), p. 171.

The two cans, one darkened by soot from a candle or black paint, the other painted white, may be set in bright sunlight to show its effect on light and dark objects. The two thermometers fit through slits made in the can covers.

the other is painted white, or it may be left with its tin surface unpainted. Each can top has a hole in it just a little larger than the thermometer that extends through to the inside. Set the two cans in the bright sunlight and keep a record of the thermometer readings. Pupils should be able to apply the findings from this dark-and-light experiment to explain why dark and light clothing is worn at different seasons or in different parts of the world. Light and dark pieces of cloth spread on the snow show similar results when the sun shines. The snow under the dark piece of cloth melts more rapidly. One application of the principle involved here is in the design of space ships where dark outside surfaces may be utilized to absorb heat energy from the sun's rays, and white surfaces may reflect the energy. By the proper use of such surfaces, satisfactory temperatures for human beings may be maintained within the ships.

As we have indicated in other chapters, it is important that children exercise caution in drawing conclusions from these experiences. Testing a few materials to see how they respond to heat, for example, will not produce sufficient evidence on which to base sweeping generalizations. The observations must be supplemented by further experiences and by reading.

EXPERIMENTING TO SEE HOW HEAT TRAVELS

An understanding of how heat is transferred from one place to another is important if pupils are to understand how their homes are heated and how temperature is controlled in other ways. It is not important for them to be able to define the terms convection, radiation, and conduction. In fact, many elementary pupils may not need to use these terms at all. They need only understand that heat travels in different ways, then come to understand how we make use of this knowledge. It is the application of such knowledge that is important. There are many kinds of experiments that pupils can perform. Some examples are given here; others will be found in textbooks and supplementary books.

TO SEE THAT AIR CARRIES HEAT

Use a lamp chimney and a candle. Light the candle and set the chimney over it on two blocks to raise it above the table surface. Note the warm air at the top of the chimney. Hold a smoking paste stick or other wooden stick at the bottom of the chimney, and the

As the flame heats the air inside the chimney, the air becomes lighter; cooler, heavier air entering the chimney at the bottom forces it up. Outdoors, such unequal heating of the air produces wind. Indoors, convection currents from heating sources (radiators, registers, etc.) heat all parts of the room.

smoke will show that air is moving into the bottom of the chimney and is traveling up past the flame to the top of the chimney. It is this moving air that carries the heat. Hold a thermometer a foot above the top of the chimney and note changes as the air is warmed. Hot-air heating systems operate on the principle of cold air pushing the warm air into the rooms that are to be heated by the furnace.

Convection currents are continually at work all around us. Winds are convection currents. If a thermometer is held near a register or radiator, it will show that the air is being warmed there. Hold the thermometer up near the ceiling either by standing on a stepladder or by attaching the thermometer to a window pole. Pupils will see that warm air has reached the ceiling. When they study the ways in which their homes are heated, they will apply what they have learned about convection as a method of heat transfer.

TO SEE THAT WATER CARRIES HEAT

Fill a flask or Pyrex baby bottle nearly full of water and heat it at the bottom. Hold a thermometer in the water at the top. It soon shows that the water is getting hot. The water at the bottom is traveling to the top, carrying the heat with it. Some grains of sand or pieces of sawdust placed in the water will show how the currents are traveling. In hot-water heating systems, heat is carried to the upstairs rooms by circulating water. The unequal heating of the water causes the movement.

TO SEE THAT HEAT IS CARRIED BY RADIATION

A fire, a candle, a toaster, or any other hot object radiates heat. Light a candle and hold a block of paraffin alongside it. The paraffin melts on the side near the flame. The higher temperature above the candle is due to convection currents, but the higher temperature beside it is caused by radiation.

TO SEE THAT SOLIDS CARRY HEAT

Place a spoon in a glass of hot water or other hot liquid. Feel the handle from time to time to note that it is getting hot. The heat has traveled along the spoon by conduction. Hot pans on the kitchen stove and fireplace tools conduct heat in this way. Pupils may compare a metal spoon with a plastic spoon to see how they differ in carrying heat.

After these experiments have been performed, pupils should be asked to look for places in their environment where heat travels from one place to another—at home, at school, in restaurants, and elsewhere. Kitchens, fireplaces, furnaces, etc., all depend, of course, upon heat transfer. This investigating will probably lead to questions about other phases of the problem of heat control—insulation and home heating.

OBSERVING THE USE OF
HEAT INSULATION

Applications of heat insulation are easy to find. Pupils should understand that the purpose of insulation is to prevent heat from going where we do not want it to go. In the school cafeteria, pupils may find out how food is kept hot. In addition, they may see that wood is used for handles of pots and cloth is used for pot holders. They may investigate refrigerators to see how insulation is used in them. They may see some of the same things in the kitchen at home.

The school custodian will be very helpful in showing pupils how heat insulators are used to retain heat in the building and in steam or other heating pipes.

It may be that the homes of some of the pupils have recently been improved with additional insulation. If so, pupils may report how the insulation was installed and, if possible, bring samples of the insulating material used. In all probability the telephone directory will carry names of builders who specialize in insulating materials. They may supply samples of different types of such materials and may have printed material that shows how the insulating material is installed. If there is a new house under construction in the neighborhood, a committee of pupils may make arrangements for a brief visit to observe how insulation is being installed.

Draw attention to "Jiffy" (insulated) bags in which ice cream is often bought. Pupils will be interested in examining the structure of the bags to see how they keep heat out.

Pupils will be interested to discover that wool usually keeps things warmer than cotton by doing the following experiment:[2] Fill three jars to the top with hot water and cover them tightly. Wipe the outside of the jars dry. Now pull a woolen sock around one jar, covering it as though it were your foot. Pull a cotton sock over the second jar. Leave the third jar as it is. Place all three jars in a cool place. After about a half hour, remove the socks and feel all the jars.

In addition to feeling the jars, place a thermometer in each and read the temperature. Such simple experiments as this serve to help pupils understand better some of the things they do every day. The third jar used as a control illustrates the emphasis that has continually been placed throughout this book on the use of the scientific attitude in experimenting.

LEARNING ABOUT HEATING SYSTEMS

A study of both the home and the school heating systems will show how the principles that have been learned are applied. Here is opportunity for planning by pupils. They may begin by settling these two problems: "What kind of plan can we develop to find out how our schoolroom is heated?" "How can we learn about how our homes are heated?" As pupils

---

[2] J. Schwartz, *It's Fun To Know Why* (New York, Whittlesey House, 1952), pp. 63–64. (Also available in paperback edition.)

consider the plan for studying the school heating system, they may decide (1) to ask the school custodian to help them by taking them to see the furnace and explaining the system to them; (2) to prepare a list of questions they want to ask the custodian, such as: "What type of furnace is it?" "What fuel is used?" "Where do the pipes lead?" and so forth; (3) to make simple diagrams that show how the furnace operates, how the heat is carried to the rooms, and how it circulates in their own classroom.

Pupils may make a similar plan for the study of their home heating system. The questions for home investigating should be definite. Examples are: "What kind of fuel is used?" "Is the furnace a hot-air, hot-water, or steam furnace?" "Where is insulation used?" "Is the heating system a good one for the house?" "Why or why not?" "If there is a thermostat, how does it work?" The thermostat operates on the principle of expansion and contraction already studied, and some of the more interested pupils may be able to explain the operation to the class.

RESOURCES TO INVESTIGATE

1. Local builders to see how homes are equipped for good heating and how they are insulated. Children's homes to see how they are heated and insulated.
2. The kitchen at home (or at school) to see how heat is controlled in utensils, stoves, refrigerators, and other equipment.
3. A bakery to find out about sources and control of heat and about utensils that are used.
4. Home economics departments for literature concerning cooking utensils and preservation of foods.
5. State university extension service for materials describing the heating of farm buildings, greenhouses, hotbeds, and other places.
6. The school building and the school custodian to learn how the school heating plant works and what science principles are involved in its operation.
7. Buildings or homes equipped with air conditioning.

CHAPTER 19A

Atomic Energy and Its Uses

Earlier in this book we looked into the vastness of space, at planets, stars, galaxies, and supergalaxies, trying to find some order in the universe. Later (in chapter 16A, which is introductory to this one) we focused on the minute molecules and atoms that make up the matter of the universe. Let us now increase our magnification to "see" the architecture *within* the atom, to find there the smallest specks yet discovered and at the same time to discover the greatest source of energy in nature.

The word *atom*, first used by the Greeks about 400 B.C. to identify what they considered to be the smallest particles of matter, means *indivisible*. But the investigations of the twentieth century have taught us that atoms are *divisible*, and that they are made of smaller, more fundamental particles.

MODEL OF AN ATOM

To learn more about these particles, SEE PAGES 479 TO 480 let us look at some atoms closely. Sir Ernest Rutherford, the father of modern atomic physics, was the first to construct a model of the interior of the atom. According to this model, a single atom is a kind of miniature solar system. In the center, corresponding to the sun, is a structure called the *nucleus*. Whirling around the nucleus, like planets, are particles called *electrons*.

Consider a specific atom, that of the element hydrogen. The hydrogen atom is the lightest and simplest of all atoms. Its nucleus consists of a single particle, called a *proton*. Around this proton, a single electron whirls round and round, as depicted in the diagram on page 458.

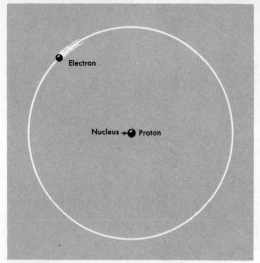

The hydrogen atom (above) has one electron whirling around a nucleus consisting of one proton. A helium atom (middle) has two electrons revolving (cont. below)

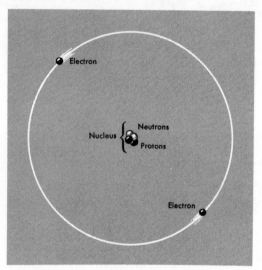

around a nucleus made of two protons and two neutrons. A carbon atom (below) has six electrons revolving around a nucleus made of six protons and six neutrons.

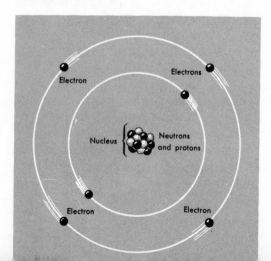

Electrons are extremely light atomic particles possessing a quantity of electricity which has been designated a *negative charge*. The electron rotates at terrific speeds around the nucleus and at a relatively great distance from it. It is held in its orbit by the nucleus, just as the earth is kept from flying off into space by the attraction of the sun. In the case of the atom, however, the attraction is due to the equal but opposite *positive charge* of electricity of the proton in the nucleus. Although the electrical charges of the electron and proton are equal, their weights are markedly different, the proton being about two thousand times as heavy as the electron.

A hydrogen atom, then, consists of one electron and one proton. Let us turn now to the heavier atoms. After hydrogen, the next heavier atom is helium. What is the architecture of a helium atom? Revolving around the nucleus are *two* electrons. As you might expect, these are prevented from flying off into space by *two* protons in the nucleus. But helium (and every other kind of atom but hydrogen) has a third kind of fundamental particle in its nucleus: the *neutron*. Helium has two neutrons. The neutron weighs about the same as a proton, but, as its name implies, it is electrically neutral—it has no electric charge.

Electrons, protons, neutrons—these seem to be the fundamental particles of atoms. (Atomic scientists have discovered others, but we will limit our consideration to these three.) As we examine atoms of the heavier elements, we find that they contain more protons and neutrons in the nucleus and more electrons outside the nucleus. In each case, the number of protons exactly equals the number of electrons. Thus, carbon has 6 protons and 6 electrons; oxygen 8 protons and 8 electrons; radium 88 protons and 88 electrons.

Just as it was hard to visualize the immense dimensions in the astronomical universe, so it is equally difficult to picture the tiny dimensions on the atomic scale.

Rule a one-inch line on a piece of paper. If you could line up hydrogen atoms along this one-inch line, there would be room for 250 million of them. Yet an electron is only 1/100,000 the size of one of these hydrogen atoms!

We found before that an atom is a sort of miniature solar system. Most of the *real* solar system, as we learned earlier, consists of empty space. The proportion of empty space, however, in an atom is ten thousand times as great as in the solar system. Assume that we want to make a giant model of an oxygen atom. If we make the nucleus of this atom fifteen hundred feet across (the length of five football fields) and place it in the center of the United States,

then its outer electrons would move in an orbit that would touch New York and San Francisco.

Indeed, all matter is filled with empty space. It has been estimated that if a giant hand could squeeze all the empty space out of the earth, until the nuclei of all its atoms touched each other, then our planet could be compressed to the size of a ball only one-half mile in diameter.

UP THE ATOMIC LADDER

There is a wonderful ladder in nature, a ladder of atoms. Begin at the first rung with one electron and one proton, and you

The space within an atom is vast compared to the size of its particles. This diagram gives some notion of where the 8 electrons of an oxygen atom would be if the nucleus of the atom were enlarged so that its diameter was one-third of a mile.

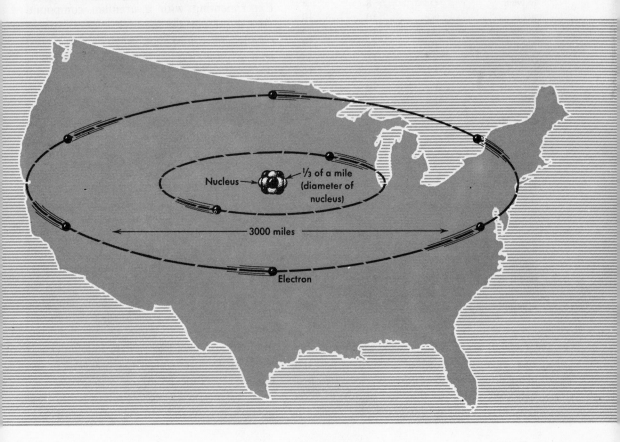

have hydrogen. Climb a rung to where there are two electrons and two protons and you have helium. Three electrons and three protons give you lithium. Rung by rung, adding one electron and one proton each time, without a break, you climb, passing atom after atom, as shown in the table, until you reach the highest rung. This has 92 electrons and 92 protons. It is uranium, the heaviest of the atoms found in nature. The number of neutral particles, or neutrons, increases too, but not in this simple arithmetic way.

The following table includes some of the familiar atoms:

Name	Symbol	No. of electrons (and protons)	No. of neutrons
hydrogen	H	1	0
helium	He	2	2
lithium	Li	3	4
carbon	C	6	6
nitrogen	N	7	7
oxygen	O	8	8
neon	Ne	10	10
aluminum	Al	13	14
phosphorus	P	15	16
sulfur	S	16	16
chlorine	Cl	17	18
calcium	Ca	20	20
iron	Fe	26	30
nickel	Ni	28	31
copper	Cu	29	34
zinc	Zn	30	35
arsenic	As	33	42
silver	Ag	47	61
tin	Sn	50	69
iodine	I	53	74
wolfram (tungsten)	W	74	110
platinum	Pt	78	117
gold	Au	79	118
mercury	Hg	80	121
lead	Pb	82	125
radon	Rn	86	136
radium	Ra	88	138
uranium	U	92	146

It is apparent that the essential difference between a substance like lead and one like gold lies in the *number* of electrons, protons, and neutrons that the atoms of these substances contain; the *kinds* of particles in each is the same. Thus, the medieval alchemists' dream of transmuting one element into another was not so far fetched after all, since all atoms are made of the same stuff. As we will soon see, moreover, the changing of atoms into other kinds of atoms occurs in nature as well as in the experiments of atomic scientists.

ATOMIC ENERGY

We have taken a quick look into SEE PAG 480 the interior of the atom and have become acquainted with some of its basic furniture. Let us now turn to a consideration of the energy hidden in it. Return to the year 1898, when the internal atomic architecture just described was unknown, when atoms were still thought of as hard, unbreakable, indivisible structures. In that year the Frenchman, Henri Becquerel, made a surprising discovery. Experimenting with a uranium compound (derived from the natural mineral, pitchblende) he found that, when it was placed near a photographic film *in total darkness*, the uranium made an impression that showed up when the film was developed. This happened even when a piece of black paper separated the film from the uranium. To understand Becquerel's astonishment, imagine yours if you were to accidentally snap the shutter of a camera in a totally dark room and find, on developing the film, an image of a necklace of pearls wrapped in a dark silken scarf that happened to be lying on the table.

Evidently the uranium compound was emitting a radiation that could pass through a sheet of paper and affect a photographic film without any outside stimulus. This was no ordinary chemical reaction, one which would soon come to an end. The uranium continued to radiate indefinitely. If this was not a chemical reaction, where did the energy come from?

The Curies became interested in Becquerel's discoveries. In the process of preparing uranium compounds, they discovered a new kind of atom, radium, which was much more active than uranium. They found that a purified sample of radium remained warmer than its surroundings and continued to radiate without dimming. In a few days, the radium emitted more energy than could be obtained from the explosion of an equal weight of TNT. But the explosion of TNT is a chemical change, in which the chemical energy is released instantaneously in a flash of light and heat. The energy of the radium, however, was steadily maintained, day after day, month after month, year after year. In 1,590 years only half of its energy would be expended.

In tracking down the source of this tremendous quantity of energy, scientists devised various tools to study the nature of radiations emanating from the radium. With these tools, three distinct varieties of radiation were found: *alpha particles, beta particles,* and *gamma rays.* As you read the following, keep in mind that scientists did not know, at the beginning of this century, that electrons, protons, and neutrons are basic parts of the atom.

Alpha particles, flying from the radium atoms at the speed of 20,000 miles a second, are specks of matter with a positive electrical charge. These were later identified as particles containing two protons and two neutrons, which, you may recall, is exactly what the nucleus of a helium atom is made of.

Beta particles, coming from uranium atoms at the speed of 160,000 miles per second, are negatively charged. These are electrons.

Gamma rays, with much greater power to penetrate than the alpha or beta particles, are akin to x-rays.

Out of radium atoms . . . came particles and energy. Thus began scientists' understanding of the architecture of atoms— of their component protons and electrons— and of the vast reservoir òf energy stored in them.

SOME ATOMS SPLIT NATURALLY.
What was the source of uranium's penetrating rays? What was the source of radium's radiations, including the high-speed particles that flew out of it? Scientists found that some of the atoms of these substances were *splitting*, without man's intervention, to form new kinds of atoms, releasing radiations at the same time. Radium and uranium are but two of a group of atoms that possess *natural radioactivity*. You can see evidence of splitting atoms if you look at the luminescent dial of a watch or clock with a magnifying glass in a darkened room. After your eyes have become accommodated to the darkness, you will see many flashes, each one representing the splitting of a single radioactive atom.

ATOMIC ARTILLERY.
The discovery of natural radioactivity not only gave scientists the clues to atomic architecture and atomic energy, it also provided them with ammunition for splitting *other* atoms. One of the bullets used was the high-speed alpha particle that could penetrate the usually impenetrable nucleus of an atom. Using alpha particles, Rutherford was able to achieve the first laboratory-controlled transmutation of an element in 1919, the first artificial changing of one atom into another. With an alpha particle as his bullet and a nitrogen atom as his target, he was able to drive an extra proton into the nucleus of the nitrogen atom. If you consult the chart on page 460 you will see that nitrogen normally has seven protons. Add one proton, and you have oxygen, with eight protons in its nucleus! Rutherford had transmuted nitrogen into oxygen.

As these discoveries became known, scientists were electrified with the new ideas implicit in them.

Atoms were no longer the basic units of the universe.

Atoms were composed of more elementary parts.

Atoms were divisible.

Atoms of one element could be transmuted into entirely new atoms.

Atoms had a vast potential of energy locked in them, far exceeding anything previously known.

$$E = MC^2$$

This algebraic expression may well become the most significant equation in all history. To understand it, we must go back to about 1900, to the then prevailing theories of the conservation of matter and the conservation of energy. Let us talk of matter first. We learned in chapter 16A that in chemical and physical changes matter may be altered in form or shape, but it is never lost, never destroyed. This principle is called the conservation of matter. Our brief reference to energy in relation to heat in chapter 18A suggested that energy too was not lost, but it was merely changed into other forms, appearing as heat, motion, light, etc. The principle of the conservation of energy states that energy cannot be created or destroyed but can only be changed into other forms.

Until 1905 these two principles reigned. Then Einstein came along and tied them together. According to Einstein matter could be converted into energy and energy into matter. Matter *could* be destroyed— but it would reappear as energy. Energy *could* be destroyed but matter would be created. This interchangeability of matter and energy was expressed in the now famous formula:

$$E = MC^2$$

E represents energy, M is mass (the amount of matter) and C is the speed of light (about 186,000 miles a second).

Energy equals mass times the speed of light times the speed of light.

Notice that energy is one side of the equation and mass (matter) is on the other. If the proper values were substituted in this equation, it would reveal that an extremely

small amount of material could be transformed into an enormous amount of energy, since the speed of light is 186,000 miles a second. If, for example, we were able to destroy completely all the atoms in a pail of sand, we would produce enough energy to supply the electric power requirements of the United States for a number of years.

All this was theory scribbled on pieces of paper, until scientists began to tinker with atoms. The proof then came from a careful study of the weight of material that went into an atomic reaction and the weight of material and the amount of energy that came out.

If you smash a piece of old furniture into kindling, all of the pieces (including the dust) when put together weigh as much as the original. When an atom is split, however, the sum of its pieces—new atoms and particles—is *less* than the original atom. What happens to the missing mass?

Scientists found that the loss of matter was accounted for by the gain in free energy, just as Einstein had predicted. Some of the energy appears as the high-speed motion of the fragments, some as wave energy.

NEUTRON BULLETS FOR CHAIN REACTIONS

All of this added up to the fact that an exceedingly small amount of matter could be transformed into a large amount of energy. A new world of power was opening up for man, if he could learn to tap the energy of the millions of atoms that were available to him, if he could find effective "bullets" in sufficient quantity to split billions of atoms and cause them to release some of their energy. The "bullets" employed before 1939 for splitting atoms were woefully inadequate for this purpose. We were, as Einstein put it, like blind men shooting at birds in a country where there were not many birds. An important clue came in the use of neutrons of the nucleus. As you recall from our discussion of the atomic architecture, the neutron is a particle of about the same weight as a proton but neutral as far as its electrical properties are concerned. It was soon discovered that the fact that the neutron was electrically neutral made it a most effective projectile in the arsenal of atomic artillery, far superior to the high-speed alpha particles. These positively charged particles are strongly repelled as they approach the nucleus, which, as you recall, is also positively charged because of its protons. Like repels like in the world of electricity and magnetism. The number of hits, therefore, made by an alpha particle, is very small compared to the number of hits made by a neutron. In this neutral atomic particle we had the key to atomic energy on a vast scale.

Using the neutron on the heaviest of the natural elements, uranium, Hahn and Strassmann in 1939 found that they could induce uranium atoms to split into fragments, producing simpler, lighter atoms like those of barium. *This was man-ordered uranium fission!* True, this was no atom bomb. There was no explosion. The energy released, however, from the splitting atoms of uranium was far in excess of any previously produced in a laboratory.

Before we go on with the fission story, we must consider a characteristic of atoms which we have not yet mentioned. As found in nature, uranium comes in several forms. Each of these types is called an *isotope*. The most common isotope is uranium 238, called U-238. The number 238 is derived by adding the number of protons to the number of neutrons in the nucleus of this atom, thus obtaining what is called the *atomic weight*.

Thus in U-238:

$$\begin{array}{r} 92 \text{ protons} \\ +146 \text{ neutrons} \\ \hline 238 = \text{atomic weight.} \end{array}$$

Uranium-235, one of the isotopes of uranium, like U-238 has 92 protons. It has only 143 neutrons, however, which gives it

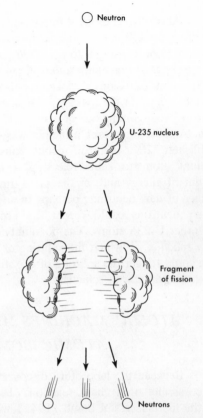

When the nucleus of a uranium-235 atom is split by a neutron, a vast amount of energy is released, as well as neutron "bullets" to split more U-235 atoms.

an atomic weight of 235. Since the chemical properties of an atom are determined by the number of protons and electrons, U-238 and U-235 are chemically identical; such chemical twins are called isotopes. The differences in weight, however, are of extreme importance in the realm of inner nuclear happenings. Most of the 92 atoms found in nature have these variant or isotopic forms.

Coming back to the uranium fission story, scientists were curious about which type of uranium was splitting. They found that, under the conditions of their experiments, only the U-235 atoms were splitting. This isotope is relatively rare in natural ores; there is only one U-235 atom for every 140 U-238 atoms.

Another fact of great importance was also discovered. When a neutron bombarded a U-235 atom, causing it to split, *other neutrons were shot out of the atom* along with the fragments of fission. Various investigators estimated that, on the average, two or three neutrons were coming out of a single U-235 atom. A most important principle was thus established. If a neutron could cause a uranium atom to split, releasing a large amount of energy and, at the same time, a number of new neutrons, perhaps these secondary neutrons could repeat the process with other U-235 atoms. The possibility of a *chain reaction*, in which the splitting of one atom could trigger the splitting of all, stirred the wildest dreams of scientists.

ATOMIC MACHINES AND ATOMIC BOMBS

Between the laboratory discovery of the possibility of a chain reaction (1940) and the first successful bomb (1945) was a period in which this dream was made a reality. The first period of the hunt between 1940 and 1942 resulted in the making of an atomic-energy machine, a predecessor of the modern peacetime atomic energy plant. From 1942 on, the problem for scientists working with the Army became the production of an atomic bomb.

THE NEUTRON POPULATION. The successful building of an atomic machine depended on the answers to questions like these:

Could a chain reaction really be kept going?

What would happen to the neutron population?

Could a chain reaction be controlled?

It will be helpful in considering these problems to think of a population of frogs in a pond. If the population is to remain steady, every couple (a male and female), on the average, must be responsible in their lifetime for the production of enough offspring so that two of them will survive to reproduce. If less than two survive, the population will decrease. If more than two survive, the population will increase. In atomic energy, the problem is the neutron population, for these are the bullets that split atoms. Let us consider a small number of U-235 atoms, one hundred, for example, that have just undergone fission in a mass of uranium containing both U-235 and U-238 atoms. Let us assume that each of these hundred atoms releases three neutrons. What will happen to these three hundred atomic bullets? Some may escape to the air. Others may be captured by U-238 atoms, which do not help in the chain reaction, since this form of uranium does not fission when bombarded with neutrons. Some neutrons may strike impurities in the material, which does not result in the production of more neutrons. Some of these neutron bullets, however, will strike U-235 atoms, which themselves will produce three new neutrons each and thus continue the chain.

The important question in the chain reaction was this: how many of the neutron bullets produced would be effective in bombarding new U-235 atoms. If 99 or less of the 300 were effective in splitting new U-235 atoms, the reaction would die down. It would not be a self-perpetuating chain. If 101 or more were effective, then we would have an ever-growing chain reaction. Each round of atomic fissions would result in more and more atoms undergoing fission. The net result—an atomic bomb. If the reaction could be regulated so that just 100 neutron bullets were effective, then we could have a controlled reaction. Atomic energy could be tapped for peaceful uses. (The term *atomic energy*, is, strictly speaking, not accurate. A better term is *nuclear energy*, since the energy comes from the nucleus of the atom. Both of these terms are in common usage.)

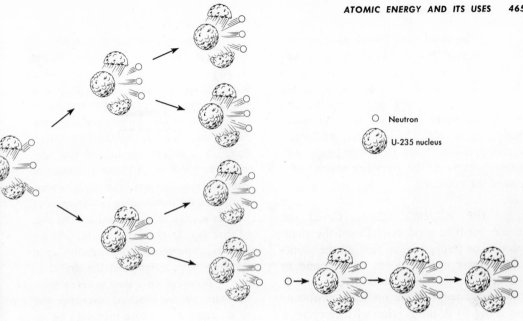

○ Neutron

U-235 nucleus

Left: *In an uncontrolled atomic reaction, as in an atomic bomb, the ever-growing chain reaction involves more and more atoms.*

Right: *In a controlled chain reaction the number of splitting atoms is maintained at a safe level.*

THE ATOMIC AGE BEGINS. The first atomic energy machine was built on a squash court, underneath the stands of Stagg Field at the University of Chicago. This machine, called an *atomic pile*, consisted of layers of uranium embedded in graphite. *Controls* made of strips of cadmium, which is a good neutron "robber," were inserted to regulate the reaction, to prevent the chain reaction from going too rapidly. The pile was built, layer upon layer until a *critical size* was reached, that is, a size that contained the right amount of uranium for a controlled reaction. On December 2, 1942, the pile received its first big test. To operate the pile, the cadmium strips were pulled out one by one. The intensity of neutrons increased rapidly as more and more U-235 atoms split, and then was maintained at a constant level. The machine worked! The atomic age had begun!

MORE FUEL. In an atomic pile there is a mixture of U-235 atoms and U-238 atoms. The U-235 atoms split when bombarded with neutrons and in turn release more neutrons. The U-238 atoms, on the other hand, absorb the neutrons into their nuclei but do not fission. What does this increase in neutron count do to the U-238 atoms? Before answering let us recall that, up to this point in history, 92 elements or kinds of atoms were known to man. In 1940, in an experiment in which U-238 was bombarded with atomic particles, two new elements, number 93, now called neptunium, and number 94, now called plutonium, were produced. When the atomic pile was invented it was found that this transmutation of atoms went on there also. Plutonium was a by-product resulting from the capture by U-238 of a neutron. Plutonium became important to atomic scientists because, like U-235, it fissions when it is bombarded with neutrons, releasing energy and more neutrons. Plutonium, then, could be used instead of the scarce U-235. A new source of atomic "fuel" thus became available.

(The word "fuel" when used in relation to atomic fission has an entirely different meaning from its use in relation to burning. In atomic fission the *nucleus* of the atom is split, releasing new particles and energy. In burning, which is a *chemical* change, atoms of the fuel join oxygen atoms, releasing energy from the interchange and rearrangements of the *electrons* which whirl around the nucleus.)

THE ATOMIC BOMB. Could an atomic bomb be produced? Could the chain reaction be stepped up so that all the atoms would fission in a millionth of a second to produce a gargantuan explosion? Or would it fizzle out slowly? Work on these problems was going on in the greatest of secrecy on a mesa about thirty miles from Santa Fe, New Mexico, at Los Alamos.

The effectiveness of a bomb depends on the liberation of a large amount of energy in a very small amount of time. To obtain this result in an atomic bomb, the chain reaction would have to produce an ever-increasing number of neutron "bullets" to hit their targets, the U-235 atoms. Experience with the pile and theoretical considerations showed that there was a size *below* which a mass of U-235 could not explode, because too many neutrons would escape from the surface of the mass and break the chain. On the other hand, if the bomb were *above* this *critical size*, it would go off at the very moment of its manufacture. How could the problem be solved?

In principle, it could be solved by separating the bomb into two masses *within its container* and then bringing the two masses together at the moment the explosion was desired. This could happen after the bomb was launched. The explosion would take place as soon as the two masses of U-235 atoms were joined, sparked by the spontaneous fissions of these atoms.

This was the theory—but would it work? The answer is best given in the words of the War Department account of the first atomic-bomb test, July 16, 1945:

Mankind's successful transition to a new age, the Atomic Age, was ushered in July 16, 1945, before the eyes of a tense group of renowned scientists and military men gathered in the desertlands of New Mexico to witness the first end-results of their $2,000,000,000 effort. Here in a remote section of the Alamogordo Air Base 120 miles southeast of Albuquerque the first man-made atomic explosion, the outstanding achievement of nuclear science, was achieved at 5:30 A.M. of that day. Darkening heavens, pouring forth rain and lightning immediately up to the zero hour, heightened the drama.

Mounted on a steel tower, a revolutionary weapon destined to change war as we know it, or which may even be the instrumentality to end all wars, was set off with an impact which signalized man's entrance into a new physical world. Success was greater than the most ambitious estimates. A small amount of matter, the product of a chain of huge specially constructed industrial plants, was made to release the energy of the universe locked up within the atom from the beginning of time. A fabulous achievement had been reached. Speculative theory, barely established in pre-war laboratories, had been projected into practicality. . . .

Nearest observation point was set up 10,000 yards south of the tower where in a timber and earth shelter the controls for the test were located. At a point 17,000 yards from the tower at a point which would give the best observation the key figures in the atomic bomb project took their posts. . . .

The time signals, "minus twenty minutes, minus fifteen minutes," and on and on increased the tension to the breaking point as the group in the control room which included Dr. Oppenheimer and General Farrell held their breaths, all praying with the intensity of the moment which will live forever with each man who was there. At "minus 45 seconds," robot mechanism took over and from that point on the whole great complicated mass of intricate mechanism was in operation without human control. . . .

At the appointed time there was a blinding flash lighting up the whole area brighter than the brightest daylight. A mountain range three miles from the observation point stood out in bold relief. Then came a tremendous sustained roar and a heavy pressure wave which knocked down two men outside the control center. Immediately thereafter, a huge multicolored surging cloud boiled to an altitude of over 40,000 feet. Clouds in its path disappeared. Soon the shifting substratosphere winds dispersed the now grey mass.

The test was over, the project a success.

The steel tower had been entirely vaporized. Where the tower had stood, there was a huge sloping crater. Dazed but relieved at the success of their tests, the scientists promptly marshalled their forces to estimate the strength of America's new weapon.

The Atomic Age had opened for good or for evil. Three weeks after the test, on August 6, 1945, an atomic bomb was dropped on Hiroshima, and three days later on Nagasaki, both with terrifying and devastating effects.

ATOMS FOR POWER

The constructive products of atomic energy are of two kinds, both created by the controlled nuclear fission in an atomic pile. One is heat, the other is a wide variety of new radioactive substances called *radioisotopes*.

THE ATOMIC PLANT. During the operation of an atomic pile, large amounts of energy in the form of heat are released by the splitting atoms. The great interest in atomic "fuel" is that it is such a compact source of heat. One pound of uranium has atomic energy equivalent to that obtained from the burning of three million pounds of coal. How do we harness this heat and put it to work? One way is to let it change water into steam, and then use the steam to turn a turbine hooked up to an electric generator. Thus heat energy is converted to electrical energy.

The Atomic Energy Commission and private industry are participating in the construction of different kinds of atomic power plants which it is hoped will be competitive in cost with those run with the conventional fuels—coal, natural gas, and oil. The heart of the atomic plant is its *reactor*, which is a chain-reacting atomic pile. One of the objectives in these projects is to maintain *neutron economy*. In any chain reaction, one of the neutrons produced by a splitting atom is needed to split another atom. Any *extra* neutrons can be used to make *new* atomic fuel. Thus, as we found before, U-238 can be converted into fissionable plutonium. The reactor becomes not only a source of energy but a breeder of new fuel!

In the selection of the original fuel, we therefore try to select one that will produce the best yield of available neutrons within the reactor. Uranium and thorium are two of the fuels being used.

Another point of interest is the efficiency with which the heat is converted into electricity. At present, the transfer of heat is a two-step process. First a fluid, called a *coolant*, circulates through the reactor, is heated, and then flows out. Second, the coolant (now hot) heats water and converts it into steam. The problem under study is: what is the best coolant? In some of the reactors being tested, water is the coolant; in others, a liquid metal, such as sodium, is employed.

Also under investigation is the possibility of producing electricity directly from the reaction of atoms in an atomic plant. Should such a breakthrough occur, there would be no need for boilers, turbines, and generators.

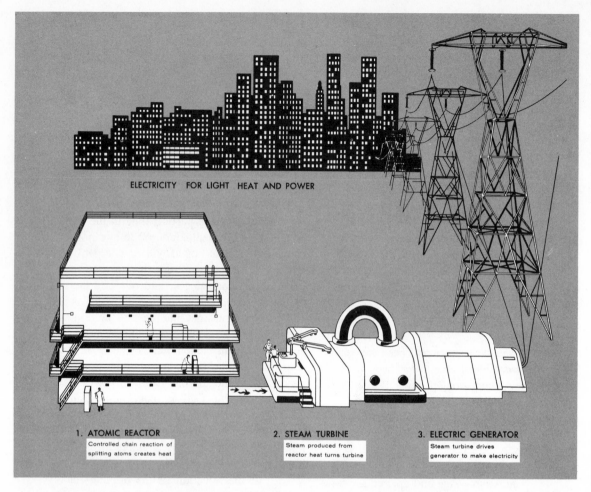

ELECTRICITY FOR LIGHT HEAT AND POWER

1. ATOMIC REACTOR
Controlled chain reaction of splitting atoms creates heat

2. STEAM TURBINE
Steam produced from reactor heat turns turbine

3. ELECTRIC GENERATOR
Steam turbine drives generator to make electricity

In an atomic power reactor the heat produced by splitting atoms changes water to steam. The steam turns a turbine to drive a generator to produce electricity.

At the present time, many nuclear power plants are either already in operation or under construction in the United States, Great Britain, France, and Russia. In 1956, Queen Elizabeth ceremoniously dedicated Calder Hall, in Cumberland, England. This, the first large-scale industrial nuclear power station in the world, is producing 140,000 kilowatts of electric power. In 1960, the Dresden Nuclear Power Station (which is shown in the frontispiece of this chapter), near Chicago, went into operation, with an electrical output of 180,000 kilowatts; this is enough electricity to serve a city of 200,000 persons.

ATOMS FOR TRANSPORTATION

In 1955, the Nautilus, the world's first atomic submarine, was launched in Groton, Connecticut. The reactor of this submarine is surrounded by a lead shield, to prevent the leakage of dangerous radiations. Water circulating through the reactor is piped to a heat exchanger. There, in turn, it heats other water, changing it into steam. The steam strikes and moves the blades of the ship's turbine, which is connected to the propeller shaft.

Because reactors can run a year or more without requiring new uranium, the atomic submarine can remain at sea almost indefinitely, cruising at speeds of nearly 30 knots for thousands of miles. Since no oxygen is needed for atomic fuel, the ship can complete missions without surfacing for air. In August 1958, the Nautilus completed its historic under-ice passage of the Arctic pack. Thus the nuclear reactor has made the true submarine a reality.

Since the launching of the Nautilus many other submarines propelled by nuclear reactors have been built. In 1962 the Enterprise, the first nuclear-powered aircraft carrier, was completed. Other nuclear-powered naval craft are under construction.

Progress toward atomic-powered aircraft is slow. One of the difficulties encountered is the weight of the shields needed to furnish protection against radiation hazards. These shields are customarily made of lead and concrete and hence add a great deal to the load of the plane. Also under consideration by the government and by industry is the use of atomic energy for surface ships and for locomotive trains. It now seems almost certain that nuclear reactors will also play an important part in space exploration, either as a supplement to other power sources or as the basic source of power for propulsion.

RADIOISOTOPES IN THE SERVICE OF MAN

A most important by-product of the atomic-energy program are the *radioactive isotopes*, also called *radioisotopes*, those "twins" of atoms, which, once produced, have the ability to give off various kinds of radiation without further stimulation. Originally these isotopes were made only in special atom-smashing machines. One of these machines, called the cyclotron, is a kind of an atomic merry-go-round, in which atomic particles are made to go faster and faster under the influence of high electric voltage, and are guided in a spiraling path by a giant SEE PAGE 480

These sketches indicate some of the ways in which isotopes are being used today.

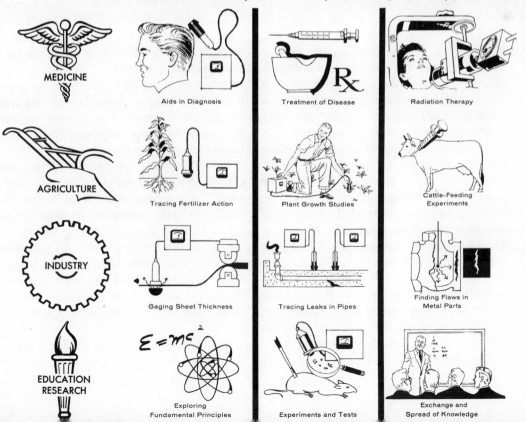

MEDICINE

Aids in Diagnosis

Treatment of Disease

Radiation Therapy

AGRICULTURE

Tracing Fertilizer Action

Plant Growth Studies

Cattle-Feeding Experiments

INDUSTRY

Gaging Sheet Thickness

Tracing Leaks in Pipes

Finding Flaws in Metal Parts

EDUCATION RESEARCH

Exploring Fundamental Principles

Experiments and Tests

Exchange and Spread of Knowledge

electromagnet. The cyclotron, invented by E. O. Lawrence of California, produces high-speed protons that smash through their target material to force their way into the nuclei of atoms. Using the cyclotron, as well as other atom-smashing machines, scientists have produced hundreds of radioisotopes.

Since 1940, the atomic pile has added considerably to the making of radioactive isotopes, sometimes called "tagged" atoms. In the pile, neutrons are the bullets which bombard the nuclei of atoms of various substances. The man-made isotopes produced in this way are then removed from the pile and placed in carefully shielded containers, ready for shipment to hospitals, to industrial laboratories, and to the many other users of these unique atoms.

TRACERS. One of the uses to which these tagged atoms have been put is that of serving as a tracer, a kind of an atomic "spy." To understand the operation of a tracer, recall the common school experiment in which a cut stalk of celery is placed in a glass of water in order to show the rise of water in the "pipelines" of the plant. The water is first colored with a dye, like red ink. The progress of the water up the stalk is easily observed. The red dye makes it possible to see *where* the water goes, in *what part* it seems to be concentrated, and *how fast* it gets there. We are "tagging" the water with a color to reveal its presence.

Radioactive atoms give off radiations that are not visible to the eye but can be detected by use of instruments such as the *Geiger counter.* Because of this, they can be traced as they move through the body of an animal or through the pipes of an oil refinery. The most complex chemical processes can be followed by substituting radioactive atoms for normal ones and then following them through invisible reactions by virtue of their tell-tale radioactivity. This method is so sensitive that incredibly small amounts can be detected and traced. It has already found many practical applications in biological research, in

agriculture, in industry, and in the diagnosis and treatment of disease.

BIOLOGICAL RESEARCH. The migration of mosquitoes from their home grounds was traced by breeding a batch in a pool containing radiophosphorus. The radiophosphorus was absorbed and retained in the bodies of the mosquitoes. Later, collections of mosquitoes made at a number of points and checked for radioactivity with a Geiger counter, revealed their range and their travel habits.

The effectiveness of a new intravenous diet of fat (one injected into the veins) was traced by injecting rats with fat containing tagged carbon atoms in its molecules. (In this, as in other tracer work with living things, the tracer corresponds in quality and in kind to the thing it traces. In the case of the fat just cited, the tagged fat molecules are chemically identical with ordinary fat. As far as biological processes are concerned, the tagged atoms are not different from the atoms normally present.) As the radioactive fat was burned, the rat exhaled radioactive carbon dioxide. The speed with which this "hot" carbon dioxide was breathed out reflected the speed with which the rat's body was using the fat.

Red blood cells have iron in them. Radioactive iron compounds were injected into the blood stream of a human being, and the rate of formation and breakdown of red blood cells was determined.

The study of photosynthesis, the process by which plants make use of the sun's energy to combine atoms from carbon dioxide and water molecules to manufacture sugar, is being studied by using radioactive carbon dioxide gas as a tracer. An important discovery made with this tracer: the oxygen which becomes part of the sugar molecule ($C_6H_{12}O_6$) comes from the carbon dioxide (CO_2) and not from the water (H_2O).

AGRICULTURE. Do fertilizers placed in the soil really reach their destination in the plants for which they are intended? This is the kind of question asked by agricultural scientists. The effectiveness of fertilizers can be evaluated by including radioactive forms of their atoms and then studying the radio-activity of the plants grown in soil containing this fertilizer. (See photograph on this page.) Thus radiophosphorus was placed in various fertilizers that employ phosphorus to find out how easily each gave up its phosphorus, how they reacted to various kinds of soils, and how best to apply the fertilizer to the soil.

Photograph of a coleus leaf made at Brookhaven National Laboratory in Upton, N. Y., taken after radioactive phosphorus had been absorbed by the plant. Studies of this kind shed light on the concentration of phosphorus necessary to maintain a healthy plant under various conditions.

INDUSTRY. Radioisotopes have already proved their value in industry, effecting savings of many millions of dollars a year. One use is the control of the thickness of sheet materials made of paper, plastic, rubber, textiles, and metals. In the machines through which these materials roll, a radioactive "gun" is placed on one side of the material to be tested and a detector on the other side. The thicker the material, the less radiation gets through. The detector is hooked up to a recorder that signals any deviation from the desired thickness to the mechanism controlling it. This operation is done mechanically. Thus, radioisotopes serve as a sensitive gauge and as an automatic control.

Industry is finding many new uses for radioisotopes. These include the cold-temperature sterilization of foods, the location of leaks in water lines, the measurement of the wear of floor waxes, gears and other materials.

DIAGNOSIS OF DISEASE. Radioactive iodine is used in the diagnosis of thyroid disorders. The thyroids are a pair of glands located on either side of the voice box. They pour a secretion into the blood, thyroxin, which regulates the body's metabolism. Thyroxin is manufactured by the thyroid gland from the iodine and other chemicals supplied to it by the blood. A patient with a suspected thyroid disorder drinks a glass of water containing radioactive iodine. The fate of the

"tagged" atoms is followed with a Geiger counter. If very little iodine is taken up and used by the gland, it may indicate that the gland is inactive. If there is a very rapid iodine intake, followed by an equally rapid discharge, the gland is probably overactive. Radioiodine is also used to detect thyroid cancers which may have spread to other parts of the body.

Radioactive phosphorus has been used in diagnosing brain tumors. This is possible because a brain tumor picks up phosphorus in greater quantity than does the surrounding normal tissue. The tumor cells do not distinguish between radioactive phosphorus and the ordinary kind. If a tumor is present, more radiophosphorus will be present in the tumor than in other areas of the brain. The surgeon searches with a needlelike

Geiger counter for the tumor, twenty-four hours after the patient has received an injection of these tagged phosphorus atoms.

TREATMENT OF DISEASE. Becquerel, described previously as the discoverer of natural radioactivity, also made the first observations of the effect of radiations on living tissues. After carrying around a tiny tube of radium salts in his vest pocket, he noticed a severe external wound, resembling a deep burn, on his abdomen. Evidently radiations from the radium salts were destroying healthy tissue.

Scientists experimented with radium to determine whether it could destroy cancerous tissue. Many cures were effected. At first, only those cancers close to the skin were treated effectively. Early malignancies of the breast and cancers of the womb, tongue, nose, and throat were checked. Later, internal growths in the stomach, liver, and intestines were controlled by radiation. In all of these, the penetrating radiations disrupted the chemical makeup of the cancer cells and destroyed them.

Radium, however, showed no selectivity: nearby healthy tissue was also destroyed. With the creation of a large number of artificially radioactive materials in atomic piles, a wide range of treatments became possible. A case in point was the use of radioactive iodine, previously mentioned as a tracer, for the treatment of cancerous thyroid glands. Taken in large doses, radioiodine is concentrated in the thyroid. There it destroys cancerous tissue. Radiophosphorus is used to treat a blood disease in which the red blood cells multiply too rapidly.

ATOMIC DATING

In chapter 6A, we saw how the natural radioactivity of uranium atoms made them a useful "clock" for determining the age of rocks. The dating of the past in this way is based on the knowledge that the average rate of disintegration of uranium in rock is constant.

The regularity in the breakdown of a quantity of atoms applies to all radioactive materials. Scientists describe the rate of destruction of these atoms in the expression *half-life*. Let us see what half-life means.

Assume that a hospital acquires a supply of radium for use in cancer research and therapy. What will happen to this supply as the years pass, if none is given away or lost? The answer is that in 1,620 years, one half of the original supply will have broken down. What happens then? In the next 1,620 years, half of the remainder breaks down again (leaving only one.quarter of the original supply). Every 1,620 years the supply of radium decreases by one half. We say that the half-life of radium is 1,620 years.

Because Uranium-238 has a long half-life, 4½ billion years, it is useful in measuring long spans of time, such as the time since the formation of rocks billions of years old. But it is too crude a "clock" to measure the age of material formed more recently. In 1947, W. F. Libby found a way of dating materials formed during the last 70,000 years. This method is based on the decay of radioactive carbon, known as Carbon-14 because its atomic weight is 14, in contrast to the common Carbon-12.

Carbon-14 has a half-life of about 5,570 years. It is found in material of plant and animal origin, such as wood, marine shells, and charcoal. How does Carbon-14 get into substances? It is believed that cosmic ray particles from outer space produce neutrons which bombard the nitrogen atoms in the atmosphere. A neutron enters the nitrogen nucleus, knocks out a proton and changes it into Carbon-14. (Consult the table on page 460 to see why the loss of a proton changes nitrogen into carbon.) The Carbon-14 then combines with oxygen to form radioactive carbon dioxide, which plants and then animals incorporate in their tissues.

This happened in the past. It is also happening now. How can we make use of

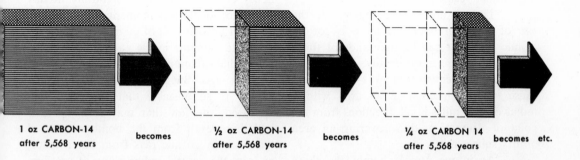

1 oz CARBON-14
after 5,568 years

becomes

½ oz CARBON-14
after 5,568 years

becomes

¼ oz CARBON 14
after 5,568 years

becomes etc.

The regularity in the breakdown of a quantity of radioactive atoms provides scientists with a "clock" for dating ancient remains. The usefulness of a particular kind of atom such as Carbon-14 for this purpose depends on its half-life, which, as shown above, is 5,568 years.

this information to determine the age of a bit of charcoal from the hearth of ancient man?

The concentration of Carbon-14 as we have stated, decreases at the rate of one-half every 5,570 years. If the charcoal specimen we are studying contains half the concentration of Carbon-14 as a plant living today, then its age is estimated to be 5,570 years.

With this new tool, scientists are dating ancient animal remains, wood from Egyptian mummy coffins, soils, sands, sediments, and peat. Volcanic eruptions have been dated with radiocarbon. Radioactive elements other than Carbon-14 are also being used to expand our collection of time clocks with which scientists are dating the past with greater accuracy.

THE HYDROGEN BOMB

The atomic bomb and the atomic pile derive their energy from the *splitting* of atoms, from atomic fission. The hydrogen bomb, with its far greater power, derives its energy from the *joining* of atoms. Essen-tially, this process, called *fusion,* involves the forming of one atom of helium from four atoms of hydrogen.

In the already "old-fashioned" atomic bomb, *heavy* atoms like those of plutonium and uranium are split into light ones; in the hydrogen bomb, the *light* atoms of hydrogen combine to form heavier ones. (In hydrogen bombs, isotopes of hydrogen, *deuterium* and *tritium,* rather than common hydrogen, are used.)

Hydrogen fusion goes on in all stars, including our sun, and is the source of their heat and light. In the center of stars, fusion can go on because the temperature there of 20 million degrees centigrade is sufficient to cause the nuclei of light atoms to overcome the powerful forces of electrical repulsion they have for each other. On earth, we have been able to induce hydrogen fusion by first exploding a uranium fission bomb to produce temperatures as high as 50 million degrees centigrade.

In both fission and fusion, energy is derived from the conversion of matter into energy in accordance with the formula $E=MC^2$. In the fission of a uranium nucleus, 1/1000 of the mass is converted into energy.

In the fusion of four hydrogen nuclei into helium, 7/1000 of the mass is so converted. But the hydrogen bomb is more devastating for another reason.

There is no limit, in principle, to the size of a fusion bomb as there is for an atomic bomb. It can be thousands of times bigger and hence more deadly. It has been estimated by scientists that an H-bomb could cause total destruction in an area with a radius of four miles in all directions from the point of detonation, thus covering an area of fifty square miles.

As in the atomic bomb, the three agencies for inflicting damage are the blast wave, the heat flash, and the radioactivity resulting from the explosion. Estimates indicate that a single H-bomb could cause almost complete destruction of any city on the earth.

Ironically, the same hydrogen fusion that gives the sun the energy to make life possible on the earth may, in the shape of man-made hydrogen bombs, be responsible for the extermination of that life.

But there is a bright side to the fusion picture! If fusion could be made to work at a steady and controllable rate, and if we could handle the enormous energy released, the world would have at its disposal a limitless source of power. Hundreds of scientists are now engaged in research which they hope will lead to controlled fusion.

NEW ATOMS

We have come a long way from the Greek idea of four basic elements—fire, water, air, and earth. We thought, a few years ago, when we reached the number 92, we would have filled in all the atoms possible in the neatly arranged table of elements. But new places had to be found when man began to tinker with the nucleus of the atom, when scientists built heavier atoms in their atomic machines. These new atoms are called the *transuranic elements* because they are heavier than uranium, the heaviest of the previously known elements. At this moment in our atomic age the total count stands at 103. We should say, however, that some of these newly created atoms exist naturally in tiny quantities for fleeting moments on the earth, and that probably all of them existed in considerable amounts in the early stages in the primordial creation of the elements billions of years ago. But all of these extra-heavy atoms are so unstable that they have disappeared; the few that may turn up now and then result from the bombardment of the earth by cosmic rays from outer space, or from the natural radioactivity of uranium or radium.

The following are the new atoms:

Name	Symbol	Number	Origin of Name
neptunium	Np	93	It is just heavier than uranium, just as the planet Neptune is beyond Uranus.
plutonium	Pu	94	Named after Pluto, the planet beyond Neptune.
americum	Am	95	Named for the Americas.
curium	Cm	96	Named in honor of Marie and Pierre Curie.
berkelium	Bk	97	Named in honor of the University of California at Berkeley, for its role in the preparation of most of the new elements.
californium	Cf	98	Named after the University of California.
einsteinium	E	99	In honor of Albert Einstein.
fermium	Fm	100	In honor of the "father of the Atomic Age" —Enrico Fermi.
mendelevium	Mu	101	In honor of the Russian chemist. Dmitri Mendelev.
nobelium	No	102	In honor of Alfred Bernhard Nobel.
lawrencium	Lw	103	In honor of Ernest O Lawrence.

Some of the important generalizations of this chapter are:

Atoms are divisible. They are composed of smaller particles that include electrons, protons, and neutrons.

The essential difference between the atoms of different substances lies in the number of particles they contain; the kinds of particles are the same.

Protons and neutrons are found in a small dense nucleus of the atom; the electrons are arranged in orbits outside the nucleus.

Some atoms, such as those of radium and uranium, split spontaneously; they possess natural radioactivity.

The splitting, or fission, of an atom results in the formation of new kinds of atoms and the release of energy.

Matter can become energy; energy can become matter.

The destruction of a tiny amount of matter results in the liberation of an enormous amount of energy, as indicated in the equation, $E=MC^2$.

In the splitting of an atom, some of its matter is converted into energy.

Neutrons are effective "bullets" for the splitting of atoms.

In a chain reaction, each splitting atom releases energy, as well as neutrons for the splitting of more atoms.

The energy produced by atomic reactors and atom bombs comes from a chain reaction of atoms undergoing fission.

Atoms can be made radioactive by bombardment with nuclear particles in the atomic pile or in "atom smashers."

These atoms, called radioactive isotopes, are useful in the fields of medicine, agriculture, and industry.

Rocks and other ancient materials may be dated by determining the percentage of certain radioactive atoms remaining in them.

In the hydrogen bomb, hydrogen atoms join to form helium atoms. This is called fusion, in contrast to the fission that occurs in the atom bomb.

The energy of the stars is derived from atomic fusion.

In both fusion and fission, matter is converted into energy.

Scientists have synthesized new atoms, heavier than uranium.

The energy of atoms has a potential for good or evil for mankind.

DISCOVERING FOR YOURSELF

1. Find out about atomic particles other than the electrons, protons, and neutrons discussed in this chapter.
2. Keep a scrapbook of the newspaper and magazine articles about atomic energy and related subjects, and summarize them by telling (1) to what important science problems they are related (2) what the possible beneficial outcomes of the discoveries may be (3) where the research is being done.
3. Use a chart indicating the structure of atoms to make three-dimensional models of some atoms.

4. Observe with a magnifying glass in a darkened room the luminous dial of a clock or watch.

5. Keep a file of news clippings that explain the use of radioisotopes in medicine, agriculture and industry.

6. Make a glossary of the scientific terms used in this chapter.

7. Find out more about Carbon-14 and about the peaceful use of atoms. (See bibliography)

8. Borrow a Geiger counter from a local high school science department. Use it to detect radioactivity in a luminous watch dial and in some kinds of rocks.

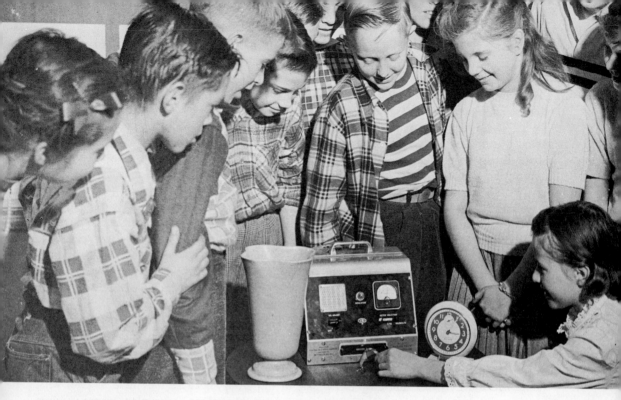

CHAPTER 19B

Teaching "Atomic Energy and Its Uses"

To quote David E. Lilienthal, former chairman of the Atomic Energy Commission: "In a democracy, atomic energy must belong to the people; and the people will have to make the decisions that govern its use. If their decisions are to be wise ones, they must be based on knowledge of what atomic energy is and what it can do."

"But what can we say and do about atomic energy in the elementary school?" you may ask. Certainly we do not wish to add to the already insecure feeling of young children; neither do we wish them to remain totally uninformed about this great force that has potentialities for unbelievable destruction as well as for improving our living through improved medical treatment, agricultural practices, and power production, to mention but three of its many possible applications.

There is much about atomic energy that is constructive. There is much about it that could lead to optimism. There is much background material about atomic energy that is no more difficult than other material that elementary school pupils handle.

Who are the "people" in Mr. Lilienthal's quotation who will make the decisions? As this is being written, the newspapers carry accounts of decisions reached by "people" in Congress and various other governmental units; these decisions are far-reaching, and it is hoped that they are wise ones. We say glibly that we live in the atomic age. The children who are today in our elementary school will soon be the "people" who make the decisions. Should they wait for their learning about atomic energy until they become the "people"? Or have they a right to expect to learn as they grow, to assimilate as much as they can as their development continues, to enter the "people" stage equipped with knowledge, attitudes, skills, and appreciations that are a sound foundation for building decisions. We believe in the second alternative.

But what shall we tell our children about the bombs? Many teachers are anxious about this question—and well they may be. This chapter would hardly be complete without some discussion of children and their reaction to the atomic bomb. Such a discussion is, of course, bound to be inadequate, for who knows how we shall need to readjust our sights as time goes on and the situation alters?

It is inevitable that children feel the insecurity and unrest that is abroad. They hear discussion of the effects of the atomic bomb; they hear talk of the use of even more powerful bombs and other atomic weapons. More than ever, while we live in uncertainty, and while there are great stresses on the emotional life of young learners, we need to give attention to the kinds of things that make for greater security on the part of children. What can we do to help children feel more secure in an uncertain, angry world? What shall be the role of the teacher in dealing with the insecurity of young children?

There are many aspects of this problem about which we cannot be certain, but of this we can be sure: it is more than ever essential that our classroom climate be designed to meet the emotional and spiritual needs of children as well as their physical and intellectual needs. What kind of climate is this? Among other things, it is one in which children feel at home because they feel that they are a part of the group, because they help to plan what goes on and are actively participating in carrying out these plans. It is a place where children are encouraged to make contributions, to do their best, to be helpful, to work with others—in fact, to use all their potentialities fully. It is a place where children feel that they are wanted and needed. It is a place where children feel that they may ask questions—all kinds of questions—and can get answers to them.

We are hardly being fair to children if we shield them from some of the facts. A degree of insecurity is probably inherent in our future existence. Quite probably we ought to educate ourselves and our children to live in an age of uncertainty. This we are not doing if we let children grow up in total ignorance of the possible future with respect to atomic and other warfare. In our day-to-day living with children, there is much that can be done through intelligent, thoughtful teaching to dispel needless fears and help them to adjust to their present world. It is well known that fears often have their source in ignorance.

What, then, are some of our intentions in including a study of atomic energy in the curriculum at the elementary school level? Our objectives are important, as we have said again and again, because they determine our selection of content and the way we teach. Here are some objectives: to create a real interest in learning about and discussing atomic energy; to teach some of the underlying scientific principles; to provide opportunity for the development of desirable attitudes with reference to getting along with others; to develop the constructive aspect of atomic energy and the importance of its wise use.

There is considerable disagreement among leading educators about how much and what kind of learning about atomic energy can or should go on at the elementary school level. Whether the study is included in the curriculum as a separate unit, is carried on incidentally, is included with social studies, or is combined with units on chemical change or electricity, depends, of course, on local choice. Our suggestions here are made to fit any of these situations.

We believe that there are certain things that children in the elementary school may do to satisfy their curiosity about atomic energy and its relationship to them and their future. Some of these activities consist in learning simple facts about atoms, molecules, and atomic energy. Some consist in developing healthy attitudes toward one another and toward the peoples of the world. The fact that scientists of all nationalities have been involved in discovering what we know of atomic energy is an important fact to be understood and contemplated. And there are other attitudes and appreciations—such as the scientific approach that has been involved in all of the research and experimentation leading to our knowledge of the atom and its potentialities—whose development goes hand in hand with learning about atomic energy.

Information about the nature of atomic energy must naturally be kept simple at the elementary school level. How far we go with the explanations and discoveries depends on the interest and abilities of each group. The preceding chapter is to be used chiefly for the interest of the teacher who wants to become informed about this important aspect of science rather than as a source of information that will be taught to pupils.

The activities in this unit might be centered around solving such problems as:

What is inside an atom?
How do atoms differ from each other?
What is atomic energy?
How can atomic energy be used?

LEARNING ABOUT ATOMS

Although the concepts of the nature and structure of atoms are difficult for young children to grasp, reading, making diagrams or models, and discussing their ideas are very helpful activities.

Reading should be directed to answer these questions: What are atoms like? How do atoms differ from each other? How do scientists study atoms? What is the connection between atoms and elements? What is the difference between fission and fusion? What are the meanings of nucleus, electron, proton, neutron?

Illustrating the structure of atoms may be done by drawings using colored chalk or by making models to show the three dimensions with cardboard, wood, plastics, clay, wire, or other materials. Drawings in this book or in other sources (see bibliography) will furnish the source. Parts of the atom—nucleus, proton, electron, etc., may be indicated. Especially interested pupils will have original ideas for illustrating atomic structure. Remember that there is a great difference between merely making a model and understanding the real structure. Models only help a little in understanding the basic structure. The learning will be more effective when pupils explain their models and as they do so indicate how atoms are different from each other as well as similar in some characteristics.

Observing flashes from self-splitting atoms[1] can be done by using a strong magnifying glass and a watch or a clock with a luminous dial—the kind that glows all night. Turn out the lights, wait ten minutes for the eyes to become adjusted to the darkness. Note the soft glow from the dial. Now hold the magnifying glass near the eye and move the watch or clock until it is in sharp focus. Look steadily at the dial and instead of a soft glow, there will be a shimmering sparkling light. A small amount of radioactive material was used on the clock hands and numbers on the watch. As the atoms of this material split, small particles shoot out. A target for the self-splitting atoms is provided in the form of a compound called

---

[1] See Julius Schwartz, *Through the Magnifying Glass* (New York, Whittlesey House, 1954), pp. 47–51.

zinc sulfide. The flashes are caused by the atomic "bullets"—actually particles from radio-active atoms—hitting this chemical.

Observing the effects of frictional or static electricity will help pupils to experience the action of electrons in atoms. Combing hair, stroking a cat's back, taking off nylon sweaters, scuffing on rugs, etc., are common examples. Children should understand that these effects occur because electrons, which are part of the atoms of all substances, may be separated from the atoms and collectively produce these electrical phenomena. (See chapters 21A and 21B for review of examples and explanation of what happens.)

EXPERIMENTING TO LEARN ABOUT ENERGY

Many of the experiments suggested in chapter 16B for the study of chemical changes are useful in learning about atoms and how they behave. The experiments that are suggested in the chapter on magnetism and electricity are also useful for this purpose. If they have already been performed by the pupils, these experiments may be reviewed here with the purpose of answering these questions: "What do these experiments show us about atoms and about energy?" "What kinds of energy have you used today?" "How has our use of different kinds of energy changed our way of living?" "How do you think the use of atomic energy may change our living?"

USING A GEIGER COUNTER

If there is a Geiger counter available in the community (perhaps for civil defense), pupils will profit by seeing it and testing materials with it. Luminous dials on clocks, some kinds of china (that contain uranium compounds), and small pieces of uranium ore will operate the counter. Interested pupils may make a report of radioactivity in their neighborhood by using a Geiger counter. Chemistry sets or mineral collections and other similar sources may have samples of rock that activate the Geiger counter. Pupils will include such observations in their reports. Pupils will see that some radiation will pass through their hands and still cause the counter to react.

REPORTING ON ATOMIC ENERGY

There are many opportunities for interested individuals to report to the class the results of investigations on such subjects as the peacetime use of atomic energy, uses of atomic energy in medicine, the atomic submarine, atoms and agriculture,[2] people who have made important contributions to our knowledge of atoms, the life of Einstein, location of the sources of uranium, and the work of the Atomic Energy Commission. These reports will of necessity be elementary. Several sources for such reports and discussions are listed in the bibliography.

---

[2] Margaret O. Hyde, *Atoms Today and Tomorrow*, 1959, *and Molecules Today and Tomorrow*, 1962 (New York, Whittlesey House).

RESOURCES TO INVESTIGATE

1. Atomic Energy Commission, Educational Services Branch, Washington 25, D. C., for teaching materials.
2. Local scientist or physics department of high school or college for a Geiger counter for examination by pupils.
3. Magazines and daily newspapers for accounts of new uses for atomic energy and for other atomic energy news events.
4. Industries that use atomic "tracers."
5. Atomic plants where electricity is being generated.

CHAPTER 20A

Machines And How They Work

SEE PAGES 496 TO 497 Machines do much of the work of the world. Walk down the street or drive through the country and you will see machines lifting, pushing, pulling, digging. Watch machines at work in the kitchen—scraping, chopping, beating, cracking, squeezing, prying, slicing. Visit a factory to see machines cutting, pounding, rolling, stamping, conveying, twisting. Watch children at play using machines for rolling, sliding, see-sawing, whirling, flying, swinging.

EARLY MACHINES

We do not know definitely what machine was first used by man, but it may well have been a club. Primitive men in many places must have discovered its effectiveness as a weapon against wild animals. Even the simple club is a machine, since it made man's work easier by permitting him to apply a force to his advantage.

When man attached a pointed stone to a club to make it into a spear, or an edged stone to make it into an ax, he became more effective in coping with his environment and raising his standard of living. When he used a stout branch of a tree to pry up a heavy stone, he was inventing a *lever*, a machine destined to find thousands of uses. From our study of the remains of stone-age man, we know that he used wood, bone, stone, or ivory to fashion tools such as axes, hammers, knives, spear points, arrow points, scrapers, drills, awls, saws, pins, and needles.

By the beginning of the Christian era, the pulley, the screw, and the windlass had been invented. The wheel, which revolutionized transportation, and without which our modern machinery would be impossible, had long been in use. We have evidence of the wheel's use from pictures and remains which show that chariots were used in Egypt and Babylonia several thousand years before the time of Christ. The American Indians, on the other hand, did not use the wheel. (Although the wheel was a great mechanical invention, it is not considered a machine when it turns around an axle of a wagon or chariot. We will see later how the wheel can be part of a machine, in the sense that physicists define this word.)

SIMPLE MACHINES

The intricate mechanism of a watch, the complex construction of an automobile, and the elaborate machinery of a factory are all combinations of a few types of simple machines. These include the lever, the pulley, the wheel and axle, the gear, the inclined plane, the wedge, and the screw. These basic machines serve any of three purposes:

1. *They increase speed. Example: an egg beater.*
2. *They increase force. Example: a house jack.*
3. *They change the direction of a force. Example: a single pulley.*

Some machines serve two of these three purposes at the same time: while they are changing the direction of a force, they either increase the speed or increase the force.

As you survey the many machines that you encounter every day, try to determine which of these three purposes they are accomplishing. Remember, however, that these machines do not produce energy but make use of the energy supplied to them.

THE LEVER

SEE PAGES 497 TO 498

Children are amused when they are told that they can lift their teacher. The only material needed for a teacher-lifting machine

is a block of wood and a plank about six feet long. The block is placed under the plank and near one of its ends. The teacher stands on the short end of the plank; the child is delighted to find that he can lift his teacher by pushing down on the other end. In using this device, which is a lever, the child is realizing one of the purposes of a machine, that of increasing force.

If the block is placed 1 foot away from the end where the teacher is standing, the child (who will be 5 feet from the block) need exert a downward push of only 25 pounds to lift his 125-pound teacher. The effectiveness of the child's muscles is multiplied fivefold. The supporting block furnishes the pivot point or *fulcrum* for the lever. The child's part of the lever is 5 times as long as the teacher's, and his force is 5 times as effective.

Is this magic? It looks as if we are getting something for nothing here—a 125-pound return for an investment of 25 pounds.

A child can give his teacher a lift—if the lever is long enough.

Here levers are being used in two different ways to do work. How they are used depends partly upon the amount of force required and partly on convenience.

This is true, but it is not the whole truth. If you watch the lever as it works, you will notice that in order to lift the teacher 1 inch the child must push down on his end of the plank for a distance of 5 inches. In other words, the child's force must be exerted 5 times the distance that the *resistance* to this force (the teacher) moves.

In the illustration just given, force is gained and distance is lost, but one thing is the same—*work*. The term work, as used by the physicist, means the use of *force through a distance*. The amount of work put in by the child is the mathematical product of the force (25 pounds) and the distance (5 inches). Compare this with the work put out in lifting the teacher (125 pounds × 1 inch) and you will see that the result is the same.

The physicist sums this up by saying that the work put in equals the work put out. This ideal situation is true, however, only if losses due to friction are disregarded. (In the other machines discussed in this chapter, frictional losses are similarly disregarded.) In the teacher-lifting machine, the work put out is slightly less than the work put in due to the friction of the plank on the block, as the plank moves.

Levers are in common use. In lifting a boulder, as shown in the diagram, the man is using the same principle as the child does in the teacher-lifting machine. Also, when a

Can you explain how each of these machines helps make the job easier?

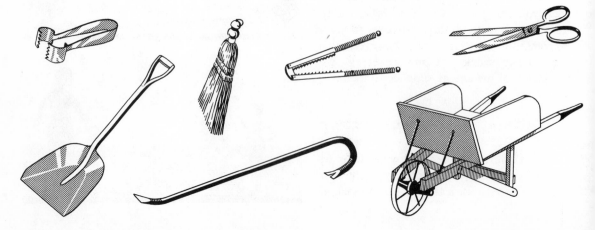

hammer is used to pull a nail, its long handle makes it possible for the user to exert a strong pull. The hammer is a bent lever; the nail offers the resistance; the point of contact of hammer with wood is the fulcrum; and the pull of the hand holding the hammer serves as the force.

In other uses of the lever, the fulcrum or balancing point is not always between the force exerted and the weight moved. In lifting a stump, as shown in the diagram, the fulcrum is near the end of the lever, where it is resting on the log. Here, again, the man's advantage is proportionate to the distance of his hand from the fulcrum as compared to the distance of the stump from the fulcrum. By using the lever, the man's force is increased, but he must also exert his force through a greater distance.

In some cases, we deliberately use a lever that gives us *less* force than we expend. One example is the use of a fishing pole. (Indoor fishermen may try this with a pencil instead of a pole.) Here the fulcrum is the butt end of the pole pressed against the fisherman's body. The force exerted is greater than the weight of the fish. However, in this case, the gain is one of *speed*. The fish is jerked out of the water; it does not have a chance to escape from the fast-penetrating hook.

THE PULLEY

EE
AGES
99
O
00

All of us have seen a flag raised to the top of a flagpole by the use of a pulley and a rope. This arrangement makes it possible to raise the flag without climbing the pole. A pulley used in this way is called a fixed or stationary pulley.

Fixed pulleys have many uses. They help to raise hay into barns, sails to the top of masts, and objects from the holds of ships to the wharves. They have many uses around factories, stores, and garages. Windows are raised with the aid of fixed pulleys and sash weights. The weight is arranged so that it will almost lift the window by itself. One has

This single pulley does not multiply either force or speed but provides a convenient means of raising loads, flags, sails, etc.

to exert only a little force to lift a window that has been properly fitted with pulleys and weights.

A fixed pulley does not increase the force but makes it more convenient to apply. With a fixed pulley, as much force is required to pull down on the rope as to lift the weight without the use of the pulley. In fact, a little more force is needed, because we must overcome the friction between the rope and the pulley wheel. It is usually easier, however, to pull down than to lift up. One reason for this is that the *weight* of the person's body helps pull the rope. Note also that with a fixed pulley the distance moved by the rope being pulled is equal to the distance moved by the rope supporting the weight.

A combination of several pulleys, in which one or more actually move, is called a compound pulley. Compound pulleys magnify force. Using the pulley shown in the illustration, a man can lift a 100-pound weight with a 50-pound pull, if the loss due to friction is disregarded. You recall that to gain force in the lever it was necessary to increase the distance through which the smaller

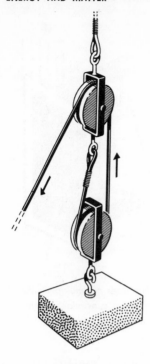

By use of this arrangement of pulleys, force is gained at a sacrifice of distance. A man must pull the rope 2 feet to raise the weight one foot, but he can raise a weight almost twice as heavy as he could with a single pulley.

force moved. The same is true here. The man must pull the rope down 2 feet to hoist the weight up one foot but, as we have seen, he need pull with a force only one half that of the weight.

Combinations of pulleys are often used in moving heavy objects. The more pulleys there are, the less force is required. Increasing the number of pulleys is, however, effective only up to a point. Beyond this point the additional friction and the resistance of the rope to being bent are greater than the advantage provided by additional pulleys.

Each combination of pulleys is called a pulley block and the arrangement of pulley blocks and their ropes is called a block and tackle. The block and tackle are in common use. Lifeboats are raised and lowered by them. Riggers hoist safes to the upper stories of buildings, and painters move their scaffolding with the block and tackle.

THE WHEEL AND AXLE

Every time you turn a door knob, you are using a machine called a *wheel and axle*. You will appreciate the value of this ma-

SEE PAG 500

There are many uses for pulleys on the waterfront.

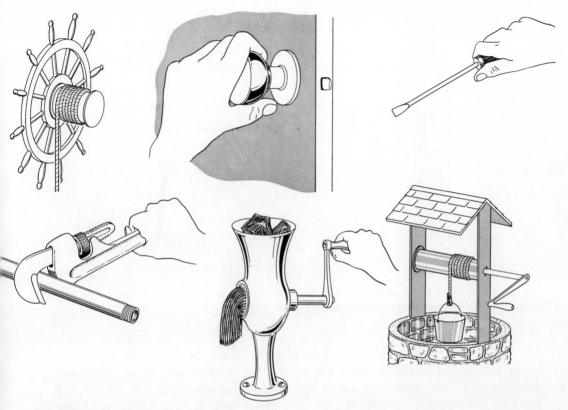

All these machines make use of the wheel and axle. In all, force is multiplied by an investment of distance.

chine if you unscrew the knob and try to turn the axle with your fingers. Restored to its normal place on the axle, the knob becomes a force-multiplying device. A little force applied on the rim of the wheel will cause a large force to be transmitted to the axle. The axle, in turn, turns the mechanism of the doorlock. The steering wheel of an automobile is another example of a wheel and axle. Of course, it is necessary to turn the wheel quite a distance to cause a small amount of turn of the front wheels.

A screw driver, when it is used for turning a screw, is a wheel and axle, with the part gripped by the hand serving as the wheel and the steel shaft as the axle. Other devices employing the wheel and axle are the fishing reel and the pencil sharpener, except that here the "wheel" has been reduced to one

"spoke," or handle, to which the force of the user is applied. A wrench, a brace and bit, a meat-chopper, a pepper mill, a wall can-opener—all illustrate the wheel and axle in use. In all, force is multiplied by applying it at a great distance from the turning axis or axle in order to overcome the great resistance at this point.

In the wheel and axle, as in the lever and in the pulley, force is gained, but at the expense of distance. Consider the simple machine (called a windlass) shown on this page for hoisting water from a well. Each time the handle (the wheel) makes one full turn the rope is wound one full turn around the axle. It is apparent that the distance traveled by the handle is greater than the distance traveled by the rope. Let us say that in this case it is 5 times as great. Then the effort needed

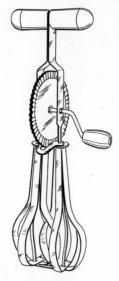 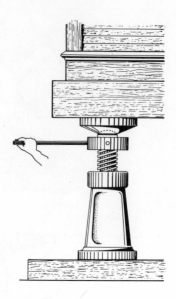

The gears in this egg beater increase speed and also change the direction of the force. The jackscrew increases force by combining two machines (see page 490).

to lift a 25-pound bucket of water will be only 5 pounds. The effort required is only one-fifth that of the weight, but it must be applied for 5 times the distance.

Two sets of wheels and axles connected by a belt can also be used to *transmit* power. You may have seen such an arrangement in a shoe repair shop. Here a continuous belt runs on two wheels. The lower wheel is turned by an electric motor. A belt transmits the motion to a wheel above, thereby turning the shaft to which the various buffing and sanding wheels are attached.

GEARS

SEE
PAGES
501
TO
502
Power can also be transmitted from one wheel to another by equipping the wheels with intermeshing teeth. Such wheels are called gears, or gear wheels (which together with their mounting are variants of the wheel and axle). The purpose of gears, as of other machines, is to increase speed, increase force, or change the direction of a force.

A close look at an egg beater will help you understand gear wheels. An egg beater has a big wheel with a handle attached. Notice this large gear wheel and the two small gear wheels. Turn the handle and watch the wheels. You will see that the small ones turn faster. Watch carefully and you will see why. The teeth of the big wheel fit into the teeth of the much smaller wheels that turn the beater. Thus, the smaller wheels make many turns while the larger wheel makes one. You can check the effectiveness of your egg beater by marking a spot on the little one with a crayon and then counting the number of turns it makes for one turn of the large one. In one common type of egg beater, the little wheel turns five times while the big wheel turns only once. Gears thus make it possible to operate the egg beater rapidly. The gears in this device also serve to change the *direction* of the force. Your hand rotates conveniently in a vertical plane; the egg beater blades swirl effectively in a horizontal plane.

Sometimes, as in a bicycle, the two gear wheels are connected by a chain. Notice

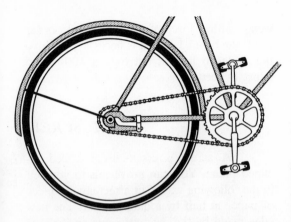

How many simple machines are involved in transmitting force from your foot to the wheel of your bicycle? Can you point out where force is gained at a sacrifice of distance and where distance is gained at a sacrifice of force?

that the front gear wheel, the one where the force is applied, is larger than the one on the rear wheel. If you turn a bicycle upside down and turn the front gear wheel one complete turn, you will find that the rear wheel makes several turns. Thus, one turn of your foot on the pedals gives you several turns of the bicycle wheel. Here again *speed* is gained by an investment of force.

THE INCLINED PLANE

SEE PAGE 502 If a man wants to raise a heavy barrel onto a truck, he uses a couple of boards, resting one end of each against the

truck floor and the other end on the ground. Then he rolls the barrel up the ramp he has made. He is using a machine called an *inclined plane*, which is simply a sloping surface. Why is the job easier this way? Is the man doing less work? Recalling the definition given before of work as a force exerted through a distance, we would find that the same amount of work is needed to roll the barrel up the incline as to lift it into the truck. Less force is used, but it has to be exerted for a longer distance. Essentially the job is easier, because at any one moment more of the weight is being supported by the planks and less by the man's muscles. The inclined plane thus serves to make the job a more gradual one.

Consider a specific example of this principle. Assume that the truck floor is 5 feet above the ground and that the plank is 15 feet long. Then the man must move the barrel 3 times as far as he would if he were lifting it straight up, but the effort required is only one-third as much.

It is believed that the huge blocks of stone used in the construction of the Egyptian pyramids were placed in position by being rolled up long, sloping hills of earth constructed especially for that purpose. We encounter inclined planes frequently. The ordinary stairway is an inclined plane, broken into steps, which makes it possible for us to elevate our bodies easily. Highways are carefully graded so that when we drive over them no steep hills are encountered.

This ramp is a simple machine in which less force is needed to do the job—but at the expense of distance.

THE WEDGE

SEE
PAGE
502
The wedge is a kind of inclined plane, but it is used in the opposite way a ramp or hill is. (A wedge is actually *two* inclined planes, fastened back to back.) On a ramp or hill, objects are raised by rolling or sliding them up the incline. A wedge, on the other hand, moves objects by being forced under them or between them. The most common use of the wedge is in separating or splitting an object. An example of this is seen when the woodsman splits logs by driving an iron wedge into the wood with heavy blows of a sledge hammer. The ax is also a wedge, as is the chisel, the knife, and even the common tack. With all of these, as with the inclined plane, less force is needed because it is applied over a longer distance.

A wedge is sometimes driven under a heavy object resting on the floor in order to lift one end of it up. Consider such a wedge, 1 inch thick at its thickest end, and 6 inches long on the side that rests on the floor. The wedge is driven with a heavy hammer under a beam which presses on the wedge with a force of 600 pounds. In order to lift the beam 1 inch it is necessary to drive the wedge 6 inches, but only a 100-pound effort is needed.

THE SCREW

SEE
PAG
503
A screw is essentially a coiled inclined plane. You can prove this to yourself in the following way. Cut a rectangular piece of paper in half by a diagonal cut. The new edge made by the cut represents an inclined plane. Now roll the paper around a pencil, beginning with one of the arms of the right triangle and continuing down to a corner. The inclined plane is now a spiral around the pencil, in the shape of a screw. On any screw, this plane is called the screw's *thread*.

In actual use the screw is a combination of two simple machines: a wheel and axle *and* an inclined plane. An example of such a combination is a wrench turning a bolt. The wrench and the body of the bolt are the wheel and axle; the thread on the bolt is the inclined plane. The advantage of one machine is multiplied by the other—hence the combined advantage can be tremendous.

As in the wedge and the ramp, a small force is multiplied by an investment of distance. Consider the jackscrew (see page 488). This machine is used to lift buildings when they are to be moved, or when the timbers which rest on the foundations are to be repaired. The jackscrew is essentially a *bolt* with a screw thread on it (to which a handle is attached), which fits into a *nut*, the base on which the jack stands. The handle serves as the wheel in the wheel and axle part of this machine. The weight to be lifted rests on the screw head. As the screw is turned, it *twists* out of the base and elevates the load resting on it. In a sense, the load is riding up a hill—the spiral hill of the thread. One complete turn of the screw may lift the weight only one-quarter of an inch, but the mechanical advantage in force may be great. The great multiplication of effort is paid for by

A wedge is a simple machine. Here, a 100-pound force is lifting a 600-pound weight.

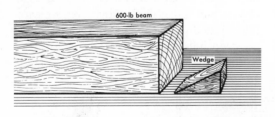

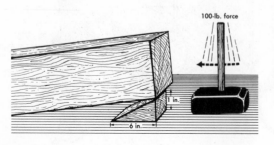

having to turn the handle of the screw through a long distance to raise the weight only a little.

The great advantage of the screw makes it useful when a very heavy object is to be moved or lifted and only a small force is available. Some automobile jacks use a screw. Derailed locomotives are moved by jackscrews.

FRICTION—LIABILITY OR NECESSITY

EE
AGES
03
O
04

Friction occurs whenever two surfaces rub against each other. The work against friction generates heat, which you can detect if you rub the palms of your hands together. In most machines, this heat represents wasted energy. In addition to being wasteful, the heat that results from friction may cause serious damage. When the bearings or rolling parts of machines are not lubricated properly, they may melt or "burn out."

What causes friction? A magnified view of the surface of an apparently smooth material would show that it possesses many irregularities, many jagged hills and valleys. According to classic theory, friction is caused by the bumping and tearing of irregular surfaces as they slide over each other. More recent studies indicate that friction arises in part from the *attraction* of the molecules of the contacting surfaces. This is the same kind of attraction that makes water stick to your hands after washing; it is called *adhesion*.

Friction is reduced in machines by the use of wheels, bearings, and rollers and by the application of lubricants. The ordinary wheels used on vehicles reduce friction, since they permit the surfaces involved to roll rather than to slide over each other. The friction of a wheel against its axle may be reduced by putting steel balls, called *bearings*, between the two. In this way, the sliding friction of the hub of the wheel against the axle is replaced by rolling friction. You can see ball bearings if you take apart the wheel of a roller skate. When we put rollers under the heavy boxes, or ball casters under furniture we are also substituting rolling for sliding.

Lubrication reduces friction, in part, because it fills in some of the irregularities of the surfaces and thus prevents their interlocking. When lubricants are used, the solid surfaces actually slide on the lubricant rather than on each other. Recent research in connection with the adhesion theory of friction, mentioned previously, indicates that the lubricant is effective because it increases the distances between the surfaces and therefore decreases the strength of the adhesive force.

A variety of lubricants, including oil, grease, soap, wax, and graphite, are used in gears and in wheels. It is important to select the right lubricant for each particular use. Lubrication not only saves energy, it also prevents unnecessary wear. This is well illustrated in the automobile. Here the entire mechanism must be constructed so that a sufficient amount of the lubricant will reach every moving part at all times.

Friction is not always a hindrance. We would not be able to walk without friction between our shoes and the ground, because our feet would slip backward. That is why walking on ice is difficult. Automobiles and trains would not be able to start without friction between the wheels and the surface beneath. Without friction, the brakes in automobiles would be useless. Everyday activities would be impossible without friction. Doorknobs would slip through our hands without turning. Chalk would not write on chalkboards. The violinist's bow would slip silently across the strings.

We often increase friction intentionally. The baseball pitcher rubs resin on his hands to get a better grip on the ball, while the opposing batter rubs his hands in the dirt to get a better hold on the bat. When roads are icy, we scatter sand over them and put chains on our tires.

ENGINES FOR POWER

We have seen how machines multiply effort or speed or change the direction of a force. We have not considered the *source* of the force that is put into the machine. Let us turn now to those devices that develop power for man, making it possible to do a great deal of work in a short time.

As long as man used only his muscles, his capacity for doing work was limited. To help his weak muscles, man pressed into service such animals as the horse, ox, elephant, and camel. But the use of power on a large scale came only when man learned how to make engines to harness the movement of the wind and the rush of falling water, the heat from burning fuels and, recently, the enormous energy within the atom. Currently scientists are experimenting with devices to capture the radiant energy of the sun. These are discussed in chapter 18A.

SAILBOATS AND WINDMILLS. When primitive man hoisted an animal skin on a pole in his hollowed-out log canoe, he was making use of the energy of the wind. Many kinds of sailboats have been built down through the centuries, but all of them are devices that capture some of the energy of the wind and use it to push the boat. Windmill blades catch the wind, too, but are so designed as to convert its energy into a rotating motion. The energy thus trapped may be used to pump water, to grind grain, or to spin an electromagnet to generate electricity.

WATER WHEELS. The energy of falling water has been harnessed by placing a water wheel in it. In the past, water wheels have furnished the power for crushing grain, for driving cloth-weaving looms, and for many other industrial purposes. Today, falling water's energy is converted into electricity. Special water wheels, called *turbines*, turn electromagnets that generate electricity. These hydroelectric generators, as they are called, are an important source of electrical energy in the United States, Canada, Russia, and many others parts of the world. (See chapter 21A for details.)

STEAM ENGINES. The invention of the steam engine was of major importance in the development of our industrial civilization. This engine uses the heat of burning fuel to change water into steam. The engine works on the simple principle that steam occupies much more space than the water it came from. One quart of water makes hundreds of quarts of steam. The energy of the expanding steam furnishes the power to run the engine.

A sail may be regarded as a machine which transfers energy from the wind to the boat.

In a steam locomotive, water is heated in a boiler and converted into steam. Each puff of steam does its job of pushing a piston in a cylinder. The back-and-forth motion of the piston is conveyed by a connect-rod to the wheels, where it is changed to a circular motion.

A steam turbine achieves smoother operation than the piston type of engine. In the turbine, many curved steel blades are set in a shaft in such a way as to receive the force of the steam. Most big ships are run by steam turbines. The spinning turbine turns a long rod, which is connected to the propeller that drives the ship. The steam turbine is also used, like the water turbine, as an engine for developing electrical power.

The burning of wood, coal, gas, and oil furnishes the energy for steam engines and steam turbines. Atomic energy is now used to convert water into steam to spin turbines that turn propellers, as in the atomic submarine, or make electricity. (See chapter 19A.)

GASOLINE AND DIESEL ENGINES.

We depend upon the gasoline engine for motive power for automobiles and airplanes and for many other purposes. In the gasoline engine, the power is derived from the rapid expansion of gases produced by the explosive burning of gasoline. This occurs inside each of the cylinders of the motor. Here, a spark from a spark plug ignites the mixture of gasoline vapor and air. The explosion that results pushes the piston down with a force of several tons. This force is then converted by the crankshaft into a rotary motion and is transmitted to the driving wheels of the automobile or the propeller of the airplane.

The diesel engine, named after its inventor, Rudolph Diesel, also works by the energy of explosions. For fuel, it uses oil instead of gasoline, which makes it more economical to run. Today, light, highspeed diesels are used more and more on trucks, buses, submarines, and locomotives. Diesels are also used to drive electric generators in places where it is sometimes convenient to have an independent or auxiliary source of electricity, as in hospitals, schools, department stores, and factories.

ELECTRIC GENERATORS AND MOTORS.

As we have seen in the preceding paragraphs, the energy of wind, falling water, expanding steam, and exploding gasoline can be converted into useful motion. We will see in the next chapter just how this motion is converted into electricity. We will also see how electric motors convert electricity into motion.

Here are some of the important generalizations about machines:

Machines help in different ways. Some produce a gain in force, some in speed; some change the direction of a force.

Work is done when a force is exerted through a distance.

Disregarding the losses due to friction, the work put into a machine equals the work put out.

A gain in force in a machine is at the expense of speed; a gain in speed requires an investment of force.

Six simple types of machines include the lever, the pulley, the wheel and axle, the inclined plane, the wedge, and the screw.

Friction occurs when any two substances rub together.

All machines lose some of their efficiency because of friction.

Wheels, rollers, and ball bearings reduce friction by substituting rolling for sliding friction.

Lubrication reduces friction by filling in the irregularities of the contacting surfaces and by decreasing the attraction between them.

Friction can be an asset: it prevents slipping and makes possible thousands of everyday activities.

Man has invented engines to harness the energy of the wind, falling water, burning fuel, the sun, and the atom.

DISCOVERING FOR YOURSELF

1. Observe the results of friction in your environment. Indicate which examples are helpful; which harmful.
2. Observe a machine at work. Name the machine, describe its work, tell where the energy came from to operate it, tell what reduces its efficiency, and list any simple machines you are able to identify that are part of the machine you are observing.
3. Examine the machines in a kitchen. Classify them according to which of the simple machines they are.
4. Observe machines in your outdoor environment and keep a record of the inclined planes, levers, and pulleys that you see in use. In each case, tell how the machine is helpful in gaining force or in some other way.
5. Observe an egg beater and a bicycle and compare their operation.
6. Watch a carpenter or a garage mechanic at work and describe and explain how simple machines help him to do work that he could not do without them.
7. Examine an antique machine and a modern machine that were designed to do the same work. Compare their efficiency of operation.
8. Observe a building under construction. Describe the machinery being used and compare such a modern operation with one of a hundred years ago.

CHAPTER 20B

Teaching "Machines and How They Work"

Children see machines at home, on their way to and from school, and wherever they go on Saturdays. Firsthand observations are important in the study of machines, just as in the other areas of science. There are many simple experiments that can be performed to deepen the pupils' understanding of the principles underlying the machines that they observe in operation.

In the early elementary grades much of the study is based on the experiences that children have with the machines around them and in answering such questions as: "How does this machine make the work easier?" In the later elementary grades, however, first steps may be taken to see the mathematical relationship between the force used and the work done by the machine.

In teaching about machines at the elementary level, the objective is to help children see the great variety of things machines do, to give them experience in seeing how everyday machines work, and to make them more observant of the machines in their environment. As in other science areas, the simpler the equipment used for experimentation the more useful it is. Kitchens provide examples. So do workshops. Many toys illustrate the concepts involved in the doing of work by machines.

Even very young children are interested in answers to "What makes it go?" Before they enter school, their toys and the tools they use have introduced them to the world of wheels and gears. The following activities emphasize observations and experiences that have been carried on with young children.

1. Look to find machines that lift, push, pull, grind, chop, dig, carry, and do other things that need to be done in everyday living.
2. Find out how machines help us to do things in the kitchen and in the workshop. Learn the name of the machine (hammer, saw, meat-grinder), find out what it does, try to tell how it makes the work easier to do, and learn how to use some of the machines safely.
3. Look at toys to find wheels, gears, levers, screws, pulleys, and other parts. Show the class how the toys work.
4. Find pictures of machines at work: on farms, in kitchens, on roads under construction, in factories, in garages, and elsewhere. Try to find out what the machines are doing, what makes the machines go, why the work of the machines is important. Arrange the pictures on charts according to some classifications: what the machines do, where the machines are at work, what makes the machines go.
5. Use machines and see how they help to do work, i.e., hammers to pull nails, saws to cut wood, shovels to dig, levers to lift, etc.
6. Watch to find what makes different machines move: which machines are moved by electricity, by wind, by water, by springs, by muscles, etc.
7. Learn about friction by rubbing hands together to feel heat. Look for places where friction wears things out—soles of shoes, automobile tires, etc. Find places where oil and grease are used to make friction less—bicycles, roller skates, lawn mowers, etc. Go on a "squeak hunt" with an oil can to eliminate squeaks in bicycles, doors, and other moving things.
8. Look to see how different people in the community use machines: a gardener, a carpenter, the milkman, the fireman, the grocer, the street cleaner, the filling-station attendant, a farmer. Find out the names of the machines, what the machines do, and what makes the machines go.
9. Ask the school custodian to show how he uses machines to: clean the school, make the school safe, clean up the schoolground, make repairs.

OBSERVING MACHINES IN THE NEIGHBORHOOD

Suggest that each pupil report to the class about two machines he has seen at work, telling where he saw each machine and describing what it was doing. Suggest to pupils that they try to find machines that no one else would think of. They may look for machines in the kitchens, the workshops, garages, filling stations, a cobbler's shop, a printer's shop, a bottling works, a creamery. Urge pupils to observe the machine long enough to see clearly what it is doing.

When pupils report their observations, a list may be compiled, entitled "Machines We Have Seen." This listing will no doubt raise questions about machines and how they work. The questions may be listed for answering as the study proceeds. Such an activity as this may be used for beginning the unit, to arouse curiosity and stimulate questions.

If there is a building project (house, store, apartment building) under way near the school, pupils may visit it as a group to see: (1) which machines are being used; (2) what kind of work they do (lift, cut, dig, etc.); (3) how they do this work; (4) what kind of force is used to make the machines operate (electricity, steam, force of muscles, etc.); (5) how the work could be done if these machines had not been invented.

These toys that move have been collected by pupils and are being studied to see what forces make them move, how these forces operate, and how they are controlled. Air pressure, springs, wind, and magnetism are involved.

Some of these points—number 3, for example—cannot be answered fully by observation but involve experimentation and reading. They are suggested here as "problem raisers" at the beginning of the study.

The list of machines made during these observations may be referred to later, after simple machines have been studied. Then pupils will be able to understand more about how these machines work and consequently can give much more detailed answers than they were able to give earlier.

It is important that pupils connect their school study of machines with things that are happening around them every day. There is almost no end to the "everyday" materials that may be brought to school for observation. We shall suggest many of them as we go along.

STUDYING THE LEVER

We have described on pages 15–16 the use of a board and a brick as a lever arrangement. A three-sided length of wood, which can easily be made in a shop, works more smoothly than the brick. A large lever that pupils can work with is useful because pupils get the "feel" that the machine actually makes the work easier to do. In accordance with the directions already given, let them try to lift one another. Let them place the brick or piece of wood at various distances from the person being lifted so that they will see that there is a relationship between the distance that the "push" moves and the ease with which the work is done. Here is an opportunity for the use of measurement to see the relationship between the distance that the force moves (downward) to the distance the resistance moves (upward). If the force moves 4 times as far as the resistance does, is it easier to move the resistance than it is if it moves only twice as far? The relationships will be obvious if pupils actually measure the two distances. Try the experiment with the fulcrum placed so that the force moves 2 feet to raise the resistance 1 foot. Then move the fulcrum so that the relationship is 3 to 1, etc. Pupils will soon feel the difference even though they will not have exact measures.

Pupils may use the words force, fulcrum, and resistance as they discuss the lever, for they will soon come to realize what each is, although the use of these words may not be considered essential. It is important that such science vocabulary be introduced but not stressed to the point of getting in the way of interest, appreciation, and understanding. At the beginning, they may substitute descriptive words such as teetering point, weight, pull, push, etc., for the more technical ones.

After using this lever, pupils may go out and use a seesaw on the playground to see that if the force is far from the fulcrum (the teetering point), more weight can be lifted. They can try various positions and various numbers of pupils to see the relationships between the force and the resistance. Again, measuring the distance that the force moves and comparing it with the distance that the resistance moves will help pupils to see why levers are useful. If the board on the seesaw is not attached, pupils can move it back and forth over the fulcrum. If it is in a fixed position, as some of them are, pupils will move their own positions instead.

After the experiments have been performed, the pupils should try to bring useful levers to school and demonstrate how they work. For each lever, they should try to see how the force and the fulcrum position are related. Suggest that pupils answer such questions as: Does the machine increase speed? Does it increase force? Does it change the direction of the force? What other advantages does it have? They will see that not all levers gain force. It is important that the levers be demonstrated so that pupils will actually see how they operate. Here are examples of levers that pupils may bring and use. (1) *A claw hammer*. Drive a nail into a board. Try to pull it out with your fingers. Then use the claw hammer. Observe how easily the nail comes out. (2) *A nut cracker* (two levers). Crack a nut with it. Observe the arrangement and see how far the force moves. (3) *A can opener* (lever type). Make the observations suggested for other levers. (4) *A pair of scissors* (also two levers).

STUDYING THE PULLEY

The flagpole is a convenient device to show pupils the use of a fixed pulley. They may observe the way in which the rope is placed through the pulley and see the advantage of a fixed pulley in getting the flag to the top of the pole. Help them to see the relationship between the distance that the force (hand pulling rope) moves down and the distance that the resistance (the flag) moves up. Fixed pulleys do not save force. They are just convenient.

Pulleys may be purchased in many stores where toys are sold, in hardware stores, in variety stores, or they may be ordered from scientific supply houses. Pulleys that can lift heavy things, as the lever that lifted a pupil, are a great asset in helping pupils understand how pulleys operate.

In order to understand how systems of pulleys are used, pupils should arrange small pulleys as shown in the illustrations. It is important for them to see that in these pulley arrangements, force is exchanged for distance. That is, much rope is pulled through the pulleys (distance) in order to make the weight easier to lift. Again they may observe to see the relationship between the distance that the force moves down and the distance that the resistance moves up. Measuring to see the exact relationship is important.

For a more definite quantitative idea, use a spring scale to show how the use of pulleys reduces the amount of force necessary to lift a weight. If possible, use wooden pulleys that can hold a heavy weight such as a pail of sand or several books tied together. Use the spring scale to lift the weight. Note the reading of the scale. Now use a block of two pulleys at the top and two at the bottom and attach the spring scale to the rope that will be pulled. Lift the weight. Again read the scale. Use different weights. If possible, increase the number of pulleys on the block to three and four and repeat in each case. Note the reading of the scale.

Using pulleys under different conditions and in various combinations along with the measuring device helps to make the scientific principles more easily understood. After such experiences children may observe the use of machines in their environment with greater understanding.

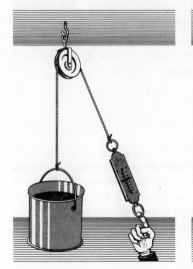

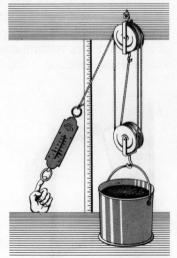

Pupils may observe pulley systems in garages, where one man easily lifts the whole front end of an automobile. In some schoolrooms, fixed pulleys are used to raise the windows and window curtains. A weight concealed in the window sash helps to lift the window, and in some window frames the pulley may be observed at the top. Clotheslines often operate by use of pulleys. A bird feeding station may be hauled away from the window on a pulley and line. Pupils may like to make one of these stations and use their knowledge of pulleys.

STUDYING THE WHEEL AND AXLE

It is not difficult to make a simple windlass that pupils can use in the classroom to lift things. The school custodian or the shop or science teacher may be willing to work with a committee of pupils in constructing it. It may be made entirely of wood of any desired dimensions and operated from the side or corner of a desk. The one illustrated here is 18 inches long; the supports at the ends are 12 inches high. A broomstick serves as the axle and the handle is made of wood and nailed to the end of the broomstick. Strong twine is used as the "rope" to lift the weights, which may be a pile of books tied together or anything else pupils may think of.

Pupils should see first of all that the handle is one spoke of the wheel and that it is fastened to the axle and turns it. As they use the windlass, they will see the relationship between the number of turns the handle makes (the distance the force travels) and the short distance the weight travels. Again this experience will be more meaningful if pupils can arrive at figures that they can compare. If there are especially interested pupils, they will discover how to measure the distance that the force travels (the circumference of the circle made by the end of the handle) and compare it with the distance that the weight travels. They will then see that here, as in the case of the other simple machines, force may be gained at a sacrifice of distance. On this handmade piece of equipment, the relationship is easy to see.

The pencil-sharpener is another illustration of the wheel and axle. So is the doorknob of the classroom. A fifth-grade teacher once unscrewed the knob of her classroom door and asked some of her pupils to try to open the door. They could not. Then she put the knob on again and pupils saw how easy it was to open the door. To make clear the idea that the knob was a wheel and axle, the pupils pushed a nail through one of the holes into which the screws fit and used it to open the door. They could see that the nail constituted a spoke of a wheel. Pupils remembered this experience because they could see how the wheel and axle, a simple machine, made it easy for them to open the door.

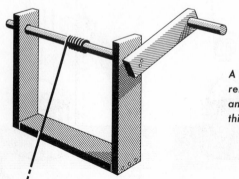

A handmade windlass such as this helps pupils to see the relationship between the distances traveled by the force and by the weight. Pupils can use their imagination in thinking of various ways to use the machine.

STUDYING GEARS

The egg beater is an example of the wheel and axle that pupils can always bring to school to observe. This observation will introduce the idea of gear wheels and make clear the relationship between the large gear wheel and the small one. Pupils will see here an example of one wheel used to turn another. Let several pupils try to determine how many times the small wheel turns while the big wheel is turning only once. Several egg beaters may be examined to compare the relationships of the turning of the large and small gears. Make a mark on one of the teeth of the large wheel so that you can tell when it has made one complete turn. Count the number of turns the small gear makes as the large one turns once. Ask the children to count the number of teeth of each of the gear wheels and see if they can figure out the relationship between the speed with which the two wheels turn. If the large wheel, for example, has 6 times as many teeth as the small gear, the small gear will make 6 turns for every one turn of the large gear. The different egg beaters may be compared by this count. Such gear wheels are used to increase speed. This is a case where force is sacrificed to increase distance. In the egg beater, pupils will see that gears also change the direction of the force.

Bicycles illustrate gear wheels and also the use of belts or chains to drive the wheels. They are, of course, easy to examine and should be brought into the classroom and demonstrated. It is easy to see how the pedal turns a wheel, and how this motion is eventually

Using machines to do work helps pupils to see that they may increase speed, change the direction of the force, or increase force. These machines are being used to illustrate these ideas. Homes, shops, and other sources supply useful machines for demonstration.

transmitted to the rear wheel. Pupils can count the number of turns of the rear wheel for one turn of the pedals.

Pupils should be urged to find other machines in which belts of various kinds are used to make one wheel turn another. Cobblers' shops, garages, and farms are good sources for examples.

STUDYING THE INCLINED PLANE

Pupils can often find examples of inclined planes in the neighborhood. If bicycles are kept in the basement of the school, for example, an inclined plane is probably used on which to move them in and out. School supplies are often unloaded by the use of an inclined plane. Stores, factories, and many other places use them too. Pupils may observe the unloading of new automobiles at the nearby sales office and see how inclined planes are used.

Pupils should make a simple inclined plane with a board and some books, and use a toy wagon to pull a load up it. If they attach a spring scale to the wagon, they can tell how much pull is needed. This may be compared with how much force it takes to lift the load up the same distance without the use of the incline. The same procedure described in the section on pulleys may be used here to compare the distance that the force travels with the distance that the weight is lifted. When the inclined plane is used, the distance is greater, but they do not need to use so much force. If the slope is not very steep, the distance is great and the force may be less. If the slope is very steep, the distance is less, of course, but more force is needed.

An ideal situation for teaching the inclined plane results if the school custodian can help pupils to make one with boards somewhere in the building or on the school grounds. Use an empty barrel as the object to be lifted. In all probability, pupils would have considerable difficulty in lifting the barrel 2 feet vertically, but with the boards used as an inclined plane they can easily lift the barrel 2 feet vertically by rolling it up the gentle slope. Experiences such as this not only help to bring about a real comprehension of the science principles involved but are thoroughly enjoyed by children.

STUDYING THE WEDGE

A wedge consists of two inclined planes put together, and, like the inclined plane, the wedge helps us to increase force. A small wedge may be driven into a piece of pine wood so that the wood will split. Pupils can then see how the wedge pushes things apart much more effectively than could possibly be done otherwise. The wedge also changes the direction of the force. Short, stubby wedges require more force to drive them than long, thin ones. Pupils may use wedges of different kinds that may be borrowed from a machine shop. Many common tools are wedges. Examples are chisels, ice picks, axes, and knives. If these tools are examined carefully, pupils can see that they are actually inclined planes that wedge between things and push them apart.

STUDYING THE SCREW

Another variation of the inclined plane is the screw. It is an incline that winds around in a spiral. If they examine a large screw, pupils can trace the spiral path of the grooves. Screws, like wedges and inclined planes, help us to gain force, but we sacrifice distance and speed. It is worth the trouble to bring an automobile jack to school to see how it enables one person to lift an automobile. Jacks are, of course, made of more than one simple machine, but the lever operates the screw, and pupils can see how the screw makes many turns in order to lift the car only a short distance.

Pupils will find many examples of screws. The piano stool, for example, uses a screw, and they can see how it operates by watching it carefully.

OBSERVING COMPOUND MACHINES

Many of the machines observed in the earlier activities are combinations of several of the simple machines—the lever, pulley, wheel and axle, and inclined plane. After a study of the simple machines, pupils may be better able to see how the compound machines are built. Garden tools used at the school may be examined to discover the various simple machines and to see how these machines and tools operate. The same thing may be done with shop tools if there is a woodworking or general shop in the school or if pupils have a workbench with tools. In one school, after the pupils had been studying machines, they asked the school custodian to show them his tool kit to see whether they could find examples of the simple machines and explain how they did the kinds of work for which they were designed.

A trip to a nearby construction project (a building, road work, or other project where compound machines are in use) is a very satisfying experience for pupils in the later elementary grades. (See suggestions on pages 31–32 for taking field trips.) Committees of pupils may be formed to find answers to such questions as: What forces are used to make the machines operate? How many simple machines can be found in one of the large compound machines? In what ways are the machines helping? How are the machines controlled by the workmen? How was the work done before some of these compound machines were invented?

OBSERVING THE EFFECTS OF FRICTION

In the study of fire, pupils learned that rubbing against the force of friction creates heat. It also wears away surfaces, and pupils should see the effect of reducing friction in machines. An easy way to show how reducing the friction between surfaces makes work easier is to take two blocks of wood with flat surfaces. First rub them together and notice how the surfaces grind against each other. Then put some oil between them, rub them again, and notice the difference. Put a little oil between your thumb and index finger and rub them together. Then wipe the oil off, rub them together, and note the difference. Pupils may talk with their fathers about what parts of the family automobile are greased and oiled when it is taken to the filling station for a grease job.

When inspired and guided, children often originate very interesting illustrations of scientific principles. Marbles and coffee cans here demonstrate ideas about friction.

A simple device for measuring smoothness and roughness of surfaces can be made by using a flat block of wood with a rubber band fastened to it. The band is used to pull the flat block on the surface. The stretch of the band shows how hard or easy it is to pull the block across a surface. Measure the stretch of the band as the block is pulled across the classroom floor, a cement sidewalk, a polished floor, a piece of glass, sandpaper and other surfaces that children will want to try. Make a chart to show the stretches on different surfaces so that it will be easy to compare them.

Reducing friction by the use of bearings is also easy to demonstrate. Roller skates, both those with bearings and those without, may be brought to school and the difference noted in the ease with which the wheels rotate. The wastebasket may be used to demonstrate how effective bearings are in reducing friction. Fill it with books and try to push it along the floor. Then set it on some marbles and try to push it along. Individual pupils can do this with piles of books to note the difference when marbles are used to reduce the friction.

SUMMARIZING INFORMATION ON MACHINES

The studying of machines lends itself to an interesting summarizing activity that can serve to: clarify ideas, provide experience in organizing, give an opportunity to use different media to express ideas.

As has been said earlier, there are many ways to make summaries. Many of the photographs in this book illustrate exhibits, bulletin boards, constructions, and collected materials that may be used. Any of these may be used to summarize the machines study.

The following important ideas are examples of themes that will give continuity and directions to a summary:

Machines have changed our ways of getting food, clothing, and shelter.
Machines help to do many things in our neighborhood.
Many different forces make machines work.
These simple machines can do many kinds of work.
These machines help us transport things.
Machines gain force, change the direction of force or gain speed.

The whole class may choose one of the themes and work on it or various pupils may choose themes that interest them and the results may then be combined into an assembly program for a group that has not studied machines. The following activities may be used to help express ideas: collecting pictures that show important facts, drawing pictures that show a sequence of ideas, collecting tools and other small machines to exhibit with appropriate labels, assembling and performing experiments that show the important principles.

RESOURCES TO INVESTIGATE

1. The kitchen at home (or at school) to observe how pulleys, levers, wheels, wedges, screws, and inclined planes are used.
2. Local buildings under construction to see use of machines.
3. Hardware store to observe kinds of machines for use in tool shops, garages, farms, buildings, etc.
4. A garage to observe the use of pulleys for lifting motors, inclined planes for storage, and many other machines at work.
5. A carpenter to explain proper use of tools and to show different kinds for different uses.
6. General merchandise catalogues for pictures of many different kinds of machines. Pictures show how complex machines are made from simple machines for the purpose of doing different types of work.
7. Toy stores to see machines used in various toys.
8. Dealers in agricultural implements to get a better understanding of machines used on the farm.
9. A manufacturing plant to see machines in operation.

1933 NORRIS DAM 1936
HEIGHT 265 FEET · LENGTH 1860 FEET
CONCRETE · 1,002,253 CUBIC YARDS
STORAGE · 830 BILLION GALLONS
RESERVOIR AREA · 45,140 ACRES
POWER · TWO 50,000 KW GENERATING UNITS
LENGTH OF LAKE · CLINCH RIVER 72 MILES · POWELL RIVER 56 MILES

CHAPTER 21A

Magnetism and Electricity

We have come to take electricity for granted, but let it for some reason or other fail us and we suddenly become aware of its importance. The following news story from the *New York Times* recounts the events that followed a power failure in Cape Cod, Massachusetts, on August 26, 1951:

INSULATORS SHOT OFF, POWER FAILS, AND THE SHOCK IS FELT BY CAPE COD— Traffic and Phones Snarled, Lights Dark —And Who Can Milk Cows by Hand? New Bedford, Mass., Aug. 27 (AP) Insulators were shot off a power line, possibly by mischievous children, in semi-rustic Wareham, where the long arm of Cape Cod begins its outward thrust into the Atlantic.

The picture of what happened Sunday night began to clear only today.

A half million people in that vacationist-loaded region were suddenly without power, without lights, without refrigeration. Street lights went out, traffic lights were extinguished, traffic snarled.

Motorists with gasoline low in their automobile tanks were stranded as filling station pumps, electrically operated, were made useless.

Theatres, churches, restaurants were darkened and closed. Cooking became impossible in homes equipped only with electric ranges. Mothers came to police barracks to have infants' milk warmed.

On telephone lines, suddenly loaded with an unexpected rush, calls had to be put through with the use of hand-operated magnetos. Traffic through the Cape Cod Canal halted an hour.

In drug stores, vaccines, cultures and serums were imperiled by refrigeration failure and the state police removed them to barracks where there was auxiliary power.

A woman subscriber called the Hyannis office of the Cape and Vineyard Electric Company, pleading, "I've got twenty cows in my barn and they all have to be milked by mechanical milkers and nobody around here knows how to milk a cow by hand."

Many homes, dependent upon electrically driven water pumps, were without water, and residents came to the police with containers of all shapes and descriptions to supply their households.

The police were called upon to dole out gasoline in small quantities to enable stalled motorists to reach hostelries —themselves darkened and without power.

These were the conditions that prevailed on a highway-crowded Sunday night all the way from Marshfield and Middleboro to the offshore island of Martha's Vineyard—for one to eight hours—when a power line failed.

MAGNETISM

TWO MERGING STREAMS. Historically, our knowledge of magnetism and our knowledge of electricity are two separate streams, originating in antiquity and merging near the beginning of the last century. In nature, magnetism and electricity are in fact intimately related forms of energy, each one capable of producing the other. Almost all of the devices referred to in the foregoing news story are indicative of how man, through his inventions, has made good use of this two-way relationship. Let us consider magnetism first. Later we will investigate electricity and see how it is linked to magnetism.

THE MAGNET AS AN IRON ATTRACTOR. The phenomenon of magnetism has been known for centuries. The fact that certain kinds of iron or iron ore had the power to attract other bits of material containing iron must have been known in ancient Greece.

The exact origin of the word "magnetism" is lost in antiquity. According to Pliny, it is derived from the name of a shepherd boy, Magnus. Says this philosopher, "As for the name Magnus that it has, it took it from its inventor and discoverer thereof, who found it upon the mountain, Ida. He . . . as he watched his beasts, observed, as he went up and down the mountainside, both the nails in his shoes and the iron tip of his staff adhering to the stone." A more accepted explanation, however, is that the name is taken from Magnesia, a province in northern Greece in which large deposits of magnetic ore were found.

THE MAGNET AS A COMPASS. A second discovery made the magnet an important instrument in navigation. It was found that if a magnet was suspended so that it could turn freely, it would swing into a north-south position. Thus the magnet becomes a compass. Some legends ascribe this knowledge to the ancient Chinese. Presumably they used magnets as compasses more than one

SEE PAGES 530 TO 531

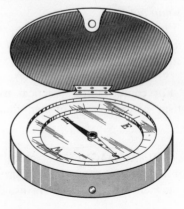

The essential part of a compass is a magnet which can swing freely.

thousand years ago. In the writings of Hebrews, Greeks, and Romans, the magnet is often referred to as a "lodestone," meaning "leading-stone" or "directing-stone." Eventually a magnetized bit of iron was used in making a crude magnetic compass, but it is thought that this valuable instrument was not used much until the middle ages. You can make a compass much like those used by early mariners by repeatedly rubbing one end of a steel darning needle in one direction only against one end of a magnet and then laying the needle on a cork floating in water. The container for the water, of course, should not be made of iron. This kind of compass is essentially the kind used by Columbus in his voyage to America. Needles in Columbus' times were made of poor steel and did not retain magnetism very long. It was, therefore, necessary to remagnitize the needle every few days by rubbing it on a lodestone.

The discovery of the magnetic compass marked an important milestone in man's struggle to explore his planet. No longer did mariners have to govern their voyaging by the North Star or by landmarks along a coast. With the compass, directions could be determined accurately when clouds or storms hid the stars from view. This new invention made it possible for men to venture out into the great unknown—the oceans of the world.

In summary, the ancients knew three important facts about lodestone:

1. *It attracted and held bits of iron.*
2. *When freely suspended, it took a north-south position.*
3. *When pieces of steel were rubbed against it, the steel acquired lodestone's power.*

For centuries the practical uses of magnetism extended no further than the compass.

NATURAL MAGNETS. Natural magnets, or lodestones, are a kind of iron ore called magnetite. Lodestones are usually ir-

Several forms of magnet: horseshoe, bar, natural lodestone, and U. Magnetism has been induced artificially in all but the lodestone.

regular in shape—that is, they look like ordinary stones you might pick up anywhere. Like the artificial magnets with which you are probably more familiar, they attract iron. Small pieces of lodestone are inexpensive and are easily obtained from scientific supply companies. Small bits of iron (iron filings) or small carpet tacks will respond to the attraction of these stones. Like other magnets, lodestones have north and south poles (sometimes several sets of these) but it is necessary to do some experimenting to find them.

ARTIFICIAL MAGNETS. The common artificial magnets found in schools are made in three shapes. Their shape gives them their name: they are known as horseshoe, bar, and U magnets. Except for their shape they are the same, for horseshoe and U magnets are essentially bent bar magnets. SEE PAGE 529 TO 530

Artificial magnets are usually made of steel. In recent years, more powerful magnets made of an alloy of iron, aluminum, nickel, copper, and cobalt, patented under the name Alnico, have found many practical uses. Magnets help close cabinet and refrigerator doors; they help us pick up pins and needles; they hold the lids of cans after the wall can-opener has removed them; they keep papers on bulletin boards; they make cloth pot holders stick to the sides of ovens; they hold kitchen knives on the wall; they are found in many toys. In all of these gadgets, either two magnets attract each other, or a magnet attracts iron or steel.

MAGNETIC ATTRACTION. If a magnet is laid flat in a dish of iron filings or small tacks and then lifted out, masses of filings or tacks cling to the ends of the magnet but very few near the middle. These ends, where the strength appears to be greatest, are called poles. All magnets, no matter what their shape, have poles. Horseshoe and U magnets are given their particular shapes in order that both poles (where the magnetism is strongest) may be used together.

Most commonly, we observe the attraction of magnets on objects that contain iron; however, cobalt and nickel also respond well to a magnet's pull. Other substances also respond to a magnet's influence, but it requires sensitive instruments to detect this.

PERMANENT AND TEMPORARY MAGNETS. Common magnets are often called *permanent magnets*; if kept properly they will retain their magnetism for a long time. Some magnets are temporary in nature. Pick up a carpet tack with a magnet. To the end of this tack, bring another tack. You will find that the first tack picks up and holds the second. The second tack will hold a third. The length of the string of tacks you can make in this way will depend on the strength of the magnet, the weight of each tack, and the extent of your patience. If you now remove the magnet from tack number one, the others drop off rather quickly. Each tack was magnetized only temporarily. A steel sewing needle, on the other hand, will retain its magnetism for a much longer time, particularly if it is given its initial magnetism by rubbing it on a magnet. Another kind of temporary magnet, and a very important one, is the *electromagnet*. This kind will be considered later in the chapter.

MAGNETISM PENETRATES THROUGH MATERIALS. Children soon discover for themselves, if they are allowed to experiment, that magnetism acts through many substances. If a magnet is brought toward tacks covered by a sheet of paper, the tacks will cling to the underside of the paper. If tacks are placed in a drinking glass, they can be manipulated from the outside by a magnet. Paper, glass, and wood, as well as air, water, copper, and many other substances are "transparent" to magnetism. On the other hand, a magnet's ability to pick up and hold tacks is reduced if an iron object is interposed between the magnet and the tacks, since the iron retains some of the magnetic influence.

ATTRACTION AND REPULSION BETWEEN MAGNETS. If a bar magnet or a magnetized steel needle is suspended in a horizontal position by a thread, it will come to rest pointing north and south. The end of the magnet that points to the north is called the north pole of the magnet; the end pointing to the south, the south pole. A magnet thus suspended, as indicated previously, is essentially a compass.

If the north pole of another magnet is now brought close to the north pole of the suspended one, the latter will swing sharply away. On the other hand, if the north pole is brought close to the *south* pole, the attraction will pull the suspended magnet to the other one. In short, *like poles repel and unlike poles attract.*

A bar magnet suspended in the manner shown here will always come to rest in a north-south line. To avoid deflecting the magnet, the support should be made of wood or some other nonmagnetic material.

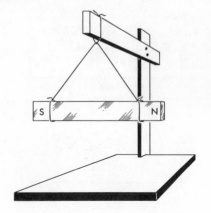

SEE
PAGE
530

MAGNETIC FIELDS.   What is the nature of magnetic attraction? We do not know the full answer to this question, but we can trace the shape, direction, and strength of the invisible *magnetic field* that exists around a magnet. This field can be explored with small bits of iron—iron filings. A bar magnet is placed on a table and covered with a sheet of paper. Iron filings are then sprinkled on the paper. A very interesting pattern develops as the iron filings come under the influence of the magnetic field. Each bit becomes a tiny temporary magnet and takes a position following the so-called lines of force that extend from the magnet. Together, the filings form a map of the field. They reveal

The magnetic field around a magnet can be explored with iron filings. The repulsion between similar magnetic poles and the attraction between opposite poles is revealed by these bits of iron.

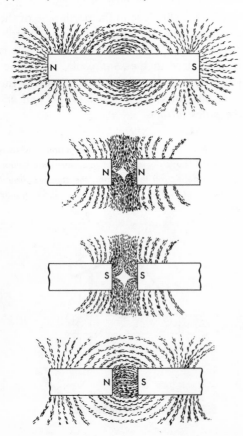

the presence of the invisible lines of force, as shown in the diagram.

If similar poles of two bar magnets are brought near each other under the paper and sprinkled with iron filings as above, the repulsion of their lines of force is shown; between two opposite poles, on the other hand, the lines of force indicate mutual attraction.

THE EARTH AS A MAGNET.   Why does a freely swinging magnet point in a north-south direction? The experiments in magnetic attraction and repulsion, described previously, suggest the answer: the earth itself acts like a magnet. The earth's magnetic field exerts an influence on all of man's compasses, causing them to line up in the direction of the field—in a generally north-south direction.

Practical mariners found that the compass needle does not point exactly toward the *geographic* north and south poles that mark the ends of the imaginary axis of the earth. Rather, it is attracted to the *magnetic* poles in each hemisphere. The magnetic pole of the Northern Hemisphere (the North Magnetic Pole) is located above Boothia Peninsula, nearly 1,200 miles from the geographic North Pole. Similarly, the magnetic pole in the Southern Hemisphere (the South Magnetic Pole) is located in Antarctica, some distance from the geographic pole. As a result, compass needles at most points of the earth point somewhat east or west of true north. Navigators of ships and airplanes carry charts showing the declination of a magnetic needle from true north for each point on the earth's globe. These charts have to be revised every few years, because the magnetic poles of the earth are shifting slowly all the time.

THE WRONG NAME.   Two facts presented in the preceding material may appear to be contradictory:

FACT 1.   Opposite poles of magnets attract each other; like poles repel.

The north magnetic pole (M) is located at a distance from the true North Pole (N). As a result, compass needles at most parts of the earth point somewhat east or west of true north. Navigators must compensate for this difference when they use the compass.

FACT 2. The north pole of a magnet, or compass, is attracted to and points toward the north magnetic pole of the earth.

Indeed, there is a contradiction here, made by history, not science. It is a contradiction in name only, not in principle. It occurred because the poles of compasses were named before the laws of attraction and repulsion were fully understood. If we could alter the course of history, we would call the end of the magnet that points to the north

its south pole, and the one that points to the south its north pole. Then the theory of opposites attracting and the terminology used would agree. To change now, however, might cause endless confusion. Some texts compromise the issue by calling the north pole of the magnet the north-seeking pole, and the south pole the south-seeking pole.

THE NATURE OF MAGNETISM

Magnetism, like many other everyday phenomena, presents many perplexing problems to scientists. What, for example, is it that makes a magnet magnetic? Scientists offer a tentative answer to this question. They point out that if you break a magnet in half, each half becomes a perfect magnet, with new poles forming at the break. If you continue breaking these halves into quarters, and so on, each new piece becomes a magnet with a north and south pole. This

Top: In an unmagnetized bar of iron, the particles show no orderly arrangement but lie with their poles pointing in all directions. Bottom: When the bar is magnetized, the particles are arranged so that all like poles point in the same direction.

leads to the theory that magnetism resides in the smallest particles of the magnet, in its atoms. Each atom is a tiny magnet—an atom magnet.

If magnetism is a characteristic that resides in atoms, then what is the difference between an unmagnetized bar of iron and a magnetized one? In an unmagnetized bar, the atoms are arranged like a group of children who, after play, have flopped on the ground to rest. They face in all directions. In a magnetized bar, the atoms are arranged like children seated in straight rows. In unmagnetized iron, the atom magnets neutralize each other; in the magnetized iron, the atom magnets add to each other to make the whole bar a magnet. Why does rubbing a steel needle on a magnet cause it to be magnetized? Under the close influence of the magnet, each of the atom magnets in the steel needle is shaken into line.

STATIC ELECTRICITY

SEE PAGE 532 Electricity that accumulates and stays on a substance is customarily called *static electricity*. But we notice static electricity more when it is not static—when it jumps. Have you observed flashes of lightening in a thunderstorm? Have you heard a crackling sound when you stroked the fur of a cat? Have you felt a tiny shock after scuffing your feet on a rug and then touching a doorknob? In all of these phenomena, two things happened:

1. *Electricity accumlated.*
2. *Electricity jumped.*

But this was not always known.

Thales, a Greek philosopher who lived about 600 B.C., experimented with static electricity. He discovered that when he rubbed a piece of amber with a woolen cloth it would pick up light objects, such as bits of straw, dried leaves, and cork. At the beginning of the seventeenth century, William Gilbert, previously described as the discoverer of terrestial magnetism, repeated some of Thales' experiments. He found that glass and sealing wax as well as amber would attract light objects when they were rubbed. Gilbert named this mysterious force electricity, after the word "electron," which means amber in Greek.

You can perform experiments similar to Gilbert's by rubbing a hard-rubber comb briskly on a woolen sweater or coat. Bits of paper will jump up to the comb and cling to it.

The study of static electricity was continued by many other scientists, and led to many important discoveries. However, its fundamental cause was not determined until the nature and structure of the atom were known. As we learned in chapter 19A, the atoms of all matter are made of electrons, which are negatively charged, whirling around nuclei containing positively charged protons (as well as other particles). You recall that there are an equal number of electrons and protons in each atom; as a result, atoms are ordinarily electrically neutral.

Now consider what happens when a comb is rubbed on a piece of cloth. The contact of these two materials causes some electrons to be torn away from the cloth and to adhere to the comb. The atoms making up the comb, for reasons we do not understand, seem to be hungrier for electrons than those of the cloth. They grab some electrons from the cloth. We say that the comb has acquired a *negative charge* of electricity.

But what of the cloth? Some of its atoms are left with an electron deficit, or what amounts to the same thing, a proton surplus. We say that the cloth has acquired a *positive charge* of electricity.

Electricity, then, is a phenomenon that stems from the electrical particles of which atoms are composed. Fundamentally, matter itself is electrical. Students often ask,

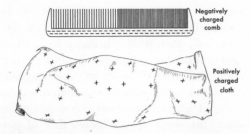

When a comb is rubbed on a cloth, the cloth loses electrons and the comb gains them. The comb acquires a negative charge of electricity, while the cloth acquires a positive charge.

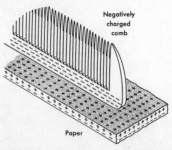

When a negatively charged comb is brought near a neutral piece of paper, the electrons on the surface of the paper are repelled, leaving it with a positive charge.

"But what is electricity?" Bertrand Russell answered this question in this way: "It is not a thing. . . . *it is a way in which things behave*. When we have told how things behave when they are electrified, and under what circumstances they are electrified, we have told all there is to tell. When I say that an electron has a certain amount of negative electricity, I mean merely that it behaves in a certain way. Electricity is not like red paint, a substance which can be put on to the electron and taken off again, it is merely a convenient name for certain physical laws."[1]

When we say that an electron has a negative charge of electricity and a proton a positive charge we are simply saying that there are two kinds of electric charges. We find that electrons repel each other and that protons repel each other, but that electrons and protons are attracted to each other.

Why does the charged comb, with its surplus of electrons, attract bits of paper which are electrically neutral? When the comb is brought *near* the paper two things happen:

1. *Some of the electrons of the paper are repelled to the side away from the comb (since similar charges repel each other).*

2. *This leaves a balance of a positive charge on the side of the paper near the comb which causes it to be attracted to the negatively charged comb.*

The comb acquires a negative charge when rubbed on wool. When, however, a glass rod is rubbed on a piece of silk, the silken cloth picks up electrons, acquiring a negative charge, and leaves the glass rod with a positive charge.

Have you ever charged your hair by combing it? The comb removed electrons from your hairs and thus left them with a positive charge. Being similarly charged, each strand of hair repels its neighbor, and so the hair tends to stand on end.

Scuffing your shoes on a rug causes you to pick up electrons from it. These accumulate on the surface of your skin. You are a charged body! When you bring your finger to an object such as a doorknob or a telephone receiver, the electrons jump from you to that object. You are discharged!

Materials, then, become charged by grabbing or shedding electrons. Why not by grabbing or shedding protons? In atoms, as we have seen, electrons move in orbits around the nucleus. They are not held too tightly to the nucleus and may be removed easily. Protons, on the other hand, are held

[1] *The ABC of Atoms* (New York: E. P. Dutton, 1923).

Lightning "strikes" the Empire State Building. Actually, the main flash travels upward. See text for details.

ward the cloud on the path taken by the leader. This upward jump of charged particles, or *return stroke*, is the main lightning stroke. It may be succeeded by further downward and upward surges in the same path. All of this takes place in less than a second.

Lightning, evidently, is a composite affair, involving up and down flow of particles: negative ones toward the earth and positive ones to the cloud. The main flash—the one that is visible and produces the thunder—travels upward. Contrary to popular opinion, lightning can strike more than once in the same place. The Empire State Building, the world's tallest building, is struck on the average of 48 times a year.

On highways you may have noticed flexible rods protruding upward from the road, adjacent to toll booths. Do you know what they are for? While your car is traveling, the rubbing of the wheel against the road causes a charge to build up on the outside of your car. This charge would be transferred to the toll booth attendant, along with the coin, if it were not disposed of. The waving rods touch the car first and lead the charge into the ground.

by powerful forces within the nucleus. To move the positively charged protons, it would be necessary to move the entire atom along with it. In solids such as the comb, glass, or silk which we have been considering, atoms are held in place and are not easily displaced by rubbing.

Lightning was discussed in chapter 9A as a weather phenomenon. Further details are in order now, since lightning is a form of static electricity. In a cumulonimbus (thunderstorm) cloud, the upper part becomes positively charged, while the lower part becomes negatively charged. As the cloud passes over the land, it repels electrons near the ground (recall the comb-paper experiment) and causes the resulting positive-charged particles to gather there. A series of streams of negative charged particles called *leaders*, lash out from the cloud toward the ground but do not touch it. When a leader finally comes close enough to the ground, the positively charged particles there jump the gap and travel upward to-

CURRENT ELECTRICITY

ELECTRON TRAFFIC. Flick a wall switch—the room is flooded with light. Push the toaster handle down—its coils heat to a red glow. Move the starting switch of the vacuum cleaner—and its motor starts spinning. Light, heat, motion, all are at your fingertips through the magic of the electric current. You are the engineer: you control the flow of electricity in these and dozens of other devices that serve you daily. More precisely, you are a kind of traffic engineer; when you throw the switch you are completing a pathway over which electrons can flow.

For current electricity, as its name implies, is a flow—a flow of electrons, the particles that are part of the atoms of all matter. Since all matter contains electrons, it is not necessary (or possible) to "make" electricity; all that is needed to push the electrons along. We will see later how this is done with batteries and with generators.

SEE
PAGE
532

THE ELECTRIC CIRCUIT. In understanding electron traffic, it is helpful to know that *current electricity travels in a continuous path*—in an electric circuit. Every time you throw a switch to light a lamp or make a motor turn, you are completing an electrical circuit, you are setting a bridge for electrons in place. Every time you snap a switch to "off," you are lifting the bridge out of the circuit.

The electric cord that connects your table lamp to the wall socket contains *two* wires in order to make a circuit possible. At any one moment, the current is flowing into the lamp through one of these wires and out through the other. To complete your "view" of the circuit it would be necessary to go all the way back from the wall socket to the electric generator in your city or town. When you flick the switch of your lamp, you are starting a movement of electrons in a continuous circuit all the way from the generating station to your lamp and back to the generating station.

HIGHWAYS FOR ELECTRICITY. The electron flow of an electric circuit takes place along a highway made of metal. Strip a lamp cord of its coverings and you find part of that highway in the twisted strands of copper wire. Examine the inside of an electric bulb and you will see the coiled filament made of the metal tungsten. From the powerhouse to the appliances in your home electrons are moving along metal paths. Materials that permit easy flow of electrons through them are called *conductors.* Silver, iron, nickel, aluminum, platinum, and lead are examples of metals that are good conductors of electricity. Carbon, though not a metal, is also a conductor of electricity.

Most nonmetals, on the other hand,

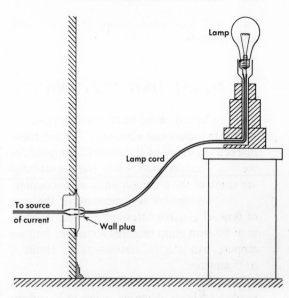

There is a continuous electric circuit between the lamp and the power station when the lamp is on.

are poor conductors of electricity. Rubber is one of the poorest conductors. Cloth, leather, glass, porcelain, and many of the new plastics are poor conductors of electricity. All of these are termed *insulators.* Insulators are used to keep electricity from going where it is *not* wanted. In a lamp circuit the plug is covered with rubber or some other nonmetallic material. The copper wires in the cord may be covered with fabric and rubber.

Electricians use rubber gloves so that they will not be shocked. Telephone and electric wires supported by poles are separated from the wooden crossarms by glass or porcelain insulators. The wood of the poles does not carry electricity when dry, but when wet can conduct electricity quite readily. Wires supported by steel towers require large insulators.

Pure water itself is not a good conductor of electricity, but almost any object becomes a good conductor when wet. Bathrooms become electrocution chambers when individuals coming out of a tub or standing on a wet floor touch lamps or radios with poor insulation.

MEASURING ELECTRICITY

Certain units have been devised by scientists to measure electricity. We see these marked on many of the electrical appliances we use. Ampere, volt, ohm, watt, watt-hour are some of the common units we encounter.

An *ampere* is a measure of the rate of flow of electrons through a wire. A common 60-watt lamp requires about one half an ampere. An electric flatiron takes about 4 or 5 amperes.

A *volt* is a unit of electrical push needed to keep electrons going at a certain rate. A new dry cell has a push of about 1½ volts; a storage battery in an auto, 6 to 12 volts, house circuits, 110 to 120 volts; long-distance electric wires, 200,000 volts or more.

The electric meter, which is located in the basement or in the kitchen or on the outside wall of almost every house, is easy to read. The present reading on the one shown here is 9,413 kilowatt hours. The amount used for any period is computed by substracting the previous reading from this one.

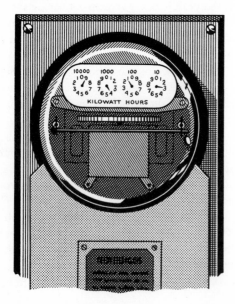

An *ohm* is a unit of electrical resistance. It measures the resistance offered by any conductor to the flow of electrons. Copper is used in electric circuits because it offers less resistance to the flow of electrons than any other metal except silver.

The *watt* is a measure of electric power. This power is a product of the number of amperes (flow) and the number of volts (push). Thus, a lamp in your 120-volt house circuit through which ½ ampere is flowing has a wattage equal to ½ × 120, or 60 watts. Since the watt is a small unit, the *kilowatt,* equal to 1,000 watts, is often used.

The *kilowatt-hour* is the unit that measures the amount of electrical work done. The power company uses this unit in calculating your bill. Thus, in a 100-watt lamp used for 10 hours, the work done is 1,000 watt-hours or 1 kilowatt-hour. If the cost of electricity is five cents per kilowatt-hour, then the cost for this will be 5 cents. Examine an electric bill and you will learn how many kilowatt-hours were used.

The names of all the units given here (and others not mentioned) are derived from the names of scientists who made significant contributions to our understanding of electricity.

FUSES—THE WEAKEST LINK

If an electric wire is carrying too much current for its size (thickness), it will heat up considerably. If this happens in the wiring of a building, it may set fire to some combustible material near it. In order to prevent this, electric fuses are included in the wiring systems of buildings. SEE PAGE 535

Examine an electric fuse of the screw-socket type. When this fuse is in place in a fuse box, electricity flows through it; it is part of the electric circuit. The essential part of the fuse is a flat strip of metal with a low melting point. You can see this strip if you look through the glass window of the fuse. If you can manage to break the seal on a fuse

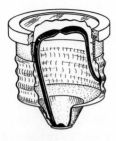

The fuse is the weakest link in the electric circuit. The heart of the fuse is a metal strip with a low melting point, shown here in black.

and take it apart, you will be able to inspect the fuse metal more carefully. Take it out of the container and apply a lighted match to its midpoint. The strip melts easily and falls apart. This is what is meant by the "blowing" of a fuse. Instead of a match, the heat is provided by the surging of too many electrons through the fuse metal. The "blowing" of a fuse, then, is really the heating, melting, and breaking of the fuse metal.

Fuses are described as the "weakest link in the electrical chain." They are made that way so that if there is any overloading of the circuit, this link will break and thus cut off the flow of electricity. Since the heating which occurs when a fuse "blows," takes place within the safe confines of the fuse, no damage is done. Excessive heating along the rest of the line and the danger of fire are averted. The destiny of a fuse, then, is its destruction.

Fuses may "blow" for two reasons: overloading or short circuiting. An electric iron plugged into a circuit already sustaining an electric broiler causes a large number of electrons to flow into that circuit from the supply that is always available from your electric company. The load may be too great for your electric wires to sustain, but, before they can heat up, the sensitive fuse metal melts and breaks the circuit. What should you do? The first thing to do is to unplug the appliance you plugged in just before the fuse melted. Then go to the fuse box, equipped with a new fuse. You will probably see that

one of the fuses looks different because of the break in the metal strip inside it. There may also be some charring on its glass window. Unscrew this fuse and screw in the new one.

A short circuit may also cause a fuse to blow. If, for example, you have a long electric cord connecting your table lamp to a wall socket, and this cord is stepped on or frequently bruised by moving furniture over it, the insulation may be worn off at some point. The two bare wires then touch. A tremendous amount of current goes racing around its new and easy path. The electrons begin to heat up the wires in the circuit, but the fuse responds immediately by melting and breaking the circuit. What should be done? Again the offending appliance (or extension cord) should be unplugged and a new fuse installed. The worn cord, of course, should be repaired or replaced; further short circuits should be avoided by having an electrician install sufficient outlets so that long cords become unnecessary. Sometimes "shorts" develop inside electrical appliances. These, of course, should be repaired. SEE PAGE 533

Extra fuse plugs should always be kept on hand. Some individuals "bothered" by fuses blowing frequently resort to dangerous alternatives. Instead of looking for the cause of the trouble, they replace a burnt-out 15-ampere fuse with a 30-ampere fuse. They are thus substituting a less effective fuse for this particular circuit; the wires in the circuit, which are designed to carry only 15 amperes safely, may overheat dangerously before this fuse melts. They are forgetting that a fuse is built not for strength but for weakness.

Another practice, even more dangerous, is the replacing of a burnt-out fuse with a penny. The penny, being made of copper, is a good conductor of electricity, in fact, too good. If the line is overloaded, or if there is a short circuit, the electric wiring system of the house is converted into a huge toaster, with the house getting the toasting.

In many homes, *circuit breakers* are replacing fuses. As you might suspect from its name, a circuit breaker is a kind of switch. In one common type, an extra surge of electricity causes an electromagnet (see page 520) to attract an iron bar. The bar trips a latch which breaks the circuit. After the source of the trouble is eliminated, the circuit breaker is restored to its original position by hand. In another kind of circuit breaker, a bimetallic (two metals) strip breaks the circuit when it is heated by the extra current.

GENERATING CURRENT ELECTRICITY

SEE PAGE 541
We found, earlier in this chapter, that we really do not manufacture electricity, that all matter has electrical particles in its atoms. Then why do we use a dry cell to ring a bell, or a storage battery to start a car? Why do we plug a lamp into an outlet? Just what are we getting when we pay for our electric bills?

Reduced to one word, the answer is a push. We pay for the energy that is used to cause electrons to move steadily through the wires of the electric circuit. It is true that each atom in the copper wires of your lamp cord has a great many electrons in it. But it is only when some of these electrons

are jarred loose from one atom and hop to the next one that we have an electric current. The atom-hopping characteristic of an electric current might be compared to a circle of jugglers, each tossing his own ninepins into the air, but occasionally flipping one of his pins to the man at his right. In the case of the atoms in a circuit, the process of electron-passing must be initiated and maintained somewhere along the line. Electron-passing may be the result of chemical action in a dry cell or battery. It may be the result of electromagnetic action in a generator. We will study each of these sources separately. Both supply the push for the electron traffic. This is what we pay for.

VOLTA'S DISCOVERY. The chemical way of making electricity in cells and batteries is the older of the two methods used in making current electricity. An Italian scientist, Volta, discovered about 150 years ago that a chemical reaction could produce a continuous flow of electricity. He found, when he placed a strip of copper and a strip of zinc in an acid solution and then connected the dry end of each of these metals with a wire, that electricity began to flow in the wire. He hazarded the brilliant guess that these metals were undergoing a chemical change in the solution, which produced an electrical force. Chemical sources of electricity dominated the field for a hundred years after Volta's discovery. Our modern dry cells and batteries are based on Volta's work.

A full understanding of how the cell worked was only possible when the inner structure of the atom was known. We will not describe the entire process involved but will instead summarize the effect of the chemical activity occurring in a zinc-copper cell:

1. *Extra electrons pile up on the zinc strip (or plate, as it is called) making it rich in electrons, or negative.*
2. *Electrons are lost from the copper plate, making it "electron-hungry," or positive.*

Chemical action in this simple wet cell produces a flow of electricity strong enough to light the small lamp.

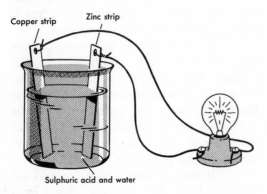

Copper strip   Zinc strip

Sulphuric acid and water

3. *If a path, such as a wire, is provided outside the cell from the zinc to the copper plate, electrons will travel through the wire from the zinc to the copper.*

Thus the cell acts as a kind of electron pump to produce on electric current.

The demonstration cell just described is called a "wet cell." The common "dry" cells used in flashlights and for portable radios are not really dry, for they would not work if they were. If you compare the dry cell with Volta's cell, you will find that it has comparable but not identical parts. Zinc is still one of the metals used; in the dry cell it also serves as the container. Instead of copper, a carbon rod is used; it stands vertically in the center of the cell. Instead of sulfuric acid in water, a moist chemical paste of ammonium chloride fills most of the cell. As in the wet cell, chemical action produces an electrical change. The zinc container accumulates electrons and becomes negative, while the carbon rod becomes positive. In the dry cell shown on this page, two posts on top serve as a convenient place for attaching wires. This dry cell is commonly used to supply current for a bell or buzzer, and also for classroom experiments. It produces 1½ volts, as do the small cells used in flashlights. The dry cell is convenient to carry about because it is compact and because there is no liquid to spill.

Storage batteries (a battery contains two or more cells) have found an important use in automobiles. Contrary to popular opinion, storage batteries do not store electricity in the sense that a can stores fruit. When it is being charged by the generator of the car, the electrical energy going into the battery produces a *chemical* change in it. Chemical energy is what is "stored." When the battery is used to turn the starter, operate the lights and heater, spark the gasoline-air mixture, or run the radio, it operates on the same principle as cells described previously. Chemical energy is converted into electrical energy.

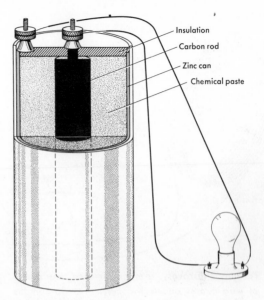

Insulation
Carbon rod
Zinc can
Chemical paste

In a "dry" cell chemical changes produce an electrical current.

The storage battery commonly used in automobiles has six cells arranged in series. Each cell produces 2 volts; the combined voltage is 12 volts.

Storage batteries are often installed in hospitals and other institutions as an auxiliary source of electricity, ready to supplant the regular supply in an emergency. They are also used in lighting buildings in country places not connected by electric lines to a central power station. These batteries are charged by a generator (to be discussed next) driven by a gasoline engine.

GENERATORS. The English scientist, Sir Humphry Davy, once said, "My greatest discovery was Michael Faraday." Michael Faraday began his scientific career as a bottle-washer in Davy's laboratory but soon took his place in the world of science. In his fifty years of research, Faraday performed 16,000 experiments which he faithfully recorded in his scientific notebooks. One, a very simple one, was destined to make possible our modern electrical world. For Faraday discovered a new and simple way of making an electric current without using

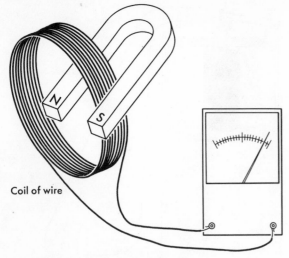

Faraday's discovery: a magnet moved near a coil of wire causes an electric current to flow in the wire.

Coil of wire

messy chemicals or clumsy batteries. He found, in 1831, that, under certain conditions, *magnetism could produce electricity.* He discovered that when he moved a magnet near a coil of wire, electricity flowed in the wire—although the wire was not connected to a battery. When he thrust the magnet into the coil electricity flowed one way through the wire. When the magnet stopped moving, the electricity stopped. When he pulled the magnet out, electricity again flowed in the wire, but in the opposite direction. When he kept moving the magnet in and out, a regular, but pulsating, current was produced. Faraday also found that moving the coil back and forth over the magnet had the same effect as moving the magnet in the coil.

Moving a magnet near a coil of wire or a coil near a magnet caused a movement of electrons in the coil. Note that only three things were needed: a magnet, a coil of wire, and motion. In the years that followed Faraday's classic discovery, scientists found how to use the rush of falling water and the pressure of steam to provide the motion needed to turn huge coils of wire near huge magnets. Today, from hundreds of stations from all over the country, power from waterwheels

or steam turbines is converted into electricity, which, a split second later, is turning a lathe in a nearby factory, cooking a dinner in a home, pumping water, and running a milling machine in a far-off farm. The frontispiece of this chapter shows a mural of TVA's Norris Dam, with the powerhouse cut away to show the water turbine and the electric generator.

AC AND DC. The electron flow in a circuit connected to a dry cell or battery is always in one direction. This kind of current is called *direct current.* A generator can produce this kind too; however, 95 percent of homes and factories in this country are supplied by generators with alternating current. In this type, the electrons flow in one direction, come to a complete halt, and then go in the opposite direction. This change of direction occurs very rapidly, usually 120 times every second. That is why your electric light does not seem to blink.

Alternating current is preferred over direct current because it can be transmitted more economically from power stations to distant places. Alternating current can be converted into direct current, where this is required for local use.

THE ELECTROMAGNET

Faraday and the American scientist Henry laid the basis for the making of enormous quantities of electricity by showing that *magnetism could be converted into electricity.* A few years before, Hans Christian Oersted, a Danish professor of physics, found that *electricity could be converted into magnetism.* While lecturing before a class, Oersted accidentally pushed a compass under a wire connected to a battery. He noticed that instead of pointing north, the magnet needle swung at right angles to the wire. This happened only when the current was on. Oersted was thus led to suspect that electricity had a magnetic influence; that a wire carrying elec-

SEE PAGE 536 TO 538

Oersted's discovery: an electric current flowing through a wire makes that wire behave like a magnet.

tricity had a magnetic field around it. Such a wire might be regarded as an "electricity-magnet," or as we call it, an *electromagnet*.

You can demonstrate the principle of the electromagnet with a piece of insulated bell wire and a dry cell. Twist the wire into a coil by winding it around a cylindrical object, like a pencil, for 40 or 50 turns. Remove

the pencil, scrape both ends of the wire free of insulation and connect them to a dry cell. The coil will then attract and hold small bits of iron (iron filings). It will also cause a compass needle to be deflected from its original position. The coil behaves like a magnet as long as current is flowing through it. To make a much stronger electromagnet, wind the insulated wire around a large iron nail. This electromagnet will pick up heavy objects like steel scissors and knives.

The electromagnet has many advantages over permanent magnets. First it can be made very strong. Its strength can be augmented by increasing the number of turns of wire in the coil or by increasing the amount of current. Perhaps you have seen huge electromagnets, attached to cranes, in junk yards, picking up a load of scrap iron and dropping it into a truck.

A second advantage of the electromagnet is that it is a temporary magnet. That is why, in the lift magnet just described; it can pick up a load of metal and then drop it. When the current is on, it is a magnet; when the current is off, it is not.

Faraday's discovery that magnetism can produce electricity led to the electric generator. In TVA's Norris Dam the rush of falling water spins turbines which turn huge coils of wire near huge magnets. The powerhouse where this occurs is shown in the middle foreground.

THE TELEGRAPH

SEE PAGES 539 TO 540

The fact that an electromagnet is a temporary magnet is the essential principle underlying the functioning of a telegraph. In 1831, Professor Joseph Henry made an exciting demonstration in his class at Albany Academy. Winding many feet of wire around an iron bar, he constructed a powerful electromagnet. He then strung a mile of wire leading from the electromagnet round and round the classroom, finally connecting its ends to a battery. Henry knew of Oersted's experiments. He knew that he could make an electromagnet acquire and then lose magnetism simply by completing and breaking the circuit. He reasoned that the switch with which he could do this might be a few feet, a few yards, perhaps a mile away from the electromagnet—if enough wire was provided.

Near the electromagnet, Henry placed a steel bar mounted on a pivot in such a way that when it moved it would strike a bell. The students were thrilled when he threw the switch completing the mile-long circuit. The steel bar, now attracted by the electromagnet, swung around and struck the bell. The students sensed that a kind of message had been sent almost instantaneously over a one-mile course.

Henry did not capitalize on his invention, but Morse did. Morse, an American painter, was intrigued with Henry's electromagnet, and he was determined to make it into a practicable telegraph. A person sending a message at one end of the line, he thought, could complete the circuit with a switch. A person at the other end, perhaps many miles away, would find that an electromagnet connected to this circuit was attracting an iron bar. When the sender broke the circuit, the iron bar would no longer be attracted, and would, if connected to a spring, return to its original position. A quick on-off movement of the sending switch would make a quick click-clack of the receiving electromagnet and bar, a "dot." A slow on-off switch action would make a slow click-clack

in the receiver, a "dash." A code of letters based on dots and dashes would make it possible to send messages instantaneously to individuals miles away.

With the help of other inventors, Morse succeeded in making a practicable telegraph. In 1844, the famous message, "What hath God wrought!" flashed over the wires from Washington, D. C. to Baltimore.

THE TELEPHONE

SEE PAC 54C

In the telegraph, a spurt of electricity causes an electromagnet to attract an iron bar and make a click. In the telephone, a spurt of electricity causes an electromagnet to attract an iron disk, which then emits speech. How is this accomplished?

The telephone is the product of two branches of science: sound and electricity. Sound will be considered in detail in the next chapter. For the moment, it will help to know that anything that makes sound, a drum for example, does so by shaking rapidly, by vibrating. This vibration is transferred to the air and thence to our eardrums.

The telephone, invented in 1876 by Alexander Graham Bell, consists of two parts, a transmitter and a receiver. The transmitter into which you talk is part of an electric circuit that extends all the way to the receiver of the person at the other end of the line. The telephone exchange, besides connecting you to your friend, provides the electricity needed for the circuit.

Inside the transmitter, there is a little box filled with thousands of grains of black carbon. These grains are part of the electrical circuit: electrons have to flow through them to complete the connection. When you speak, the vibration produced by your vocal cords causes the sides of the carbon box to move in and out. Each time the sides move in, the carbon grains are squeezed together. Each time the sides move out, the grains spread farther apart. This squeezing and unsqueezing does something to the flow of electricity.

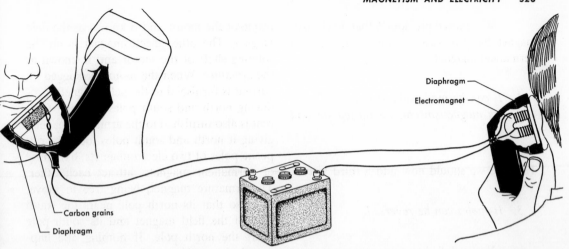

Diaphragm

Electromagnet

Carbon grains

Diaphragm

When you speak into the mouthpiece of a telephone you make the diaphragm vibrate. This affects the electric current, which in turn causes the diaphragm in the receiver to vibrate and to duplicate the original sound. For details see text.

When the carbon particles are squeezed together, they are in close contact, making a broad, solid path for electricity. Electricity flows easily through them. When the pressure is released, the carbon particles spring apart and touch each other more lightly. Now the electrical path is thin and broken—resistance is increased—and the electricity flows weakly.

The effect of speaking, then, is to cause electricity to travel in irregular "spurts," now strongly, now weakly, through the circuit that connects the speaker to the listener. Note that *the sound vibration does not travel through the wires*. Instead, it causes electrons to move in varying amounts instead of their usual steady stream. The sound vibration has been converted into a kind of electrical vibration that is transmitted with lightning speed from speaker to listener.

The telephone receiver converts the electrical vibrations back into sound vibrations. The essential parts of the receiver are an electromagnet and an iron disk. Let us see what the effect of a current varying in strength has on these essential parts. A strong flow of electricity makes the electromagnet

stronger. It pulls harder on the disk. When the flow is weaker, the disk moves back. In this way, the fluctuating electrical circuit causes the disk, or *diaphragm*, to vibrate. The vibrating disk causes the air nearby to vibrate. The air vibrations strike the eardrum of the listener, and he hears a sound that is a duplication of the speaker's voice.

To summarize:

1. *Sound vibrations are changed to electrical vibrations in the transmitter of the telephone.*
2. *Electrical vibrations are transmitted along the line to the receiver.*
3. *In the receiver, the electrical vibrations are changed back to sound vibrations.*

THE ELECTRIC MOTOR

In the telegraph and telephone, an electromagnet attracts a piece of iron. In a motor, there are two electromagnets, one of which drives the other.

SEE PAGE 540

We learned previously that an electro-magnet has two distinct advantages over a permanent magnet:

1. *It can be made very strong.*
2. *Its magnetism can be turned on and off.*

To these we should now add a third virtue:

3. *Its poles can be reversed.*

You recall that a permanent magnet has a definite north and south pole. An electromagnet does too, but the location of its poles depends on the direction in which the current is flowing. When the direction of the current is reversed (as it is when the connections of its wires to a dry cell is switched), the position of its poles is reversed: north to south and south to north.

One of the electromagnets in a motor is fixed in position. It is attached to the outer

In a motor the poles of the field magnet attract the opposite poles of the armature, causing it to turn. Small arrows show electron path.

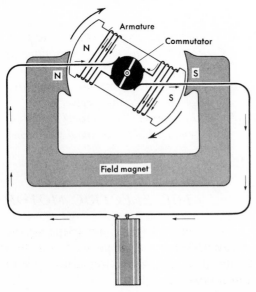

frame of the motor and is known as the *field magnet.* The other electromagnet is on the rotating shaft of the motor and is known as the *armature.* When the motor is plugged in, current is furnished to the field magnets, producing north and south poles in them. Current is also furnished to the armature magnet, giving it north and south poles too. The opposite poles of two electromagnets, like those of permanent magnets, attract each other. The armature magnet, being free to move, turns so that its north pole nears the south pole of the field magnet and its south pole nears the north pole. If nothing else happened, the motor would come to a complete standstill. However, just before the unlike poles reach each other, the direction of the current is reversed in the armature electromagnet, thus reversing the position of its poles. North is now near north, south near south. These repel each other, so the motor keeps turning.

Just how is the current reversed in the armature? Inspect the diagram on this page. At the moment depicted, electrons are flowing from the outside (left) post of the dry cell to one side of the *commutator,* which is shown as a black circle in the center of the armature. Thence the electrons flow through the coiled wire of the armature, back to the other half of the commutator, and then back to the dry cell. What do you think will happen when the armature makes a half turn? Do you see that the ends of the wires (actually the *brushes*) will touch opposite sides of the commutator? As a result, the electrons will now flow in the opposite direction through the armature coil. When this occurs, the magnetic poles are also reversed: north becomes south and south becomes north.

The commutator, then, is the device which makes it possible to reverse the direction of the current and consequently the poles of the armature. The commutator, which is actually a split metal ring, acts as a switch to halt the flow of electrons in one direction, and start them in the opposite direction at just the right instant.

The electric motor is the reverse of the electric generator. In the generator, motion produces electricity; in the motor, electricity produces motion.

ELECTRICITY FOR HEAT AND LIGHT

EE
AGES
40
O
41

Many household appliances, such as electric toasters, percolators, irons, ranges, and heaters, change electrical energy into heat energy. Some of the energy of the moving electrons is turned into heat as the electrons are forced to move against the resistance offered by the wires of the appliance. This resistance is increased by making the wires thin or by using wires of some highly resistant material such as iron or nichrome (an alloy of nickel, chromium, and steel).

The common electric bulb uses a very thin filament, which, because of its high resistance, becomes hot enough to glow brilliantly, but, because it has a high melting point, does not melt.

The phenomenon of glowing when hot is called *incandescence*. Edison began his experiments leading to the invention of the electric lamp in 1877. Many scientists prior to this date had searched for a practical way of using electrical energy to produce light. It remained for Edison to show that a successful incandescent lamp has to have a hairlike filament in order to provide the necessary high resistance. This filament was enclosed in a sealed space devoid of oxygen so that it would not burn up. This was achieved by removing the air from the bulb and sealing it, thus creating a vacuum.

The first filaments were bits of charred or carbonized paper. Later, after a long search, certain kinds of bamboo fibers, when charred, were found to produce a stronger filament. Carbon filaments were used in lamps for about twenty-five years. Eventually they were replaced by the more economical tungsten filament, which not only uses less electricity but also can be heated

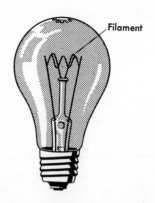

The electric bulb uses a very thin filament, which, because of its high resistance, becomes hot enough to glow brilliantly.

to higher temperatures without melting, thus yielding a whiter light. Another change, one that increased the life of bulbs, was the filling of the lamp with inactive gases, such as argon, that do not support burning. In these new lamps, the evaporation of the filament was reduced; consequently the lamps lasted longer.

The following generalizations are some of the more significant ones in the foregoing material:

Objects made of iron (and several other metals) are attracted by magnets.

When freely suspended, a magnet aligns itself in a north-south position. It becomes a compass.

Magnets are strongest at their poles.

Like poles of magnets repel, unlike poles attract each other.

The earth acts like a magnet.

The magnetism of a substance is due essentially to the magnetic qualities of its atoms and to the arrangement of its atoms.

A steel needle or rod can be magnetized by stroking it with a magnet.

Electricity stems from the electron and proton make-up of atoms.

The contact and separation of two surfaces may permit electrons to be torn away from one and deposited on the other. Both acquire a charge of static electricity.

The object that loses electrons acquires a positive charge; the one that gains electrons, a negative charge.

Like charges repel; unlike charges attract.

Lightning is an abrupt discharge of electricity through the air.

Current electricity is the flow of electrons in a circuit.

A fuse is the weakest link in the electric circuit.

In cells and batteries, chemical action starts electrons moving in one direction to make a current.

Moving a coil of wire near a magnet or a magnet near a coil of wire causes electrons to flow in the coil. This is the principle of the generator.

When electricity flows through a wire, the wire becomes a magnet. This is the principle of the electromagnet, which is fundamental in the electric motor, the telegraph, the telephone, and many other devices.

Electrical energy can be converted into other forms of energy—into heat, light, sound, and mechanical energy.

DISCOVERING FOR YOURSELF

1. Read an electric meter and explain how you did it.
2. Survey your environment to find unusual uses for permanent magnets.
3. Examine three different kinds of worn-out electrical appliances. Make a list of the science principles in electricity that were used in constructing the appliance to make it efficient and useful.
4. Make a list of places in a house where accidents with electricity might occur and suggest precautions that should be taken.
5. Find examples of static electricity in your environment. Keep a list of the places where you observed the phenomena and explain what conditions caused the charge to be generated.
6. Find out how tall buildings in the community are protected against lightning.
7. Discover the following things about a specific house: Where does electricity enter? How many fuses are there? Which appliances use the most electricity? What is the source of the electrical supply?
8. Locate the storage battery in a car. Find out its voltage. Find out why frequent addition of water is necessary. Find out what uses are made of the electricity that is generated.
9. Make a survey of electrical appliances in a house. Find out which ones use an electric motor, which use wires of high resistance, which use electromagnets.
10. Examine a neon sign to discover where it is connected to the main circuit, how a complete circuit is made, and how it is turned on and off.
11. Objects containing iron, such as radiators, railings, and food cans often acquire magnetism from the earth's magnetic field. Use a compass to determine the north and south poles of these objects.
12. Saran wrap is very good for demonstrating static electricity. Crease a piece 2″ x 10″ over a pencil, so that it forms an inverted V. Place your hand between the two "wings" thus formed. What happens? Why? Try various objects such as a pen rubbed on cloth, a piece of glass rubbed on silk, etc. Are the wings attracted or repelled?

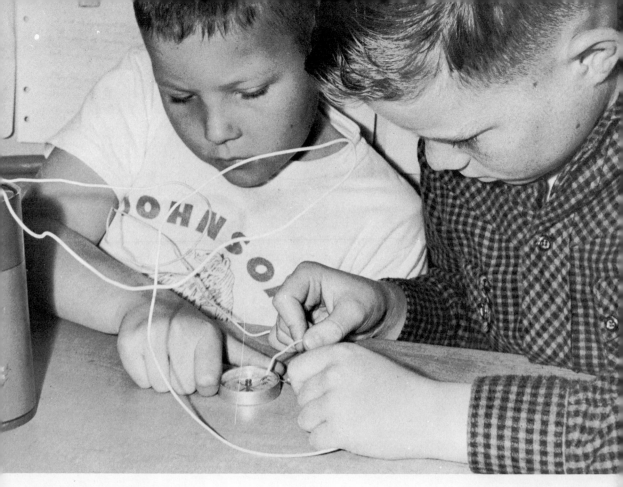

CHAPTER 21B

Teaching "Magnetism and Electricity"

Magnetism and electricity are everywhere in the lives of children—in their homes, the school, and the community. Children bring magnets and magnetic games to school and they like to demonstrate what they discover by using them. They find out that magnets attract some things and not others. When magnetic compasses are brought, questions come up about why the compass points north and south. Installing a doorbell in a playhouse at school or arranging Christmas-tree lights raises problems about electricity. The natural tendency that children have to explore and manipulate comes into play; through these activities and observations in their surroundings, children raise very sensible and searching questions about magnetism and electricity, and plan ways to answer them—a most desirable situation.

If you are going to help children work with magnetism and electricity, remember that:

1. Many children are sources of information and other help. They can bring magnets, worn-out electrical appliances such as heating pads, toasters, worn out dry cells, fuses, light bulbs, to take apart and examine.

2. The school custodians can be of great help with switches, meters, fuses, wiring, electric heating and lighting and the way in which they are used in the school building.

   A parent who is an electrician may be a helpful source of material and information. Junior high school science teachers often have special abilities in this area that the elementary school teacher may draw on. Such exchange as this often marks the beginning of a better understanding between teachers of various grade levels.

3. It is important to keep the ideas simple and to apply these ideas to real situations. Remember that electricity is being used at home, at school, in the neighborhood, and that what is discovered in studying electricity may be applied to understanding the things seen every day.

4. You cannot get a shock from a dry cell. Their wires sometimes become heated but there is no other danger. If you try some of the experiments yourself, you may develop more interest than you thought possible.

In primary grades, the unit problems in this field may be:

What things can we do with magnets?
How and where do we use electricity?

In later elementary grades, the problems will be more inclusive:

What is static electricity?
How do we use electrical circuits?
How is electricity used in communication?
How is electricity produced and distributed?
What can electricity do?

The following activities have been carried out successfully in primary grades. Other activities suggested throughout this chapter may also be used.

1. Make a compass.
2. Learn how to find directions with a compass.
3. Look at home to find different things that electricity does for us.
4. Find games that use magnets and learn how they work.
5. Use magnets to make discoveries such as: where the magnetism is strongest, what it will travel through, what a magnet will attract, etc.
6. Wire (with the help of the teacher or older children) a light or doorbell on a playhouse in the schoolroom.
7. Find out the many different things that electricity does at the school.
8. Look at appliances that use electricity to find out if the electricity makes heat, makes light, or makes something move.
9. Examine a flashlight to see how it works.
10. Take a walk to see some of the things electricity does in the community.

EXPERIMENTING WITH PERMANENT MAGNETS

Pupils should be encouraged to manipulate magnets to make whatever discoveries they can by themselves. This may take place before class begins in the morning or at noon or during any free time. The class experience with magnets may begin by letting various pupils show the class any important discoveries they have made. This is a good opportunity for pupils themselves to devise experiments. Most of the experiments are quite simple.

The following problems may be answered by simple experiments that pupils can devise:

How can we show that some magnets are stronger than others? (By seeing how many paper clips the magnet can hold, by determining the number of pieces of paper through which the magnets can hold a paper clip.)

How can we tell where the strongest parts of the magnets are? (By observing how many paper clips are attracted at various places on a magnet.)

How can we make a needle into a magnet?

How can we tell whether a lodestone has poles? (Use a compass.)

How do the poles of magnets act toward each other?

How can we make a simple compass with a bar magnet?

How can we tell whether a piece of metal is a magnet?

What kind of things will a magnet attract?

Through what kinds of things will magnetism travel?

How can we make an object a temporary magnet by using one of our magnets?

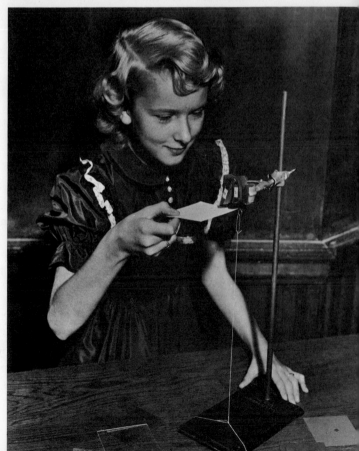

This girl in a Chicago public school is testing to see whether the magnetic force will go through paper. The Alnico magnet in the clamp holds the iron paper clip in midair. She will test other materials too.

Using a rubber ball to represent the earth and a magnet thrust through it to represent the earth's magnetism, pupils can use a compass to help them understand how it shows directions. Note that the magnet is inserted so that it emerges from the ball's surface at the position of the magnetic, not the geographic, pole.

Pupils may work in small groups to prepare their experiments to show to the class. First the whole class may work out a plan for each small group to follow. This procedure is especially important if pupils are just beginning to learn to work in small groups.

When children are experimenting, as with all experiments, caution them not to generalize from one trial. For example, an experiment with one pin or nail is not sufficient evidence from which to conclude that "magnets attract all nails and pins." Children can discover that it is the material that a thing is made of that is important, not the name of the thing itself. Lifting a tin can with a magnet is no basis for saying that magnets attract tin. They do not, you know. Tin cans are made of steel and are merely covered with a very thin coating of tin, and the magnetism travels *through* the tin and attracts the steel inside it, just as it travels *through* paper and attracts iron filings or tacks placed on it.

DEMONSTRATING THE MAGNETIC FIELD

Place a magnet on a table with a piece of paper over it. Sprinkle iron filings on the paper. A definite pattern is formed, showing how far and in what direction the magnetism extends around the magnet. The activity is more meaningful when children understand that this is a way of "seeing" the invisible force of magnetism and not just a new way to play with a magnet. In effect, the filings form a map of the invisible field of force surrounding the magnet. A piece of glass may be substituted for the paper. Such an experience as this is more appropriate for the middle grades than for the primary grades.

MAKING AND USING A COMPASS

By suspending a bar magnet from a support, pupils can make a very crude compass. The bar magnet swings into a north-and-south position. Boy Scout manuals contain directions for making simple compasses. Some pupils may volunteer to get together and make

Through what different kinds of materials will the force of a magnet travel? Various kinds of materials and magnets are used in this investigation. Many trials are made to be sure.

one for the class, or the materials (a flat cork, a magnet, a needle, and a saucer of water) may be assembled, and pupils may make the compass in class. The needle is magnetized by rubbing it (in one direction, not back and forth) on one of the poles of the magnet and is then laid on the cork, which is floating on the water. The needle will soon point north and south. Although the floating-needle compass is interesting historically (originally a lodestone was used in this manner) a compass made by suspending a darning needle by a thread inside a milk bottle (as shown here) is easier to make. It is helpful to have a commercially made compass for examination.

Compass study may center around answering some of the following: What are some of the different kinds of compasses in common use? How can we use a compass to tell where the sun is at different times of the day? How can you use a compass to tell where your house is from school, what direction your school faces, which way the wind blows, or to put directions on a map of your neighborhood?

When several compasses are made, they may be used as a check against each other. Urge pupils to discover different ideas for making them.

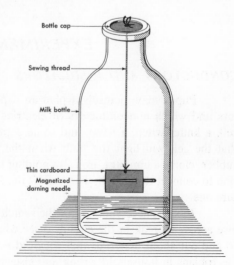

EXPERIMENTING WITH STATIC ELECTRICITY

Pupils can do many experiments about static electricity by themselves. They may demonstrate activities such as combing their hair, rubbing a rubber comb on a wool sleeve, or holding tissue paper against the blackboard and rubbing it rapidly with a silk cloth. The demonstration illustrated here may be done by using a piece of glass, two books, some scraps of paper, and a piece of silk cloth. Lay the two books on the table about four inches apart. Sprinkle the scraps of paper on the table between the books. Lay the piece of glass over the books so that it covers the paper. Rub the glass vigorously with the silk cloth. The paper will jump up from the table to the glass. Experiment with books of various thickness to see how far the pieces will jump. Try to make measurements of the distance on different days.

Some experiences with static electricity are more effective if they take place in the dark so that pupils can observe the sparks. Pupils are then more likely to see the connection between static electricity and lightning. In the elementary school, in most circumstances it is considered neither important nor desirable to go into detailed explanation of the behavior of electrons. There are, however, individual pupils who can, on their own initiative, explore further to find out the behavior of electrons in relation to static electricity.

Static electricity experiments work better on dry days than on humid ones. Pupils will be interested to experiment on different days to see that this is true. Some kinds of material such as Saran wrap show the effects of static electricity in almost any kind of weather.

Rubbing a glass with a silk cloth is one way to demonstrate the phenomenon of static electricity.

EXPERIMENTING WITH ELECTRIC CURRENT

CONDUCTORS AND INSULATORS

Pupils may themselves plan an experiment to discover which materials are conductors and which nonconductors of electricity. To do this they need a simple circuit—a dry cell, a knife switch, a lamp, and some copper wire. Connect the dry cell to the lamp to see that the cell will light the bulb when the switch is closed. Now open the switch and test rubber, cloth, aluminum, iron, by holding them across the two poles of the switch in a position to connect the switch. The bulb is the kind used in a flashlight and the socket is a miniature one.

It is not necessary to use the switch; the materials to be tested may be held anywhere else across a break in the circuit to see whether they will complete it. Pupils may use books to find out about materials that they did not test and to see how nonconductors are used by electricians in household wiring and elsewhere.

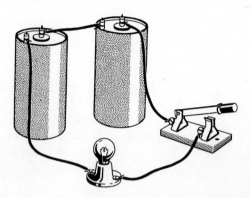

A knife switch is used between the dry cells and the lamp to make and break the circuit.

SHORT CIRCUITS

Connect a dry cell to an electric lamp using copper wires that have had their insulation removed in several places. Touch a bare spot on one wire to a bare spot on another. Pupils will devise variations of this experiment to show other ways to make short circuits. This experiment has application to the cause of fire in buildings and to use of worn extension cords.

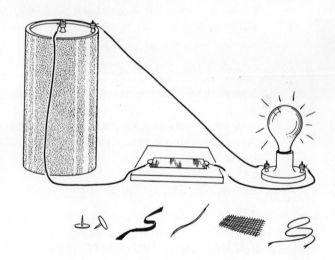

A simple piece of apparatus may be used to find out if materials are conductors or non-conductors of electricity. Materials to be tested may be laid across the two thumbtacks. The pupils will think of many materials to test.

Since the safe use of electricity is of importance to all of us, here are some general rules, stated simply and organized according to their application.[1] Rules such as these should not be merely memorized by children. As children study electricity, they come to understand the reason for the precautions and consequently they see the sense of observing them. The rules apply to home, school, and any other place where electricity is used, but they are useful only if they are learned in a functional manner and not merely memorized. It is important to stress that children should not work with house current or replace fuses.

---

[1] From W. L. Beauchamp, G. O. Blough, and M. Williams, *Discovering Our World*, Book 3 (Chicago, Scott, Foresman, 1957).

SAFETY RULES FOR USING ELECTRICAL APPLIANCES

1. Disconnect all electrical appliances when they are not being used.
2. If there is a switch on an electrical appliance, turn it off before you disconnect the appliance. Also be sure that the switch is turned off before you connect the appliance.
3. Never use an electrical appliance or an electric cord that you know is out of order.
4. Never try an experiment with an electrical appliance or an electric cord that is connected to the current in your home or at school.
5. Never touch an electrical appliance with wet hands. Also be sure not to touch it if any part of your body is touching a water pipe.

SAFETY RULES FOR USING ELECTRIC WIRES

1. Never touch electric wires or use an electric cord on which the covering is worn.
2. Keep electric wires and cords from rubbing against things or becoming kinked. Rubbing may wear off the covering, and kinking may break it.
3. Stay away from broken wires that hang down from poles or buildings.
4. Never climb a pole that supports electric wires.
5. Never touch an electric wire or cord with wet hands. Also, do not take hold of a wire or cord while any part of your body is touching a water pipe, faucet, or radiator.

SAFETY RULES FOR USING FUSES

1. Never try to repair a "burnt-out" fuse. Use a new one.
2. When a fuse "burns out," always put in a new fuse that will carry the same current. If the old fuse is labeled 15A, the new fuse should be labeled 15A.
3. Never try to use a penny instead of a new fuse. The penny is made of copper. It will not melt until the copper wires do too. (See experiment on fuses, page 535.)
4. Always turn off the current when you put in a fuse. Otherwise you may get an electric shock.

SAFETY RULES FOR USING SWITCHES

1. Have a switch repaired at once if you get a shock when you use it to turn current on or off.
2. Never touch a switch with wet hands. Also, do not touch a switch when any part of your body is touching a water pipe, faucet, or radiator.

SAFETY RULES FOR USING ELECTRIC HEATERS

1. Never use a knife, fork, or spoon to get bread out of an electric toaster while it is turned on. You may get a shock or a burn, or you may cause a short circuit.
2. Do not use a damp cloth to clean the outside of an electric heater while it is turned on. Disconnect the heater and wait until it cools.

3. Do not go away and leave an electric iron connected. It may set the ironing board on fire.
4. Do not hang wet clothes on an electric heater to dry. You may cause a short circuit or even a fire.
5. Never touch an electric heater while you are in a bathtub or while any part of your body is touching a water pipe, a faucet, or a radiator.
6. If you use an electric heating pad, be sure that it has a waterproof cover. You may get a shock if perspiration soaks into it.

As children study electricity, they may make their own safety rules from the knowledge they have gained. These rules may be checked against those given here and any important ones that have been omitted may be added. Children should be encouraged to take this list home and to talk it over with their parents to decide which rules apply especially to their homes.

FUSES

The drawing illustrates a simple demonstration that shows how a fuse protects a house. Use a block of soft wood, two thumbtacks, a dry cell, some copper wire, and a piece of metal foil. Press the thumbtacks into the wood, connect them with the narrow strip of foil, making sure that the foil makes a good connection with the tacks, and connect the wires to the cell. It is helpful to cut a notch on either side of the metal foil near the center to make a very narrow place in the foil. The foil melts. (If the demonstration does not work at first, let pupils decide why. It may be because the foil strip is too wide or because the connections are not properly made. The problem-solving involved in trying to decide why the demonstration does not work may be as important as understanding the demonstration itself.)

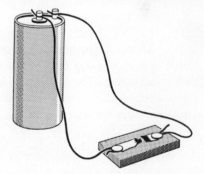

A piece of foil (from a chewing-gum wrapper or similar source) is used to illustrate how a fuse works. Pupils will learn that foil must be cut in a very narrow strip before electricity will melt it.

MAKING SWITCHES

Switches—devices for breaking and completing circuits—are readily purchased, but the two pictured here are easily made. In the making, pupils may understand more clearly the nature of an electric current.

The switches are made of the following materials: A sandpapered block of soft wood, about 1½" × 3" × ½", 2 brass screws, a piece of copper 1" × 3" × ½", or a piece cut from a tin can (use tin shears), a cork, 2 lengths of bell wire (long enough to reach to a bell or buzzer and to the dry cell).

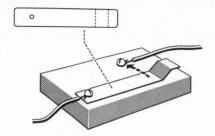

Homemade apparatus such as this sometimes teaches science principles better than any other materials.

Cut out the metal arm as shown, and make a hole at one end for the screw. Insert the screw through the hole and screw it part way into the block. Remove insulation from one end of the wire and twist the wire clockwise around the screw. Tighten the screw but leave it loose enough so that the switch arm can be moved. Mark on the block the location of the second screw and drive this screw in halfway. Remove the insulation from a second length of wire, bend the end clockwise around the screw, and tighten the screw. When the switch arm is in the position shown in the drawing the circuit is open, or broken. When the arm is moved over to touch the second screw, the circuit is closed. This switch may be used in any of the circuits for lighting lamps, operating electromagnets, etc.

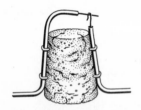

Pupils can think of variations of this cork switch by substituting materials and construction.

A second type of switch is made by using a large cork as shown in the drawing above. Corks such as this one are sold by drugstores and by supply houses, or children may bring them from home. The switch shown here was made from a cork 1½ inches in diameter (large end). Insulated staples were used in making it, but any small staple will do. Remove insulation from the wires, as shown, bend one end of the bare wire into the shape of a hook, and connect both wires as shown. When the straight bare wire is hooked under the hook of the other wire so that the two wires touch, the circuit is closed. Otherwise it is open.

EXPERIMENTING WITH AN ELECTROMAGNET

Use one or two dry cells, two or three feet of insulated wire, a large nail, and some iron thumbtacks. (The wire is wound around the nail, and the ends of the wire are connected to a dry cell. Be sure that the wires are not left connected for very long or you will wear out the dry cell.) Instead of reading directions from a book, pupils may be asked to see whether they can make the nail into a magnet by using the materials. Test the nail first to see that it is not magnetized. If they are not successful, they may go to their books, read the directions carefully, and make the electromagnet. Such procedure is likely to provoke much more thinking from pupils than following directions in a book from the beginning.

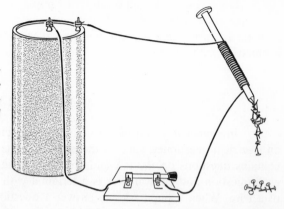

When electricity flows through it, the electromagnet can pick up objects of iron. When the circuit is broken, it drops them. An electromagnet is temporary; its strength can be changed and its poles reversed.

Questions about the need for taking the insulation off the ends of the wire will probably be raised, and a discussion of what insulation is and what materials are insulating materials may follow.

Pupils may now try to make the electromagnet stronger, following the same procedure used for making it. (They will find that using more than one dry cell or winding more turns of wire around the nail may produce the desired results.) After the electromagnet has been made and used, pupils may be asked to hunt for places where electromagnets are used at home and at school. After the investigations, the class may make a list. (It will include doorbells, electric motors, telegraph sets, etc.)

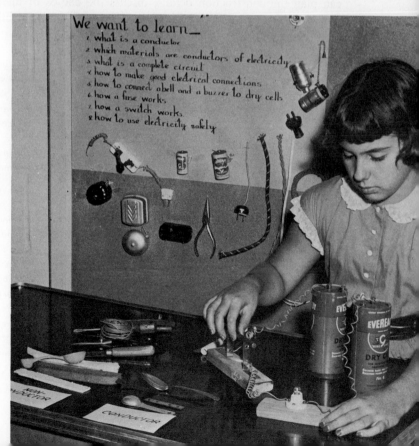

The apparatus here is being used to test conductors and non-conductors by placing them in a gap in the circuit (under pupil's right hand). Pupils have made the apparatus.

Here again is an opportunity for pupils to use mathematics to help to discover relationships. Have them discover how many tacks (or paper clips) are picked up with 6 turns of wire, 12 turns, etc., or with one dry cell, two dry cells, etc. They may devise a chart to summarize their results.

MAKING AN ELECTRICAL QUESTIONER

In connection with their study of electric circuits, pupils may be interested in making an electrical questioner, such as the one shown here. This device uses cards, each of which contains questions on the left and answers (in scrambled sequence) on the right. Next to each question and each answer is a terminal with which electric contact is made by means of a wire. When a pupil tries to answer a question, he touches the question terminal with one wire and the answer terminal with another. If he touches the correct answer, an electric light bulb goes on.

The terminals may be made of copper fasteners, stove bolts, or any other conducting material. Each "question" terminal is connected, in back of the board, to one "answer" terminal by means of insulated copper wire. Also behind the board is a flashlight battery to which are connected two lengths of copper wire long enough to reach all the terminals on the front of the board. One of these wires is connected through the circuit of the light bulb, which is mounted on the front of the board. When one wire is touched to a "question" terminal and the other to the correct "answer" terminal, the wire which connects the terminals behind the board completes the circuit and the light goes on.

The building of the questioner can be an interesting and profitable activity. Pupils can plan the construction details, discuss the choice of materials, solve problems as they arise in the construction, and learn to work together efficiently.

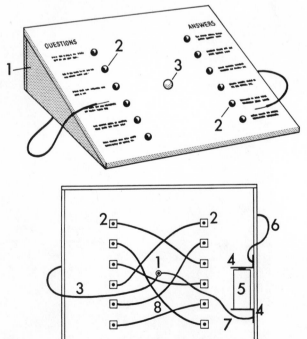

Front view: The questioner uses cards that have the questions on the left side and the answers on the right, but the answers do not correspond in sequence to the questions. 1, wedge-shaped side board; 2, terminal made of stove bolt or copper fastener; 3, flashlight bulb.

Rear view: Behind the board, each "question" terminal is connected to an "answer" terminal. 1, socket for flashlight bulb; 2, ends of terminals; 3, wire that reaches from flashlight bulb to front of board for contact with terminal; 4, copper strips for holding flashlight battery; 5, flashlight battery; 6, wire that reaches from flashlight battery to front of board for contact with terminal; 7, wire from battery to light bulb; 8, wire connecting pairs of terminals.

Once completed, the questioner may be used for bird and wildflower identification or for the answering of questions encountered in the study of science. The preparation of question cards involves skills in art and in language arts.

MAKING A TELEGRAPH SET

Constructing a telegraph key and sounder is a very exciting activity for elementary school pupils. The picture on this page and the following description are from a book for sixth grade.[2]

> You can easily learn how a telegraph works if you make a telegraph set like the one in the picture. First, make the sounder. This is the part that clicks when a telegraph is working. Get two pieces of soft wood. Use one piece for the base and the other for the back. Make the electromagnet by winding twenty-five or thirty turns of insulated copper wire around a large nail. Drive the nail part way into the base. It is a good idea to drill a small hole in the wood before you drive the nail. The hole will keep the nail from splitting the wood. Now nail the back to the base.
>
> Next, cut a strip from a tin (pie plate). The strip should be about three quarters of an inch wide and four inches long. Of course, you know that the tin (pie plate) is made of steel covered with a very thin layer of tin. Drill a little hole in one end of the strip. Then fasten it to the wood base with a screw. Bend the strip so that one end is about one eighth of an inch above the top of the nail. The strip will be the *armature*. It is the part that moves. Drive a small nail in the wood back just above the armature. To make binding posts for the wires, put two screws in the wood base. Connect the ends of the wire from the electromagnet to the binding posts.

By using such easily obtainable materials, pupils can construct this key and sounder. A group of especially interested pupils may wish to do the construction and demonstrate the results to the class. Problems that arise through this experience are often real learning situations.

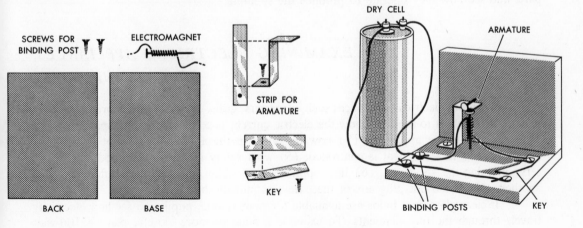

SCREWS FOR BINDING POST — ELECTROMAGNET — STRIP FOR ARMATURE — KEY — BACK — BASE — DRY CELL — ARMATURE — BINDING POSTS — KEY

---

[2] W. L. Beauchamp, G. O. Blough, and M. Williams, *Discovering Our World*, Book 3 (Chicago, Scott, Foresman, 1957).

Now make the *key*. Use a strip from a (tin pie plate). The strip should be the same size as the armature. Drill a small hole in one end of the strip. Fasten the strip to the wood with a screw, in the position shown in the picture. Bend the strip so that the other end is off the wood. Put another screw under this end of the strip. The strip should touch this screw when you push the end down. Connect the key and the sounder to a dry cell, as shown in the picture.

STUDYING THE TELEPHONE

A detailed study of the telephone mechanism is not generally included in science courses of the first six grades. Pupils with unusual interest and ability in electricity and communication may go ahead under their own initiative with such assistance as the teacher may provide or help them obtain elsewhere. See bibliography for books on electricity.

STUDYING AN ELECTRIC MOTOR

A toy electric motor, which pupils may bring from home, is easy to operate and enables pupils to see the parts. There is a small wheel connected to the armature that turns with it, and this may be used to turn the wheels of toys. Pupils will show considerable ingenuity in working with such a motor. In the elementary school, it is hardly advisable, except in cases of unusual interest on the part of individual pupils, to go into detail on how the electric motor operates. It is possible for them, however, to understand how the attraction and repulsion of the poles of magnets (usually electromagnets) is used to produce spinning motion. One very simple and inexpensive one, which operates on dry cells, may be purchased ready for assembly from G. W. Moore, Inc., 100 Beaver Street, Waltham 54, Massachusetts. The directions for assembling it are included. Toy stores and many ten-cent stores carry similar motors. Many of the books in the bibliography supply directions for making different kinds of motors. Children may make a list of the many everyday appliances that make use of motors. If there is a St. Louis motor available, pupils can see the moving parts and see how they operate to produce the spinning.

EXAMINING ELECTRICAL APPLIANCES: HEAT AND LIGHT

Worn-out electrical appliances such as toasters, grills, etc., that pupils bring to school may be taken apart to see: (1) how the electric current is completed in the appliance; (2) what gets hot in the appliance; (3) how the wires in the appliance are kept from short-circuiting; (4) how the heat is controlled; (5) what safety measures are important to observe in using the appliance; (6) how appliances are alike and how they differ from one another. (Note: Do not plug any of these devices into the building current.)

If clear glass light bulbs are available for examination, pupils can see how electricity travels through the tiny filaments. To examine a filament more closely, place a 100-watt bulb in a double paper bag and break it with a hammer. Examine the filament with a 10X lens to see how it is made.[3] An electrical-appliance dealer may be able to furnish some printed material helpful in understanding how light bulbs work. Someone from the store may explain to the pupils how neon and other electrical signs work. Some appliance dealers have replicas of Edison's first lamp, which they are glad to lend to schools. If fluorescent lights have recently been installed anywhere in the school, the school custodian may be able to supply the class with information about them. Someone in the class may like to find out about Thomas Edison's invention of the electric lamp and report his findings to the class.

FINDING OUT WHERE ELECTRICITY COMES FROM

Pupils will probably be interested in finding out where the electricity that they use at home and at school comes from and how it gets to the places where it is used. It may be feasible to make a field trip to a power plant. Here, pupils may see how the energy of burning fuels, of running water, or perhaps of atomic energy is converted into electrical energy. Dry cells may be cut in half and examined, and some pupils may find out about the storage batteries in their cars.

OBSERVING ELECTRICAL INSTALLATIONS

If a new house is being constructed near the school, pupils can see applications of many of the things they have studied. Arrangements for the trip should be made carefully, as previously suggested for field trips. Pupils may go to see where electricity enters the house; where the meters, fuses, and house switches are to be installed; how the wires are installed; where insulation is used; and how safety precautions are exercised.

The school custodian may be willing to show pupils some of these same things in the schoolhouse so that they will have a clearer understanding of how electricity is carried through the school buildings. Pupils should be encouraged to learn about electricity in their own homes.

RESOURCES TO INVESTIGATE

1. An electrical shop for odds and ends of wire, insulating materials, magnets, and other materials, as well as for information about electricity.
2. Ten-cent store for purchase of inexpensive electrical equipment for use in experiments.
3. A junk shop for metals to test as conductors, for magnets, and for other odds and ends.
4. The local power company for information about the source of electricity, its cost, etc.
5. Western Union and the local telephone company for a visit to see how electricity is used in communication.

---

[3] Schwartz, Julius, *Through the Magnifying Glass* (New York, Whittlesey House, 1954).

6. The school custodian to show pupils where electricity enters the school, the fuse box, the electric meter, the switches, how insulating materials are used for safety; to provide burned-out fuses; to read the electric meter; and for other similar purposes.

7. A local electric-appliance dealer for information on the various uses to which electricity is put in the community.

8. Children's homes for illustrations of the ways in which electricity is used to do various kinds of work in the home.

9. The community for examples of the many kinds of work done by electricity in factories, in homes, in stores, in public buildings, on the streets, etc.

10. Local hardware store or department store to see how many tools and appliances use magnetism and electricity.

11. Local radio or television station to see how programs are put on the air.

12. A hydroelectric plant for information about the generation of electricity.

13. Local electrical contractors for regulations related to electrical installations and uses of electricity.

14. Toy store for toys that use magnetism or electricity.

15. The local doctor for information on the uses of magnetism and electricity in the instruments that he uses.

CHAPTER 22A

Sound and How We Use It

We live in a world of sound. Sounds excite, frighten, soothe, inform. Our language reflects our keen awareness of sound. In the country we mark the *hum* of mosquitoes, the *rustle* of leaves, the *lowing* of a cow, the *flutter* of wings, the *roar* of a waterfall. In the city we note the *blare* of automobile horns, the *rumbling* of trains, the *blast* of factory whistles, the *patter* of children's feet, the *cries* of street vendors. Each season, each mood of nature is announced by its own special sounds. Man also makes his contribution in the complex sound combinations that he evokes from musical instruments—from violin strings, organ pipes, drumheads, and from his own vocal cords.

This chapter is the story of sounds. It is the story of how sounds are made, how sounds differ, how sounds travel, how sounds are detected, how sounds may be controlled.

WHAT CAUSES SOUND?

Pluck a stretched rubber band and listen to its sound. Look at it and observe the rapid back-and-forth motion—its vibrations. When the vibrations stop, the sounds stop. SEE PAGES 556 TO 557

Put your fingers on your throat and say "ah." Something inside is vibrating, something very much like the rubber bands. These vibrators are your vocal cords.

Place a thin plastic twelve-inch ruler across the edge of a table so that about half of it protrudes. Hold it down firmly, with one hand placed just above the edge of the table. Slap it lightly with the other hand. Hear, feel, and see the vibrations.

Whenever a sound is produced, something is quivering, trembling, shaking back and forth—vibrating. That something may be a string, a membrane, a reed, a column of air. It may originate in an insect's wings, a ticking watch, an animal's throat, a tuba's horn or a thunderbolt.

HOW IS SOUND CARRIED?

SEE PAGE 558 A tree crashes in a far-off forest. No human, no animal at all is present to hear the crash. Was a sound produced? The answer, of course, depends on our definition of sound. If sound is defined only as that which is heard, then no sound was produced. If sound is defined as a certain kind of vibration, then sound was produced, whether it reached the ears of a living thing or not.

Sounds from crashing trees or vibrating violins or people's throats usually reach our ears through the air. Just how do sounds travel?

Consider a bell tinkling from the impact of its clapper. As the bell shakes it imparts its rhythmic back-and-forth motion to the air particles—molecules—immediately around it. These molecules in turn pass the vibratory motion to the air molecules adjacent to them and so on. In this way, the vibration travels outward in all directions from its source. A small part of the air wave strikes a little membrane in your ear—your

eardrum—and starts it trembling in the same way that the bell was trembling. A vibration originating in a bell has been transferred to air molecules and from air molecules to your eardrum. Later we will see how we become *aware* of the sound.

SOUND WAVES.   A *sound wave* set in motion by a bell has reached our ears. The only thing that has traveled is a vibratory motion; the sensation the sound evokes within us is quite another thing. A sound wave is often compared to what happens when a pebble is dropped into a quiet pond. A wave spreads outward until it strikes the edge of the pond.

So, when we say that sound is traveling through the air, we really mean that a certain kind of wave is proceeding through the air. This may be compared to what happens when a policeman tries to hold back a curious crowd. As he pushes against the individuals near him, they are forced back. In turn they force those behind them back, and so on over an ever-widening area. Each individual may have taken only one step backward, but the wave of "compression" has traveled many feet through the crowd.

In a sound wave, the particles of air between the sounding object and your ear—

A tinkling bell starts a sound wave of condensation (air particles jammed together) and rarefaction (air particles spread apart). The wave moves away from the bell in all directions.

drum move back and forth only a tiny distance. Each impulse started by a vibrating object, such as a violin string, starts a wave in which air particles are successively jammed together and then spread apart.

A MEDIUM FOR SOUND. The first space travelers to land on the moon will have to communicate with each other by radio, for there is no air there. In a classic experiment in physics, the air is pumped out of a jar in which a ringing alarm clock is suspended. As the air is gradually exhausted from the jar, the sound gets fainter and fainter until it cannot be heard, although the clapper of the bell is seen moving. As air is admitted into the jar, the alarm is heard again.

Gases such as air are not the only medium for the transmission of sound. When two stones are clapped together underwater, divers many feet away can hear the sound through the water. The American Indians put their ears to the ground to hear the sound of far-off hoofbeats. The rumblings of a train many miles away can be detected by placing one's ear against the train rail, which carries sound more effectively than air. These illustrations show that sound travels well through liquids and solids.

THE SPEED OF SOUND

SEE PAGES 558 TO 559

A flash of lightning is seen several seconds before the crash of thunder is heard, although both occur at the same time. The sound of a woodsman's ax reaches a distant observer's ears after he has seen the ax strike the wood. The white clouds puffing from a whistle of a far-off locomotive are seen before the shrill blast is heard.

These and many other observations and experiments make it apparent that it takes time for sound to travel from the sounding object to our ears, certainly much more time than light takes to reach our eyes.

The speed of sound through air was determined by the Dutch scientists Moll and Van Beek in 1823. Two high hills eleven miles apart were used for this experiment. A cannon on one of the hills was fired. An observer on the other hill noted the flash of fire (the experiment was done at night to make it more visible) and then counted the number of seconds until he heard the report. The experiment was repeated a number of times. It was also checked by firing a cannon on the opposite hill, in order to cancel any error that might have been caused by the wind. From this experiment, the average speed of sound was calculated to be about 1,100 feet per second. (In these experiments, it was assumed that light travels instantaneously. Actually, light travels at the rate of about 186,000 *miles* a second; this obviously would not affect the interpretation of the results of the experiment appreciably.)

Careful observations have shown that the speed of sound through air is 1,090 feet per second when the temperature is 32° F. (0° C.). Perhaps an easy way of remembering this is to consider that it takes sound about 5 seconds to travel a mile. In chapter 9A, this fact is used to provide a method for determining the distance of a lightning flash from an observer. At temperatures higher than 32°, sound travels faster, and at lower temperatures more slowly.

Sound travels more quickly through liquids and solids than through air. It travels about 4 times as fast through water, about 10 times as fast through pine wood, and about 17 times as fast through steel as it does through air.

SOUND BOUNCES

ECHOES. Have you ever heard your voice come back to you as an echo from a cliff, a building, or a hill? An echo is heard because sound bounces off these structures, just as a ball bounces off a wall. An echo also resembles the reflection of light from a mirror. An echo is a sound reflection.

Echoes are heard as separate sounds only if they reach the listener one-tenth of a second or more after the original sound. It takes at least that time for the human ear to separate one sound from another. If you want to hear your echo, you must stand at least 55 feet away from the reflecting wall. If you shout against a cliff 55 feet away, the sound will travel 55 feet to the cliff and bounce 55 feet back to you, a total distance of 110 feet. Since sound travels about 1,100 feet per second, it can make this trip in one-tenth of a second. The echo will reach your ear one-tenth of a second after you hear your own original voice. You will, therefore, just be able to distinguish it as an echo.

If, on the other hand, the reflecting wall is only 11 feet away, as it might be in your living room, the sound bounces back too fast, taking only one-fiftieth of a second for the trip. In this case the sound reflection only *prolongs* the original sound; it is not detected as an echo.

SEE PAGE 558 An echo may interfere seriously with hearing, particularly in a large gymnasium or in an auditorium. The echoes overlap the words of the speaker in such a way as to cause confusion. Such a difficulty may be overcome by using sound-deadening materials for the walls, ceilings, and floors. Soft materials, such as canvas, curtains, soft wall boards, and rugs absorb sound waves and reflect little sound. Auditoriums often have soft wood walls for this reason.

CONCENTRATING SOUND. Sound waves may be reflected from curved surfaces and concentrated in such a way as to increase audibility. Large auditoriums often have stages that are curved at the back like the reflector in an automobile headlight. Sound waves strike the curved surface and are reflected out into the auditorium to add to the audibility.

Cheerleaders often use megaphones to shout directions to their "rooters." Mega-phones, like band shells, permit sound to go out in only one direction. The energy is thus concentrated rather than dissipated over a wide space.

Before electronic hearing aids were common, partially deaf people used ear trumpets, which are essentially megaphones used in reverse. The large end gathers more sound waves than the ear alone could catch. Your own outer ear is a sound catcher, although you could hear very well without it. If you cup your ears, you collect more sound waves and thus convey their energy to your eardrums.

The stethoscope is used by physicians to detect heart and other internal sounds that furnish clues to the condition of the body. The end of this instrument which is placed against the patient contains a diaphragm that is much larger than the human eardrum and consequently collects more sound energy. The tubing of the stethoscope channels the sound to the doctor's ears without much loss.

MEASURING DISTANCE BY SOUND

Echoes have been put to practical use by navigators for determining the depth of water under their ships. A vibrator attached under water to the hull of the ship sends sound waves into the water. These hit the bottom and bounce back to the ship. The time between the emission of the sound and its reception as an echo is noted and the depth is calculated. If, for example, one second is required, the sound has traveled 4,500 feet. (The speed of sound in water is about 4 times its speed in air.) The bottom, therefore, is 2,250 feet down.

Sonar, a modern sounding device, gives both the direction of the returning waves and the time required for the round trip. In this way, a detailed picture of the ocean depths is obtained. This picture may include underwater reefs, wrecks, mines, and even schools of fish.

Sound pulse

Echo

Sonar makes it possible for a ship to determine the depth to the ocean floor. The time elapsed between the sending of the sound from the sonar vibrator and its reception as an echo by the ship provides the information needed to determine the depth of the water.

BATS AND THE BLIND. How can a bat fly through the total darkness of a cave, avoiding all obstacles in its path? Before 1800, Lazzaro Spallanzani of Italy discovered that if the *ears* of a bat were covered, the bat would collide helplessly with large conspicuous objects. Thus, scientists were led to associate the agility of a bat in the dark to its hearing. But the almost silent flight of bats made them ask: just what do they hear?

In 1920, an English physicist, H. Hartridge, suggested that bats might be hearing *ultrasonic* sounds. These are sounds that are too high-pitched for human ears to detect. Donald Griffin and Robert Calambo, American scientists, studied the problem intensively between 1938 and 1941. They found that the bats themselves emitted these ultrasonic sounds from their mouths and that their ears

were designed to receive them. They tested the skill of bats by having them fly through a darkened room divided in half by a row of wires hanging from the ceiling and spaced about a foot apart. The bats were successful in flying through without touching the wires. Stopping the ears of the bat *or* covering their mouths with tape reduced their scores to the level of pure chance. In short, bats find their way around by sending sound waves out and by receiving echoes that tell them of nearby objects.

Studies have shown that the extraordinary skill shown by some blind people in "sensing" and avoiding obstacles is due to their heightened ability to detect reflected sounds. They "see" with their ears. At Innsbruck University in Austria, scientists working with the blind tested this theory. They covered all exposed parts of the body of a blind individual possessing this "sense," in order to exclude the possibility of the *skin* serving as a detector. Only the ears were left exposed. The tested individual displayed the same agility as he usually possessed. However, when his ears were stopped, this skill was lost.

In both bats and people, the emitted sound and the echo reflected from close objects are not heard separately; rather, the echo changes the quality of the original sound —just as footsteps sound different in different rooms of your house.

SOUNDPROOFING

Most new school buildings, public auditoriums, and broadcasting and television studios are soundproofed to reduce the noise in each room and to prevent sounds from disturbing people in the next one. In schools, this is done for music and woodworking rooms and for lunchrooms. Porous wood products, rugs, draperies, porous plasters, fiber boards, and felts are among the materials used to deaden sounds and thus to reduce echoes.

In all of these materials, sound energy is absorbed instead of being reflected. The regular motions of the air molecules that constitute a sound wave are converted into irregular motions (heat) in the pores of the absorbing materials. In an automobile, the sound of the exhaust is reduced by conveying the sound waves through the winding path of the muffler before they escape to the air. In this way, the energy of the sound waves initiated by the explosions in the cylinders is dissipated.

CHARACTERISTICS OF SOUND

How do we distinguish among the multiplicity of sounds that we hear, when, for example, we listen to a full orchestra playing a symphony? There are three characteristics by which we identify sounds: loud-

ness, pitch, and quality. All of these have to do with the nature of the vibrations that are producing the sound.

LOUDNESS. It is obvious that when the tympanist strikes his drum hard, a louder sound is produced than when he taps it gently. A powerful stroke causes the drumhead, and consequently the particles of air next to it, to move back and forth for a greater distance than a gentle stroke. A powerful wave travels from the drum to you, making your eardrums vibrate vigorously. The loudness of the sound you hear depends, then, on how far the sound waves make your eardrums move in and out. In a literal sense, the tympanist has "your ear."

Loudness depends also, of course, upon the distance of the listener from the source of the sound. Since more and more air is set in motion by the sound wave as it advances in all directions from the drum, its energy is spent in many directions. In an auditorium, this is compensated for by the reflection and the concentration of sound by the sides, back, and top of the hall.

The loudness of a sound may be measured by means of a sound-level meter. The unit for measuring sound is the *decibel* ("bel" from Alexander Graham Bell). The rustling leaves in a light breeze have a rating of about 10 decibels, sounds within the average home about 20 decibels, a large railroad station about 55 decibels, a boiler factory 100 decibels. At 120 decibels, sounds become physically painful. Continuous noise above 50 decibels is thought to be harmful to a person's emotional well-being.

PITCH. If sound is compared to an ocean wave, then loudness is associated with the *height* of the wave. Pitch, by the same analogy, is a characteristic determined by the *number* of waves that pass a point in a given period of time. In the science of sound, we say that pitch depends upon the number of vibrations per second made by the vibrating body. By definition, one vibration, some- SEE PAGE 557 times called a *cycle*, includes both the backward motion and forward motion of the vibrating body.

If you draw your fingernail over the back of a linen-covered book, the nail will produce a sound because it is being vibrated by the many little ridges in the cloth. As you increase the speed with which you move your finger, the pitch increases to higher and higher tones. The pitch of the note depends on the rapidity with which your nail is quivering, i.e., the frequency of its vibration. Few vibrations per second produce a low tone; many vibrations per second a high tone.

The ear of a human being is able to pick up vibrations ranging from 16 to 20,000 vibrations per second, with the greatest sensitivity around 1,000 to 4,000 vibrations per second. There are some sounds that the human ear cannot hear at all, although some insects and other animals may detect them. Special dog whistles produce a high-pitched, ultrasonic sound that is audible to dogs but not to people.

There is quite a range of pitch represented in an orchestra. The middle C of a piano vibrates 256 times per second if the piano is in tune. (The standard middle C tuning fork of the physics laboratory also has a frequency of 256 vibrations per second.) Some of the high piano strings vibrate 3,500 times per second. An organ can produce a frequency as low as 16 vibrations per second.

How are sounds of different pitch produced in string instruments? If you look inside a piano, you will see that three factors are responsible for the difference in pitch of the various strings: length, weight (which depend on the thickness and the material used), and tightness. Low notes are produced by the long, heavy, loose strings; high notes by the short, light, more tightly stretched strings.

In general, a long string (or a heavy or loose one) vibrates slowly; consequently a low-pitched note is produced. A short string (or a light or more tightly stretched one)

vibrates rapidly, producing a high-pitched sound.

In wind instruments, the air in the instrument is made to vibrate by the player. Here the pitch is determined principally by the length of the column of air producing the sound. Different pitches are obtained by changing the length of the air column. Shorter air columns produce higher-pitched sounds; longer columns, lower pitched sounds.

QUALITY. As we listen to a symphony orchestra, we are aware not only of pitch and loudness, but also of the quality of the sound of different instruments. The oboe sounds different from the clarinet; the bassoon different from the violin. How are differences in quality produced?

We recall that loudness depends on the strength and that pitch depends on the frequency of the sound wave. Quality depends on the "shape" imposed on the sound waves by the *overtones*. The production of overtones can be demonstrated by a simple experiment.

If you stretch a guitar string between two screws which are firmly set in a board, and pluck the string, it will vibrate throughout its entire length, producing a musical tone. This, the lowest tone that the string is capable of producing, is called its *fundamental*. If you now press down the middle of the string tightly with one finger and pluck either half-string, that part will vibrate to produce a tone one octave higher than when the whole string vibrates. This note is called the *first overtone*. Now, if you remove your finger quickly while half of the string is vibrating, the string will vibrate not only in half its length but also as a whole— *at the same time.* You then should hear two sounds—the note made by the string vibrating as a whole and the note made by the string vibrating in half its length.

If you now place your finger one-third of the way from the end of the string (either end) and hold it down, plucking this third of the string will produce a note higher than the first overtone. This is the *second overtone*. Many other overtones are possible.

In the playing of musical instruments, a large number of overtones are produced simultaneously with the fundamental tone. These overtones are different in different instruments. Thus, A flat on a clarinet sounds different from A flat on a violin because different overtones are produced. In singing or speaking, some individuals are able to produce more overtones than others. They can do this in part because they are skilled in controlling their voices. The number of overtones given off by a violin and by other musical instruments depends upon their construction as well as upon the skill of the musician.

The difference in character of two tones of the same pitch and loudness is due, then, to the difference in the relative prominence of the fundamental and the various overtones.

MAKING SOUNDS LOUDER

The crashing of cymbals starts a large wave moving across a concert hall. The strings of a piano, on the other hand, are not large enough to cause very much of a "splash" in the air. In order to make their sounds louder, the strings are connected to a sounding board. The sounding board is set vibrating by the ends of the strings connected to it. Its broad area permits it to set a large amount of air into motion at any given moment. The same principle obtains in the violin, cello, and all other stringed instruments.

To demonstrate this principle, rap the prongs of a fork against a heel of your shoe and listen for the sound. Do this again, but this time press the end of the handle against a wooden table. The sound is louder because the fork's vibration is transmitted to the table, which, in turn, causes a large amount of air surrounding it to begin vibrating.

SYMPATHETIC VIBRATIONS

It is possible for one vibrating object to make another object vibrate without touching it. If you open a piano, press down on the loud pedal to remove the damper from the strings, and sing into the strings, you will hear some of the strings sing back at you. Which strings? Those in tune with the pitch of your voice, with its fundamental tone and overtones. We call this a *sympathetic vibration*. If you sing at a different pitch, different strings will sing back. SEE PAGE 559

You probably have noticed that loose windows rattle and knives and forks chatter when certain notes are sounded on a piano or a radio. This happens because each sounding object has a natural frequency of vibration. If sound waves of that note strike it, it will respond sympathetically. Some singers are reputed to be able to shatter a fine crystal glass by singing loudly into it at its natural pitch.

Why does a seashell held to the ear seem to have the "sound of the sea" in it? The air in the seashell reinforces the slight sounds that are present by vibrating sympathetically with those in tune with it. The waves are bounced back and forth in such a manner that the reflections from the wall of the seashell add up and strengthen the sound. These sounds, of course, are not the sounds of the sea unless you are listening to a seashell on the seashore. This quality of responding sympathetically to certain sounds and reinforcing them is called *resonance*.

The human voice, produced by the vibration of the vocal cords, is reinforced by the sympathetic vibration of the air in the throat, mouth, and nose and is thus given its resonant quality.

MUSICAL INSTRUMENTS

For thousands of years, people have invented and played musical instruments of various kinds. Drums, stringed instruments, SEE PAGE 559 TO 560 and wind instruments have been found among the relics of very early man.

There are three general groups of musical instruments: the stringed instruments, such as violins, violas, bass violas, harps, and cellos; the percussion instruments, such as the drum and xylophone; and the wind instruments, such as the cornet, flute, and saxophone.

STRINGED INSTRUMENTS. In most stringed instruments, the strings are usually held down by the fingers of the left hand and are plucked, strummed, or bowed with the right. Various tones can be obtained by varying the length of the strings. The harp is an exception to this. It has 46 separate strings, since a change of length is not possible. However, the pedals on the harp can change the tension of the strings to make sharps and flats.

The wood and the air spaces in the body of a violin, along with the strings, are essential in producing a good tone. A good violin has the special virtue of vibrating faithfully with each string and with every pitch, even the high ones. A poor violin tends to "play favorites," amplifying some vibrations and neglecting others.

PERCUSSION INSTRUMENTS. Percussion instruments, such as the drum, depend upon the vibration of a flexible head that is struck with sticks or with the hands. The head is stretched over a wooden or a metal body. The vibrations of the head and of the body of the drum produce the sound. Pitch on some types of drums can be altered by stretching or loosening the skin. The kettledrum player loosens and tightens the head of the drum during the playing of a symphony.

WIND INSTRUMENTS. In stringed instruments, the musician causes strings to vibrate. The vibration is passed to the rest of the instrument, which causes the air to vibrate and produce the sound that reaches your ears. In wind instruments, the player makes the air vibrate directly.

Blow across the tops of a series of bottles that have different amounts of water in them. Those with more *air* in them make a lower tone than those with little. The longer air column, like the longer string, produces the deeper tone.

In most wind instruments, from a piccolo to an organ, pitch is changed by changing the length of the column of air. In instruments like the fife, flute, clarinet, saxophone, oboe, and bassoon, the player lengthens the column of air by covering the holes in the instrument, and shortens it by uncovering the holes. He does this with his fingertips directly, or with the help of keys and pads.

In the trombone, the lengthening and shortening of the air column is done by sliding a U-shaped tube in and out. In other brasses, such as the cornet, trumpet, tuba, and French horn, there are three curved tubes, each controlled by a key. As the key is pressed down, the column of air that it controls is added to the total; when the key is released, the column is removed, or subtracted, from the total. By forming different combinations of these separate air tubes, the musician is able to evoke the different notes needed.

In some wind instruments—for example, the cornet, tuba, trumpet, French horn, and trombone—the air is caused to vibrate by the vibration of the player's lips. In the clarinet, bassoon, saxophone, and oboe, on the other hand, wooden reeds are caused to vibrate by the blowing of the player. These, in turn, set air columns in the instrument vibrating.

The bugle has a fixed column of air. Tightening or relaxing the lips causes the rate of vibration to vary and thus produces the different tones.

HOW WE SPEAK

Like all other sounds, speech is produced by vibrations. Stretched across the inside of the voice box, or *larynx*, are two folds

SEE PAGE 560

of tissue called the *vocal cords*. It is the vocal cords that vibrate when we speak. The cords are elastic fibers that can be stretched and relaxed by the action of muscles in the voice box. You can illustrate the way that sound is produced by blowing upon the edges of a wide rubber band, stretched so that its edges are close together.

All the air that is breathed in and out passes through the voice box. Ordinarily the vocal cords are relaxed on the two sides of the voice box. The air passes in and out between the vocal cords without producing sound. When you talk or sing, your brain sends messages along the nerves to the muscles controlling the vocal cords. The muscles pull the vocal cords together so that there is only a narrow slit between the cords, like that between the edges of the wide rubber band that you stretched. As the diaphragm and chest muscles force air out of the lungs, the air makes the vocal cords vibrate. The pitch of the sound is controlled by making the vocal cords tighter or looser.

The natural range of pitch of the voice is determined largely by the length of the vocal cords. Women have higher pitched voices than men because their vocal cords are shorter. Children's voices are higher than those of adults, for the same reason.

The voice box is not the only part assisting in the making of speech. The lips, tongue, teeth, palate, and mouth help in the formation of spoken sounds. When we whisper, the sounds are produced by placing the mouth and tongue in the required positions, without vibrating the vocal cords.

The quality of the human voice depends on the many spaces that resonate sympathetically with the vocal cords. These include the sinuses, the nasal cavities, the mouth, throat, windpipe, and lungs, as well as the voice box itself.

HOW WE HEAR

The ear is essentially a mechanism for the reception of sound waves and for the conversion of sound waves into nerve impulses. The ear consists of three parts: the outer ear, the middle ear, and the inner ear. The outer ear collects air vibrations; the middle ear amplifies them and passes them along to the inner ear; the inner ear changes the vibrations into nerve messages. The explanation that follows will be easier to understand if frequent reference is made to the drawing below.

OUTER EAR.   The outer ear is composed of a shell of flexible cartilage and skin attached to each side of the head, leading to a canal that funnels inward. The outer ear

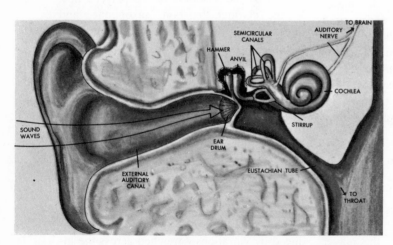

The delicate mechanism of the ear is shown here. Can you describe how the parts function in the process of hearing?

acts on the principle of a hearing tube, that is, it collects and concentrates sound waves and conducts them, so that they strike against the eardrum. In man the value of this is slight—we could hear almost as well without the outer ears. In many animals, however, the external ear can be turned toward the source of the sound and can play an important function in collecting sound waves.

The *eardrum* is set obliquely across the auditory canal, thereby providing a greater surface for receiving vibrations than if it were stretched squarely across it. It is a wonderfully designed membrane, with many delicate fibers running in concentric circles around it to make it elastic and springy, and with coarse fibers arranged like the ribs of an umbrella to give it strength.

MIDDLE EAR. Within the middle ear is a chain of three little bones. The outer one, called the *hammer*, is attached to the eardrum. The hammer is connected by means of a joint to the bone called the *anvil*. This in turn is jointed to the *stirrup*. The foot plate of the stirrup rests against the *oval window* of the inner ear.

The three bones act as levers, magnifying the strength of the initial vibration received by the eardrum about 22-fold. This strengthened impulse is conveyed to the membrane covering the oval window.

Before leaving the middle ear we should mention the *Eustachian tube*, which connects the middle ear to the throat. The purpose of this tube is to permit the equalization of pressure on both sides of the eardrum. If, for example, you ascend in an elevator, the pressure on the outside of the eardrum decreases with the altitude. The air inside the middle ear tends to push the eardrum outward. However, some of the air escapes through the Eustachian tube into the throat, thereby equalizing the pressure on the eardrum. Chewing or swallowing helps because it opens the end of the Eustachian tube near the throat. (This is why airline hostesses distribute gum when the pressure is being changed in the cabin.) When you descend in an elevator, the pressure increases; the Eustachian tube permits air to flow from the throat *into* the middle ear.

INNER EAR. The inner ear is composed of the *cochlea* and the *semicircular canals*. Only the cochlea will be discussed here, since it is the auditory sense organ. (The canal apparatus is concerned with balance and with the sense of position. It is discussed in chapter 13A.) The cochlea is a snail-shaped structure with two and one-half turns in it. It is filled with lymph, a fluid resembling blood except that it has no red blood cells in it. The sound waves from the eardrum are transmitted by the three bones to the fluid in the cochlea. Running through the cochlea is the important *basilar membrane*, upon which is a structure containing 24,000 *hair cells*. These cells are thought to be the true receptors of hearing.

Thousands of sensory nerve fibers are connected to the hair cells. These fibers join to form the auditory nerve which leads from the cochlea to the brain. By a number of complex mechanisms, not fully understood, sound waves in the fluid of the cochlea are converted into electrical energy which triggers nerve impulses in the nerve fibers. These impulses travel along the auditory nerve to the brain, where they are perceived as sounds of varying pitch, loudness, and quality.

To sum up our discussion of how we hear: sound waves pass from the eardrum to the three bones, then to the cochlea where they initiate nerve impulses, which are then transmitted to the brain.

CARE OF THE EARS

The ear is a complex organ that deserves the best of care. Any kind of severe blow on the ears may rupture the eardrum and injure the delicate adjustments of the three bones in the inner ear. It is good common sense "not to poke anything into your ear smaller than your elbow."

Violent nose-blowing should be avoided because it forces air through the Eustachian tube into the middle ear. This may injure the eardrum and may also force germs into the middle ear and cause an infection.

It is important that the ears be kept clean so that bacteria may not get into the inner section. Wax, a normal secretion of the outer ear, seems to protect our hearing by catching dust and other foreign particles that might otherwise carry germs into the ear. If too much wax accumulates, however, or if it becomes too hard, it should be removed by a physician.

In this chapter we have discussed the essential aspects of the phenomenon of sound. Here are some of the generalizations:

Sounds arise from vibrations.

Sound vibrations travel in a wave motion in all directions from their source.

Sound vibrations travel through gases, liquids, and solids.

Sound travels through the air at the rate of about 1,100 feet a second.

An echo is a reflected sound.

Porous, soft materials are good sound-absorbers.

Sounds are characterized by their loudness, pitch, and quality.

Pitch depends on the number of vibrations per second made by the sounding body.

Sounds cause our eardrums to vibrate.

The inner ear converts sound vibrations into nerve impulses.

DISCOVERING FOR YOURSELF

1. Listen for sounds in your environment. Make a list of the things that make the sound. Explain what causes each sound to change in loudness and pitch.
2. Observe the inside of a piano to discover how sounds are made, what gives them quality, and how they are controlled.
3. Devise some original experiments that show that some substances carry sound better than others.
4. Examine a public building (a schoolhouse, auditorium, or other building) to see how sounds are controlled.
5. Examine a variety of musical instruments to see how they make sounds, and how the sounds are controlled.
6. Examine a hearing aid to see how it works.
7. Collect some "sound-making" insects and try to see how they produce sounds.
8. Find out what a *decibel* and *phone* are and what *ultrasonic* and *supersonic* mean.
9. Find out what some cities and institutions do to reduce noise.
10. Prepare a number of experiments to show what determines the pitch, loudness, and quality of sound.
11. Examine a phonograph record (78 rpm) with a 10-power magnifying glass.[1] See if you can find the waves in the grooves that produce the sounds. Do the waves differ in length and in height? How would such variations affect the sound?

---

[1] See *Through the Magnifying Glass* by Julius Schwartz. (New York, Whittlesey House, 1953.)

CHAPTER 22B

Teaching "Sound and How We Use It"

Children live in a world of sound. They are stimulated, mystified, informed, and delighted by many sound impressions. It is easy to capitalize on children's fascination and experiences with musical instruments, to teach them some of the important principles of sound—its production, its nature, and its control. There are all sorts of things children can make—toy xylophones, for example—to illustrate principles of sound, and there are many simple experiments and experiences that they can either originate or find in books. This is one of the most interesting units to teach in the elementary grades, and if it is kept at the appropriate level it has very few aspects that are difficult to understand.

Some of the things that younger children may do include:

1. Listen to various sounds and describe them, i.e., tell if they are loud or soft, high or low, pleasant or unpleasant. Try to tell how they are made.
2. Try to feel vibrations from bodies that are making sound, such as the drum, xylophone, radio, phonograph, cymbals, triangle, piano, etc.
3. Listen to the sounds made by familiar animals such as birds and other pets, farm animals, zoo animals, insects; learn how to identify the animal by its sound.
4. Make sounds in some of the ways described in this chapter and try to tell what makes the sounds and how they are different from each other.
5. Examine toys and instruments of different kinds (drums, whistles, guitars, harmonicas) and tell what part of the instrument makes the sound, and how the sound is made (plucking, blowing, beating, etc.).

DISCOVERING THE CAUSE OF SOUND

Many experiences will help pupils to understand that sound is caused by vibration. One involves the use of a triangle, which may be obtained from a kindergarten. Strike the triangle to make it vibrate. Listen to the sound. Touch it to stop the vibration. Listen again and you will hear no sound. In order to see that the triangle is actually vibrating, thrust it into water after it has been struck and note the waves of water that travel out from it. They are caused by the vibrations. (Tuning forks may be used for this if they are available. They may be ordered from scientific supply houses. Some music teachers have small ones.) Touching the vibrating triangle or tuning fork with their fingernails will help make the vibrations real to children.

Ask pupils to suggest other experiments that will help them understand that vibration causes sound. Here are some possibilities: Stretch a rubber band; pluck it; listen to it; stop it from vibrating; listen again. This may also be done with a violin string. Touch a piano or radio while it is playing to feel the vibration. Then stop the sound. Hold the fingers against the throat while making a sound. Stop the sound and feel the throat. After several such experiences pupils may *tentatively* conclude that "all sound is caused by vibration." This conclusion may then be checked by reading and investigating further.

OBSERVING THINGS THAT MAKE SOUND

Urge each child to bring some sound-maker and demonstrate it to the class to see whether the pupils can decide what vibrates to make the sound. Suggest that pupils try to exercise originality in their selection. They may bring toys or musical instruments, use their own voices, etc. After they have tried to decide in each case what vibrates to make the sounds, several pupils may, one at a time, make the sounds again and the class may be asked to tell how these sounds differ from each other. Pupils will discover that sounds differ in loudness, pitch, and quality, although they will not necessarily state their observations in

The principles of how sounds are produced and how they vary are more easily understood when pupils construct apparatus such as this.

these terms. This will lead to the problem of why sounds differ from one another. Such an experience as this may be used to open a unit of study. Through it pupils will raise questions and problems to start the study. This is more effective than expecting pupils to respond to a question from the teacher: What would you like to know about sound? Such an approach may produce some nonsense questions unless some preliminary experiences have given the pupils a basis for asking good questions.

EXPERIMENTING WITH PITCH

An empty wooden chalk box or cigar box and some rubber bands can be used to make high and low sounds and to demonstrate how they are made. Stretch a rubber band across the opening of the box and pluck it. (Thumbtacks may be placed at different distances down the sides of the box to hold the bands as they are stretched tighter and tighter.) Listen to the sound. Keep on tightening the rubber band and plucking it. The tighter it is stretched, the higher the sound will be. Now stretch a wide and a narrow rubber band across the box about equally tight. Pluck each and listen to the sound. Increase the tension of both and listen to each.

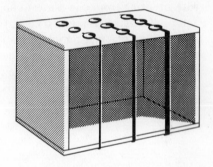

Rubber bands stretched across a chalk box illustrates the concepts of pitch. Experiments may be performed with bands of various thicknesses and various tensions.

From these experiences, pupils begin to see that the more tightly the bands are stretched, the higher the pitch, and that thin bands produce a higher pitch than thick ones. If they watch the bands carefully, they may be able to see that this difference is due to the speed of vibration. The use of a flexible ruler, as suggested in the next section, will also serve to show pupils the relationship between speed of vibration and pitch. Urge pupils to originate other examples to show these ideas. The thick band and the loosely stretched ones vibrate so slowly that they can be seen moving back and forth, whereas in the thin and the tightly stretched bands the vibrations are too fast to be seen.

These principles can also be observed on a violin. In many classes, one or more of the pupils take violin lessons or at least have an instrument available. Pupils may notice the effect of stretching and loosening the strings, and they may hear the difference between the sounds of the thick strings and those of the thin ones. On the violin they can also see the effect of the length of the string on the pitch. Pressing down on the string keeps part of it from vibrating. Consequently, they can see that the shorter the string, the higher its pitch, and that long strings make sounds of lower pitch. Pupils may examine other stringed instruments to see the same idea.

EXPERIMENTING TO LEARN HOW
SOUND IS CARRIED

If there is a place in the school where iron pipes go from one floor to the next, pupils can learn how sound travels through metal by noting that sound (made by tapping the pipe) will travel along the pipe from one floor to another.

There are many other experiences which help children see that some things are better carriers of sound than others. For example, if one child strikes a tuning fork at one end of a table and holds it in the air, children at the other end of the table cannot hear it. But if he sets the stem of the vibrating tuning fork on the table and the other children put their ears down to the table, they can easily hear the sound. They can experiment to see which carries the sound of a tuning fork better, a yardstick or a necktie. A long window pole may be used to demonstrate how solids carry sound by using the tuning fork—strike a tuning fork and then touch its base to one end of the pole while a student places his ear at the other.

An interesting way to learn more about how sound travels is through the use of a tin-can telephone.[1] This, of course, does not operate on the same principle as a real telephone, but it serves to show how vibrations from the human voice can be transmitted along a wire or string from one place to another.

To make it, use two cans, two buttons, and several feet of wire or string. The cans should have one end removed neatly so that they will be safe to use. Punch a small hole in the center of the bottom of each can. Thread one end of the string through this hole to the inside of each can and tie it to the button. The telephone is used by two pupils standing far enough from each other to pull the string taut. One speaks into the can, holding it close around his mouth. The other holds the can to his ear. In answering, the process is reversed.

OBSERVING SOUNDPROOFING

In most schools, there are rooms in which materials to deaden sound have been used. The school principal will help to locate these places for pupils to observe. Some probable places are the library, the auditorium, and the cafeteria.

Broadcasting studios, of course, furnish excellent examples of the use of soundproofing materials. A committee of pupils may arrange to visit a station to see how the rooms are soundproofed and report their observations. Building-supply firms will probably be able to furnish some samples of the materials used to deaden sound. Pupils should be alert to note examples of soundproofing in auditoriums and similar places and to report their findings.

LEARNING ABOUT THE SPEED OF SOUND

When pupils have learned that light travels much faster than sound, they can demonstrate this fact on their school grounds. Let a pupil carry a large drum or something else that will make a loud sound a block or so away from the rest of the class. Let him strike the drum with a broad gesture that can be seen at a distance. Pupils will soon observe that they

---

[1] G. O. Blough and M. H. Campbell, *Making and Using Classroom Science Materials in the Elementary School* (New York: Holt, Rinehart and Winston, 1954), pp. 159–162.

do not hear the sound until the drummer's arm is ready to strike the drum again. They see the drummer because light travels from him to them. They hear the drum because sound travels from the drum to them. But the sound travels very slowly compared with the light. Pupils may recall that they have watched a man hammering on a roof in the distance and heard the sound when the hammer was already in the air ready to hit the nail again, or that they see lightning before they hear the thunder even though both occur simultaneously.

USING A MEGAPHONE

While the pupils are outdoors with the drum, they may use a megaphone to see how effectively sound may be directed. Let a pupil walk several yards away from the group and shout to the class with and without the use of the megaphone. Pupils may make small megaphones from paper. It is interesting for them to listen to the tick of a watch through a megaphone and then try to hear it from the same distance without using the megaphone. Pupils may look for other devices which direct sound. By talking into one end of a garden hose extending from one room to another pupils may discover how sounds can be directed.

DEMONSTRATING SYMPATHETIC VIBRATIONS

An experiment with tuning forks will show the principle of sympathetic vibration. Use two tuning forks that produce the same number of vibrations per second (256, for example, which is middle C on the piano). Place one with its base resting on a table or other hard surface. Do not make it vibrate. Strike the second one, and while it is vibrating place its base on the same surface an inch away from the first fork and in the same position. After a moment, stop the vibrating fork by touching the prongs. Listen closely to the first fork and you will hear a faint hum coming from it. It is vibrating.

If tuning forks are not available, let pupils sing into the open strings of a piano at different pitches to hear the notes sing back. Or, they may ring a bell near open piano strings. Pupils may recall experiences they have had with sympathetic vibrations at home when vases or other things have been set on the piano.

EXAMINING MUSICAL INSTRUMENTS

Many pupils take music lessons and it is appropriate to apply the facts and principles they have learned in science to the instruments they play. Pupils who have had instruction from their music teachers about how the instrument produces sounds can demonstrate this knowledge to the class.

As the musical instruments are demonstrated, pupils may observe and listen to discover: what vibrates to make the sound; how the sounds are varied in pitch and loudness; what influences the quality of the sound produced. For demonstration purposes, pupils may be asked to play a scale.

Many pupils have never seen the inside of a piano. The boards are not difficult to remove, and the strings and hammers are easy to observe. The three observations suggested in the preceding paragraph are appropriate for learning about the piano, as they are for the saxophone, cornet, violin, or any other instrument pupils are likely to bring in. A mouth organ is especially interesting to examine. If there is one available that is no longer usable, the cover may be removed. Pupils can see the differences among the reeds inside.

If there is a music teacher in the school or in the community, it is important and very helpful to invite her to join in the study of these instruments. She will be able to contribute information that will not only help the pupils to understand the instruments but will enrich their study of sound.

The chart[2] on the facing page summarizes activities and learnings related to musical instruments commonly found in elementary schools.

LEARNING HOW WE MAKE SOUNDS

A picture of human vocal cords will help pupils learn something about the mechanism of the voice box. Feeling the vibrations in their own throats will also help them to understand how vocal cords vibrate. It is also important for pupils to learn how the teeth, tongue, and lips help to formulate different sounds and how they themselves may improve their pronunciation of words by using these organs correctly and by breathing properly.

Instrument	*What Children Do*	*What Children Learn*
Drums	Children play on them with sticks or with their hands. Place small, tightly rolled up bits of paper on drumhead. Drum to see them dance. Hit drum gently; hit drum hard. Play on small drums and big drums.	Drums shake (vibrate) while they are played. A hard tap makes a louder sound than a gentle tap. Small drums make high sounds; big drums make low sounds.
Xylophone	Strike the bars with the sticks.	The long bars make the low notes; the short bars make the high notes.
Piano	Open the cover of the piano and look at the strings: Notice how the sound is produced when a key is struck. Notice that the strings are of different length. Feel the piano while it is being played.	Felt covered hammers strike the strings to make the sounds. Short strings make the high notes; long strings make the low notes. When the piano is played we can feel a vibration.
Triangle	Strike the triangle. Listen to it. Strike it again. Touch it with fingertips. Grasp the triangle firmly and strike it.	The triangle makes a sound when we strike it. While it is sounding it quivers (vibrates). If it is held in the hand and struck, a dull sound is produced.
Cymbals	Strike the cymbals. Listen. Strike the cymbals. Touch the surface of one with the fingertips. Rub one of the cymbals gently with the fingers. Strike the cymbals. Put your hand on one of them.	Cymbals make sound when they strike each other. While the cymbals are sounding they shake. Rubbing a cymbal produces a muffled sound. Putting your hand on a sounding cymbal stops the sound.

[2] From *Sound and Light in Communication*, Brooklyn 1, N. Y. Board of Education of the City of New York, Publication Sales Office, 110 Livingston St. (50¢)

SPECIAL ACTIVITIES ABOUT SOUND

Individuals or small groups especially interested in sound may undertake projects related to some of the principles they have learned. A few such projects are described here; many others are suggested in books in the bibliography.

MAKING FLOWERPOT CHIMES

Pupils can produce chimes by using flowerpots of graduated sizes. Hang the pots upside down by the use of twine attached to buttons large enough not to slip through the hole in the bottom of the flowerpot. The pots may be hung from a broomstick extended from one chair back to another. A small hammer or any other hard object may be used to tap the flowerpots to make the sound. Pupils should be able to explain why the pots make different sounds.

PRODUCING A SCALE WITH DRINKING GLASSES

With some experimenting and patience, pupils can make drinking glasses filled with graduated amounts of water produce a musical scale. A series of test tubes will also produce this effect. Sounds may be produced in the glasses by striking them and in the test tubes by blowing across them. Again, pupils should apply the science principles they have learned.

MAKING A XYLOPHONE

Pieces of hard wood sawed to graduated lengths and placed across two longer pieces of wood as in a real xylophone may be arranged so that a scale and even a tune can be played on them. A large iron nail may be used for striking them.

RESOURCES TO INVESTIGATE

1. The local motion-picture theater and other public buildings to see how sound-proofing and other sound controls are accomplished.
2. The school and the custodian to learn about the soundproofing in the school auditorium and elsewhere in the building.
3. Music teachers to show various musical instruments and explain how they produce and control sounds.
4. A music store to see and examine instruments and hear about how they produce and control sound.
5. A speech teacher to explain how we produce and control sound and how voices may be improved.
6. A collection of sound-producing insects to observe how they produce sounds and how they can cause changes in sounds.
7. Building-supply company to note soundproofing materials.

CHAPTER 23A

Light and How We Use It

A beam of light, originating in the excited atoms of the sun, starts on its way to the earth. Eight minutes and 93 million miles later, it has reached the sidewalk outside your home. A child races through the steady stream of light, interrupts it momentarily, and causes a shadow to fall on the walk. Some of the light is reflected from the sunlight-bathed objects to your eyes, making it possible for you to see the scene outside your window.

Light is a messenger, bringing us news of the universe. Light excites the most important sense, that of sight, initiating nerve impulses that our brain interprets as a distant star, a glorious sunset, a friendly face.

Light rules life. Plants and animals are governed by the rhythm of day and night. Sunlight provides the energy for the food-making process in green plants and consequently is essential for all life on our planet. The fossil fuels—coal, gas, and oil—have stored within them energy that winged down from the sun millions of years ago.

LIGHT TRAVELS

One of the most important discoveries made concerning light is that it travels, racing through space at the rate of about 186,000 miles per second. Nothing in our everyday experiences conveys this concept. When we pull up the shade of a darkened room, the light seems to fill it instantaneously. Distances on earth are too short for the travel time of light to make much difference. It does have significance, however, for the viewing of heavenly bodies. If the sun were suddenly to stop shining, we would continue to see it for about eight minutes, for, at the speed given above, it takes that time for light to travel from the sun to the earth. Moonlight (which is really reflected sunlight) takes about 1⅓ seconds to travel the 238,000 miles from the moon to the earth. Other interesting implications of the traveling of light through space are discussed in chapter 8A. We learned there that the distance covered by light in a year furnishes us with a yardstick, the light year, for measuring the universe.

WHAT IS LIGHT?

This question has been the subject of controversy for many centuries. Plato and other ancient philosophers believed that light was a kind of emanation *from* the eye that made objects visible. Sir Isaac Newton proposed the corpuscular theory of light in 1700. He believed that light was a stream of particles or corpuscles shot off by a luminous body. At about the same time, Christian Huygens, a Dutchman, countered with the theory that light was a vibration, a wave that rippled through space. Each of these theories, those of Newton and Huygens, explains some phenomena satisfactorily but not others. Einstein theorized that a beam of light is a shower of small packets of energy, which he called photons. At present, we can at least agree to define light as the kind of energy that causes us to see.

SHADOWS

SEE PAGE 578

Perhaps the simplest picture that nature paints of an object is its shadow. We notice shadows most in the early morning or late afternoon, when opaque objects, such as trees or people, cast elongated silhouettes. A moment's consideration will show that the object is not really "casting" anything, instead it is blocking the sunlight, which, streaming past its edges, traces the form of the object on sidewalk or lawn.

The earth, too, casts a shadow—into space. When the moon enters this cone-shaped shadow, we have a lunar eclipse.

When the moon's smaller shadow sweeps across the earth, we have a solar eclipse.

Of course, not all substances are opaque to light. Glass and some plastics are transparent; they permit light from objects to pass through. Our ancestors used oiled paper in their windows to permit light to enter their houses. Substances such as oiled paper or frosted glass, which allow some light to go through, but through which objects cannot be clearly seen, are called *translucent*. In lighting our homes and schools we make use of various materials that transmit light differently.

SEEING THE THINGS AROUND US

A red rose in a glass vase is set on a white doily on a dark table—in a totally dark room. Your eyes are wide open, but you do not see any of these objects. Light a candle and they become visible. Why? Just how, for example, do you see the rose?

Light travels from the candle source to the petals and stem. Here, some of it is absorbed by the atoms of these plant structures, and some is reflected in various directions from the surface of the flower. Part of the reflected light enters your eye and causes an image to be formed in the back of it. This stimulates the nerve endings there to carry impulses to your brain which interprets these impulses as a flower.

Although the flower reflects the candle *light* to your eye, you do not see the candle as you would in a mirror. This is because it reflects light irregularly—in such a way as to reveal its own texture and shape, rather than that of the candle. In other words, it is the *effect* of the surface texture on light that makes the object visible. A perfectly smooth reflecting surface would not be visible; the source of light rather than the surface would be seen. It would be a mirror. SEE PAGE 578

Even if you put a dark screen between the candle and the flower you would still see the flower, because some of the

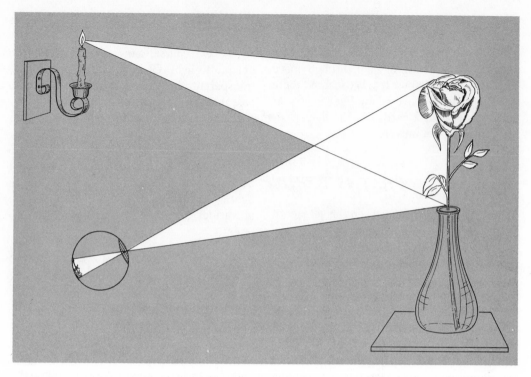

We see a rose because light travels to it and is reflected to our eyes. See text for further details.

candle light would be reflected from the walls and the ceiling to the vase. Light from the candle travels in all directions and is reflected in all directions.

The table appears darker to your eyes than the flower, the flower darker than the doily. Why? The atoms of the table surface *absorb* a good deal of the light (photons or waves) that strikes them, and convert it into heat. Very little is reflected to your eye. The red flower absorbs some light but reflects more than the dark table does. The white doily reflects the most light, absorbing very little. Thus, the variation in brightness of different surfaces under equal illumination is due to the different amounts of light energy soaked up and "bounced off" by their constituent atoms.

COLOR

Why do the rose petals look red, the stem green? What makes an object have a color? To understand color, we must know a little more about the nature of light itself. If a narrow beam of the white light from the sun or from a lamp passes through a triangular glass prism, a rainbow of colors appears on a screen or wall on the opposite side. The white light fans out to form a spectrum of red, orange, yellow, green, blue, and violet, in that order, each color merging imperceptibly into the next. White light, then, consists of a mixture of many colors. Sir Isaac Newton showed this in a simple but ingenious experiment, using two prisms. A beam of white light was directed at the first prism and emerged on the opposite side as a spectrum of colors. Newton then placed the second prism, upside down with respect to the first, in the path of these colored rays. The rays joined in the second prism to form a spot of white light on a screen.

White light, then, can be separated into colors; these colors can combine to make white light. If, on the other hand, a narrow beam of green light were allowed to pass

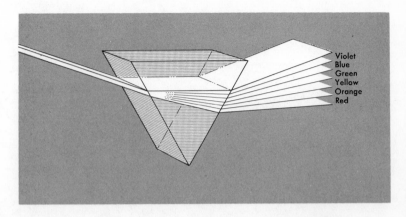

When a beam of white light is passed through one side of a triangular glass prism, a rainbow of colors emerges from the other. White light is a mixture of many colors.

Violet
Blue
Green
Yellow
Orange
Red

through a prism, it would emerge as a green light.

The reason that we are discussing white light is that we live in a world that is bathed in it. The colors we see "in" objects (except for those that make their own light) are influenced by the fact that these objects are "painted" by a white light that is a combination of red, orange, yellow, green, blue, and violet.

To come back to the original question, why do the rose's petals appear red and its stem green? Bathed in white light, the petals are receiving red, orange, yellow, green, blue, and violet rays. All of these are absorbed as energy into the atoms of the pigment of the petals *except the red ones*. This color is reflected; in your eye it stimulates certain nerve endings, resulting in the sensation of red. In other words, the color of an opaque object is determined by the kind of light it does *not* absorb, by the kind that bounces off it. *The red you see "in" the rose is the red originally in the white light bathing the rose and then reflected from it.* The green stem appears green because it absorbs most colors except those near the green part of the spectrum; it reflects green. (See next page.)

White light fans out to form a spectrum of colors; the colors rejoin to form white light.

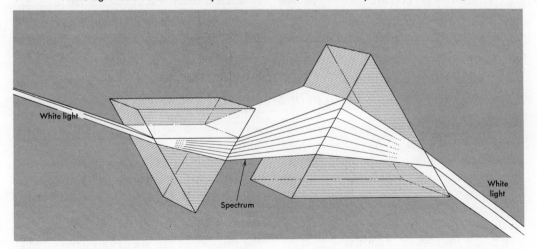

White light

Spectrum

White light

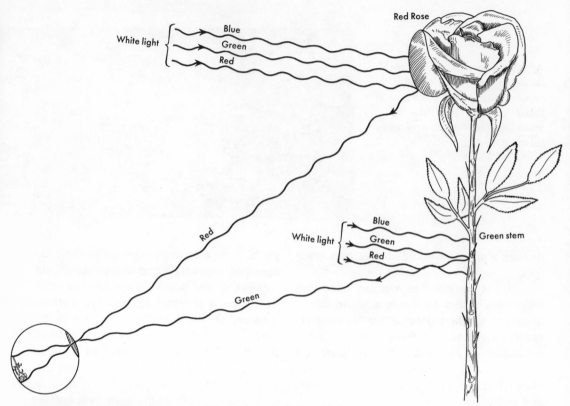

Roses are red because they absorb all the colors in white light except red. This color is reflected to your eye. Why is the stem green?

A white flower reflects a large percentage of *all* of the different colors in white light and so appears white. In nature, there are very few objects that are pure red or blue or green. A red apple, for example, reflects more red than the other colors, but it also reflects a little blue and green.

RAINBOWS

White light, as we have learned, is a mixture of many colors. When white light, traveling through the air, passes obliquely through a substance of different density like a glass prism, or a body of water, the various colors separate to produce a spectrum. We see this in a classroom, sometimes, when sunlight passes through an aquarium.

Spectrum-making on a large scale occurs when nature displays a rainbow in the sky. Here nature's "prisms" are the thousands of water droplets left slowly settling in the sky after a shower. Each droplet fans out the white sunlight into a tiny spectrum, but the angle of vision of the viewer on the ground permits him to see only one of these colors in each of the bands that characterize a rainbow. From the highest part of the arch, red is bent to the eye; then, in descending order, we can see the bands of orange, yellow, green, blue, and violet.

You can make a small but real rainbow by spraying a shower of droplets from a garden hose. Do this in the late afternoon when the sun is more than halfway down from overhead. Standing with your back to the sun, adjust the nozzle to the finest spray and direct it toward the east at a rather high angle. The rainbow will be more beautiful if the spray is directed toward a shaded or dark background. This homemade rainbow is produced in the same way as nature's larger ones.

WHY IS THE SKY BLUE?

Of course, the sky may also be red, orange or other colors, gray, or black. Before answering the question, it must be understood that the color we ascribe to the "sky" is an effect produced only in the lower part of the atmosphere—in the air up to twenty or thirty miles above the surface of the earth. The lower atmosphere is dense with molecules of its component gases and with dust particles. The blue color in sunlight is reflected and scattered in every direction by the gases and particles in the lower atmosphere. Some of these blue rays are reflected to the earth and enter our eyes, so we see a blue sky. The sun itself appears yellow, which is a combination of the remaining colors in the sunlight—that is, those left after the blue has been subtracted.

Sky color, then, is a characteristic of our lower atmosphere. As flights into space take us out of the lower atmosphere, the sky above appears black at all times, since there are no atmospheric particles to scatter the sunlight. On the moon, which has no atmosphere at all, the sky is always black, even when the sun is shining.

MIRRORS

SEE PAGE 579

We noted previously that a perfectly smooth reflecting surface would not be visible, that the source of the light rather than the surface would be seen, that this kind of surface would be a mirror. How is an object seen "in" a mirror?

Light, like a ball, bounces away from objects it strikes. If you throw a ball at an angle against a smooth, even surface such as a new hardwood floor, it will bounce away in a predictable direction. If, now, seven of your friends join you in a line, each throwing a ball at the same angle and at the same time, but against different points on a line on the floor (see illustration on page 568), then eight balls will bounce together and be deflected in eight parallel paths. If we erected a net in the path of the eight rebounding balls, each ball could be caught and held in place. The pattern formed by the balls in the net would duplicate the pattern formed by the eight balls in the players' hands. To carry this analogy to a mirror, the net corresponds to our eye, the smooth floor to a mirror and the eight balls in the hands of the throwers as the original "picture." A mirror faithfully bounces rays of light emanating from an object to the viewer and thus makes a point by point reproduction of the original.

We commonly speak of looking *into* a mirror in order to see our reflection there. Obviously, nothing occurs behind the mirror. It is true, however, that light coming from any point in front of a mirror, such as the light of a candle flame, *appears* to come from a point an equal distance behind the mirror. At this latter point, there is formed what is called the *image* of the original object. Although we speak of "mirror images," the image is actually formed in your eye from the light that the mirror has reflected to it.

Most mirrors are made of glass, the back being coated with a substance, such as silver, that will reflect light readily. Unbreakable mirrors are made of highly polished steel, although such mirrors do not reflect light as well as the glass ones.

Convex mirrors, the kind that bulge out in front, produce small images of a large area. Because of this, they are commonly used as rear-view mirrors on autos.

Concave mirrors are used in reflecting telescopes to gather light from a distant object such as a star and focus it so that it may be viewed. The stars are too far away to be magnified, but the reflecting telescope can make them appear a million times as

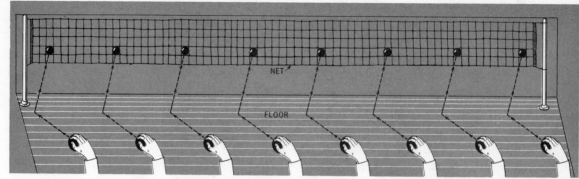

In this analogy to reflection by a mirror (see text), the net corresponds to the eye, the floor to a mirror, and the eight balls in the player's hands to the original "picture."

bright. The sun, the moon, and the planets, however, *are* magnified in such a telescope. Concave mirrors also are used in headlight reflectors of cars, in searchlight reflectors, and as shaving mirrors.

LIGHT BENDS

SEE
PAGE
578
If you have ever tried to catch a goldfish with your hands, you know that the fish is not where it appears to be. Why is this so?

Light is bent as it passes obliquely from one medium to another if the mediums differ in density. To the man on the bank, the fish appears to be in the position of the unshaded fish. Actually, it is in the position of the shaded one.

Light travels in straight lines, but its direction is changed when it passes from a medium of one density to another. The fish fooled you because the rays of light reflected from it were bent as they passed from the water to the air. For the same reason, a pencil or a spoon partly submerged in water looks crooked. So does the handle of a fishnet or the oar of a rowboat. Men spearing fish must aim below the spot where the fish appears, or they will miss it. In all of these examples, we do not see light being bent; we see the effects of this bending.

The bending of light as it passes obliquely from one media to another is known as *refraction*. The apparent "twinkling" of stars (stars actually do not twinkle) is due to the bending of starlight as it passes through the various shifting layers of hot and cold air in the atmosphere.

The refraction of light by the earth's atmosphere makes it possible for us to see the sun when it is actually below the horizon. At sunrise and sunset, the rays of the sun pass obliquely through the dense air of the lower atmosphere and are bent toward the earth. They no longer come in a straight line from the sun to the viewer. Thus, the rays are bent to our eyes, even though the sun is below the horizon. The effect of all this is to make the day longer than it would be if the earth had no atmosphere.

LENSES

EE
PAGES
80
O
81

The first lens used by man was the one that he has in his own eye. We have extended the use of this lens with the aid of many others. Lenses in eyeglasses correct the deficiencies in our eyes. Lenses in telescopes extend our view into space; lenses in microscopes permit us to penetrate into the mysteries of the minute; lenses in cameras help us make a record of the present for the future.

Lenses are useful because they are effective light-benders: they are designed to refract light according to the purpose of the optical device they are used in.

There are two principal types of simple lenses. Those thicker in the middle than at the edges are called *convex lenses* or *converging lenses*. Those thinner in the middle than at the edges are called *concave lenses* or *diverging lenses*.

PICTURES FROM LENSES.

A magnifying glass is a common example of a convex lens. A simple experiment that you can perform with such a lens will reveal what it does to light. First go to a room with a window brightly illuminated by light from the sky. Draw the blinds or shades on the *other* windows to darken them. Stand near a wall on the side of the room opposite the illuminated window and tack a sheet of white paper to it. Hold the magnifying lens near the paper. Move the lens back and forth until you see a sharp image of the window on the paper. (If you are reading this at night, you can get the same effect by using a bright lamp instead of a bright window.) Look at the image carefully and you will notice that it is upside down. The convex lens (see illustration, page 571) bends the light and causes it to form a small, inverted image of the window.

THE CAMERA.

SEE
PAGE
581
If you place a piece of unexposed photographic film on the wall instead of paper and then develop it in the usual manner, you will find that you have

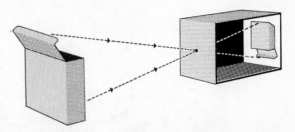

The camera in its simplest form is a light-tight box with a tiny pinhole at one end. This diagram shows how an inverted image is produced.

made a negative of the image, in the same way that a camera does. You have stripped the camera down to its two most basic essentials—lens and film. A *pinhole camera* even disposes of the lens, using instead a tiny hole to admit the light. A study of the diagram of this camera will show why cameras produce inverted images.

The common box camera is essentially a light-tight box with a lens in front, an opening for light, a shutter for allowing light to enter the opening for a fraction of a second, and a device in back for holding and turning the film. Light admitted by the shutter and passing through the lens is focused on the film. There it produces a change in the silver salt that is embedded in a gelatin layer on the film. This change is made visible by development, which also serves to preserve the image on the film. Since *light* actually causes *dark* grains of silver to be deposited on the film, the developed film is a negative. White teeth are black in a negative; black hair is almost colorless since it reflects little light. In making a print, light is made to shine through the negative to the photographic paper, which is also coated with a sensitive silver compound. Thus, a reversal of the image is effected, and a positive is produced.

In the previously described experiment with the magnifying glass, focusing was done by moving the lens back and forth. In a box camera, and in other kinds of fixed-focus cameras, the only focusing that is done

This is a negative of the picture on page 562 of this book. Note that in the negative the light and dark areas are reversed from those on the positive. When the negative is placed over the printing paper and exposed to light, the light shining through the light areas causes the printing paper to turn dark. The dark areas on the negative block the light and leave the printing paper lighter in color.

is accomplished by moving the entire camera; the lens is not moved in relation to the camera. Because of this, the box camera is somewhat limited in its use; however, it can take satisfactory pictures of subjects that are from six feet away to as far as the eye can see. Cameras with focusing devices permit the lens to be moved back and forth to secure sharp focuses for each picture.

MOTION PICTURES. The process by which pictures are made to produce the illusion of motion may seem complicated but actually is quite simple. The principle is illustrated by a certain kind of picture book in which the pictures are printed close to the edge of the page. One holds the book's edge with the thumb, bends the pages and then releases them rapidly one by one. If the pages slip by rapidly enough, the illusion of motion is created.

Motion pictures are simply a series of still pictures projected on a screen in rapid succession. Each picture is motionless while it is being shown. Our eye receives each of these pictures and focuses it on its own "screen," the retina, in the back of the eyeball. The movie projector is constructed to make each image persist for 1/24 of a second on the screen. The retina retains a picture for as long as 1/15 of a second after it has disappeared. This phenomenon is known as *persistence of vision*. Because of the rapidity with which the pictures appear, the eye blends each image with the following one so

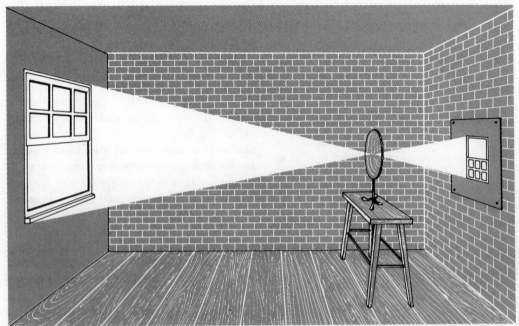

Your room can be a camera. All you need is a magnifying glass. How does the image compare with the original?

that we get the impression of continuous, lifelike motion.

THE EYE

SEE PAGE 582

The eye is often compared to a camera. The eye is a light-tight box, with dark pigment on the inside to prevent the bouncing around of light. It has a lens to focus light and a light-sensitive screen in the back on which an image is actually formed. It has an opening in front comparable to the opening of a camera; the size of this opening can be varied, as in a camera, to admit more or less light. It has a kind of shutter, the eyelid, that can exclude light (the eyelid also serves as a kind of windshield wiper to keep the eyes clean). The resemblance of eye and camera is even more detailed and striking than indicated by these items. We will note some other similarities as we go along.

THE OUTER EYE. Observe your own eye in a mirror to find some of its external structures. It will be helpful if you refer to the diagram on page 572 as you make this study. You are looking at a portion of an almost spherical ball about one inch in diameter. You are looking right through a thin transparent membrane that guards the front of the eye, called the *conjunctiva*. This membrane is continuous with the inner surface of the eyelids. The conjunctiva is kept free of dust and is lubricated by the tears that are spread in a thin film every time you blink. After flowing over the surface of the eye, the tears are drained by two tiny tubes, one in the inner corner of each eye, into the nose cavity. The continual washing and lubrication of the eyeball by tears prevents the delicate conjunctiva from becoming dry and inflamed. The tears also contain the substance *lysozyme*, which destroys bacteria.

Under the conjunctiva is the "white of the eye," the *sclera*. The sclera is made of tough, fibrous tissue that extends around the entire eye to make up the "box" of this instrument. The sclera becomes transparent over the *iris* and *pupil*, forming the somewhat bulging *cornea*. The pupil is a hole in the iris through which light is admitted into the eye. It appears black because it is the opening into the dark cavity of the eyeball. The pupil is surrounded by the doughnut-shaped iris, which is the pigmented or colored portion of the eye. The iris is a muscle that controls the size of the pupil. You can see it at work if you sit for a few minutes in a dimly lighted room, with just enough light to see your iris and pupil in a mirror. When you switch on a nearby light, the iris gets bigger and the pupil smaller. This reflex action of the iris automatically regulates the amount of light entering the eye. The need for such control becomes apparent when one realizes that the light from a sunny beach is thousands of times as strong as the light in a dimly lighted theater. In dim light, the pupil opening is large, in order to admit as much light as possible; in bright light, it becomes small to reduce the amount. In a camera, too, a diaphragm is adjusted by the photographer to permit more or less light to enter the opening at its center.

The eyeball lies in a bony socket of the skull and is manipulated by the muscles that are attached to it. These muscles tilt the eyeball up and down, left and right, and in a rotary motion.

INSIDE THE EYE.   The internal structure of the eye can be understood with the aid of the diagram, which represents a vertical section of the eyeball from front to back. In this section, we recognize some structures previously seen in the external view: the eyelids, cornea, iris, pupil, and sclera. In addition, we note two important structures—the *lens* and the *retina*, and two fluids—the *aqueous humor* and the *vitreous humor*. The aqueous humor is a watery fluid in front of the lens, and the vitreous humor is a denser fluid behind the lens that fills most of the eyeball.

THE EYE MAKES A PICTURE.   The lens of the eye acts like the lens of a camera: it gathers light, bends it, and forms a picture. The light rays are focused to make a sharp image on the light-sensitive retina in the back of the eye. As in the camera, the image is an inverted one.

The lens of the human eye is not focused by moving it back and forth. Instead,

A. Front view of eye. B. Vertical section of eye. Which of the eye's structures can be seen in the front view? See the text for a description of how the eye functions.

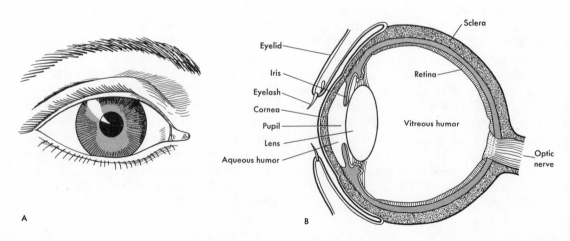

A   B

focusing is accomplished by *changing the shape of the lens*. The eye lens is a transparent disk, convex on both sides and about one-third of an inch in diameter. It is within the globe of the eye, just behind the iris. It is made of a material whose shape can be altered by the action of muscles attached to it. When the lens is thin and flat, it is adapted for focusing faraway objects. When it is fatter and rounder, it is adapted for close vision.

The ability to adjust the lens shape is called *accommodation*. This works well in most young people. In older individuals, the lens loses some of its elasticity, and eyeglasses are required to compensate for this.

THE SCREEN OF THE EYE.

The parallel between eye and camera holds for the light-sensitive retina, which is analogous to photographic film. In the retina there are two kinds of sensitive cells, the rods and the cones. Cones are sensitive to light of different colors and are also used in bright light. Rods are sensitive to dim light; when stimulated they produce sensations only of light intensity—of varying shades of gray. As you might expect, the retinas of some night animals contain only rods.

In light of intermediate strength, both the rods and the cones respond. As brightness increases, the cones take over entirely. This change corresponds to the photographer's use of "fast" or "slow" film in his camera.

The cones, then, are used in bright light, and respond to varying colors in that light. How does the eye see color? It is thought that human color vision is dependent on the responses of three different kinds of cones, each with a different light-sensitive pigment. One type is sensitive to red light, one to green light, and one to blue-violet light. Color sensation is the sum of responses to impulses from all three types of cones. Thus, the human retina resembles not only black and white film but color film, which also contains three different chemicals sensitive to different colors.

SEEING WITH OUR BRAINS.

Impulses initiated by the 130 million light-sensitive cells in each retina are sent over nerve fibers to the brain. These are nerve impulses, not light waves. The brain interprets them according to the type of cell over which the impulse comes and the particular spot in the brain where the impulse is received. The brain produces some kind of a replica (not a picture) of the image on the retina.

What happens in the brain is fantastically complex; what one "sees" depends on many factors. An ink blot means different things to different people. Seeing is not simply a matter of the physics of light: it depends on the operation of the mind, on psychology.

THE KEYBOARD OF LIGHT

Light is similar to sound in a number of ways. Both are messengers, carrying information of the world about us to our senses. Both travel, although light travels almost a million times as fast as sound. Both apparently are wave phenomena; a wave-like disturbance proceeds in all directions from a source. In both, the length of the wave (from "crest" to "crest") varies; in sound, varying wavelengths produce sounds of different *pitch*, in light, different *colors*.

Color, then, is akin to pitch. Just as each note has a different wavelength, so each color has its particular wavelength. The deepest red visible to the eye as a color has a wavelength of about 1/30,000 of an inch; the deepest violet at the other end of the spectrum has a wavelength of 1/60,000 of an inch.

We recall that some sound waves (the ultrasonic ones) cannot be detected by the human ear. This has its parallel in "invisible" light waves. Just beyond the violet is the invisible *ultraviolet*, with a shorter wavelength than violet. Ultraviolet radiation, found in sunlight, is important to life because

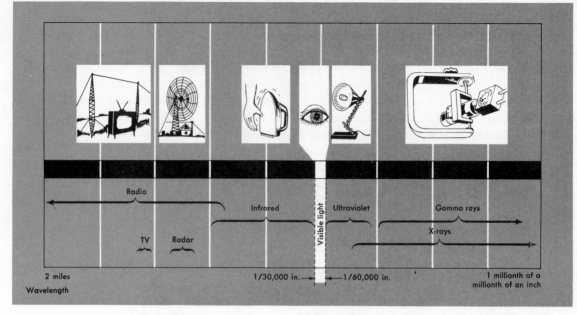

Radio

TV   Radar

Infrared

Visible light

Ultraviolet

Gamma rays

X-rays

2 miles
Wavelength

1/30,000 in. →   ←—1/60,000 in.

1 millionth of a
millionth of an inch

Visible light is a small part of the electromagnetic spectrum.

it stimulates the production of Vitamin D in organisms exposed to it. Ultraviolet radiation is also responsible for the sunburning and suntanning effects of exposure to sunlight. Although not detected by the eye, ultraviolet does affect photographic film, and therefore the appearance of the developed image.

At the other end of the spectrum, just beyond the deepest red, is *infrared*. These waves, also occurring in sunlight, are extremely important, for these are the radiant heat waves that warm the earth. All warm bodies radiate infrared light. Infrared radiation affects special photographic film that is sensitive to this invisible color.

BEYOND THE
REDS AND BLUES

Beyond the reds and blues, there exists a larger spectrum of waves known as the *electromagnetic spectrum*. We can compare this spectrum to a super-grand piano, containing not seven octaves but seventy. On the keyboard of this imagined piano, which

is ten times as long as the conventional grand piano, visible light occupies only one octave, near the center.

As you run your eye over the keyboard (see illustration) you discover that this piano is capable of many effects: radio, television, radar, visible light, x-rays, and gamma rays. Note that as you move from radio waves at one end to gamma rays at the other, the wavelength decreases progressively from about 2 miles to a millionth of a millionth of an inch.

Electromagnetic waves, first described in 1865 by James Maxwell, are another example of the basic unity of nature. In chapter 19A, we found that all matter consists of the same fundamental particles—electrons, protons, neutrons, and others. The electromagnetic spectrum demonstrates that many forms of radiation consist of waves of the same fundamental nature which travel at the same speed of 186,000 miles per second.

The following generalizations may be made from the material in this chapter:

We are able to see objects because they reflect or emit light to our eyes.

A mirror image is produced by the regular reflection of light by the reflecting surface to the viewer.

The light that is not absorbed by opaque objects is reflected by them.

Light is bent or refracted when it passes obliquely from a medium of one density to another.

Lenses are light-benders.

The eye resembles the camera in many ways.

The color of light is determined by its wavelength.

Sunlight is a mixture of many colors.

The color of an opaque object viewed in sunlight is determined by the portion of the sun's colors that it reflects.

When white light passes through a triangular prism, it fans out into a spectrum.

Rainbows are formed when sunlight is separated into its colors by water droplets in the air.

Light behaves in some respects like waves and in others like a shower of energy packets.

Light travels through space at the rate of about 186,000 miles per second.

Visible light resembles other forms of radiation such as radio, x-rays, and cosmic rays in that all are produced by waves and all travel at the same speed.

DISCOVERING FOR YOURSELF

1. Examine and use various kinds and shapes of lenses to see how they differ in their effects.
2. Experiment with sunlight (using lawnspray, prisms and other pieces of glass, an aquarium, etc.) to break it into its colors.
3. Look in your environment for examples of: refraction, reflection, indirect lighting, direct lighting, glare, sodium lights, fluorescent lights.
4. Perform a carefully controlled experiment to prove that plants need sunlight.
5. Examine and use a light meter.
6. Observe the use of photoelectric cells in your environment.
7. Use light to make a blueprint and explain what happens.
8. Examine a camera to see how it controls and uses light.
9. Examine a projection machine to see how it controls and uses light.
10. Experiment with production of shadows to see changes in size and sharpness.
11. Some astronomical societies help their members make their own telescopes. Join one.
12. Find out about those powerful sources of light, called lasers.

CHAPTER 23B

Teaching "Light and How We Use It"

Children note reflections, rainbows, colors, shadows, sunsets, moonlight. They use cameras, magnifying glasses, and mirrors. They play shadow games; they mix colored paints. Problems come from observations and experiences such as these.

The following experiences illustrate how an alert teacher used an experience to help her pupils to observe, then guided them in making conclusions that they could apply to other situations.[1]

In our kindergarten we had a problem of "What makes the lights on the ceiling of our room?" We called the lights "Our Lunch Box Light," "The 'Doughnut' Light," "The Pale Balls of Light," and "The Dancing Light." These lights were seen over a period of several months in a room where there is much sunlight. The following account describes briefly what took place:

One day, hearing the children laugh, I looked up to see Donna making a reflection on the ceiling with the bottom of her tin lunch box.

I asked Donna why she didn't use the top of her lunch box (which was painted dark red). She said it wouldn't work. I asked her to let me try it. I was sitting on the shady side of the room and it wouldn't work. I suggested to the children that they try to make a light on the ceiling with any kind of object. They tried

[1] This account of experiences in a kindergarten in Louisville, Kentucky, has been prepared by the teacher, Anne W. Anderson.

paper, cardboard, a piece of wood, a towel, a pair of scissors, pocketbooks, and an aluminum pitcher. The scissors and pitcher made faint streaks of light, but the lunch box was the best.

As we discussed our observations, we agreed that to make a light on the ceiling, two things were necessary—something *shiny* and *sunshine*. One child said one day, "I know what you call it. It is a reflection." After we got this far, I produced about 12 or 15 small mirrors and let all the children make bright reflections.

On another day, on the ceiling, there was a bright reflection in the shape of a ring. We called it the "doughnut" light. What made it? It must be something shiny in the sun. Children took turns trying to decide what it was. They examined everything on the sunny side of the room. One child decided that it was a 4-inch aluminum cap on the radiator. We covered the cap with cardboard and the reflection disappeared. When the cap was uncovered, the reflection reappeared. Many children covered it to see—so we were sure.

On another day, there were 6 or 8 pale balls of light on the ceiling. What made them? Here was the toughest problem we had struck. Again everything on the sunny side of the room was examined. All the vases and flowerpots were moved off the plant table. The problem remained unsolved for several weeks—just coming up now and then to pester us. On cloudy days there were no lights of any kind. On sunny days the pale balls were there. Upstairs, in the hall, too, there were beautiful balls of light on the ceiling!

Finally, one boy thought of climbing up on a chair and looking out on the yard. He discovered some pieces of broken glass outside and thought they might make the pale reflections. So he went out with a box and picked up the broken glass. Our pale balls of light were gone. But we made him go out and put the glass back! Upstairs, we climbed on chairs and sure enough the lower roof was covered with many pieces of broken glass.

On another day, a large pale reflection danced all over the ceiling and then settled down to a small bright spot. After the same trial-and-error method of examination, we found that it came from a cup of water on the plant table. When the water shook, the light danced; when the water was still, the light was still. One day, after a rain, we had pale dancing reflections and found clear puddles outside. The wind was ruffling the puddles.

Some activities that may be useful for primary grades are:

1. Observe shadows to see how they are made, and how they may change.
2. Look through a prism to see the colors.
3. Observe rainbow colors through an aquarium or lawn spray and name the colors.
4. Use a magnifying glass to look at many different kinds of things and materials.[2]
5. Use a mirror to reflect light.
6. Observe reflections on different surfaces.
7. Mix colors and observe the effects.
8. Take pictures to see how important light is in the process.

---

[2] Julius Schwartz, *Through the Magnifying Glass* (New York, Whittlesey House, 1954), 142 pp.

OBSERVING SHADOWS

Children like to watch shadows and play shadow games. A study lamp or other lamp with an opaque shade may be used to help pupils discover: What makes a shadow? What makes shadows change length? What kinds of things make dark shadows? Observing outdoor shadows at different times of the day helps pupils see how the sun behaves as the day passes. Pieces of wrapping paper may be used to draw an outline of a pupil's shadow at 9:00 A.M., 12:00 M. and 3:00 P.M., or at other hours that will show the relationship of shadows to the height of the sun in the sky.

EXPERIMENTING WITH REFLECTING SURFACES

To see that smooth surfaces reflect more light than rough surfaces, use a large mirror and a dusty chalk eraser. Dust chalk on half of the mirror and leave the other half smooth. Notice the difference. The same idea may be illustrated by shining one shoe to make it a smooth surface and dusting chalk on the other one. Urge children to find other examples.

EXAMINING ARTIFICIAL LIGHTS

The progress of our methods of lighting is an interesting study. A series of pictures may be collected or drawn to illustrate this progress. These pictures would include early torches, whale-oil lamps, and candles. Many encyclopedias have pictures, and local stores that sell lighting fixtures sometimes have printed matter illustrating the history of lighting.

If it is possible to obtain a clear glass electric light bulb, pupils can see the tungsten wires inside and note how they are stretched out or coiled on the inner flame. The local offices of the power company may be able to supply a replica of the first lamp invented by Edison or at least supply literature on the history of electric lighting. Pupils could look for such literature in their town libraries as well.

Encourage pupils to observe the many artificial lights in their environment and to see their different characteristics and uses. Such observations will include their homes, their streets, their schools. Examples of lights in these places are: flashlights, traffic lights, headlights, street lights, fluorescent lights, etc.

OBSERVING HOW LIGHT PASSES
THROUGH DIFFERENT THINGS

Pupils may observe in their school to find examples of things (1) through which all or almost all the light striking it can pass (transparent); (2) through which part of the light travels (translucent); (3) through which no light travels (opaque). They may discuss how these various things are useful because of the way in which they transmit or do not transmit light.

Examining the structure of the kaleidoscope will help to understand the principles of light and reflections that are involved. Several science problems will be encountered as pupils work.

EXPERIMENTING WITH MIRRORS

Pupils may make a collection of different kinds of mirrors, i.e., hand mirrors, pocket book mirrors, shaving mirrors, etc., and examine them to see what they can learn by looking at their own images. They may use mirrors to reflect beams of light. If they experiment, they will soon see the relationship between the way the light beam strikes the mirror and the way in which it is reflected. Another way of illustrating this idea is to use a large mirror in front of the classroom and ask selected pupils to tell which pupils they can see in the mirror and why, if they can explain. Pupils may observe the uses of mirrors in store windows, in automobiles, in elevators, in barber shops, and in dentists' offices, and report on why the mirrors are shaped as they are and why they are placed as they are.

MAKING A PERISCOPE

It is easy to construct a homemade periscope to see around corners or over fences or out of windows when the window sills are high. You need two mirrors and four pieces of cardboard about 12 to 15 inches long and 3 or 4 inches wide with which to make an elongated box. Both mirrors must be fastened in place at a 45-degree angle, so that they are parallel to each other. (See drawing on following page.)

Light from the objects is reflected by the mirror on the top of the periscope to the mirror at the bottom. You look at the bottom mirror through the hole in the lower portion of the periscope and thus see the image as it is reflected by the top mirror. The periscope is a useful teaching device because it helps pupils understand that mirrors reflect light, and that they can change the path of light. In a periscope the path is changed twice.

The mirrors can be fastened in place with either adhesive or mechanic's tape. The box can be put together with brads, glued, or fastened with tape. Several pupils in the class may like to make periscopes and demonstrate their use to their classmates.

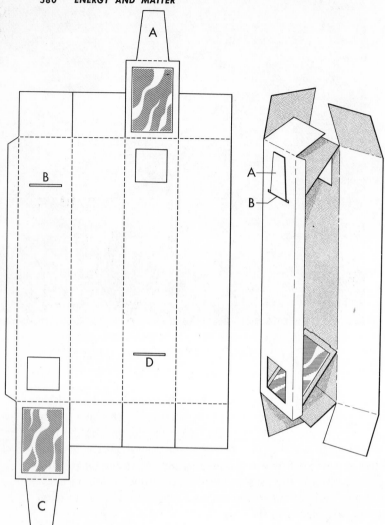

This pattern for a periscope can be cut out of heavy cardboard. Tabs A and C fit into slots B and D, but before the flaps are glued down you should make certain that the mirrors are at the proper angle. You can determine this by trying out the periscope before you apply the glue.

FINDING OUT WHAT LENSES
ARE USED FOR

Although the details of how lenses form images are too difficult for most elementary school pupils to comprehend, all pupils can observe that the thickness and curvature of the glass affect the direction of the light as it passes through. The lens from a flashlight, a magnifying glass, a projector, and the eyeglasses of pupils in the class are all useful as illustrations of what lenses do. Pupils should certainly not be encouraged to wear one another's glasses, but looking through the various lenses to see how objects appear through them will help them to see how lenses differ.

A magnifying glass may be used in bright sunlight to focus light strong enough to burn paper. There is a safety precaution to be observed here. It is possible for pupils to burn themselves or one another by careless use of the glass. It is easy for pupils to see how moving the lens back and forth focuses the light and to see how the lens acts as a light "gatherer." Children should realize that it is dangerous to look at the sun with any kind of lenses and that light from the sun should never be reflected into anyone's eyes.

In connection with the study of lenses it is very helpful to have a nurse or doctor discuss how the eye sees, show pupils how eyes are checked by the use of a chart, and explain briefly and nontechnically to the class what happens when drops are put into the eyes and how lenses are used to determine the kind of eyeglasses to be prescribed. The nurse or doctor may help pupils to set up certain rules for the care of the eyes and discuss with them things that they might do in their schoolroom to improve light conditions—such as adjusting window shades, using chalkboards, and rearranging seating.

EXAMINING A CAMERA

In almost any upper elementary class there are pupils who have cameras and know well enough how to operate them in order to tell the class about them. Urge children to bring their cameras, explain simply the operation, and then insert film and take pictures of the class. They may demonstrate loading the films, holding the camera, getting proper light, using the finder, etc. They may describe various cautions in the use of the camera to ensure good results. In some instances it is even possible for them to explain how the film is developed. Pupils should understand where light enters the camera, where the lens is, what the shutter does, and how the picture is focused on the film. The demonstrator may also introduce pupils to the light meter and show how it behaves under various light intensities. Because so many adults are enthusiastic about photography, more and more children have access to cameras. The use of the camera may demonstrate many of the science principles involved in the study of light.

MAKING BLUEPRINTS

Using light to make simple blueprints helps pupils to see how light can produce a chemical change on sensitive paper. Blueprint paper may be purchased at camera or art supply shops and in some drug stores. Since this paper changes color after a period of time, even in the dark, it should be purchased fresh in small quantities. Small pieces of glass will serve to hold in place the paper and the objects to be printed. Leaf blueprints, for example, are made by laying a leaf on the blueprint paper, covering it with a piece of glass, and holding it up to the bright sunlight for several seconds. After the blueprint is exposed, wash it in cold water. The leaf print will appear white, the remainder of the paper blue. Blueprint paper is covered with light-sensitive chemicals. These chemicals will dissolve in water. Wherever light strikes the paper, the chemicals change. The new chemical that is produced is blue and does not dissolve in water. Sunlight strikes the paper and produces the new chemical in every place except under the leaf.

A film negative (instead of a leaf), placed on top of blueprint paper and exposed as described previously, will help pupils understand how a print is made from a negative.

INVESTIGATING AND CORRECTING
LIGHTING CONDITIONS

In all probability, a local store that sells lighting fixtures can furnish printed materials that illustrate principles of good lighting. The school principal may have studied school lighting and may be prepared to talk to pupils about how the lights in the school have been designed to give the proper amount of light. He may bring a light meter to the room and show the pupils how to check the amount of light at various places in the room. If the amount of light is not adequate, it may be possible for the class to urge that steps be taken to improve it. Pupils may take home some of the printed material[3] that describes good lighting and discuss their home lighting situation with their parents. There have been instances when such an activity has resulted in improved lighting both at home and in school.

Teachers have the responsibility of seeing that lighting is adequate in their schoolrooms. Children seldom speak for themselves about things of this sort. Others must speak for them. Often administrators and boards of education are unaware that lighting is not what it should be. Sometimes, too, this problem is not presented to them forcibly enough to receive adequate attention. Public-school officials, constantly being bombarded by demands, do not intentionally disregard children's needs, but they may have to have these needs brought to their attention emphatically and often. Teachers should accept the responsibility of seeing that children do not undergo unnecessary eyestrain even if it means frequent and loud reminders.

Blackboards of the traditional type sometimes produce glare. Many new buildings now have sight-saving green boards on which yellow chalk is used. Given proper "blackboards" and chalk, teachers have the responsibility of writing large enough and legibly enough so that children do not strain their eyes making out tiny or unrecognizable figures or words.

STUDYING THE EYES[4]

Children may be encouraged to look carefully at their own eyes in a mirror or at the eyes of a classmate to see the tiny opening (pupil), the colored part of the eye (the iris) that regulates the size of the pupil, and the eyelids and eyelashes that protect the eyes. They may feel their eyes through their lids to understand the roundness. They may cover their eyes for a few minutes and let their classmates see the before and after effects on the size of the pupil. They may observe what happens to the pupil near a bright window and then in a darker place in the room. They may draw up a set of rules for protecting their eyes.

RESOURCES TO INVESTIGATE

1. Local photographers, camera shops, camera clubs, and camera manufacturers for information about photography.
2. An optician for discarded lenses that may be used in performing simple experiments with light.
3. The power company or electrical institute to learn about the measurement of light, types of lighting, and the amount of light necessary for various activities.

---

[3] National Society for the Prevention of Blindness, Inc., 1790 Broadway, New York 19, N. Y. Write for catalogue of materials.

American Standard Practice for School Lighting, Illuminating Engineering Society, 51 Madison Ave., New York, N. Y.

[4] For further information, see J. Perry, *Our Wonderful Eyes* (New York, Whittlesey House, 1955), 158 pp.

4. Hardware and electrical supply stores to observe the various types of light fixtures and to learn how science principles are used in their construction.
5. The school building and the school custodian to learn how the school is lighted and, with the use of a light meter, to see how much light is used for various purposes in school.
6. Children's homes to observe the different kinds of lighting fixtures and how they are related to the light needs.

CHAPTER 24A

Flight and Space Travel

Over the desolate sands at Kitty Hawk, North Carolina, an odd machine made of wood, cloth, wire, and bicycle chains, and powered by a crude 12-horsepower engine, rose into the air for 12 seconds, and flew a distance of 120 feet. Thus, on December 17, 1903, did Wilbur and Orville Wright make an ancient dream of man come true. This trip, the first heavier-than-air, powered flight, was the beginning of the air age. It marked the first time in history that a machine carrying a man had raised itself by its own power into the air in full flight, had flown without loss of speed, and had landed at a point as high as the place from which it had started.

For many centuries man dreamed of flying like a bird. Alexander the Great is supposed to have made a flying machine by harnessing two strong eagles to a yoke on which he was seated. According to this legend, the eagles followed the direction in-

dicated by Alexander's spear, on the point of which was a piece of meat.

Leonardo da Vinci, the fifteenth-century painter and sculptor, was also an engineer and inventor who applied his genius to the problem of flight. Studying the flight of birds, he designed several wing-flapping machines to help man soar in the air. He also suggested the use of rotating wings, thus anticipating the modern helicopter. Da Vinci is also credited with the invention of the "air screw" to pull a machine through the air, thus pointing the way to the modern propeller.

Da Vinci was the first to make a reasonable estimate of what is entailed in keeping a man in the air. From his examination of birds, he found a relationship between wing span and body weight. On this basis, he estimated that a man would need wings with a 12-foot span to support him. In this, da Vinci was much more realistic than some of the ill-fated experimenters who followed him.

There is no evidence that any of da Vinci's machines ever worked, or that his theories influenced the development of aviation. Indeed, it was not until 1930 that his full works were published. A man whose theories did influence aviation was Sir George Cayley, an English scientist. In 1809, he made a remarkably astute statement on the problem of flight. He said that flight would be possible if we could make a *surface* support a weight by the application of *power* to the *resistance of the air*. In this, Cayley was giving proper recognition to:

1. *The supporting surface (the wings of the modern plane).*
2. *Power (the motor and propeller—later the jet—that would pull or push the wings through the air).*
3. *The air itself (the "resistance of the air," as we will see, provides the "lift" on the wing needed to overcome gravity).*

Cayley established the principle of the fixed wing, that is, the wing held fast to the body of the plane, in contrast to the flapping wing considered by previous flight enthusiasts. He conducted many experiments with model gliders to test his theories.

Glider experiments were of utmost importance in the development of aviation: test flights with these unpowered flying devices made it possible to improve the design and the shape of planes and thus make them more airworthy. Otto Lilienthal pioneered in designing and flying gliders that could carry a man. He developed the curved or arched wing. In his book, *The Art of Flying Based on the Flight of Birds,* published in 1889, he stated that in the arched wing "there lies in all probability the whole secret of the art of flying."

Lilienthal made over 2,000 successful glider flights, sometimes achieving distances of 200 to 300 yards in his gliding machines.

We will return to the airplane later and examine it carefully to find out just how it works. For the moment, however, let us consider an entirely different approach to flight, that of the balloon.

BALLOONS

In June 1783, the French brothers Etienne and Joseph Montgolfier built a balloon and flew in it for a mile at an altitude of 1,000 feet. Their balloon was actually a large paper bag lined with linen and filled with hot air. Since hot air is less dense than cold air, the balloon had enough buoyancy to rise and to support the weight of the men in the gondola attached to it.

The Montgolfier brothers started a wave of balloon flights. Balloon ascensions were familiar sights at country fairs. The balloon bag was tied down to pegs in the ground over a wood fire and kept there until it filled with hot air. Then a balloonist took his place on a trapeze attached to a parachute, which in turn was attached to the balloon. When the inflated balloon was released it sailed into the air with a loud "whoosh." When the bag was as high in the air as it could go, the daredevil balloonist pulled a cord which detached the tip of the parachute from the balloon. The balloonist came floating down, while the bag, losing attitude as the hot air cooled, went drifting off to be recovered later from a pasture or field.

In later flights, hydrogen, the lightest of all gases, was used instead of hot air. In one of the first high-altitude balloon flights, in 1862, two balloonists, Coxwell and Glaisher, rose 7 miles into the air.

But free-floating balloons were never efficient for practical purposes of transportation, although they did provide many thrills as well as much scientific information about conditions of the atmosphere. One balloonist was able to remain aloft long enough

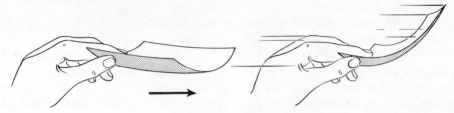

The "kite effect." When a surface is pushed against the air, the air pushes back. The text tells how this gives an airplane part of its lift.

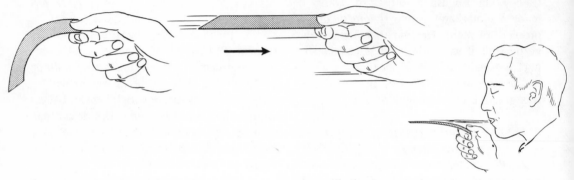

The "vacuum effect." The pressure on the upper surface is decreased. How does this effect help to lift an airplane?

to drift, with favorable air currents, 2,000 miles from Paris to Moscow. With the addition of a steering mechanism and an internal combustion engine and propeller to furnish motive power, the airship, a lighter-than-air machine, was developed. This type of craft reached its greatest development with the huge airships, or dirigibles, of Count Ferdinand von Zeppelin. These airships could carry heavy loads of freight and passengers.

Lighter-than-air craft are still used for military reconnaissance and for carrying advertisements. But the amazing development of heavier-than-air planes with power to carry cargoes of more than 300 people or 35 tons of freight has rendered the dirigible practically obsolete.

Balloons are still important in the scientific exploration of the upper atmosphere (see chapter 9A) and in providing a clearer view of the heavens (see chapters 7A and 8A).

WHAT MAKES AN AIRPLANE FLY?

Air is a real substance, just as real as liquid water or solid earth. A parachute falling through air descends slowly because its inside surface encounters and pushes against many air molecules. The crowded molecules, in turn, push back against the parachute, retarding its downward drop. If the chute fails to open, however, it plummets to earth rapidly. SEE PAG 611 TO 612

THE "KITE" EFFECT. Because air is a substance, it offers resistance to the movement of objects through it. At first, this might seem to be only an obstacle to horizontal flight. But a simple experiment will reveal that this resistance can serve a helpful purpose too. Hold one end of a 9-by-12-inch sheet of paper (as shown in the illustration), forefinger on top, and supported by the thumb and second finger underneath. Hold it in a horizontal position, curved slightly so that it does not droop. Now tilt it at a slight angle, so that the opposite end of the paper is slightly higher than the end you are holding. Now push the paper directly forward, but hold on to it. You find that the free, leading edge tilts up. Why?

As the surface of the paper is pushed against the air molecules, it crowds them together. The crowded molecules, in turn, spring back and push against the paper. Part of this air resistance impedes the forward progress of the paper, but, since the crowded molecules beat against the paper in all directions, *part of the resistance serves to lift the paper*, tilting its free end up. With a little practice, you can flick the paper or a piece of cardboard so that on leaving your hand, the upward push serves to lift the entire sheet against the pull of gravity.

The sheet of paper that you have experimented with has some of the characteristics of an airplane wing. You have used it in a way that fulfills Cayley's requirements for heavier-than-air flight. You have applied power (the push of your hand) to the resistance of the air, and in that way you have achieved a small amount of "lift."

You have found that when a tilted surface is pushed against the air, the air pushes back, partly slowing it down, partly lifting in up. A kite rises for the same reason, except that here the air (wind) moves against the surface to be lifted, instead of the surface moving against the air.

THE "VACUUM" EFFECT. Now take a look at a real airplane to find the flat, tilted surface that presses against the air. You discover it in the wings, set at an angle so that their front edge, called the leading edge, is higher than their back edge, called the trailing edge. However, only the lower surface of the wings is flat; the upper surface is curved or arched. Why? To find the answer, perform a second experiment with paper, this time with a strip about 2 inches wide and about 6 inches long. Hold it at

one end between your thumb and forefinger, thumb on top (as shown in the illustration), so that it falls in a curve not unlike that of the top of an airplane wing. Now *pull* the paper through the air. It's free end rises, as in the first experiment. You may argue, and with good reason, that the lower surface is being pushed up, as in the previous experiment, by the impact of the air from underneath. This is true, but it is only part of the truth. To discover the role of the upper surface alone, bring your fingers and the paper under your lips and blow over the *top* of it only. The paper rises again. Why?

We recall again that air is a real substance, made of bouncing molecules. We should also recall that, because of the never-ceasing bouncing of these molecules, air, even when it is not moving as a mass (wind), exerts a push in all directions—up, down, sideways. At sea level, this pressure amounts to about 15 pounds on every square inch of surface that the air impinges on. When an airplane is at rest on the ground on a windless day, the pressure on top of the wing is counterbalanced by an equal pressure from the bottom. The net effect is zero. But when the wing begins to move forward through the air, an interesting thing happens. The air flowing over the curved upper surface is forced to travel a greater distance and at a greater speed than the air on the lower surface. Rushing over the upper surface of the wing, the air expends some of its energy in motion and consequently loses some of its pressure. Thus, the pressure on the upper surface becomes less (forming a partial vacuum) than the pressure on the lower surface. The higher pressure underneath lifts the wing, and therefore the plane, against the pull of gravity.

To summarize, two factors operate to give a moving wing its lift:

1. *The impact of air against the lower surface of the wing (the "kite" effect).*
2. *The decreased pressure on the upper surface of the wing (the "vacuum" effect).*

Of the two, the second contributes more to the total lift of a plane, accounting for about 80 percent of it.

THE PROPELLER'S JOB.   In your experiments, the power to move the paper "wing" was supplied by your muscles. In the propeller plane, the power is supplied by the engine. This power is conveyed by a shaft to the propeller, sometimes called an "airscrew." The propeller resembles an electric fan; its whirling blades are twisted at an angle so that they push the air behind them. The air offers resistance to this and so pushes the blades forward. Since the propeller is attached to the plane, the plane is pulled forward at a speed necessary to give the wings their "lift."

Contrary to the impression that some individuals have, the job of the propeller is *not* to blow a stream of air over the wings. Usually, the propellers are placed so that this air stream or *wash*, as it is called, will not interfere with the normal flow of air over the wings. The job of the propeller is to pull the plane forward so that air will flow over the wings.

As an airplane races down the runway, the propeller pulls it along the ground faster and faster until the impact of the air and the excess pressure on the under surface of the wings is sufficient to lift the plane into the air.

In jet planes, no propellors are required—jet action thrusts the plane through the air. Jet action will be explained later.

HOW AN AIRPLANE IS CONTROLLED

Before heavier-than-air flight could be achieved, three problems had to be solved:

The control surfaces of a plane permit it to change its position in three ways. The text explains how the elevator, the rudder, and the ailerons are manipulated to control pitching, yawing, and rolling.

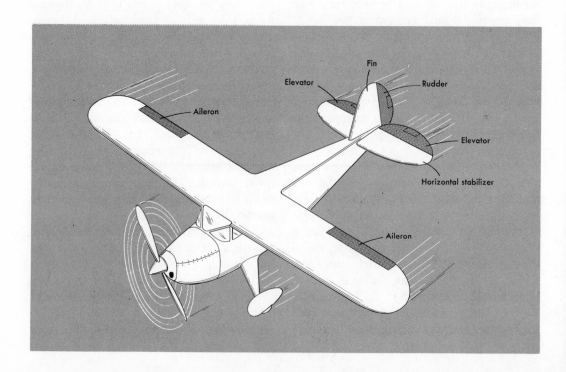

1. *Efficient surfaces to support the weight had to be provided. We have seen how the arched wing solved this problem.*
2. *Adequate power without excessive weight had to be furnished. This had to wait on the development of light internal-combustion engines.*
3. *Stability and maneuverability in flight had to be attained. We will consider some aspects of this problem now.*

THE CONTROL SURFACES.   Airplanes move in three-dimensional space. Reference to the accompanying diagram will show three kinds of changes in position relative to this space. It might be helpful in understanding these to think of *yourself* as a plane, arms outstretched, flying through space like Superman. You might want to change your *pitch*, so that the length of your body is tilted with respect to earth, pointing up or pointing down. The word pitch is also applied to a similar motion of a ship at sea. You might want to *yaw*, that is, alter the direction in which you are heading toward the left or toward the right. You might want to *roll* (or bank) so that one of your arms is higher than the other. Rolling is also a nautical term, well known to those who have suffered from seasickness.

The pilot is able to cause these changes in position by manipulating adjustable control surfaces that are hinged to the plane and can be turned like a door. When these surfaces are turned to "catch the breeze," they alter the position of the plane in the air.

Pitching is effected by moving the *elevator*, part of the tail of the plane. When the elevator is tilted up, the plane's tail goes down and its nose up. When the elevator is down, the opposite movement occurs.

Yawing to the left or right is effected by moving the *rudder*, also part of the tail of the plane.

Rolling, also called banking, requires the operation of the two *ailerons*, which are hinged strips, each attached to the trailing edge of the plane's wings. The ailerons work in opposition to each other, so that when one is turned up, the other automatically moves down.

One other control should be mentioned here, the engine *throttle*, which regulates the amount of forward *thrust* supplied by the propellers.

Having given the functions of the *movable* controls of a plane, we must hasten to correct an impression that some may have about the function of the rudder. It is natural to assume that it serves exactly as a rudder does on a ship; that is, that it is used in a similar way by a plane to execute right and left turns in the air. The rudder does help, as we shall see, but it is the ailerons and the wings which are the chief factors in turning. We quote from page 43 of the *Flight Instruction Manual* of the United States Civil Air Authority (Technical Manual #100, April 1951) in this regard:

Turns are *not* made with the rudder. Turns are made in an airplane by tipping, or canting, the direction of the lift of the wings from vertical to one side or the other, causing this "lift" to pull the airplane in that direction as well as to overcome gravity. This is done by using the ailerons to roll the airplane toward the side to which it is desired to turn.

The *Manual* goes on to say that the rudder is used while banking in a turn in order to correct the tendency of the plane to yaw toward the outside of the turn.

In other words, turning is done by tilting the plane so that part of the lift on the wings is used to pull the plane to the left or right. To try to turn by using the rudder alone is like trying to make a sharp turn in an auto while traveling rapidly on an icy road. The car may point in a new direction but it continues skidding off in the original one.

BUILT-IN STABILITY.   In addition to the elevator, rudder, and ailerons, all subject to the control of the aviator, the plane as a whole must possess inherent stability, that is, it must be designed to correct slight alterations in its position caused by upward, downward, and horizontal gusts of winds or by the plane's own movements. Flying would be impossible if the aviator had to adjust for each of these disturbances. To a great extent, a plane must be able to take care of itself. In the tail of the plane, a fixed vertical *fin* keeps the plane from yawing sideways. The horizontal stabilizer keeps the nose and tail from bobbing up and down. The wings prevent the tendency to roll. The placement of the wings at an upward-sloping angle (dihedral angle) to the body or *fuselage* of the plane increases the effectiveness of the wings as stabilizing surfaces.

PILOTING THE PLANE

TAKE-OFF.   When the pilot has completed his check of the plane and all the passengers have boarded, he obtains permission via radio from the control tower of the airport to taxi. He warms the engine of the plane with the landing wheels braked. With the propellor spinning satisfactorily, he unlocks the brakes, taxis down the runway assigned to him by the control tower, and heads the plane into the wind. Again he must receive permission by radio from the control tower, this time to take off.

The pilot pushes the throttle forward, and the plane rushes down the runway into the wind, all three wheels still on the ground. As the speed increases, the lift on the wings is almost equal to the weight of the entire plane. The pilot pushes the *joy stick* (or wheel) forward slightly, causing the elevator to tip down. The tail of the plane is lifted. The plane moves faster and faster until it reaches its take-off speed. The elevators are now tipped slightly upward. The plane is lifted gently off the ground. The landing gear

is retracted into the plane, which climbs until the desired elevation is reached. The elevators are then leveled.

LEVEL FLIGHT.   In level flight, the pilot uses the ailerons and rudder to make whatever turns are needed. The ailerons are controlled by the same joy stick or wheel that controls the elevator. To move the ailerons, the stick is moved to the right or left. To make a right turn, the stick is moved to the right; the right aileron is raised and the left one lowered. This results in the tipping of the plane toward the right, with right wing down and left wing up. The plane swings into a right turn. As indicated previously, the pilot moves the rudder slightly in making a turn. The rudder is controlled with the *foot pedals*. In a right turn, the rudder is moved toward the right by pushing the right pedal forward. In a left turn, the joy stick is moved to the left and the left foot pedal is pushed forward.

LANDING.   The pilot gets ready to land by lowering the nose of the plane in a slight glide and by "throttling down" the motor, thus slowing the plane. With a drop in speed, there is a loss of lift. The plane begins to sink slowly. The pilot obtains permission from the control tower of the airport to make a landing and receives instructions about which runway to use. When the plane has lost sufficient altitude and speed, it enters the runway with the nose tilted slightly down. When the ground is nearly reached, the pilot pulls the nose up to make a level landing.

On the large airliners you may have noticed something looking like a second wing attached to the trailing edge of each of the real wings, between the ailerons and the fuselage. These are called *flaps*. Flaps are used in landing and in taking off. When a plane is ready to land, the flaps, which ordinarily are set inside the wings, come out. By extending the surface of the wing, and, in effect by increasing its curvature, they give it more lift so that the plane can come down gently. These flaps also serve as air brakes, slowing down the plane. When the plane is taking off, the flaps also are used to provide as much lift as possible.

NAVIGATING THE PLANE

If you have ever flown across the ocean or been in a thick fog in an airplane, you know how important it is for aviators to have dependable methods of navigation. Your safe, direct flight from New York to London in a matter of hours is the result of expert navigation. We shall deal briefly with some of the methods used in air navigation.

In *contact flying*, the pilot determines his position chiefly by observing such known landmarks as cities, villages, lakes, railroad tracks, and rivers. In the early days of aviation, barnstorming pilots coming on unfamiliar terrain would sometimes swoop down on a railroad station, read the sign to find out where they were, and zoom up again. Of course, a pilot over unfamiliar territory can identify the landmarks by referring to a map. Contact flying is used over land on days when the visibility is such that the ground can be seen from the plane.

When the weather is bad or when a pilot is flying over trackless water, *dead reckoning* may be used. This method is based on a knowledge of the direction in which the plane has traveled, the speed, and the number of hours spent in flight. A plane flying due east at the rate of 200 miles an hour should be 800 miles east of the starting point at the end of four hours, provided it has not been slowed down, speeded up, or deflected by winds. The accuracy of dead reckoning is largely dependent upon the accuracy with which the wind velocity and direction is determined.

In *celestial navigation*, the pilot determines his position by reference to known heavenly bodies. An instrument called a sextant is used to measure the altitude (angle with the horizontal) of such bodies as the sun, moon, Venus, Polaris (the North Star), and Arcturus. This information is then checked against prepared tables and charts and the position of the plane determined. Celestial navigation is particularly useful in flying over oceans and other large bodies of water where there are no landmarks, or in areas where there are no radio beams to guide the plane.

In *radio navigation*, the pilot follows a directional flight path provided by special stations called radio range stations. The plane flies on the "beam," which is a highway of radio signals in the sky. These skyroads form a network connecting large cities over the whole world, with radio range stations placed at intervals along them. Each station sends out radio waves that are strongest in *four* narrow paths or beams to guide the pilot.

Radar is also used as an aid to navigation when visibility is poor. Radar (a word made from italicized letters of the words "*ra*dio *d*etection *a*nd *r*anging") is based on the use of a radio "echo." From the radar set in a plane, a powerful burst of high frequency radio energy is broadcast. When the radio waves strike an object, part of their energy is reflected back to their source, producing a spot of light on a tube resembling a television tube. Ships at sea use radar to prevent collision with other ships, icebergs, or jutting coast lines. In the air, radar reduces the hazards of night flying and low visibility. Collisions with planes, with mountains, and other air obstacles can thus be averted. Control towers at airports are also equipped with radar. When landing conditions are difficult, as in a thick fog, the control operator is able to see just where the incoming plane is and to "talk the plane down," that is, give precise landing instruction to the pilot by two-way radio-telephone.

Man-made satellites will soon be in use as aids to navigation. Present plans call for four *Transit* satellites in proper orbit. These will broadcast accurate navigation data to ships and aircraft throughout the world every 1½ hours to enable navigators to calculate their locations accurately.

SEE PAGE 614 *WEATHER AND AVIATION.* In aviation, as in many other things, the straight line is not always the shortest distance between two points. A pilot modifies his flight path according to the prevailing weather conditions.

Special weather forecasts are issued by the Weather Bureau every six hours, covering conditions over all civil airways and about 250 airports in the United States. The forecasts include information about clouds, fog, winds, storms, icing conditions, and other phenomena. Knowing these conditions, a pilot will work out a flight plan that avoids dangerous storms, headwinds, and icing conditions. It may be necessary for the pilot to land at an alternate airport if weather conditions at the original destination are hazardous.

The installation of radar equipment in commercial planes aids the pilot in "seeing" the weather. With radar in the cockpit, the pilot gets a clear picture of the weather as much as 150 miles ahead, even through clouds and darkness. Radar enables the pilot to fly through the smoothest corridors of the weather pattern, thus insuring safer, more comfortable, and more dependable travel. Other aspects of weather in relation to aviation are discussed in chapter 10A.

JETS

The propeller, as we have seen, is a device that makes use of the air to pull the plane forward. Jet planes, however, generally have no propellers. How do they work? SEE PAGE 614

A simple experiment with a toy balloon illustrates the jet principle. If a balloon is inflated and then released, it zips around as the air escapes. We note that the balloon zips in the opposite direction from that of the escaping air. Why does the balloon behave in this way?

Jet action is an example of *Newton's third law of motion*, which states that for every action there is an equal and opposite reaction. When someone dives off your shoulders into water, you feel a violent shove backward at the moment of diving. The jumping of the diver (action) resulted in your being pushed back (reaction).

In the balloon experiment, the escaping air is comparable to the diver, and the balloon itself to the person supporting the

This pulse-jet illustrates some of the features common to all jets. The rapid burning of fuel in a combustion chamber causes a blast out of a rear opening. The reaction to the blast thrusts the plane forward.

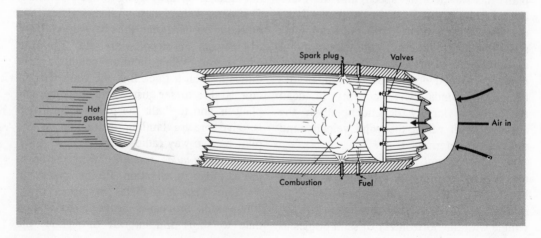

diver. The air streaming out of the opening produces a kick backward or a *thrust* on the inside of the balloon in the opposite direction. Thrust does not depend on the presence of air in the room, for, as we shall see later, jet action is possible in airless space.

There are a number of kinds of jet planes, but all work on the same principle. In all, a large quantity of gas is produced by the rapid burning of fuel in a combustion chamber. In all, the gas is blasted out of an opening in the rear end. And in all, the reaction thrusts the plane forward—from the inside.

The differences in the various jet planes are related to the method in which the air needed for burning is admitted into the combustion chamber. The *ramjet* engine is sometimes called the "flying stovepipe" because it looks like a simple pipe or tube. When the ramjet is moving through the air at high speed, air is packed or rammed through a funnel-like opening in the front end of the "stovepipe." Kerosene is then sprayed into the wider combustion chamber of this pipe, where it mixes with the air streaming in. It burns rapidly and continuously, producing a large volume of hot gas that roars out of the large opening in the rear. A forward thrust is developed which pushes the plane to great speeds.

Since the ramjet must be moving fast, about 300 miles per hour, to admit enough air for combustion, it obviously cannot start by itself. One way of launching a ramjet plane is to carry it under another plane and then release it when it is moving fast enough. Another is to fire rockets fastened to the ramjet to boost it up to its operating speed.

The *turbojet*, however, can start from the ground without assistance. In the turbojet, a rotating, bladed wheel or *turbine* near the rear end of the pipe is spun by the escaping gases. The turbine is connected by a shaft to a fan in front. As the turbine spins, it turns the fan, which forces air from the outside into the combustion chamber.

The *turboprop* is a jet plane, resembling a turbojet, but its turbine also serves to turn a propeller. Both propeller action and jet action are used to move these planes, most of the thrust being supplied by the propeller. The turboprop combines some of the advantages of the propeller and jet planes. The propeller, as we recall, depends on its impact on the surrounding air for its effectiveness. Near the surface of the earth, where the air is dense, it is most effective; at high altitudes, however, there is not enough air for it to "bite" into. Jet action, on the other hand, does not require air to push against. It functions effectively at high altitudes. At low altitudes and at slow speeds, propeller action is better because it requires less fuel.

The turboprop is therefore a good passenger plane for trips of several hundred miles. At low altitudes, when the plane is taking off, climbing, or landing, the propeller is most effective. At very high altitudes, the jet does more of the work.

The development of an atomic-powered plane has been an object of research. With a lump of uranium no bigger than a man's fist it should be possible to travel vast distances without "refueling." No combustion is needed; fission of atoms in a reactor would provide heat that would cause air to expand and to blast out of the exhaust tubes as in a jet plane. However, several major obstacles must be overcome before an A-plane can take its place beside the A-submarine in our emerging atomic age. The greatest difficulty has been the construction of an atomic reactor light enough to move a plane at supersonic speed, yet heavy enough to shield the crew and passengers from radiation.

THE SOUND BARRIER

As planes travel faster and faster, new obstacles to flight develop. When a plane is moving at a speed of 750 miles per hour, approaching the speed of sound, a

The United States will soon develop civilian supersonic transports that will make it possible to fly across the country in less than two hours. Shown here are four models of aircraft that fly faster than sound.

curious thing begins to happen. The plane begins to shake and bounce. Going still faster, at the very speed of sound, the shaking increases, becoming so violent that the wings are sometimes wrenched off the plane. At still greater speed, the plane has smooth sailing again.

The plane has passed through an invisible wall in the air—the *sound barrier*. Just what is this barrier?

You recall from chapter 22A that sound moves in a wave of compression; molecules of air are pushed closer together as the wave proceeds. This wave of compression advances at about 1,100 feet a second or about 760 miles per hour at sea level.

When a plane moves slower than the speed of sound (roughly 660 miles per hour at an altitude of 35,000 feet), the sound made by the plane speeds away from it. But when the speed of sound is reached, the plane keeps pace with its own sound waves. The compression waves cannot speed away from the plane. They pile up in front of the wings and body of the plane, forming a veritable wall called a *shock wave*.

Shock waves interfere with the smooth flow of air around the plane and cause irregularities in the forces which act on the plane. At about the speed of sound,

two shock waves form at a distance from the airplane. These are heard on the ground as an explosive sound known as *sonic boom*, usually heard as two powerful bangs in quick succession.

When the plane succeeds in breaking through and flying at *supersonic speed*, that is, faster than the speed of sound, the sound waves no longer bother it, for they are left behind the plane.

Planes have been designed to move through the sound barrier without damage. A long, needle-like nose and thin, swept-back wings enable the plane to slip through the sound barrier smoothly. The *delta* or triangular wing is common in craft designed for flight at supersonic speed.

At present, plans are under way for the development of civilian supersonic air transport. Planes which will travel from two to three times the speed of sound are now being designed. The first such U.S. plane will probably travel at 1,700 miles per hour and transport 150 persons. Thus it will be possible to fly from Boston to San Francisco in less than 2 hours. This means that one can leave Boston 1 hour before breakfast and arrive in San Francisco 2 hours before breakfast! One will be able to take a trip from the United States to Europe in only about 2½ hours.

THE ROCKET PLANE

Perhaps the ultimate stage in the flying machine is the rocket, which does not rely in any way on the air to sustain its motion. With the development of more and more powerful power systems, the thrust provided by the rocket is sufficient to overcome the pull of gravity even without the "lift" provided by the wings of the conventional plane. When rocket planes leave the lower atmosphere and fly at heights of hundreds of miles or more, the air is too "thin" for wings to be of any use anyway.

The rocket engine, unlike any of the others discussed in this chapter, carries its own oxygen supply (or other chemicals which serve as oxidizers) for the burning of fuel and is therefore not limited to flight within the atmosphere. This, plus the enormous power-to-weight ratio, makes it the only known engine that can drive manned or unmanned vehicles into space.

Gunpowder, the traditional fuel used in the older military rockets and in rockets used for firework displays, is not suitable for long-distance flights. Instead, new liquid and solid fuels are used. A rocket is propelled in the same way as a jet. The burning of fuel produces gases under high pressure which stream out of the nozzle. The jet action produced in this way creates the thrust that makes the rocket go.

On August 2, 1960, Major Robert M. White flew to an altitude of 136,500 feet —about 25 miles—in the X-15, a rocket-propelled plane. Since then speeds of more than 4,000 miles per hour and altitudes up to 67 miles have been reached in the X-15. This experimental plane was built to investigate the problems of re-entry into the atmosphere from high altitudes while traveling at extremes of speed. Special design was required to make the X-15 maneuverable at high supersonic speed. The plane's structures also had to withstand the high temperatures created by the air resistance as it plunged into the earth's atmosphere.

THE HEAT BARRIER

Another obstacle to rapid flight is the *heat barrier*. We get some notion of this barrier when we observe meteorites enter our atmosphere. The friction between the meteorite, falling at the rate of 25,000 miles per hour, and the air causes it literally to "boil" away, leaving behind a trail of luminous gas, popularly called a "shooting star." Similarly, when a plane flies through the atmosphere, air friction heats the plane's metal skin; the faster the flight, the more intense the heat. Supersonic planes are affected by the heat barrier; their design and the materials used in their construction must be adapted for this condition. The heat generated is a menace also to the pilot, who would be roasted in his cockpit if it were not for refrigeration equipment installed in these planes.

ROCKETS AND SPACE FLIGHT

(Note: In the material on space flight which follows, the authors have been guided by *Space: The New Frontier*, a publication of the National Aeronautics and Space Administration.) SEE PAGES 614 TO 615

The history of rockets is closely related to the history of space travel, since only with the rocket principle is space travel possible. The first recorded use of rockets occurred in 1232 A.D., when the Chinese repelled Mongols with "arrows of flying fire," which were actually incendiary firecrackers. Rockets were brought to Europe shortly after. In 1379, a crude rocket powered with gunpowder scored a lucky hit which destroyed a defending tower in the battle for Isle of Chiozza during the Venetian-Genovese War.

In the nineteenth century, Sir William Congreve of Great Britain developed a rocket which was used extensively in the Napoleonic Wars. The "rockets' red glare" in the *Star-Spangled Banner* refers to the Congreve rocket missiles that the British fired against Fort McHenry during the battle for Baltimore in the War of 1812. A humanitarian use of the Congreve rocket was first patented in 1838. This was a device which carried a line from shore to a stranded vessel, enabling the distressed crew to be pulled to shore on a breeches-buoy.

All of the rockets up to the twentieth century employed a solid fuel, such as gunpowder. In 1903, a Russian schoolteacher, Konstantin Ziolkovsky, proposed an interplanetary rocket in an article "Investigating Space with Rocket Devices." Here he urged that a spaceship be powered by a liquid-propelled engine supplied with liquid hydrogen and liquid oxygen. It is interesting to note that Ziolkovsky said that "probably the first seeds of the idea were sown by that great, fantastic author, Jules Verne."

Ziolkovsky's ideas remained unknown outside of Russia, and at that time the Russians gave them little attention.

Working separately, Herman Oberth, a Rumanian-German, and Robert H. Goddard, an American, laid the basis for modern rocketry. Oberth stimulated experimental rocket work in Germany with his book, published in 1923, "The Rocket into Interplanetary Space."

Dr. Goddard, a professor at Clark University in Massachusetts, in 1919 sent to the Smithsonian Institution a copy of a 69-page manuscript entitled "A Method of Reaching Extreme Altitudes." This paper attracted the attention of the press because of a brief comment on the possibility of shooting a rocket to the moon and exploding a load of powder on the surface. Shortly after, God-

This is an illustration from the first edition of Jules Verne's science fiction novel, "From the Earth to the Moon," published in 1865. Here the passengers in Verne's spaceship enjoy their first feeling of weightlessness.

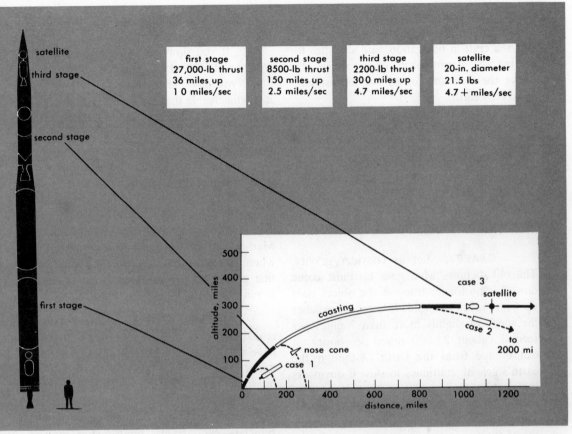

satellite

third stage

second stage

first stage

first stage	second stage	third stage	satellite
27,000-lb thrust	8500-lb thrust	2200-lb thrust	20-in. diameter
36 miles up	150 miles up	300 miles up	21.5 lbs
1 0 miles/sec	2.5 miles/sec	4.7 miles/sec	4.7 + miles/sec

case 3

satellite

coasting

case 2

to
2000 mi

nose cone

case 1

altitude, miles

500
400
300
200
100

0   200   400   600   800   1000   1200

distance, miles

A three-stage rocket. See discussion on page 599.

dard hypothesized that a liquid fuel would be superior to the powder pellets which he had been using to power his rockets. Between 1919 and 1926, Dr. Goddard worked to perfect his ideas. On March 16, 1926, a momentous day for rocket flight, the world's first liquid fuel rocket was launched. Although it covered a distance of only 184 feet, it proved that this kind of a rocket would work. Dr. Goddard continued his research in the more open spaces of southwestern United States. In 1935, his rockets achieved altitudes of 7,500 feet and speeds of over 700 miles per hour.

Rockets played an important part in World War II. The V-2, a rocket-propelled missile, was fired at London and Antwerp. It has been estimated that had the Germans been given another six months of production time with the rocket, they could have turned the tide of war.

On October 4, 1957, the first man-made satellite, Sputnik I, was rocketed into orbit in the Soviet Union. Less than four months later, on January 31, 1958, the United States launched its first satellite, Explorer I. The Spage Age opened.

SATELLITES INTO ORBIT

Circling the earth today are many satellites which, unlike the moon, were placed there by man. Included in the new array of man-made heavenly bodies are satellites for watching the weather picture, satellites for relaying telephone and television messages around the earth, satellites for assisting air and sea craft in navigation, and satellites for serving as astronomical observatories far above the dust and fog of our atmosphere-blanketed earth.

To place a satellite into orbit, it is necessary to contend successfully with two important conditions. First, one must cope with the earth's gravity, which never releases its influence. Secondly, one must overcome the resistance offered by the earth's atmosphere, through which the space vehicle must plow on its way into orbit.

GRAVITY.   Let us consider gravity. The old dictum "what goes up must come down" is no longer true—if the object goes up with sufficient speed. If a rocket reaches the speed of slightly more than 7 miles per second (about 25,000 miles per hour), it can escape from the earth. Although the earth's gravity continues to slow it down, its initial velocity is sufficient to permit it to escape, perhaps to proceed to the moon, Venus, or Mars, perhaps to become a satellite of the sun.

If a rocket is propelled upward at a speed of only 10,000 miles an hour, gravity will slow it down sufficiently to cause it to fall back to earth.

To place a satellite into orbit around the earth at an altitude of 200 miles, it is necessary to make it reach a speed of about 18,000 miles an hour. The gravitational attraction of the earth is then counterbalanced by the force produced by the satellite's speed in orbit.

Consequently, to answer the question "what keeps a satellite up?" it is necessary to understand the action of gravity and the effect of the speed of the satellite in orbit. A simple way of demonstrating this principle is to fasten a weight to the end of a string and then swing the weight. When the weight reaches "orbital" speed, it stretches the string in a straight line from your hand. The weight is held in its orbit both by the force created by its swinging motion and by the pull of the string ("gravity").

If you slow the swinging motion, the weight will fall "out of orbit." If, on the other hand, you increase the speed of the weight, it is conceivable that the string (which represents the pull of gravity) might break and the weight fly away. The weight will have achieved an "escape" velocity.

The earth itself is an example of a body moving rapidly enough (about 18 miles a second) in its orbit not to fall into the sun, but not so rapidly that it tears out of the solar system to wander in the Milky Way galaxy. Man-made satellites become less mysterious when we realize that they obey the same laws that govern all of the planets in their orbits around the sun.

STAYING IN ORBIT.   When people realize that once in orbit man-made satellites have no engines for propulsion (except for minor adjustments of position), they ask the question "what keeps a satellite moving?" This is a perfectly natural question since our experiences on earth teach us that moving vehicles—cars, trains, boats—stop moving unless continuously propelled by some kind of engine. However, what is not always understood is that these moving objects are constantly opposing the force of friction which results from their contact with the ground, water, air, etc. Without friction, a moving car could coast along forever with the motor turned off. Newton expressed this idea in one of his laws when he stated that a body continues in uniform motion unless acted on by an unbalanced force.

At altitudes of 100 or more miles above the earth, the effect of the atmosphere is negligible, so that there is nothing to slow down the speed of satellites. Of course, some satellites have had a short life, not by design but because they were launched into orbits which cut across the lower, denser portion of the earth's atmosphere.

THE ATMOSPHERE.   Early in this discussion we said that the earth's atmosphere was a factor to be contended with. We have just seen how a satellite must be above the atmosphere since the slowing effect will tend to rob the satellite of the speed necessary to match the pull of the earth's gravity.

The atmosphere must also be taken into consideration in planning the trip from the moment of launch on the surface of the earth until the space vehicle is above the air. The vehicle must be streamlined so that air resistance is kept to a minimum. Speed in the lower atmosphere must not be too great, since friction increases with speed. Moreover, frictional heating results in temperatures which may adversely affect the material of the spacecraft.

A rocket rises slowly from its launching pad and gradually gains speed as it climbs. Thus it passes through the dense lower layers of the atmosphere with speeds at which friction heating does not constitute a serious problem. The rocket reaches full speed at heights where the air is too thin to cause any important resistance to flight.

MULTISTAGE LAUNCHING. Multistage rockets with two, three, four, or more stages, mounted on top of each other in piggy-back fashion, are often used for orbital or space flight. In succession, each part of the vehicle separates from the space vehicle after it has burned its fuel, ultimately leaving only the payload—which may be a satellite orbiting the earth or a spaceship on its way to the moon, Venus, Mars, or elsewhere. A typical three-stage launch is shown in the illustration on page 597. What are the advantages of a multistage vehicle?

1. *All the stages after the first stage have the speed of the prior stage imparted to them.*
2. *Dropping the stage after it has burned its fuel gives the succeeding stages less "dead weight" to carry as they push the vehicle into higher and higher speeds.*

THRUST. The force produced by the huge rocket engines is measured in pounds of *thrust.* To boost a spacecraft into orbit from the ground requires a thrust greater than the total weight of the launch vehicle. Two factors determine the amount of thrust that a rocket can deliver: the rate at which the fuel is burned, and the speed at which the resulting gases are exhausted from the jet.

To place an object in orbit around the earth requires that enough energy be imparted to (1) lift the object against the force of gravity to the desired height, and to then (2) give it enough speed in its orbital path to counteract the force of gravity. The illustration on page 597 shows how a typical rocket is launched. In the sample selected, a Vanguard vehicle is used to launch the satellite. The diagram and the data given show the following:

1. *Each stage increases the speed of the vehicle, and then separates from it.*
2. *The first two stages boost the satellite to a height of 300 miles and give it a speed of 2½ miles per second. The third stage pushes the satellite in its orbit up to a speed of 4.7 miles per second and then separates from it.*
3. *The third stage may continue in orbit for some time. The other stages fall back toward earth, and, like a flaming meteor, are heated to incandescence and burned up because of friction of the air.*

SPEED AND ORBITAL DISTANCE. What speed is required to maintain satellites in orbit at distances other than 300 miles from the earth? Since gravity decreases with distance, the speed required decreases with distance from the earth. The following table shows the effect of distance on velocity in orbit (assuming that the satellite takes a circular orbit).

Height Above Earth in Miles	Velocity in Feet Per Second	Time For One Orbit
0	25,900	*84.5 minutes
100	25,600	88 minutes
400	24,700	98 minutes
1,000	23,100	118 minutes
23,000	10,060	1 day
230,000	3,360	27 days

* Neglecting slowing caused by the earth's atmosphere.

This chart shows a number of other interesting relationships:

At a distance of about 23,000 miles from the earth, the orbital period is one day. Since the earth is spinning at the rate of one turn a day, such a satellite would appear to stand still! At present writing, a satellite named Syncom is in such an orbit. It will be used to relay telephone and teletype messages. Three such stationary-type satellites can provide a global communication network with uninterrupted 24-hour-a-day television and telephone service, since each satellite can "see" approximately one-third of the earth.

At a distance of 230,000 miles from the earth, the period for one revolution is 27 days. There is such a satellite in existence—the moon itself!

Actually, the orbit of an earth satellite is not circular but elliptical. The point at which the orbit is closest to the earth is called the *perigee* and the point of greatest distance is called *apogee*. In the historic flight of John Glenn, perigee was approximately 100 miles and apogee 160 miles from the earth.

MAN INTO SPACE

When we place a man in a spaceship, we are adding a complex and delicate structure to it. We can alter the non-living mechanisms in a space vehicle to fit the conditions of space. But we have to take man more or less as he is—and alter the conditions to fit his needs. Man cannot be re-engineered; he takes his way of living with him. He must breathe air and obtain from it about 150 gallons of oxygen in one day. His body temperature of 98.6° F. can be maintained only if the temperature around him is not too high or too low. Man's body is fitted to exist at or near the sea level pressure of about 15 pounds on every square inch of his body; if he is thrust unprotected into the zero pressure of space, the internal pressure in his blood vessels and lungs would make him explode. To continue to function, the body mechanism requires a constant supply of food and water. Wastes from his skin, kidneys, bowels, and lungs must be disposed of.

On earth, man can survive the normal radiations from the sun and space which filter down through the atmosphere; in space outside the atmosphere, he must be protected from powerful cosmic ray particles and intense ultraviolet radiation. The rain of stones —meteoroids—which bombard the earth are burned up by friction with the atmosphere; in space these could be a hazard to the spaceship and the men in it. Man is a sensitive being, accustomed to the rhythm of day and night, to working, moving, eating, to making changes in his earth environment. In space, he faces the possible danger of fatigue because of the confinement of his "home" and his commitment to his major task there. Experiments on earth teach us that fatigue can result in a decline in power of perception, in indecision and impaired judgment. On earth, man moves in vehicles which accelerate him gently; in space vehicles, he must endure for several minutes the strain of violent launch acceleration that multiplies his weight approximately 10 times. Deceleration on landing has the same effect. On earth, man is subjected to the constant steady pull of earth's gravity; in a satellite or spaceship, he enters the strange world of weightlessness.

In spite of these limitations, man brings to a spaceship his intelligence, courage, determination and creativity—characteristics which we have not been able to build into a machine. By adding man, we increase the chances of success of space mission. When the automatic control system for the Mercury's position in orbit became faulty,

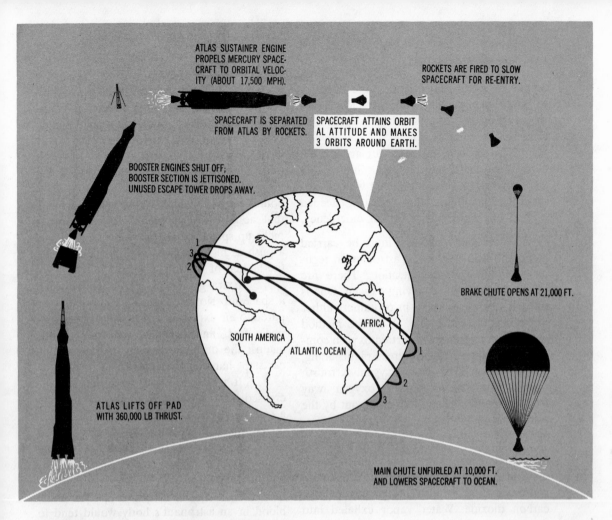

ATLAS SUSTAINER ENGINE PROPELS MERCURY SPACECRAFT TO ORBITAL VELOCITY (ABOUT 17,500 MPH).

ROCKETS ARE FIRED TO SLOW SPACECRAFT FOR RE-ENTRY.

SPACECRAFT IS SEPARATED FROM ATLAS BY ROCKETS.

SPACECRAFT ATTAINS ORBITAL ATTITUDE AND MAKES 3 ORBITS AROUND EARTH.

BOOSTER ENGINES SHUT OFF; BOOSTER SECTION IS JETTISONED. UNUSED ESCAPE TOWER DROPS AWAY.

BRAKE CHUTE OPENS AT 21,000 FT.

AFRICA

SOUTH AMERICA

ATLANTIC OCEAN

ATLAS LIFTS OFF PAD WITH 360,000 LB THRUST.

MAIN CHUTE UNFURLED AT 10,000 FT. AND LOWERS SPACECRAFT TO OCEAN.

THE ORBITAL FLIGHT OF ASTRONAUT GLENN.

Lift off at Cape Kennedy: 9:47 a.m. EST February 20, 1962.

Apogee (peak altitude): 141.2 nautical miles; perigee (low point in orbit): 86.84 nautical miles. (About 160 and 100 miles, respectively, in statute miles.)

Touchdown, in the ocean southeast of Cape Kennedy, near Grand Turk: 2:43 p.m. EST.

Total time, launch to touchdown: 4 hours, 56 minutes.

Total time weightless: 4 hours, 38 minutes.

Total miles flown, 81,000.

Acceleration forces: During launch, 8 G; during re-entry, over 8 G.

Glenn took over and was able to control the capsule's movements by hand.

LIFE SUPPORT FOR MAN IN SPACE

PRESSURE. How do we protect and support man in space? Although the precise methods will vary with the nature of the vehicle and the duration of the trip, certain guiding principles can be stated. We must encase man in an airtight vehicle that protects him from the vacuum of outer space in which he travels. Pressure inside the cabin need not be as high as that on earth, which is 15 pounds per square inch. By reducing the pressure to about 5–7 pounds per square inch, the weight of the air that the spaceship must carry is reduced. Moreover, the strain on the structure of the capsule—the tendency to burst open—is also reduced. (Reduction of air pressure in pressurized airplanes is done for the same reason.)

To protect an astronaut against the consequences of a possible break in the cabin wall, he wears a close-fitting suit which automatically maintains the pressure needed around his body in case of an emergency.

OXYGEN.   Oxygen must be carried along and delivered to the astronaut in regular and uniform concentration. There are several methods of supplying oxygen. One is to carry the total supply in containers either in gaseous or liquid state. A second method is to obtain oxygen from certain oxygen compounds. A third is to have green plants along, such as algae, to produce oxygen. A fourth method would be to split the oxygen away from the carbon dioxide breathed out by the astronaut.

WASTES.   Waste gases such as carbon dioxide and water vapor must be removed from the cabin's atmosphere. Lithium hydroxide is a chemical which can remove carbon dioxide. Water vapor exhaled into the atmosphere can be removed by condensation on a cold surface. The condensed water can then be reused as drinking water.

TEMPERATURE.   Reliable equipment for conditioning the air to the right temperature is essential. In the project Mercury the evaporation of water from the capsule into the vacuum of space provided the necessary cooling. In longer space flights, a mechanical refrigeration system will be utilized.

ACCELERATION.   As a rocket ship picks up speed on its way up, the astronaut feels heavier and heavier. This is similar to the experience we have when we are riding in a car and the driver suddenly steps on the gas. We feel ourselves thrown hard against the back of the seat. When a rocket ship accelerates, the astronaut feels the extra push. The strength of this push is measured in "g's." The astronaut's weight on earth is, as

we know, just the amount that the earth's gravity pulls on him. This amount is called "1 g." The little g represents gravity's pull. When a rocket leaves the launch pad, it may have a push of about twice that of gravity's pull. The astronaut then would feel a 2-g push. A spring scale placed under a 150-pound astronaut at this time would indicate that he weighs 300 pounds. As the rocket picks up speed the astronaut may experience a push as high as 8 g's, as Glenn did during the launch of his ship.

Extra g's are also experienced when a spaceship slows down. This may be compared to the experience of pushing down with one's feet, and bracing with one's hands against the dashboard when the driver of a car steps hard on the brakes.

It is important to note that the increased g's result not from speed but from a *change* in speed. When we travel in jet airliners across the country at speeds of 400 miles an hour, we often feel that we are motionless, unless we look at passing clouds and the landscape.

As a spaceship picks up speed, the blood in an astronaut's body would tend to pool in the lower part of his body—if he sat upright. His heart could not supply the force needed to carry blood to his brain, and he would lose consciousness. If, on the other hand, the astronaut lies on his back with his legs elevated the blood will not collect in the lower part of his body. In this position, also, the astronaut does not have to support the full weight of head, arms, and torso. The extra g's are distributed over the astronaut's back area.

WEIGHTLESSNESS.   When the spaceship ceases to accelerate, that is, when the rockets are not blasting and the ship is "coasting" at constant speed, the astronaut experiences 0 g's or weightlessness. This occurs when he is in orbit around the earth or for much of the time when he is traveling in space to the moon, Venus, Mars, and beyond.

Artist's conception of the Mercury spacecraft showing cutaway view of the astronaut in the capsule and also the escape tower and retrorockets. The escape tower drops away two minutes after blastoff.

Prolonged weightlessness is a new experience for man. The weight of any object, as we have seen, means the pull of gravity on it. Weightlessness occurs when the effects of an object's motion just cancel the pull of the earth and other heavenly bodies. It is not necessary to leave the earth to be weightless. During free fall, a diver, a jumper, and a parachutist (before his parachute opens) undergo weightlessness, if we disregard the slowing down caused by air pressure.

Imagine a man in an airplane high above the earth standing on a spring-weighing scale to which his shoes are glued. The scale reads 160 pounds. The bottom of the plane falls out and so does the man, with the scale still attached. But the scale now registers 0 pound. A man's weight in free fall is zero; he is in effect weightless. (Another name for weightlessness is zero gravity.) When he hits the ground his weight returns—actually the scale would register hundreds of pounds at the moment of impact.

John Glenn was weightless for 4 hours and 40 minutes in the orbital flight of the Mercury. So too was the entire capsule and the objects in it. Said Glenn to a Joint Meeting of Congress on February 26, 1962: "Zero g or weightlessness—at least for this period of time—appears to be no problem. As a matter of fact, lack of gravity is a rather fascinating thing.

"Objects within the cockpit can be parked in mid-air. For example, at one time during the flight, I was using a hand-held camera. Another system needed attention; so it seemed quite natural to let go of the camera, take care of the other chore in the spacecraft, then reach out, grasp the camera and go back about my business." On eating, Glenn said, "I had one tube of food that was squeezed into my mouth out of the tube. This presented no problem swallowing or getting it down at all.

"I think the only restrictions of food would be that it not be particularly crumbly, like cookies, with a lot of little particles that might break off, because you wouldn't be able to get all these back unless you had a butterfly net of some kind."

FOOD. From what we have just quoted, it is apparent that it would not be comfortable for a weightless individual to eat the same way as he does on earth. The cereal lifted on a spoon by a spaceman to his mouth would keep on traveling after the spoon had stopped, and land on the roof of the space craft. Solid food will have to be placed directly into the mouth—by squeezing it in from tubes. Liquid, such as water, cannot be poured into one's mouth since there is no gravity to cause it to leave the glass. A straw would do the trick, however, since this method relies on the use of air pressure.

For long space trips, the total food required cannot be stowed and lifted from the earth. Some method of growing food must be provided. Algae, which can be grown in tanks, are often suggested. They reproduce rapidly, provide a high protein food, and at the same time remove carbon dioxide from the cabin's atmosphere and supply necessary oxygen.

Water must be produced or reclaimed during flight. Water from the astronaut's urine, feces, breath, and sweat is one source. The wastes will be processed to reclaim water and chemicals which may be utilized to promote the growth of plants. Another possible source is the water formed by auxiliary rockets when hydrogen is burned (H plus O yields H_2O).

NEXT TARGETS IN SPACE EXPLORATION

The orbital flight of astronaut Glenn marked the realization of a major goal of Project Mercury. This step in manned space flight demonstrated:

1. *That an astronaut can work effectively while weightless, at least for the period tested.*
2. *That manual control by the astronaut is feasible.*
3. *That food in tubes can be consumed with no difficulty.*

PROJECT GEMINI. The National Aeronautics and Space Administration has a long-range plan of space exploration. Project Gemini (named for the twin stars Castor and Pollux, together in the constellation, Gemini) calls for a two-man crew. Two missions assigned to Project Gemini are:

1. *Development of techniques for bringing together two vehicles in space.*
2. *Operation of orbital flights lasting from a few days to a week to carry out a variety of scientific investigations that require man's participation and supervision. In the Gemini, astronauts will learn how to live and work together in space. They may try climbing out of spacecraft more than 100 miles above the surface of the earth and performing various tasks there.*

Among the space skills the Gemini astronauts must learn are those of rendezvous and docking. In a rendezvous, a spacecraft finds and moves close to another object or craft in space. Docking means the actual joining of one orbiting object to another. These skills are essential in the fulfillment of

A *two-man Gemini spacecraft closes in on an unmanned rocket stage in an orbital rendezvous experiment (artist's conception). At nearly identical velocities, the two craft are latched together.*

the nation's first great assignment in space exploration—a successful round-trip expedition to the moon. It is hoped that this feat will be accomplished in the next 5 to 8 years.

PROJECT APOLLO. Project Apollo is the next step in the United States space program. Apollo will carry three astronauts who will engage in various projects, such as maintaining an earth-orbiting space laboratory, making flights in the vicinity of the moon, making a landing on the moon, and returning to earth. Journeys into space for periods up to two weeks are planned. One of the first trips will be a journey around the moon. Later in the 1967–1970 period, an Apollo landing on the moon and return to the earth is planned.

Since the flights of the Apollo may last as long as two weeks, the astronauts must be able to work without being hampered by space suits. In order to make this possible, it will be necessary to create an earth-like environment within the spaceship.

To escape from the earth, a speed of about 25,000 miles per hour will be required. When this speed is reached, there will be a period of about three days of weightless coasting en route to the moon. The flight path will be curved, and, like a duck hunter's shot, in front of the moon's line of travel. When Apollo is in the right location, control rockets will guide it into a circular orbit around the moon. According to one plan, two of the crewmen will make their way into a space ferry which is joined nose to

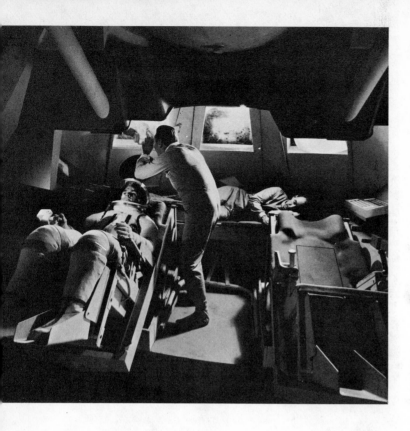

In this model of a three-man Apollo spacecraft, one astronaut is shown on his couch flying the spacecraft, the second is sleeping, and the third is taking a navigational bearing. They wear light comfortable coveralls while on their 2½-day journey to the vicinity of the moon. Pressure suits are in the craft and can be donned quickly in an emergency.

nose with the main "command" capsule. The space ferry or "bug" (so-called because of its spindly legs used in the lunar landing) will separate from the command capsule. Rockets will ease the ferry down to a sunlit area on the moon.

It is planned that the astronauts will stay 24 hours or less on the first visit. Since the moon has only one-sixth of the earth's gravity, much less thrust than that required on earth will be needed to launch the vehicle from the moon. Finally the lunar explorers will take off and soar back to the mother craft. They will then cut loose the ferry, and rocket back to earth. Re-entry and recovery procedures for return to earth will be similar to that of the Mercury. However, since the Apollo's speed will be greater than Mercury's, it will need to enter the atmosphere over a longer course—or possess more heat shielding. Also the Apollo astronauts may have to be subjected to greater "g" forces than the Mercury astronauts.

The exploration of outer space is no longer fantasy. Man-made satellites now orbit around the earth. Astronauts have orbited around the earth. Details for moon probes and moon landings have been worked out, and men are at work at building the ships for these exploits. Later will come flights to Venus and Mars. Still later may come flights beyond the solar system—perhaps to other worlds in space whirling around other stars.

The following are some of the important generalizations in this chapter:

Balloons and dirigibles are filled with lighter-than-air gases.

The movement of the wings of a plane through the air provides the lift needed to offset the pull of gravity.

The lift on a wing moving through the air arises from: (1) the impact of air on its lower surface, and (2) the decrease in pressure on its upper surface.

The propeller's or the jet's function is to provide the forward thrust necessary to move the plane through the air.

The position of a plane in the air may be altered by the movement of hinged surfaces—the elevator, the rudder, and the ailerons.

In jets, fuel is burned rapidly in a large chamber, producing a large volume of gas. The gas streaming out of the opening of the jet produces a backward kick or thrust which moves the vehicle.

Rockets work on the jet principle; unlike jets, however, they carry their own oxygen supply and consequently can operate in airless space.

Rockets have made space travel possible.

To place a satellite into orbit, it is necessary to contend with the resistance offered by the earth's atmosphere and with the pull of gravity.

If a rocket reaches the speed of about 7 miles per second or about 25,000 miles per hour, it can escape from the earth.

If an object reaches a speed of about 5 miles a second or 18,000 miles per hour it can orbit the earth at an altitude of several hundred miles.

To stay in orbit, a satellite must move fast enough to counterbalance the gravitational attraction of the earth.

Satellites maintain their speed in orbits high above the earth because there is no air there to slow them down.

The earth itself is a body in orbit around the sun, moving at the rate of about 18 miles a second.

Since gravity decreases with distance, the speed required to maintain a satellite in orbit decreases with distance from the earth.

To support life of man in space, we must cope with such factors as pressure, food and oxygen supply, suitable temperature, disposal of wastes, acceleration, radiation, and weightlessness.

Weightlessness occurs when a body moves at a speed sufficient to counteract the gravitational pull of any other body on it. Weightlessness is experienced by astronauts in spaceships orbiting the earth or "coasting" through space.

The next targets in space exploration are the moon, Mars, and Venus.

DISCOVERING FOR YOURSELF

1. Find out more about how progress in weather prediction has influenced aviation.
2. Prepare a chart to show similarities and differences of various jet-type planes.
3. Examine an airplane to see how the principles you have learned in this chapter are put into operation. Examine the wings, the fuselage, the tail, and other parts. Examine the instrument panel and find out what the pilot can tell by looking at the various indicators.
4. Visit a museum, if possible, to see various historic and modern aircraft.
5. Make a kite and fly it. Apply what you learn to understanding how an airplane gets into the air.
6. Visit an airport to observe as much as you can that will help you to understand the material in this chapter.
7. Assemble a simple model airplane and use it to learn the parts of aircraft.
8. Study models of aircraft and compare them for size, shape, and angle of the wings.
9. Watch the flight of a helicopter and an airplane and list characteristics of each.
10. Keep a record of newspaper and magazine aviation news for one month, indicating: problems, progress, safety, and other factors.
11. Compare the source of thrust of a jet, an airplane, a helicopter, and a rocket.

12. °Collect information about some of the rocket and space projects currently underway.

13. Examine models of various rockets, satellites, or other space vehicles to see how they are shaped and constructed to perform their specific functions.

14. Swing a ball on a string in a vertical plane. Find out whether the length of the string or the weight of the ball affects the speed necessary to keep the ball "in orbit."

15. Various satellites (Syncom, Telstar, etc.) are in orbit at different altitudes from the earth. Find out why.

16. Watch the newspapers for the time to observe the sphere satellite, Echo. Observe it for a number of evenings and try to answer these questions. How long does it take to traverse the sky? What direction is it moving in? What is the source of light that makes it visible? Why does the direction and time of orbit change? Why are there long periods when Echo cannot be seen?

17. Design a demonstration of[1] "escape velocity" by experimenting with the following materials:

   a. a steel ball (bearing) to represent a satellite.

   b. an incline (cardboard shaped into a trough) which will be tilted at different angles to give varying speeds to the ball.

   c. a table on which the ball will roll from the incline.

   d. a magnet (to *represent* the pull of gravity) placed on the table near the path of the ball.

---

[1] Compare your demonstration with that given in *Science Shows You How* by Kenneth M. Swezey (New York, McGraw-Hill, 1964).

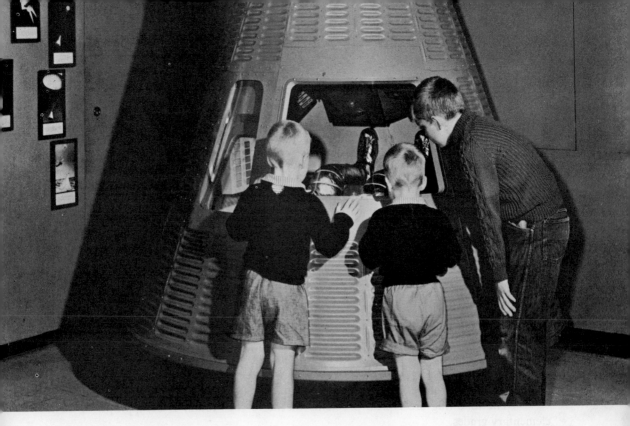

CHAPTER 24B

Teaching "Flight and Space Travel"

Flight and space travel are a natural part of the elementary school curriculum for we are certainly living in the air and space age, and children are well aware of it. Satellites are in orbit; how they are launched and kept going is of great interest to children. The influence of gravity on rockets, satellites, and spaceships, weightlessness and the many other aspects of space exploration are fascinating to them. Scarcely a week passes without newspapers, magazines, television, and radio reporting new ventures or plans. Along with this, a visit to an airport, the sight of a jet plane, and even a look at small aircraft are still exciting experiences for most children. This curiosity is well used when it is directed toward science experiences of experimenting, observing, and assembling information to solve problems that help children understand the principles underlying flight.

A study of flight and space travel affords an excellent opportunity for experiences that involve the use of other subject matter areas along with science. The social studies, language-arts, and arithmetic are involved when pupils study the progress of air and space travel and the problems that have been and still remain to be solved as we go farther from the earth.

No teacher can know all of the answers about flight and space travel. This is not necessary. A knowledge of the material in the preceding chapter is helpful for guiding the learning activities. In addition to this, the bibliography suggests easily obtainable resources that will help answer children's questions and solve their problems.

Many state departments of education have issued aviation instruction aids and space information material of one kind or another that contain helpful suggestions. A teacher who

Observing the effects of wind on surfaces helps pupils to understand the principles underlying airplane flight. Many variations of the experience pictured here are possible.

has had an airplane trip is almost sure to use it to make a study of air transportation a vital experience for pupils. A teacher who keeps up with the current news reports and gathers a clipping file of such material will find herself much better prepared to help her pupils.

The following are typical problems that have been found to be appropriate for the elementary grades.

How are satellites launched and what do scientists discover by their use?
What keeps a satellite going?
What is gravity and what is its influence on rockets, satellites, and spaceships?
What propellants are used in rockets?
How long does it take to reach various objectives (planets, the moon, etc.)?
What are some of the difficult problems that must be solved in space travel?
What is weightlessness and what effects does it have?

Here are some experiences that have been successful in primary grades:

1. Go to the airport to get a "feeling" of what happens there by observing planes as they land and take off, observe the runways, and get a general notion of what happens at the airport.
2. Go inside a large transport plane to see what it is like.
3. Make and fly kites to see how they are kept up and balanced.
4. Make and launch parachutes made of paper or cloth and string.
5. Find pictures of different kinds and uses of airplanes.
6. Name the different parts of a plane and find out what each part does.
7. Find out what things in the community are transported by air, i.e., fruit, flowers, mail, etc.
8. Examine models of different kinds of planes, name the different parts, and describe them. Find out what each is used for and how it is built to serve this purpose. Make an exhibit of the planes.

Models of various shapes and sizes are being constructed to learn about the effects of air currents on plain and curved surfaces. Some are original designs. Some are taken from books on aviation.

9. Do simple experiments to see how wind lifts things and to see that air presses on things.
10. Make paper gliders and see how they work in the wind and in a room where there is no wind.
11. Discuss why the earth may be called a spaceship.[1]
12. Blow up balloons and let them go "jetting" into the air.
13. Examine and "launch" various kinds of toy rockets which are sold in variety stores (none with combustible or explosive devices).
14. Stage a toy airplane show or rocket show.

OBSERVING THE RESULTS OF AIR ON SURFACES

First-hand observations of how a current of air moving on a surface has various results is shown by the use of these models and similar devices that pupils will originate.

LEARNING WHAT MAKES AN AIRPLANE FLY

Pupils will perhaps need to review some of their experiments with air pressure, especially those which show that air pressure is exerted in an upward as well as a downward direction. Holding a cardboard over a full glass of water and inverting the glass (see page 203), for example, it will help them to see that air can press up under the wings of an airplane.

---

[1] Julius Schwartz, *The Earth is Your Spaceship* (New York, Whittlesey House, 1963).

The Plane Goes Up?

Be sure to have materials to illustrate your explanations.

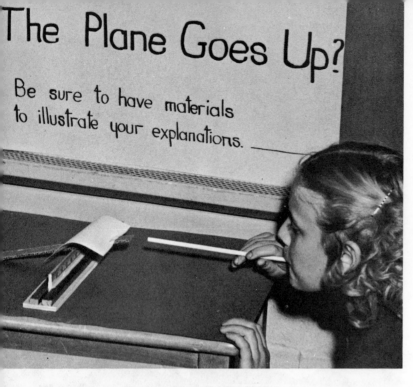

Elaborate equipment is not at all necessary to an understanding of airplane flight. Here the "wind" is being directed by means of a soda straw, and the "airplane" is made of paper and a strip of cardboard.

To show the effect of an air current's passing over a surface, let pupils hold strips of paper (2 inches wide and 4 or 5 inches long) so that they can blow a stream of air over the top (see photograph). Until they begin to blow, the papers hang down. As soon as air is forced over them, they stand out straight. This helps pupils to see what happens when air travels over the top of an airplane wing.

The paper model airplanes pictured here will help pupils see more clearly how the parts of a plane respond to wind currents.

An arrangement such as the one with the ruler and straw helps pupils to understand how an airplane is lifted. The use of the rudder is illustrated by the paper "rudder," and the handmade gliders are also very useful in teaching the principles of flight.

Paper model airplanes, with wings and rudder surfaces folded, can be used to demonstrate how real aircraft are controlled. They can be supported by knitting needles or a cork pivot in the wind of an electric fan. The cross section of an airplane wing, made of paper and supported by a knitting needle, will behave in a wind in much the same manner as a real airplane wing.

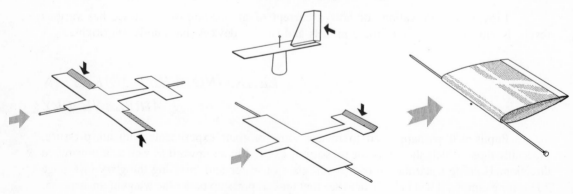

A "rudder" can be made from two file cards, one folded as shown, the other arranged to turn freely on a pin pivot. The boy is blowing on this "rudder" from several directions to observe its action.

VISITING THE AIRPORT

The questions about how airplanes are controlled, types of aircraft, and "goings on" at an airport can be answered in the course of a well-planned visit to an airport. Preparation for the trip will consist of listing things pupils want to do and see at the airport, such as: see the instrument board of an airplane, get a close view of the ailerons and other parts of a plane and see how they work, examine a propeller at close range, look at the engines of jet planes, go inside a big plane to see the kitchen and other facilities, go to see the weather instruments, observe the control tower and its location, observe the safety devices on the landing field, watch the refueling and loading or unloading of an airplane, and talk with a pilot, a stewardess, and control-tower personnel. If the trip to the airport is made at or near the end of the study of aviation, pupils will have a clearer understanding of what they see and can use the trip as an opportunity for gaining information.

A trip to the airport made by these Washington, D. C., pupils was an instructive and enjoyable experience. Pupils have just explored the inside of the plane and asked questions of the pilot.

Obviously this experience is enjoyable. It is also instructive as pupils try out materials that explain science principles related to physical science phenomena.

STUDYING THE WEATHER

Although we have given in chapter 9B many suggestions for the study of weather, the emphasis is somewhat different when weather is being considered in connection with aviation. The following questions were asked by a fifth grade on a visit to an airport, and illustrate the weather emphasis: "What instruments are used at the airport weather station?" "Does the airport forecast weather or does it use the forecast of the weather bureau?" "How are pilots kept informed of weather changes?" "How often are weather forecasts changed during a day?" "What weather reports are essential for rocket launching?"

LEARNING ABOUT JET PROPULSION

Since "jets" are now common, some understanding of how they work is important. The jet propelled balloon pictured here will help pupils to understand the principle.

The "track" is made of wire stretched from one side of a room to the other. The balloon is held to the track by strings attached to paper clips. Inflate the balloon and as the air escapes, the "jet" moves along the wire. The speed may be controlled by inserting a plug in the open end of the balloon that will regulate the amount of air that escapes. Make the plug of paper. Pupils will experiment with the size of the plug and get varying results.

LEARNING ABOUT ROCKETS
AND SPACE TRAVEL

There are a variety of activities that pupils can do to give them a better concept of what is going on in this important scientific field. Some involve reading, others experimenting, others assembling materials to show certain aspects of space travel. The bibliography contains excellent material written especially for this purpose.

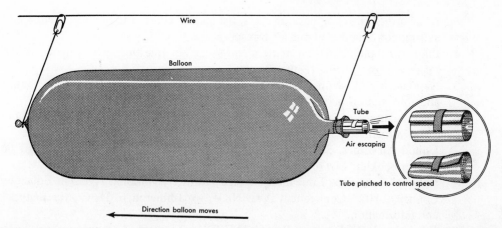

Some concepts about jet propulsion are more easily understood through the use of this apparatus (explained on page 614). Although this experiment may come under the category of "fun," it provides opportunity to see how pressure operates to provide a push forward and how various factors may be regulated to control speed. The books in the bibliography describe other ways of arranging materials to illustrate these same principles.

Reporting on current happenings: Daily papers, magazines and other sources are excellent places that help pupils keep track of current events such as speed and distance records, new discoveries, new inventions, importance of information, etc.

Collecting models and pictures that show various types of rockets and space vehicles: Telling the story of important facts by captions is a very interesting procedure. Some of the toy rockets currently available illustrate science principles. (The use of combustible or explosive devices should be discouraged in school.)

Demonstrating why a satellite remains in orbit: Whirl a ball (or other weight) on the end of a string as suggested on page 598. Whirl in a vertical plane so that the circle described by the ball does not vary. What happens when the ball is allowed to slow down? "Roll a ball along a table top and allow it to fall off at the end. Roll it again, but much faster. The second time, the ball will fall to the floor, but at a greater distance from the table top. In this demonstration, the table top represents outer space while the floor represents the earth. Now imagine the ball moving very fast (in outer space). If the ball could go fast enough, it would never reach the earth because as it fell, it would follow the curvature of the earth."[2]

RESOURCES TO INVESTIGATE

1. Local airport to learn how airplanes fly and how they are controlled, to see types of aircraft, landing fields, and hangars, and to gain other information.
2. *Current Science*, a magazine for later elementary and junior high school grades, for information about planes, air transportation, rockets, and satellites. (Order sample copy from American Education Press, Columbus, Ohio.)

[2] From *Earth in Space*, Board of Education of the City of New York.

3. Local airline ticket offices, for maps, pamphlets, charts and other printed matter, and motion pictures about air transportation.
4. Pilots, to explain aviation matters and to answer questions about flying. Radio, for reports on "flying weather."
5. National Air Museum, Smithsonian Institution, Washington, D. C., for pictures and information about historic airplanes.
6. Manufacturers of airplanes or airplane parts, for materials and information about airplanes, parts, and instruments.
7. United Air Lines, School and College Service, P. O. Box 8800, Chicago 66, Ill., for booklet: *List of Free Aviation Education Material and Services.*
8. National Aerospace Education Council (formerly National Aviation Education Council), 1025 Connecticut Ave. N. W., Washington 6, D. C., for materials and information.
9. Educational Publications Branch AFEE-1, National Aeronautics and Space Administration, 4th and Maryland Ave. N. W., Washington 25, D. C., for materials and information.
10. *Space*, a general magazine about space, monthly except July and August, 4211 Colie Drive, Silver Spring, Maryland.
11. Communicative Arts, P. O. Box No. 11017, San Diego 11, California. Write for price list of wall charts, film strips, and other teaching materials on space science.

BIBLIOGRAPHY

PART ONE: TEACHING ELEMENTARY SCIENCE

PROFESSIONAL PUBLICATIONS FOR TEACHERS

Baker, Tunis. *Baker Physical Science Packet. Baker Nature Study Packet*. Holland, Mich., Revised 1961. Card packets describing more than 300 science experiments.

Blackwood, Paul E. *How Children Learn to Think*. U.S. Office of Education Bulletin No. 10. Washington, D.C.: G.P.O., 1951, 19 pp. Discussion of the ways in which pupils arrive at conclusions.

Blough, Glenn O. *It's Time for Better Elementary School Science*. Washington, D.C.: National Science Teachers Association, National Education Association, 1958, 48 pp.

——. *You and Your Child and Science*. Washington, D.C.: National Education Association, 1963, 28 pp. For teachers and parents.

——, and Paul E. Blackwood. *Science Teaching in Rural and Small Town Schools*. U.S. Office of Education Bulletin No. 5. Washington, D.C.: G.P.O., 1949, 55 pp.

——, and ——. *Teaching Elementary Science*: Suggestions for Classroom Teachers. U.S. Office of Education Bulletin No. 4. Washington, D.C.: G.P.O., 1948, 40 pp. A "know-how" guide for beginning and for improving elementary science teaching.

——, and Marjorie H. Campbell. *Making and Using Classroom Science Materials in the Elementary School*. New York: Holt, Rinehart and Winston, 1954, 229 pp. Directions for making and using materials and apparatus commonly needed in elementary schools.

Burnett, R. Will. *Teaching Science in the Elementary School*. New York: Holt, Rinehart and Winston, 1953, 540 pp. Subject matter and teaching methods.

Cornell Science Leaflets. (Originally Cornell Rural School Leaflets). V. Rockcastle (Ed.). Ithaca, N.Y.: Cornell University Press. Available at a yearly subscription rate of one dollar (payment in advance).

Craig, Gerald S. *Certain Techniques Used in Developing a Course of Study in Science for the Horace Mann Elementary School*. Contributions to Education No. 276. New York: Teachers College, 1927.

——. *Science in Childhood Education*. New York: Teachers College, Columbia University, 1944, 86 pp.

——. *Science for the Elementary-School Teacher*. Boston: Ginn, 1958, 894 pp. Teaching suggestions and subject matter.

——. *What Research Says to the Teacher: Science in the Elementary School*. Washington, D.C.: National Education Association, 1957, 33 pp.

Dunfee, Maxine, and Julian Greenlee. *Elementary School Science: Research, Theory, and Practice*, Washington, D.C.: Association for Supervision and Curriculum Development, 1957, 67 pp.

Fifty-ninth Yearbook of the National Society for the Study of Education. Part I, *Rethinking Science Education*. Chicago: University of Chicago Press, 1960, 338 pp.

Fitzpatrick, Frederick L. (Ed.). *Policies for Science Education*. New York: Teachers College, 1960, 219 pp. Policies and improvements in science programs at all levels.

Forty-sixth Yearbook of the National Society for the Study of Education. Part I, *Science Education in American Schools*. Chicago: University of Chicago Press, 1947, 296 pp.

Guidelines for Science and Mathematics in the Preparation Program of Elementary School Teachers. Order from state directors of teacher education. 1963, 15 pp. Recommendations of the Teacher Preparation-Certification Study.

Hone, Elizabeth B., and others. *A Sourcebook for Elementary Science.* New York: Harcourt, 1962, 552 pp. Techniques and procedures for teaching science.

Hubler, Clark. *Working with Children in Science.* Boston: Houghton Mifflin, 1957, 425 pp. Emphasizes physical science.

Improving Instruction in Elementary School Science. Bulletin No. 1382. Albany N.Y.: University of the State of New York, 1949. A guide for study groups.

Jacobson, Willard L., and Harold E. Tannenbaum. *Modern Elementary School Science: A Recommended Sequence.* New York: Teachers College, 1961, 194 pp. Help in selecting and organizing an elementary science program.

Kambly, Paul E., and John E. Suttle. *Teaching Elementary School Science.* New York: Ronald, 1963, 492 pp. Methods and resources.

Lewis, June E., and Irene Potter. *The Teaching of Science in the Elementary School.* Englewood Cliffs, N.J.: Prentice-Hall, 1961, 381 pp. Teaching suggestions and subject matter.

Navarra, John G. *The Development of Scientific Concepts in a Young Child.* New York: Teachers College, 1955, 147 pp. A research study of children's experiences in relation to the development of science learnings.

———, and Joseph Zafforoni. *Science Today for the Elementary School Teacher.* New York: Harper & Row, 1960, 470 pp. Teaching suggestions and subject matter.

Operation New York: Using the Natural Environment of the City as a Curriculum Resource. Brooklyn, N.Y.: Board of Education, City of New York. Suggestions applicable to any city.

Piltz, Albert. *Science Equipment and Materials for the Elementary School.* U.S. Office of Education Bulletin No. 28. Washington, D.C.: G.P.O., 1961, 66 pp. Selecting and using scientific equipment.

———, and William J. Gruver. *Science Equipment and Materials: Science Kits.* U.S. Office of Education Bulletin No. 332. Washington, D.C.: G.P.O. Details of selection and use of specialized science equipment.

Science for Today's Children. Thirty-second Yearbook, Bulletin of the Department of Elementary School Principals. Washington, D.C.: National Education Association, 1953, 311 pp. Philosophy, curriculum, and methods of instruction in elementary science.

Tannenbaum, Harold E., and Nathan Stillman. *Science Education for Elementary School Teachers.* Boston: Allyn and Bacon, 1960, 340 pp. Stresses child development.

Thirty-first Yearbook of the National Society for the Study of Education. Part I, *A Program for Teaching Science.* Bloomington, Ill.: Public School Publishing Co., 1932, 370 pp. Contains a treatment of trends, and recommendation for further work. Treats practices, criticism of practices, contributions of science teaching, and so forth.

Zafforoni, Joseph. *New Developments in Elementary School Science.* Washington, D.C.: National Science Teachers Association, National Education Association, 1963, 56 pp. Summary of a national survey.

GENERAL SUBJECT-MATTER
BACKGROUND BOOKS FOR TEACHERS

Beauchamp, Wilbur L., and others. *Everyday Problems in Science.* Chicago: Scott, Foresman, 1963, 576 pp.

Beiser, Germaine, and Arthur Beiser. *Physics for Everybody.* New York: Dutton, 1960, 184 pp. Nonmathematical approach for adults.

Boylan, Paul J. *Elements of Chemistry.* Boston: Allyn and Bacon, 1962, 696 pp.

———. *Elements of Physics.* Boston: Allyn and Bacon, 1962, 666 pp.

Brandwein, Paul F., and others. *You and Science.* New York: Harcourt, 1961, 702 pp.

Cox, Louis. *Energy.* Darien, Conn.: Teachers Publishing Corporation, 1964, 96 pp.

Dull, Charles E., and others. *Modern Chemistry.* New York: Holt, Rinehart and Winston, 1962, 694 pp.

———. *Modern Physics.* New York: Holt, Rinehart and Winston, 1963, 662 pp.

Fitzpatrick, Frederick L., and others. *Living Things.* New York: Holt, Rinehart and Winston, 1962, 420 pp. A general biology text.

Heller, Robert L. *Geology and Earth Science Sourcebook.* New York: Holt, Rinehart and Winston, 1962, 496 pp. For elementary and secondary schools.

Joseph, Alexander, and others. *A Sourcebook for the Physical Sciences*. New York: Harcourt, 1961, 674 pp. Reference for subject matter and sources.

Moon, Truman J., and others. *Modern Biology*. New York: Holt, Rinehart and Winston, 1963, 759 pp.

Moore, Ruth. *The Coil of Life*. New York: Knopf, 1961, 418 pp. The story of the great discoveries in the life sciences.

Morholt, Evelyn, and others. *A Sourcebook for the Biological Sciences*. New York: Harcourt, 1958, 506 pp. Reference for subject matter and sources.

Namowitz, Samuel N., and Donald B. Stone. *Earth Science*. Princeton, N.J.: Van Nostrand, 1960, 438 pp. A high school text.

Palmer, E. Laurence. *Field Book of Natural History*. New York: McGraw-Hill, 1949, 664 pp.

Pauli, Wolfgang F. *The World of Life*. Boston: Houghton Mifflin, 1949, 653 pp.

Ramsey, William, and Raymond A. Burckley. *Modern Earth Science*. New York: Holt, Rinehart and Winston, 1961, 630 pp.

Schwab, Joseph J. (Supervisor). *Biology Teachers' Handbook*. Biological Sciences Curriculum Study. New York: Wiley, 1963, 585 pp.

Trinklein, Frederick E., and Charles M. Huffer. *Modern Space Science*. New York: Holt, Rinehart and Winston, 1961, 550 pp.

Trump, Richard F., and David L. Fagle. *Design for Life*. New York: Holt, Rinehart and Winston, 1963, 664 pp. Modern approach to the study of living things.

United States Department of Agriculture. *Yearbooks: Climate and Man*, 1941; *Grass*, 1948; *Trees*, 1949; *Insects*, 1952; *Plant Diseases*, 1953; *Water*, 1955; *Soil*, 1957; *Land*, 1958; *Food*, 1959. Washington, D.C.: G.P.O.

STATE AND CITY BULLETINS AND COURSES OF STUDY IN ELEMENTARY SCIENCE[1]

California State Department of Education. *Looking Ahead in Science*. Sacramento, Calif.: 1960.

———. *Science Curriculum Development in the Elementary School*. Sacramento, Calif.: 1963.

District of Columbia Public Schools. *Elementary Science Curriculum*. Washington, D.C.: 1957.

Florida State Department of Education. *Science for Children in Florida's Elementary Schools*. Rev. ed. Tallahassee, Fla.: 1961.

Georgia Department of Education. *Science for Georgia Schools Vol. 1 Primary*, and *Science for Georgia Schools Vol. 2 Intermediate*. Atlanta, Ga.: 1960.

Illinois State Superintendent of Public Instruction. *Handbook for Science Workshops Grades 4, 5, 6*. Springfield, Ill.: 1960.

Maryland State Department of Education. *Planning for Effective Science-Learning*. Baltimore: 1956.

Michigan State Department of Education. *Guidelines for the K–12 Science Program*. Lansing, Mich.: 1961.

New Jersey Department of Education. *Teaching Science*. Trenton, N.J.: 1957.

New York: University of the State of New York. *Science for Children: K–3* and *Science for Children: 4–6*. Albany, 1964.

New York City Board of Education. *Science K–6:* (1) *Magnetism and Electricity*, (2) *Earth and Space*, (3) *Living Things*, (4) *Sound and Light in Communication*, (5) *Weather*, (6) *Motion and Force in Transportation*, (7) *Earth and Its Resources*. Brooklyn, N.Y.

North Carolina State Superintendent of Public Instruction. *Science for the Elementary School*. Publication No. 227. Raleigh, N.C.: 1953.

North Dakota Department of Public Instruction. *An Elementary Science Source Book, Vol. 1* and *Vol. 2*. Bismark, N.D.: 1962.

Ohio State Department of Education. *Science Education for the Elementary Schools of Ohio*. Curriculum Bulletin No. 3. Columbus, Ohio: 1946.

---

[1] These are some of the states that issue their science courses of study or bulletins under separate cover. Many others have material in this field but include it with their general elementary curriculum material.

Many cities, towns, and counties have issued bulletins and courses of study that are most useful. These often may be obtained from libraries or sometimes may be purchased from the issuing sources.

Pennsylvania Department of Public Instruction. *Microbiology for Elementary School Children.
Earth and Space Science.* Harrisburg, Pa.: 1963.
South Carolina State Department of Education. *Guide for Teaching Science Grades 1–6.* Columbia, N.C.: 1962.
Texas Education Agency. Science Grades 1–9. *Suggested Lists of Principles and Terms.* Austin, Texas: 1961.
Virginia State Board of Education. *A Tentative Guide for Science Grades 1–12.* Part I, *Grades 1–9.* Richmond, Va.: 1956.

MAGAZINES FOR USE IN SCIENCE TEACHING

American Forests. Washington, D.C.: American Forestry Association.
Audubon. Harrisburg, Pa.: National Audubon Society. Published bimonthly.
Curious Naturalist, The. South Lincoln, Mass.: Massachusetts Audubon Society. For children. Ten issues a year.
Current Science, Science and Math Weekly, and *My Weekly Reader.* Columbus, Ohio: American Education Press. Published weekly during school year.
Geographic School Bulletins. Washington, D.C.: National Geographic Society. Published weekly by School Service Division.
Journal of Research in Science Teaching. Easton, Pa.: National Association for Research in Science Teaching. Published quarterly.
Junior Astronomer, The. Silver Spring, Md.: Benjamin Adelman. The latest news in astronomy for pupils and teachers.
Metropolitan Detroit Science Review. Detroit, Mich.: Metropolitan Detroit Science Club. Published quarterly.
National Geographic School Bulletin. Washington, D.C.: National Geographic Society. Published each week (October to May).
National Parks Magazine. Washington, D.C.: National Parks Association.
Natural History. New York: American Museum of Natural History. Published monthly (except July and August).
Nature and Science. New York: American Museum of Natural History. Sixteen issues per school year. For children.
School Science and Mathematics. Menasha, Wisc.: Published monthly, except July, August, and September.
Science and Children. Washington, D.C.: National Science Teachers Association. Published eight times a year.
Science Digest. Chicago: Science Digest. Published monthly.
Science Education. Published in February, March, April, October, and December. Send subscriptions to C. M. Pruitt, Editor, University of Tampa, Tampa, Fla.
Science News Letter. Washington, D.C.: Science Service. Published weekly.
Science Teacher, The. Journal of the National Science Teachers Association. Washington, D.C.
Science World. Englewood Cliffs, N.J. A magazine for high school science students. (Good teacher background.)
Scientific American. New York: Published monthly. The advancing front of science, written by scientists.
Sky and Telescope. Cambridge, Mass.: Sky Publishing Corp. An astronomy magazine published monthly.
Skylights. Washington, D.C.: National Education Council. A fact sheet for teachers and students interested in aviation education.
Space Science. Silver Spring, Md.: Benjamin Adelman. Published monthly except July and August.

GENERAL: BOOKS FOR CHILDREN

Adler, Irving. *Dust.* New York: John Day, 1958, 122 pp. Nature and effects of dust.
––––––. *Monkey Business.* New York: John Day, 1957, 128 pp. Methods used to discover so-called scientific frauds.
––––––. *The Tools of Science from Yardstick to Cyclotron.* New York: John Day, 1958, 128 pp.

Interesting information about the tools and instruments used by many different kinds of scientists.

Barr, George. *More Research Ideas for Young Scientists.* New York: Whittlesey, 1961, 158 pp. More ideas for discovery.

———. *Research Ideas for Young Scientists.* New York: Whittlesey, 1960, 158 pp. An excellent discovery book of experiences and experiments.

———. *Young Scientist Looks at Skyscrapers.* New York: Whittlesey, 1963, 159 pp. For "sidewalk superintendents" interested in the science of building.

———. *Young Scientist and Sports, featuring Baseball, Football, and Basketball.* New York: Whittlesey, 1962, 159 pp. Answers to science questions related to common sports.

———. *Young Scientist Takes a Ride: Guide to Outdoor Observation from a Car Window.* New York: Whittlesey, 1960, 160 pp. Interpreting the scientific world from a car window is informative and interesting.

———. *Young Scientist Takes a Walk: Guide to Outdoor Observation.* New York: Whittlesey, 1959, 160 pp. Exciting suggestions for discovering science in the immediate environment.

Bendick, Jeanne. *All around You.* New York: Whittlesey, 1951, 48 pp. The child's physical world. An easy book.

Blough, Glenn O. (Ed.). *Young People's Book of Science.* New York: Whittlesey, 1958, 446 pp. Interest-catching selections from many sources.

Brown, Vinson. *How To Explore the Secret Worlds of Nature.* Boston: Little, Brown, 1962, 174 pp. Discovering natural history in the immediate environment.

Burlingame, Roger. *Scientists behind the Inventors.* New York: Harcourt, 1960, 192 pp. The work of scientists and its influence on common conveniences.

Cooper, Elizabeth K. *Science in Your Own Back Yard.* New York: Harcourt, 1958, 192 pp. Interesting well-written information about common things including living things, weather, soil, and so forth.

Crouse, William H. *Science Marvels of Tomorrow.* New York: Whittlesey, 1963, 192 pp. Scientific principles explain many future scientific marvels.

———. *Understanding Science.* New York: Whittlesey, 1963, 221 pp. Revised edition of an excellent introduction to physical science.

Freeman, Mae, and Ira Freeman. *Your Wonderful World of Science.* New York: Random House, 1957, 84 pp. Easy-reading general science.

Froman, Robert. *Wanted: Amateur Scientists.* New York: McKay, 1963, 102 pp. What especially interested and talented pupils can do about science discoveries.

Hyde, Margaret O. *From Submarines to Satellites.* New York: Whittlesey, 1958. The advancement in national defense.

Kadesch, Robert R. *The Crazy Cantilever and Other Science Experiments.* New York: Harper & Row, 1961, 175 pp. Experiments that help solve knotty and interesting everyday science problems.

Milgrom, Harry. *Explorations in Science: A Book of Basic Experiments.* New York: Dutton, 1961, 128 pp. Exciting experiences that help children understand their world.

———. *Further Explorations in Science: A Second Book of Basic Experiments.* New York: Dutton, 1963, 124 pp.

Ruchlis, Hy. *Discovering Scientific Method: With Science Puzzle Pictures.* New York: Harper & Row, 1963, 190 pp. An interesting approach to science through problems. Not for beginners.

Schneider, Herman, and Nina Schneider. *Let's Find Out.* New York: W. R. Scott, 1946, 39 pp. A science picture book with simple experiments.

———, and ———. *Let's Look inside Your House.* New York: W. R. Scott, 1948, 40 pp.

———, and ———. *Science Fun with Milk Cartons.* New York: Whittlesey, 1953, 159 pp. Constructing things in order to understand science principles.

Schwartz, Julius. *It's Fun to Know Why: Experiments with Things around Us.* New York: Whittlesey, 1952, 125 pp. Experiments with iron, coal, paper, bread, and other common materials.

———. *Now I Know.* New York: Whittlesey, 1955, 32 pp. Finding the answers to puzzling aspects of the environment by experience and observation. For very young children.

———. *Through the Magnifying Glass: Little Things That Make a Big Difference.* New York:

Whittlesey, 1954, 142 pp. Using the simple magnifying glass to make discoveries about crystals, plants, animals, and man-made things.

Somerville, John. *The Way of Science: Its Growth and Method.* New York: Abelard-Schuman, 1953, 172 pp. Scientific methods: nature and use.

Sonneborn, Ruth. *The Question and Answer Book of Everyday Science.* New York: Random House, 1961, 69 pp. Simple answers to questions that children ask.

Wyler, Rose, and Gerald Ames. *Prove It.* New York: Harper & Row, 1963, 64 pp. Very easy to read and to do experiments.

Note: See other bibliographies for related experiment books.

BOOKS ON IDENTIFICATION

General

Palmer, E. Laurence. *Field Book of Natural History.* New York: McGraw-Hill, 1949, 664 pp. Excellent, comprehensive, important for the elementary school library.

Animals

Abbott, Robert T. *Sea Shells of the World: A Guide to the Better-Known Species.* New York: Golden Press, 1960, 160 pp.

Cavanna, Betty. *The First Book of Sea Shells.* New York: Watts, 1955, 38 pp.

Dudley, Ruth H. *Sea Shells.* New York: Crowell, 1953, 149 pp.

Evans, Eva Knox. *The Adventure Book of Shells.* New York: Capitol Publishing Co., 1955, 93 pp.

Lutz, F. E. *Field Book of Insects.* New York: Putnam, 1935, 510 pp.

Palmer, E. Laurence. *Palmer's Fieldbook of Mammals.* New York: Dutton, 1957, 321 pp.

Peterson, R. T. *A Field Guide to the Birds.* Boston: Houghton Mifflin, 1934, 167 pp.

Wild Animals of North America. Washington, D.C.: National Geographic Society, 1960, 399 pp.

Zim, Herbert S., and others. *Golden Nature Guides.* New York: Simon and Schuster, 1949–1956, 160 pp. *Insects; Birds; Mammals; Seashores; Reptiles and Amphibians; Fishes.*

Rocks, Minerals, and Stars

Jensen, David E. *My Hobby Is Collecting Rocks and Minerals.* New York: Hart Publishing Co., 1955, 121 pp.

Joseph, M. J., and S. L. Lippincott. *Point to the Stars.* New York: McGraw-Hill, 1963, 96 pp.

Pearl, Richard M. *How To Know the Minerals and Rocks.* New York: McGraw-Hill, 1954, 380 pp.

Rey, H. A. *Find the Constellations.* Boston: Houghton Mifflin, 1954, 72 pp.

———. *The Stars: A New Way to See Them.* Boston: Houghton Mifflin, 1952, 144 pp.

Shuttlesworth, Dorothy. *First Guide to Rocks.* New York: Doubleday, 1963, 30 pp.

Zim, Herbert S., and Robert H. Baker. *Stars.* New York: Simon and Schuster, 1951, 157 pp.

———, and E. K. Cooper. *Minerals: Their Identification, Uses, and How To Collect Them.* New York: Harcourt, 1943, 368 pp.

———, and Paul R. Shaffer. *Rocks and Minerals.* New York: Simon and Schuster, 1957, 160 pp.

Plants

Collingwood, G. H. *Knowing Your Trees.* Washington, D.C.: American Forestry Association, 1937, 109 pp.

Everett, T. H. *Field Flowers, Garden Flowers, Woodland Flowers.* Racine, Wis.: Whitman, 60 pp. each.

Gottscho, Samuel. *A Pocket Guide to Wild Flowers.* New York: Washington Square Press, 1951, 192 pp.

Harvey, Jane. *Wild Flowers of America.* Racine, Wis.: Whitman, 1932, 96 pp.

Moldenke, Harold N. *American Wild Flowers.* Princeton, N.J.: Van Nostrand, 1950, 453' pp.

Parsons, Frances T. *How To Know the Ferns.* New York: Scribner, 1922, 215 pp.

Peterson, Maude G. *How To Know Wild Flowers.* New York: Macmillan, 1933, 383 pp.

Rogers, Matilda. *The First Book of Tree Identification.* New York: Random House, 1951, 95 pp.

Saunders, Charles F. *Western Flower Guide.* New York: Doubleday, 1917, 286 pp.

Stefferud, Alfred. *How To Know the Wild Flowers*. New York: Holt, Rinehart and Winston, 1950, 144 pp.

Thomas, William S. *Field Book of Common Mushrooms*. New York: Putnam, 1936, 392 pp.

*BIBLIOGRAPHIES OF BOOKS**

American Association for the Advancement of Science. *Science Book List for Children*. Washington, D.C.

————, and the National Science Foundation. *An Inexpensive Science Library*. A selected list of paperbound science books. Washington, D.C.

Association for Childhood Education International. *Bibliography of Books for Children*, and *Children's Books for $1.25 or Less*. Washington, D.C.

Bibliography of Reference Books For Elementary Science. Washington, D.C.: National Science Teachers Association, 40 pp.

National Aeronautics and Space Administration. *Aeronautics and Space Bibliography*. Washington, D.C.: Government Printing Office, 1961. For elementary grades.

National Aeronautics and Space Administration. *Aeronautics and Space Bibliography of Adult Aerospace Books and Materials*. Washington, D.C.: Government Printing Office, 1961.

National Council of Teachers of English. *Adventuring with Books: A Reading List for Elementary Grades*. Champaign, Ill.

Piltz, Albert. *Science Publications: An Annotated Guide to Selected Listings*. U.S. Department of Health, Education, and Welfare OE-29046, Circular No. 705. Washington, D.C.: Government Printing Office, 1963, 65 pp. A source book.

Schwartz, Julius, and Herman Schneider. *Growing Up with Science Books*. New York: Library Journal, 32 pp.

PART TWO: THE EARTH AND THE UNIVERSE

THE EARTH'S SURFACE

For Children

Crosby, Phoebe. *Junior Science Book of Rock Collecting*. Champaign, Ill.: Garrard Publishing Co., 1962, 63 pp. Easy reading about common rocks and their uses.

Evans, Eva Knox. *The Adventure Book of Rocks*. New York: Capitol Publishing Co., 1955, 93 pp. Collecting and studying rocks.

Fenton, Carroll Lane, and Mildred Adams Fenton. *Riches from the Earth*. New York: John Day, 1953, 156 pp. Minerals and ores, their usefulness and other information.

————. *Rocks and Their Stories*. New York: Doubleday, 1951, 112 pp. Studying and identifying rocks and minerals. Photographs.

Goetz, Delia. *Deserts*. New York: Morrow, 1956, 64 pp. Information about deserts, their cause, and the adaptation of living things to such a habitat.

————. *Mountains*. New York: Morrow, 1962, 64 pp. Kinds of mountains and life on them.

Irving, Robert. *Rocks and Minerals*. New York: Knopf, 1956, 175 pp. A general treatment.

————. *Volcanoes and Earthquakes*. New York: Knopf, 1962, 123 pp. Cause and action of these phenomena with helpful drawings.

Lauber, Patricia. *All about the Planet Earth*. New York: Random House, 1962, 138 pp. The earth's surface, the waters, the changes through the ages, and some of the methods of study.

Parker, Bertha M. Basic Science Education Series. New York: Harper & Row, 1958–1959, 36 pp. *The Earth's Changing Surface; Gravity; Soil*.

* Book lists are revised periodically. Check to get the latest.

Pearl, Richard M. *1001 Questions Answered about the Mineral Kingdom*. New York: Dodd, Mead, 1959, 326 pp. An excellent source book.

Pine, Tillie S., and Joseph Levine. *Gravity All Around*. New York: Whittlesey, 1963, 48 pp. Easy reading.

Polgreen, John, and Cathleen Polgreen. *The Earth in Space*. New York: Random House, 1963, 77 pp. The earth's relation to other planets as well as to the universe. Easy reading.

Poole, Lynn, and Gray Poole. *Volcanoes in Action*. New York: McGraw-Hill, 1962, 79 pp. Answers to questions curious children ask about volcanoes.

Ravielli, Anthony. *The World Is Round*. New York: Viking, 1963, 46 pp. The earth's shape described for beginners.

Reed, W. Maxwell. *The Earth for Sam*. New York: Harcourt, 1960, 244 pp.

Ruchlis, Hy. *Your Changing Earth*. Irvington-on-Hudson, N.Y.: Harvey House, 1963, 40 pp. The earth's origin and its changing forces through the ages.

Shuttlesworth, Dorothy. *The Story of Rocks*. New York: Garden City, 1956, 56 pp. Colored illustrated guide.

Strahler, Arthur S. *The Story of Our Earth*. New York: Home Library Press, 1963, 56 pp. Illustrated story of the earth and the forces that act on it.

For Teachers

Bates, D. R. (ed.). *The Earth and Its Atmosphere*. New York: Basic Books, 1959, 312 pp. Fifteen scientists present background needed to understand International Geophysical Year.

Croneis, C., and W. C. Krumbein. *Down to Earth*. Chicago: University of Chicago Press, 1950, 502 pp.

Hubble, Lawrence. *The Earth*. Darien, Conn.: Teachers Publishing Corporation, 1964, 96 pp. One in the series produced with the National Science Teachers Association. Information about geology, astronomy, and oceanography.

Namowitz, Samuel N., and Donald B. Stone. *Earth Science*. Princeton, N.J.: Van Nostrand, 1960, 614 pp. General comprehensive treatment.

Ramsey, William L., and Raymond E. Burckley. *Modern Earth Science*. New York: Holt, Rinehart and Winston, 1961, 630 pp. A comprehensive text.

Sullivan, Walter. *Assault on the Unknown: The International Geophysical Year*. New York: McGraw-Hill, 1961, 460 pp. Background material.

ASTRONOMY

For Children

Adler, Irving. *The Stars*. New York: John Day, 1956, 125 pp. A simple explanation of the evidence and the reasoning that led to astronomers' conclusions.

——. *The Stars: Steppingstones into Space*. New York: John Day, 1956, 156 pp. Astronomy for the especially curious and interested.

——, and Ruth Adler. *The Sun and Its Family*. New York: John Day, 1958, 126 pp. Story of solar system with the methods of discovery. For the especially interested.

Blough, Glenn O., and Ida B. DePencier. *How the Sun Helps Us*. New York: Harper & Row, 1958, 36 pp. Easy.

Branley, Franklyn M. *The Big Dipper*. New York: Crowell, 1962, unpaged. Easy reading with large drawings.

——. *Exploring by Satellite*. New York: Crowell, 1957, 40 pp. The story of Project Vanguard.

——. *Mars: Planet Number Four*. New York: Crowell, 1962, 116 pp. Discusses possibilities of life.

——. *The Nine Planets*. New York: Crowell, 1958, 74 pp. A guide to understanding the planets.

——. *The Sun: Our Nearest Star*. New York: Crowell, 1961, 44 pp. Easy. The nature of the sun and our dependence on it.

Freeman, Mae, and Ira Freeman. *Fun with Astronomy*. New York: Random House, 1953, 58 pp. Ideas for demonstrations and experiments in astronomy.

——, and ——. *The Sun, the Moon, and the Stars*. New York: Random House, 1959, 84 pp. The earth, the solar system, galaxies, and universe.

Freeman, Mae, and Ira Freeman. *You Will Go to the Moon.* New York: Random House, 1959, 62 pp. Easy. Illustrated account of a trip to the moon.

Gallant, Roy A. *Exploring the Moon.* New York: Garden City, 1955, 63 pp. Surface of, conditions on, origin of, and other information about the moon.

———. *Exploring the Planets.* New York: Garden City, 1958, 121 pp. Informative and well-illustrated.

———. *Exploring the Sun.* New York: Garden City, 1958, 57 pp. The development of man's knowledge of the sun.

———. *Exploring the Universe.* New York: Garden City, 1956, 62 pp. Elementary material about our expanding universe.

Hyde, Margaret O. *Exploring Earth and Space: The Story of the International Geophysical Year.* (Revised). New York: Whittlesey, 1959, 157 pp. Excellent story of all phases of science being stressed during International Geophysical Year.

Joseph, Maron Joseph, and Sarah Lee Lippincott. *Point to the Stars.* New York: McGraw-Hill, 1963, 93 pp. Locating stars and constellations; maps and drawings. For especially interested.

Lewis, Claudia. *When I Go to the Moon.* New York: Macmillan, 1961, unpaged. The wonder and mystery of earth as viewed by a space-child on the moon.

Ordway, Frederick I., and Ronald C. Wakeford. *Conquering the Sun's Empire.* New York: Dutton, 1963, 128 pp. Modern astronomy and possible future discoveries through space travel.

Parker, Bertha M., The Basic Science Education Series. New York: Harper & Row, 1958–1959, 36 pp. *Beyond the Solar System; The Earth's Nearest Neighbor; The Sun and Its Family.*

Piper, Roger. *The Big Dish: The Fascinating Story of Radio Telescopes.* New York: Harcourt, 1963, 159 pp. How the telescope works as well as some of the exciting discoveries made by the use of such instruments.

Posin, Dan Q. *Life beyond Our Planet.* New York: McGraw-Hill, 1962, 125 pp. A scientist explores the exciting possibilities and life on other planets.

Richardson, Robert S. *Astronomy in Action.* New York: McGraw-Hill, 1962, 191 pp. Astronomers and how they work.

Schloat, Warren. *Andy's Wonderful Telescope.* New York: Scribner, 1958, 48 pp. The principles of the reflecting and refracting telescopes pictorially explained.

Schneider, Herman, and Nina Schneider. *You among the Stars.* New York: Scott, 1951, 60 pp. General easy material.

Schwartz, Julius. *The Earth Is Your Spaceship.* New York: McGraw-Hill, 1963, 32 pp. Easy reading about the movements of the earth through space, and their effects.

Simack, Clifford D. *The Solar System: Our New Front Yard.* New York: St. Martins, 1962, 280 pp. The solar system in relation to space travel and its problems. Fuller treatment than many books give.

Wells, Robert. *Alive in Space: The Science of Bio-Astronautics.* Boston: Little, Brown, 1961, 176 pp. New material about the biology of space.

Zim, Herbert S. *Comets; Shooting Stars; The Sun.* New York: Morrow, 1953–1958, 64 pp. Interesting astronomy for beginners.

Note: For rocket and space travel books *see* Aviation bibliography.

For Teachers

Alter, Dinsmore, and Clarence H. Cleminshaw. *Pictorial Astronomy.* New York: Crowell, 1952, 296 pp.

Assimov, Isaac. *The Kingdom of the Sun.* New York: Abelard-Schuman, 1960, 151 pp. The methods of astronomy and their results.

Atkins, J. Myron, and Stanley P. Wyatt, *Astronomy: Charting the Universe* and *Astronomy: The Universe in Motion.* Urbana, Ill.: University of Illinois Press, 1962. Experimental material.

Caidin, Martin. *Vanguard.* New York: Dutton, 1957, 288 pp.

Davidson, Martin. *Astronomy for Everyone.* New York: Dutton, 1953, 494 pp.

Editors of *Scientific American. Planet Earth.* New York: Simon and Schuster, 1957.

———. *The Universe.* New York: Simon and Schuster, 1957, 142 pp.

Hoyle, Fred. *Astronomy.* New York: Doubleday, 1963, 320 pp.

Hynek, J. Allen, and Norman D. Anderson. *Challenge of the Universe*. New York: McGraw-Hill, 143 pp. Excellent background materials.

Leyson, Captain Burr W. *Man, Rockets, and Space*. New York: Dutton, 1954, 188 pp.

Pickering, James S. *Captives of the Sun*. New York: Dodd, Mead, 1961, 326 pp. Astronomy of the solar system.

Richardson, Robert S. *Exploring Mars*. New York: McGraw-Hill, 1954, 261 pp.

————. *Second Satellite*. New York: Whittlesey, 1956, 191 pp.

Watson, Fletcher G. *Between the Planets*. New York: Doubleday, 1962, 224 pp. Astronomy and its methods.

Whipple, F. L. *Earth, Moon, Planets*. Cambridge, Mass.: Harvard University Press, 1952, 293 pp.

THE AIR AND THE WEATHER

For Children

Adler, Irving. *Hurricanes and Twisters*. New York: Knopf, 1956, 143 pp. Cause and behavior of hurricanes and tornadoes.

Antoine, Tex. *Wonders of the Weather*. New York: Dodd, Mead, 1962, 63 pp. With helpful diagrams.

Bendick, Jeanne. *Lightning*. Chicago: Rand McNally, 1961, 61 pp. Explanation of the phenomena and answers to questions.

Blough, Glenn O. *Not Only for Ducks*. New York: Whittlesey, 1954, 48 pp. The story of rain.

————. *Water Appears and Disappears*. New York: Harper & Row, 1959, 36 pp. The story of evaporation and condensation, leading to an understanding of weather. Easy.

Branley, Franklyn M. *Air Is All around You*. New York: Crowell, 1962, unpaged. Easy book about air.

Fenton, Carroll L., and Mildred A. Fenton. *Our Changing Weather*. New York: Doubleday, 1954, 110 pp. Weather information with illustrations.

Gallant, Roy. *Exploring the Weather*. New York: Garden City, 1957, 64 pp. Illustrated, well-organized study.

Hitte, Kathryn. *Hurricanes, Tornadoes, and Blizzards*. New York: Random House, 1960, 82 pp. Origin and nature of these storms.

Irving, Robert. *Hurricanes and Twisters*. New York: Knopf, 1955, 144 pp. Cause, courses, case histories, and other facts about storms.

Milgrom, Harry. *The Adventure Book of Weather*. New York: Capitol Publishing Co., 1959, 96 pp. Experiments and general information.

Parker, Bertha M. The Basic Science Education Series. New York: Harper & Row, 1949–1959, 36 pp. *The Air About Us; Ask the Weatherman; Clouds, Rain, and Snow; Our Ocean of Air; The Ways of the Weather*.

Pine, Tillie, and Joseph Levine. *Air All Around*. New York: Whittlesey, 1960, 48 pp. Easy. Properties of air and experiments to demonstrate them.

————, and ————. *Water All Around*. New York: Whittlesey, 1959, 48 pp. Easy. Experiments with evaporation and condensation and other properties of water.

Schneider, Herman. *Everyday Weather and How It Works*. New York: Whittlesey, 1961, 189 pp. Weather information with experiments.

Wolfe, Louis. *Let's Go to a Weather Station*. New York: Putnam, 1949, 47 pp. How a meteorologist gathers, communicates, and analyzes data.

————. *Probing the Atmosphere: The Story of Meteorology*. New York: Putnam, 1961, 160 pp. The history of weather science and the men who made it.

Wyler, Rose. *The First Book of the Weather*. New York: Watts, 1956, 62 pp. An excellent introduction.

Zim, Herbert S. *Lightning and Thunder*. New York: Morrow, 1952, 64 pp. Interesting information and answers to questions frequently asked.

———— and others. *Weather*. New York: Simon and Schuster, 1957, 160 pp. Weather study as a hobby.

For Teachers

Atkins, J. Myron, and R. Will Burnett. *Air, Winds, and Weather*. Elementary School Science Activities Series. New York: Holt, Rinehart and Winston, 1958. 58 pp.

Blair, Thomas. *Weather Elements*. Englewood Cliffs, N.J.: Prentice-Hall, 1937, 402 pp.

Brands, G. *Meteorology*. New York: McGraw-Hill, 1944, 235 pp.

Forrester, Frank. *1001 Questions Answered about the Weather*. New York: Dodd, Mead, 1957, 419 pp. A mine of useful information.

Kimble, George H. T. *Our American Weather*. New York: McGraw-Hill, 1955, 322 pp.

Lehr, P. E., and others. *Weather*. New York: Simon and Schuster, 1957, 157 pp.

Snow, Frost, and Ice. Cornell Science Leaflet, Vol. 41, No. 3. Ithaca, N.Y.: Cornell University Press, Winter 1947–1948, 32 pp.

Taylor, George F. *Elementary Meteorology*. Englewood Cliffs, N.J.: Prentice-Hall, 1954.

PART THREE: LIVING THINGS

THE EARTH'S LIVING FAMILY

For Children

Arnold, Oren. *Marvels of the Sea and Shore*. New York: Abelard-Schuman, 1963, 152 pp. Animals of the shore and waters and discussion of the behavior of the sea.

Bentley, Jack. *Enjoying Pets*. New York: Vanguard, 1956, 240 pp. Keeping and learning about animal pets.

Blough, Glenn O. *After the Sun Goes Down*. New York: Whittlesey, 1956, 48 pp. The story of animals at night.

———. The Basic Science Education Series. New York: Harper & Row. 1957–1959, 36 pp. *An Aquarium; The Insect Parade; The Pet Show; Useful Plants and Animals.*

———. *Christmas Trees and How They Grow*. New York: Whittlesey, 1961, 48 pp. The story of the growth of a tree, tree nurseries, and conservation.

———. *Not Only for Ducks*. New York: Whittlesey, 1954, 48 pp. How rain helps plants and other living things.

———. *Wait for the Sunshine*. New York: Whittlesey, 1954, 48 pp. Plants and the seasonal changes, with emphasis on food manufacture in plants.

———. *Who Lives in This Meadow?* New York: Whittlesey, 1961, 48 pp. Animal life, its adaptation to environment and interrelationship.

———. *Who Lives at the Seashore?* New York: Whittlesey, 1962, 48 pp. Animal life along the shore and how to observe it.

———, and Marjorie Campbell. *When You Go to the Zoo*. New York: Whittlesey, 1955, 128 pp. Habits of zoo animals and details about how they are cared for.

Bridges, William. *Zoo Doctor*. New York: Morrow, 1957, 126 pp. An engaging account of how zoo animals are cared for, by the curator of publications of the Bronx Zoo.

———. *Zoo Expeditions*. New York: Morrow, 1954, 191 pp. Interesting and unusual information about the exciting business of collecting animals.

Cooke, Emogene. *Fun-time Window Garden*. Chicago: Childrens Press, 1957, 31 pp. Raising house plants from seeds and slips.

Darling, Louis. *Chickens and How To Raise Them*. New York: Morrow, 1955, 63 pp. How eggs hatch and chickens grow.

Fenton, Carroll Lane, and Dorothy C. Pallas. *Birds and Their World*. New York: John Day, 1954, 96 pp. Habits, adaptations, and other information.

Garelick, May. *What's Inside?* New York: Scott, 1955, unpaged. The hatching and early life of a gosling.

Green, Ivah. *Animal Masquerade*. New York: Coward-McCann, 1955, 64 pp. Protective adaptations of many kinds of animals.

Harvey, Tad. *Exploring Biology*. New York: Doubleday, 1963, 121 pp. A large, fully illustrated book that introduces children to the plant and animal world.

Hogner, Dorothy Childs. *Earthworms*. New York: Crowell, 1953, 51 pp. Interesting information about these common animals. Easy.

Hutchins, Ross E. *This Is a Flower*. New York: Dodd, Mead, 1963, 153 pp. Excellent photographs accompany comprehensive treatment of the flower.

Kirkus, Virginia. *The First Book of Gardening*. New York: Watts, 1956, 65 pp. Describes gardening from planting to harvesting.

McCarthy, Agnes. *Creatures of the Deep*. Englewood Cliffs, N.J.: Prentice-Hall, 1963, 24 pp. Information about the habits of sea animals.

Morgan, Alfred. *A Pet Book for Boys and Girls*. New York: Scribner, 1949, 246 pp. Practical book on care of many different kinds of pets.

Parker, Bertha M. The Basic Science Education Series. New York: Harper & Row, 1950–1959, 36 pp. *Adaptation to Environment; Animals of the Seashore; Animals We Know; Dependent Plants; Domesticated Plants; Fishes; Flowers, Fruits, Seeds; Gardens Indoors; The Garden and Its Friends; Plant and Animal Partnerships; Plant World; Reptiles; Seeds and Seed Travels; Toads and Frogs.*

Riedman, Sarah R. *Naming Living Things*. Chicago: Rand McNally, 1963, 124 pp. Information about classification not easily found elsewhere.

Schloat, G. Warren. *The Wonderful Egg*. New York: Scribner, 1952, unpaged. Photographic story of egg to chicken, including suggestions for raising chickens.

Schwartz, Julius. *Through the Magnifying Glass: Little Things That Make a Big Difference*. New York: Whittlesey, 1954, 144 pp. Flowers, roots, stems, and other common things examined under a magnifying glass.

Selsam, Millicent E. *Plants That Move*. New York: Morrow, 1962, 127 pp. Includes experiments with leaves, flowers, and vines.

———. *Play with Plants*. New York: Morrow, 1949, 63 pp. A book full of experiments with plants that may be done indoors.

———. *Play with Seeds*. New York: Morrow, 1957, 93 pp. Experiences with and information about common seeds and how they are formed.

———. *See along the Shore*. New York. Harper & Row, 1961, unpaged. The world of tides, animal, and plant life along the ever-changing shore.

Simon, Hilda. *Wonders of the Butterfly World*. New York: Dodd, Mead, 1963, 63 pp. Excellent material about the habits of common butterflies.

———. *The Young Pathfinder's Book of Snakes*. New York: Hart Publishing Co., 1963, 127 pp. Information that will satisfy young readers.

Stefferud, Alfred. *The Wonders of Seeds*. New York: Harcourt, 1956, 111 pp. Formation, structure, and germination of seeds.

For Teachers

Air-Borne. Cornell Science Leaflet, Vol. 49, No. 2. Fall 1955, 32 pp. Air-borne seeds and how they are distributed and details of animal flight.

Barker, Will. *Wildlife in American History*. Washington, D.C.: Robert B. Luce, 1962, 108 pp. Excellent background science–social-studies material.

Dubos, René. *The Unseen World*. New York: Oxford, 1960, 110 pp. The relationship between microbes and other forms of life.

Galston, Arthur W. *The Life of the Green Plant*. Englewood Cliffs, N.J.: Prentice-Hall, 1961, 116 pp. A modern view of the way a green plant functions.

Gordon, Eva L. *Green Factories*. Cornell Science Leaflet, Vol. 49, No. 3. Winter 1956, 31 pp. How plants manufacture food.

Keeping Animals in the Classroom. Cornell Science Leaflet. Fall 1960. Valuable suggestions.

Platt, Rutherford. *This Green World*. New York: Dodd, Mead, 1959, 196 pp. A naturalist supplies the details of the plant world in a thoroughly interesting way.

Schery, Robert W. *Plants for Mankind*. Englewood Cliffs, N.J.: Prentice-Hall, 1952, 564 pp.

Storer, John H. *The Web of Life*. New York: Devin-Adair, 1956, 142 pp. The story of interdependence of living things on the earth. Easy, interesting reading.

Wailes, James. *Living Things*. Darien, Conn.: Teachers Publishing Corporation, 1964, 96 pp. One in the series produced with the National Science Teachers Association. Information and activities.

LIVING THINGS AND THE SEASONS

For Children

Blough, Glenn O. *Bird Watchers and Bird Feeders*. New York: Whittlesey, 1963, 48 pp. Birds in winter.
———. *The Basic Science Education Series*. New York: Harper & Row, 1958–1959, 36 pp. *Animals Round the Year; Birds in the Big Woods; Plants Round the Year.*
———. *Soon after September*. New York: Whittlesey, 1959, 48 pp. Living things and the seasons.
Bronson, Wilfred S. *Starlings*. New York: Harcourt, 1948, unpaged. Life story of birds told through observation of starlings. Informative drawings.
Goetz, Delia. *Deserts*. New York: Morrow, 1956, 64 pp. How plant and animal life adapt to desert conditions.
———. *Tropical Rain Forests*. New York: Morrow, 1957, 64 pp. An environmental study describing the living things in the rain forests.
Hausman, Leon A. *Beginner's Guide to Attracting Birds*. New York: Putnam, 1951, 127 pp. A practical book on taking care of bird visitors.
Hawkinson, Lucy, and John Hawkinson. *City Birds*. Racine, Wis.: Whitman Publishing Company, 1957, unpaged. Tells about the most common birds found in almost all cities.
Hussey, Lois J., and Catherine Pessino. *Collecting Cocoons*. New York: Crowell, 1953, 70 pp. How to collect, care for, and identify cocoons, and how to raise the insects.
Parker, Bertha M. The Basic Science Education Series. New York: Harper & Row, 1958–1959, 36 pp. *Birds; Birds in Your Backyard; Animal Travels.*

For Teachers

Barker, Will. *Winter Sleeping Wildlife*. New York: Harper & Row, 1958, 136 pp.
Cornell Science Leaflets. Ithaca, N.Y.: Cornell University Press, 1950–1957, Vol. 50, No. 4, *Beetles*; Vol. 38, No. 4, *Cover*; Vol. 43, No. 4, *Fish Bait*; *Paned Desert Laboratories*; Vol. 50, No. 2, *Fruits of Woods and Fencerows.*

ANIMAL WAYS

For Children

Bartlett, Ruth. *Insect Engineers*. New York: Morrow, 1957, 128 pp. Describes the anatomy, social habits, and engineering feats of ants.
Blough, Glenn O. *After the Sun Goes Down*. New York: Whittlesey, 1956, 48 pp. Life in the forest at night.
———. *Animals That Live Together*. New York: Harper & Row, 1959, 36 pp. Easy reading about common social animals.
———. *Animals and Their Young*. New York: Harper & Row, 1958, 36 pp. Easy reading about how some of our common animals care for their young.
———. *Who Lives in This House?* New York: Whittlesey, 1957, 48 pp. Habits of animals that inhabit a deserted house.
———. *Who Lives at the Seashore?* New York: Whittlesey, 1962, 48 pp. Adaptation of animals to a tide environment.
Cooper, Elizabeth K. *Insects and Plants: The Amazing Partnership*. New York: Harcourt, 1963, 142 pp. Details of the interrelationship of plants and insects.
———. *Science on the Shores and Banks*. New York: Harcourt, 1960, 180 pp. Exploring the water's edge and discovering about the animals and plants that live there.
———. *Silkworms and Science*. New York: Harcourt, 1961, 160 pp. The story of silk and the insects that make it.
Fenton, Carroll Lane, and Dorothy Constance Pallas. *Insects and Their World*. New York: John Day, 1956, 95 pp. Information that includes life cycle, habits, and structure.
George, Jean. *The Hole in the Tree*. New York: Dutton, 1957, unpaged. Many creatures use the hole in the tree as it grows in size from a tiny place to a large one.
Hecht, Bessie M. *All about Snakes*. New York: Random House, 1956, 139 pp. Anatomy, habits, and other interesting information.

Hyde, Margaret O. *Animals in Science: Saving Lives through Research*. New York: McGraw-Hill, 1962, 143 pp. A comprehensive picture of the usefulness of animals in medical discoveries.

Hylander, Clarence J. *Animals in Fur*. New York: Macmillan, 1956, 202 pp. Information on the adaptation of common mammals to a variety of habitats.

————. *Sea and Shore*. New York: Macmillan, 1950, 242 pp. Information on animals and plants living in the sea, with illustrations to help identify them.

Mason, George F. *Animal Homes*. New York: Morrow, 1947, 96 pp. Descriptions of the homes of common animals.

Parker, Bertha M., and others. The Basic Science Education Series. New York: Harper & Row, 1957–1959, 36 pp. *Insects and Their Ways; Six-Legged Neighbors; Insect Societies; Insect Friends and Enemies*.

Peattie, Donald Culross. *The Rainbow Book of Nature*. New York: Harcourt, 1957, 319 pp. A nature book that is a complete natural history in itself.

Perry, John, and Jane G. Perry. *Exploring the Seacoast*. New York: Whittlesey, 1961, 185 pp. Kinds of seacoasts, their nature, their living things, and the explorers' methods of discovery.

Phillips, Mary Geisler. *The Makers of Honey*. New York: Crowell, 1956, 155 pp. The life and work of the honeybee.

Platt, Rutherford, and staff. *Walt Disney Secrets of Life*. New York: Simon and Schuster, 1957, 124 pp. A beautiful color-illustrated introduction to living things.

————. *Walt Disney's World of Nature*. New York: Simon and Schuster, 1957, 176 pp. Colored pictures and informative text about living things.

Reed, W. Maxwell, and Wilfred S. Bronson. *The Sea for Sam*. New York: Harcourt, 1960, 233 pp. The sea, its tides, its floor, and its living things.

Selsam, Millicent E. *How Animals Live Together*. New York: Morrow, 1963, 90 pp. Social life of animals interestingly presented.

Simon, Hilda. *Exploring the World of Social Insects*. New York: Vanguard, 1962, 114 pp. Excellent material, helpfully illustrated, clearly written.

Sterling, Dorothy. *Insects and the Homes They Build*. New York: Doubleday, 1954, 125 pp. Common and unusual insect homes and the habits of the insects that build them.

Teale, Edwin W. *Insect Friends*. New York: Dodd, Mead, 1956, 96 pp. General information about a variety of insects. Photographs.

————. *The Junior Book of Insects*. New York: Dutton, 1953, 249 pp. Recognizing, collecting, and learning about insects.

For Teachers

Allee, W. C. *The Social Life of Animals*. New York: Norton, 1938, 293 pp.

Barker, Will. *Familiar Animals of America*. New York: Harper & Row, 1956, 300 pp.

————. *Familiar Reptiles and Amphibians of America*. New York: Harper & Row, 1964, 236 pp.

Breland, Osmond P. *Animal Life and Lore*. New York: Harper & Row, 1963, 388 pp.

Cornell Science Leaflets. Ithaca, N.Y.: Cornell University Press, 1945–1952, Vol. 41, No. 4, *Apple Tree Animals*; Vol. 43, No. 3, *Hunters and Hunted*; Vol. 44, No. 1, *Nature Writings*; Vol. 40, No. 1, *Outdoor Education*; Vol. 38, No. 3, *Over the Ground*; Vol. 45, No. 4, *Reptiles*.

Devoe, Alan. *The Fascinating Animal World*. New York: McGraw-Hill, 1951, 303 pp.

————. *Our Animal Neighbors*. New York: McGraw-Hill, 1953, 278 pp.

Grout, Roy A. *The Hive and the Honey Bee*. Hamilton, Ill.: Dadant and Sons, 1963, 556 pp. Life in the hive and a comprehensive treatment of beekeeping.

Lincoln, Frederick C. *Migration of Birds*. U.S. Department of Interior. Circular 16, Fish and Wildlife Service, Washington, D.C.: G.P.O., 1950, 102 pp.

Scott, John P. *Animal Behavior*. Chicago: University of Chicago Press, 1958, 252 pp. Behavior of animals with a record of methods of experimentation and observation.

Walker, Ernest P. *First Aid and Care of Small Animals*. New York: Animal Welfare Institute, 1955, 45 pp.

THE HUMAN BODY

For Children

Callahan, Dorothy, and Alma Smith Payne. *The Great Nutrition Puzzle*. New York: Scribner,

1956, 189 pp. Emphasizes scientific method and experimenting to find the facts of foods and nutrition.

Coy, Harold. *Doctors and What They Do*. New York: Watts, 1956, 173 pp. The scientific aspect of the work of a doctor.

Grant, Madeleine P. *Wonder World of Microbes*. New York: Whittlesey, 1956, 157 pp. Microbes and their effect on our lives.

Hyde, Margaret O. *Medicine in Action*. New York: Whittlesey, 1956, 160 pp. Details of health practices, the duties of doctors, and research methods.

Lauber, Patricia. *Your Body and How It Works*. New York: Random House, 1962, 77 pp. Illustrated text presenting details of anatomy and physiology.

Lerner, Marguerite R. *Who Do You Think You Are?: The Story of Heredity*. Englewood Cliffs, N. J.: Prentice-Hall, 1963, 61 pp. The story of heredity reduced to its simplest form. Material not easily found elsewhere.

Ludovici, L. J. *The World of the Microscope*. New York: Putnam, 1959, 128 pp. The importance of the achievements made through the use of the microscope.

Parker, Bertha M. The Basic Science Education Series. New York: Harper & Row, 1958–1959, 36 pp. *Community Health; Foods; How We are Built; Keeping Well; You As a Machine*.

Perry, John. *Our Wonderful Eyes*. New York: Whittlesey, 1954, 158 pp. Marvels of the eye and sight, with experiments to help understand.

Reidman, Sarah R. *Shots without Guns*. Chicago: Rand, McNally, 1960, 232 pp. The story of vaccination.

Schneider, Leo. *You and Your Senses*. New York: Harcourt, 1956, 132 pp. The operation of human sense organs and how to care for them.

Selsam, Millicent E. *Microbes at Work*. New York: Morrow, 1953, 95 pp. The work of bacteria, molds, and yeasts, with experiments suitable for children.

Spingarn, Natalie Davis. *To Save Your Life*. Boston: Little, Brown, 1963, 210 pp. The story of the U.S. Public Health Service.

Sutton-Vane, S. *The Story of Eyes*. New York: Viking, 1958, 214 pp. The history of the development of sight in animals from the simple to complex.

Weart, Edith L. *The Story of Your Brain and Nerves*. New York: Coward-McCann, 1961, 64 pp. How the nervous system works.

For Teachers

Baron, A. L. *Man against Germs*. New York: Dutton, 1957, 320 pp.

Burgdorf, Otto P. *Golden Adventure Book of Human Biology*. New York: Golden Press, 1962, 94 pp. An introduction to human anatomy and physiology from the experimental viewpoint.

Busch, Phyllis S. *Smoking and Lung Cancer*. Trenton, N. J.: New Jersey State Department of Education, 1963, 77 pp. A teaching guide for this important subject, intended for grade five to college.

Moore, Ruth. *The Coil of Life*. New York: Knopf, 1961, 418 pp. The great discoveries of the last 200 years in biology, biochemistry, and allied sciences that have led to our understanding of the chemistry of life.

Simon, Harold J. *Microbes and Man*. New York: McGraw-Hill, 1963, 160 pp. The interactions of microbes and men—friend and foe.

Stanley, Wendell M., and Evans G. Valens. *Viruses and the Nature of Life*. New York: Dutton, 1961, 224 pp.

CONSERVATION

For Children

Blough, Glenn O. *Lookout for the Forest*. New York: Whittlesey, 1954, 48 pp. A conservation story.

———. *The Tree on the Road to Turntown*. New York: Whittlesey, 1953, 48 pp. Conservation aspects of a tree's life.

———. *Useful Plants and Animals*. New York: Harper & Row, 1959, 36 pp. How we use animals and plants in daily living. Easy.

Farb, Peter. *Living Earth*. New York: Harper & Row, 1959, 167 pp. Soil, its use and conservation.

Fenton, Carroll Lane, and Mildred Fenton. *Riches from the Earth.* New York: John Day, 1953, 158 pp. Origin and use of many minerals.

————, and Dorothy C. Pallas. *Trees and Their World.* New York: John Day, 1957, 96 pp.

Fox, William. *Rocks and Rain and the Rays of the Sun.* New York: Henry Z. Walck, 1958, 90 pp. The forces of nature as they relate to the needs of man.

Gionnoni, Frances, and Seymour Reit. *Golden Book of Gardening: How To Plan, Plant, and Care for the Home Garden.* New York: Golden Press, 1962, 68 pp. Essential information about gardening.

Green, Ivah. *Water: Our Most Valuable Natural Resource.* New York: Coward-McCann, 1958, 96 pp.

Lauber, Patricia. *Dust Bowl: the Story of Man on the Great Plains.* New York: Coward-McCann, 1958, 96 pp. Wind, weather, and dust storms in our "semiarid" areas.

————. *Our Friend, the Forest.* New York: Doubleday, 1959, 61 pp. Trees, soil, plants, and animals in the forest.

Meyer, Jerome S. *Water at Work.* New York: Harcourt, 1963, 90 pp. Physical properties, importance, many uses, and future problems of water supply.

Milne, Lorus J., and Margery Milne. *Because of a Tree.* New York: Atheneum, 1963, 149 pp. Interdependence of living things and adaptation to environment.

Parker, Bertha M. The Basic Science Education Series. New York: Harper & Row, 1957–1959, 36 pp. *The Earth, A Great Storehouse; Leaves; Saving Our Wild Life; Trees.*

Pinney, Roy. *Vanishing Wildlife.* New York: Dodd, Mead, 1963, 182 pp. A naturalist discusses conservation of wild life beginning with extinct species and highlighting the many conservation problems. Excellent photographs.

Smith, F. C. *The First Book of Conservation.* New York: F. Watts, 1954, 69 pp. Beginning study.

For Teachers

Archer, Sellers G. *Soil Conservation.* Norman, Okla.: University of Oklahoma Press, 1956, 286 pp. A full treatment of this aspect of the total problem of conservation.

Ashbaugh, Byron, and Muriel Beuschlein. *Things To Do in Science and Conservation.* Danville, Ill.: Interstate Printers & Publishers, 1960, 164 pp. A comprehensive helpful resource.

Bates, Marston. *The Forest and the Sea.* New York: New American Library, 1961, 216 pp. (Paperback.)

Bathurst, Effie S., and Wilhelmina Hill. *Conservation Experiences for Children.* Washington, D.C.: G.P.O.

Bibliography of Conservation Books, Booklets, and Teaching Aids. Washington, D.C.: National Wildlife Federation, 1954, 44 pp.

Books, Booklets, and Bulletins on Soil and Water Conservation. U.S. Department of Agriculture, Soil Conservation Service. Washington, D.C.: G.P.O., 1953, 30 pp.

Chase, Stuart. *Rich Land, Poor Land: A Study of Waste in Natural Resources.* New York: McGraw-Hill, 1934, 361 pp.

Conservation Education in American Schools. Washington, D.C.: American Association of School Administrators, National Education Association, 1951, 527 pp.

Conservation Education in Rural Schools. Washington, D.C.: National Education Association, 1943, 114 pp.

Concepts of Conservation. New York: Conservation Foundation, 1963, 64 pp. A guide to discussion of some fundamental problems.

Cornell Science Leaflets. Ithaca, N.Y.: Cornell University Press, 1946–1952, Vol. 40, No. 2, *Hedgerows;* Vol. 39, No. 4, *The Story of Conservation;* Vol. 46, No. 2, *The Story of Conservation in New York;* Vol. 42, No. 3, *Wood;* Vol. 44, No. 4, *Wooded Laboratories.*

Fox, Adrian, and George E. Rotter. *Learning about Soil and Water Conservation.* Lincoln, Nebr.: Johnson, 1958, 64 pp. A text-workbook.

Materials to Help Teach Forest Conservation. List of teaching aids. Washington, D.C.: U.S. Department of Agriculture, 1953, 4 pp.

Munzer, Martha E., and Brandwein, Paul F. *Teaching Science through Conservation.* New York: McGraw-Hill, 1960, 470 pp.

Osborn, Fairfield. *Limits of the Earth.* Boston: Little, Brown, 1953, 238 pp.

————. *Our Plundered Planet.* Boston: Little, Brown, 1952, 217 pp.

An Outline for Teaching Conservation in Elementary Schools. U.S. Department of Agriculture, Soil Conservation Service PA-268, Washington, D.C.: G.P.O.

Peterson, Roger Tory, and James Fisher. *Wild America.* Boston: Houghton Mifflin, 1956, 425 pp. Two naturalists tour United States and record their fascinating observations.

Storer, John H. *The Web of Life.* New York: New American Library, 1956, 128 pp. (Paperback.)

Additional Information Sources

American Forest Products Industries, Inc., Washington, D.C.

American Forestry Association, Washington, D.C.

Conservation Foundation, New York.

Fish and Wildlife Service, U.S. Department of Interior, Washington, D.C.

Forest Service, U.S. Department of Agriculture, Washington, D.C.

National Association of Audubon Societies, New York.

National Park Service, U.S. Department of Interior, Washington, D.C.

Soil Conservation Service, U.S. Department of Agriculture, Washington, D.C.

Note: Many Bulletins and teaching aids are available from your state department of education or state conservation department at the state capital. Many states have the following resources: forestry agencies, extension foresters, park agencies, fish and wildlife agencies, soil conservation offices, and agencies that deal with minerals and waters. Be specific about your needs. If children write, send *only* one letter that has been carefully checked.

ANCIENT ANIMALS AND PLANTS

For Children

Andrews, Roy C. *All about Dinosaurs.* New York: Random House, 1953, 141 pp. Formation of fossils and how they are found and studied.

————. *All about Strange Beasts of the Past.* New York: Random House, 1956, 142 pp. The story of early mammals and the scientific expeditions that have unearthed their fossil remains.

Blough, Glenn O. *Discovering Dinosaurs.* New York: Whittlesey, 1960, 48 pp. Information and an account of how scientists work to make discoveries.

Darling, Lois, and Louis Darling. *Before and after Dinosaurs.* New York: Morrow, 1959, 64 pp. A comprehensive study of the development and adaptation of these huge beasts.

Dickinson, Alice. *The First Book of Prehistoric Animals.* New York: F. Watts, 1954, 92 pp. Illustrated historical treatment of ancient animal life.

Epstein, Sam, and Beryl Epstein. *Prehistoric Animals.* New York: F. Watts, 1956, 210 pp. History of the development of life on the earth and how such knowledge has developed.

Fenton, Carroll Lane. *Prehistoric World.* New York: John Day, 1954, 126 pp. General treatment of ancient animals.

Holsaert, Eunice, and Robert Gartland. *Dinosaurs.* New York: Holt, Rinehart and Winston, 1959, unpaged. A book to begin on.

Parker, Bertha M., The Basic Science Education Series. New York: Harper & Row, 1958–1959, 36 pp. *Animals of Yesterday; Life through the Ages; Stories Read from the Rocks.*

Shuttlesworth, Dorothy E. *The Age of Reptiles.* New York: Garden City, 1958, 57 pp. The rise and fall of the reptiles.

Swinton, William E. *The Wonderful World of Prehistoric Animals.* New York: Garden City, 1961, 88 pp. Picture history of animal world.

Williams, Henry L. *Stories in Rocks.* New York: Holt, Rinehart and Winston, 1948, 151 pp. Origin of the earth and the story of its development and of life on it.

Zim, Herbert S. *Dinosaurs.* New York: Morrow, 1954, 64 pp. Discovery and study of fossils and how they are formed.

For Teachers

Colbert, Edwin H. *Dinosaurs.* New York: Dutton, 1961, 300 pp. Discovery, study, and the resulting information.

Fenton, Carroll L. *Life Long Ago: The Story of Fossils.* New York: Reynal, 1937, 280 pp.

Fenton, Carroll L. *Our Amazing Earth*. New York: Doubleday, 1945, 340 pp.

———, and Mildred Fenton. *The Fossil Book*. New York: Doubleday, 1958, 458 pp. An excellent background, with very helpful illustrations.

———, and ———. *The Rock Book*. New York: Doubleday, 1945, 357 pp.

Matthews, William H. *Fossils: An Introduction to Prehistoric Life*. New York: A. S. Barnes, 1962, 322 pp. Detailed, useful background information.

Moore, Raymond C. *Introduction to Historical Geology*. New York: McGraw-Hill, 1958, 656 pp. Changes in rock and in plant and animal life. Richly illustrated.

Moore, Ruth. *Man, Time, and Fossils*. New York: Knopf, 1961, 436 pp. The evolution of man.

PART FOUR: ENERGY AND MATTER

WHAT THINGS ARE MADE OF

For Children

Asimov, Isaac. *The Search for the Elements*. New York: Basic Books, 1962, 158 pp. Discovery and nature of the elements. A history of chemistry.

Carona, Philip. *The True Book of Chemistry*. Chicago: Childrens Press, 1962, 46 pp. Easy reading about the elements and how they act.

Cooper, Elizabeth K. *Discovering Chemistry*. New York: Harcourt, 1959, 184 pp. Chemistry experiments, their meaning and application.

Freeman, Ira, and Mae Freeman. *The Story of Chemistry*. New York: Random House, 1962, 80 pp. For beginners.

Gallant, Roy A. *The ABC's of Chemistry*. New York: Doubleday, 1963, 88 pp. Large book organized alphabetically to introduce young readers to the words and world of chemical change.

———. *Exploring Chemistry*. New York: Garden City, 1958, 119 pp. Illustrated and diagramed.

Irwin, Keith G. *Chemistry First S-T-E-P-S*. New York: F. Watts, 1963, 49 pp. Chemistry applied to everyday phenomena.

Parker, Bertha M. The Basic Science Education Series. New York: Harper & Row, 1959, 36 pp. *The Everyday Atom; Matter and Molecules and Atoms; What Things Are Made of*.

Poole, Lynn, and Gray Poole. *Carbon 14 and Other Science Methods That Date the Past*. New York: McGraw-Hill, 1961, 160 pp. The fascinating story of the methods of science that date the past; expertly told.

Seaborg, Glenn T., and Evans G. Valens. *Elements of the Universe*. New York: Dutton, 1958, 245 pp. Comprehensive treatments of the elements and how they behave.

Schwartz, Julius. *It's Fun to Know Why: Experiments with Things around Us*. New York: Whittlesey, 1952, 125 pp. Simple experiments that show how man obtains and uses salt, iron, coal, glass, paper, bread, wool, cement, rubber, and soap.

———. *Through the Magnifying Glass*. New York: McGraw-Hill, 1954, 142 pp. Exploring crystals, atoms, and other wonders with a simple magnifier.

For Teachers

Asimov, Isaac. *Building Blocks of the Universe*. New York: Abelard-Schuman, 1957, 256 pp.

Jaffe, Bernard. *Chemistry Creates a New World*. New York: Crowell, 1957, 321 pp.

Matter, Energy, and Change: Explorations in Chemistry for Elementary School Children. Washington, D.C.: Manufacturing Chemists' Association, 1960, 50 pp. Experiments and subject matter for teachers' background.

Trieger, Seymour. *Matter (Chemistry)*. Darien, Conn.: Teachers Publishing Corporation, 1964, 96 pp. One in the series produced with the National Science Teachers Association. Information and activities.

FIRE AND ITS PREVENTION

For Children

Adler, Irving. *Fire in Your Life.* New York: John Day, 1955, 128 pp. The story of fuels and fire.

Hough, Walter. *The Story of Fire.* New York: Doubleday, 1928, 198 pp. General account of fire and its uses.

Parker, Bertha M. *Fire.* New York: Harper & Row, 1959, 36 pp. What happens when a fire burns, and how we use fire.

————. *Fire, Friend, and Foe.* New York: Harper & Row, 1959, 36 pp. The nature of burning and the story of useful and destructive fires.

For Teachers

Fire Prevention Education. New York: National Board of Fire Underwriters, 1945, 355 pp. Contains self-inspection blanks for schools and home-inspection blanks for school children. Much important material. The board also has other material available.

Fire Prevention Education. Bulletin No. 1311. Albany, N.Y.: University of the State of New York, 1957, 63 pp.

Mackintosh, Helen K. *A Curriculum Guide to Fire Safety.* Bulletin No. 8. Washington, D.C.: Government Printing Office, 1946, 31 pp.

National Fire Protection Association, Boston. Many publications especially useful for elementary schools.

Wildfire. Cornell Science Leaflet, Vol. 41, No. 2, Fall 1947, 32 pp. Discussions of various kinds of fires and their consequences, fire patterns, fire prevention, and fire fighting.

HEAT AND HOW WE USE IT

For Children

Parker, Bertha M. *Heat.* New York: Harper & Row, 1958, 36 pp. How heat travels and how it is measured and used.

————. *Thermometers, Heat, and Cold.* New York: Harper & Row, 1959, 36 pp. Kinds, uses, and construction of thermometers and the effects of heat and cold.

Ruchlis, Hy. *The Wonder of Heat Energy.* New York: Harper & Row, 1961, 186 pp. A story of the vital part heat plays in our world.

ATOMIC ENERGY AND ITS USES

For Children

Beeler, Nelson F., and Franklyn M. Branley. *Experiments with Atomics.* New York: Crowell, 1954, 156 pp. Atomic structure and important phases of atomic energy for the more-than-a-little interested pupil.

De Vries, Leonard. *The Book of the Atom.* New York: Macmillan, 1960, 264 pp. Historical account and present knowledge.

Haber, Heinz. *The Walt Disney Story of Our Friend, the Atom.* New York: Simon and Schuster, 1956, 160 pp. Historical development of our knowledge of the atom.

Hyde, Margaret O. *Atoms Today and Tomorrow.* Rev. ed. New York: Whittlesey, 1959, 156 pp. For readers with some information on the subject.

Jaworski, Irene D., and Alexander Joseph. *Atomic Energy: The Story of Nuclear Science.* New York: Harcourt, 1961, 198 pp.

Kohn, Bernice. *The Peaceful Atom.* Englewood Cliffs, N.J.: Prentice-Hall, 1963, 66 pp. The story of the nature and use of the atom with discussion of discoveries. Easy reading.

McKown, Robin. *The Fabulous Isotopes: What They Are and What They Do.* New York: Holiday, 1962, 184 pp. Helpfully illustrated treatment that introduces nuclear science.

Radlauer, Edward, and Ruth S. Radlauer. *Atomic Power for People.* Chicago: Melmont Publishers, 1960, 47 pp. Information not easily available elsewhere about the work of atomic power plants.

Ross, Frank. *Superpower: The Story of Atomic Energy.* New York: Lothrop, 1955, 185 pp. History and detailed information.

Schneider, Herman, and Nina Schneider. *How Big Is Big: From Stars to Atoms*. New York: Scott, 1950, 48 pp. Relative sizes compared from a child's point of view.

Yates, Raymond F. *Atomic Experiments for Boys*. New York: Harper & Row, 1952, 132 pp. An introduction to atoms and atomic energy.

For Teachers

Asimov, Isaac. *Inside the Atom*. New York: Abelard-Schuman, 1956, 170 pp. Information about atoms and the uses of atomic energy.

Eidinoff, M. L., and Hy Ruchlis. *Atomics for the Millions*. New York: Whittlesey, 1947, 276 pp.

Evans, Hubert M., and others. *Operation Atomic Vision*. Washington, D.C.: National Association of Secondary-School Principals, National Education Association, 1948, 95 pp.

Fermi, L. *Atoms in the Family*. Chicago: University of Chicago Press, 1954, 267 pp.

Hughes, Donald J. *On Nuclear Energy*. Cambridge, Mass.: Harvard University Press, 1957, 263 pp.

Living with the Atom. Albany, N.Y.: Bureau of Secondary Curriculum Development, New York State Department of Education, 1952, 68 pp. A source book for teachers.

Martin, Charles Noel. *The Thirteen Steps to the Atom: A Photographic Exploration*. New York: F. Watts, 1958, 251 pp. With detailed information.

May, Julian. *There's Adventure in Atomic Energy*. Chicago: Popular Mechanics, 1957, 174 pp.

Woodbury, D. O. *Atoms for Peace*. New York: Dodd, Mead, 1955, 259 pp.

Note: Write to Superintendent of Documents, Government Printing Office, Washington, D.C., for list of government publications on various phases of atomic energy.

MACHINES AND HOW THEY WORK

For Children

Blackwood, Paul E. *Push and Pull: The Story of Energy*. New York: Whittlesey, 1959, 192 pp. The origins and uses of energy.

Blough, Glenn O. *Doing Work*. New York: Harper & Row, 1959, 36 pp. Easy story of simple machines and how they work.

Buehr, Walter. *The Story of the Wheel*. New York: Putnam, 1960, 47 pp. Changes in the world due to the development and use of the wheel.

Corbett, Scott. *What Makes a Car Go*. Boston: Little, Brown, 1963, 44 pp. Easy reading, helpful illustrations, information not easily available.

Hogben, Lancelot. *The Wonderful World of Energy*. New York: Garden City, 1957, 69 pp. Large book describing history and uses of all kinds of energy.

Irving, Robert. *Energy and Power*. New York: Knopf, 1958, 140 pp. The history of energy and power up to and including atomic energy.

Lewellen, John. *The True Book of Toys at Work*. Chicago: Childrens Press, 1953, 45 pp. Easy explanations of how simple toys such as whistles, electric trains, balloons, and so forth work.

Meyer, Jerome S. *Machines*. New York: Harcourt, 1958, 64 pp. The basic operation of machines.

Parker, Bertha M. *Machines*. New York: Harper & Row, 1959, 36 pp. Principles and use of simple machines.

———. *Toys*. New York: Harper & Row, 1957, 36 pp. How some of the common toys work.

Pine, Tillie S., and Levine, Joseph. *Friction All Around*. New York: Whittlesey, 1960, 46 pp. Easy. Explains friction and its importance.

Schneider, Herman. *Everyday Machines and How They Work*. New York: Whittlesey, 1950, 192 pp. Illustrated.

———. *Let's Look under the City*. New York: Scott, 1954, 40 pp. How water, gas, electricity, and telephone calls come to the buildings in the city.

———, and Schneider, Nina. *Let's Look inside Your House*. New York: Scott, 1948, 40 pp. Experiences with water, heat, and electricity as they are used.

———, and ———. *More Power to You*. New York: Scott, 1953, 119 pp. Development and use of power.

Schwartz, Julius. *I Know a Magic House*. New York: Whittlesey, 1956, 32 pp. Explanations for everyday home happenings; for beginners.

Sharp, Elizabeth. *Simple Machines and How They Work*. New York: Random House, 1959, 83 pp. Descriptions of the simple machines with helpful experiments.

Wyler, Rose, and Gerald Ames. *What Makes It Go?* New York: Whittlesey, 1958, 64 pp. Experiments to develop the concepts of the study of power.

For Teachers

Dunn, Lois. *Motion*. Darien, Conn.: Teachers Publishing Corporation, 1964, 96 pp. One in the series produced with the National Science Teachers Association. Information and activities.

Rockcastle, Verne N. *Simple Machines*. Cornell Science Leaflet. Ithaca, N.Y.: Cornell University Press, 1960.

MAGNETISM AND ELECTRICITY

For Children

Bendick, Jeanne. *Electronics for Young People*. Rev. ed. New York: Whittlesey, 1955, 189 pp. Electronics, what it can do and how we use it.

Bendick, R., and J. Bendick. *Television Works Like This*. New York: Whittlesey, 1959, 64 pp. Illustrated behind-the-scenes story of telecasting.

Branley, Franklyn M., and Eleanor K. Vaughan. *Mickey's Magnet*. New York: Crowell, 1956, unpaged. Easy. Discovering magnets by experimenting and observing.

————. *Rusty Rings a Bell*. New York: Crowell, 1957, 32 pp. Easy. Story of a boy who discovers how an electric current works.

Feravolo, Rocco V. *Junior Science Book of Electricity*. Champaign, Ill.: Garrard Publishing Co., 1960, 59 pp. For beginners.

Mandelbaum, Arnold. *Electricity. The Story of Power*. New York: Putnam, 1960, 157 pp. Methods of discovery, the history of development of electricity.

Morgan, Alfred P. *The Boys' First Book of Radio and Electronics*. New York: Scribner, 1954, 221 pp. Technical and detailed information.

————. *A First Electrical Book for Boys*. New York: Scribner, 1951, 263 pp. Diagrams and clear explanation.

Parker, Bertha M. *Electricity*. New York: Harper & Row, 1959, 36 pp. The nature and uses of electricity.

————. *Magnets*. New York: Harper & Row, 1958, 36 pp. Easy story of magnetism; what it can do and its uses.

Pine, Tillie S., and Joseph Levine. *Electricity and How We Use It*. New York: Whittlesey, 1962, 48 pp. Easy. Electrical circuits and how they are used.

————, and ————. *Magnets and How To Use Them*. New York: Whittlesey, 1959, 48 pp. Easy. Simple experiences and information about magnets.

Reuben, Gabriel. *Electronics for Children*. New York: Sterling, 1960, 84 pp. Series of experiments and experiences, useful learning about magnetism, electricity, electronics, and nuclear energy.

Schneider, Herman, and Nina Schneider. *Your Telephone and How It Works*. New York: Whittlesey, 1952, 96 pp. Information about how sound and electricity make the telephone work.

Schwartz, Julius. *I Know a Magic House*. New York: Whittlesey, 1956, 32 pp. First experiences with electrical devices and other "magic" in the house.

For Teachers

Atkins, J. Myron, and R. Will Burnett. *Electricity and Magnetism*. New York: Holt, Rinehart and Winston, 1958, 58 pp.

Dunsheath, Percy. *Electricity: How It Works*. New York: Crowell, 1960, 248 pp. Useful reference for teachers who need background.

Morgan, Alfred. *The Boys' First Book of Radio and Electronics*. New York: Scribner, 1954, 229 pp.

————. *The Boys' Second Book of Radio and Electronics*. New York: Scribner, 1957, 276 pp.

————. *The Boys' Third Book of Radio and Electronics*. New York: Scribner, 1962, 277 pp. For especially talented and interested.

Rockcastle, Verne N. *Electricity and Magnetism*. Cornell Science Leaflet, Vol. 50, No. 3. Ithaca, N.Y.: Cornell University Press, 1957.

SOUND AND HOW WE USE IT

For Children

Berger, Melvin, and Frank Clark. *Science and Music from Tom-tom to Hi-fi*. New York: Whittlesey, 1961, 176 pp. How musical instruments produce sounds and how sounds are recorded.

Irving, Robert. *Sound and Ultrasonics*. New York: Knopf, 1959, 146 pp. For beginners.

Kettlekamp, Larry. *Drums, Rattles, and Bells*. New York: Morrow, 1960, 48 pp. The story of sounds and how they are produced.

———. *The Magic of Sound*. New York: Morrow, 1956, 62 pp. Principles and uses.

Parker, Bertha M. *Sound*. New York: Harper & Row, 1957, 36 pp. The nature of sound and application to everyday experiences.

Pine, Tillie S., and Joseph Levine. *Sounds All Around*. New York: Whittlesey, 1958, 46 pp. Easy. Simple activities to teach basic principles.

Podendorf, Illa. *The True Book of Sounds We Hear*. Chicago: Childrens Press, 1956, 47 pp. An easy book about common sounds and their causes.

LIGHT

For Children

Beeler, Nelson E., and Franklyn M. Branley. *Experiments with Light*. New York: Crowell, 1958, 143 pp.

———, and ———. *Experiments with a Microscope*. New York: Crowell, 1957, 154 pp. Making discoveries through use of the microscope in examining common and uncommon things. Unusual information.

———, and ———. *Experiments in Optical Illusion*. New York: Crowell, 1951, 114 pp. How eyes work and how illusions occur.

Feravolo, Rocco V. *Junior Science Book of Light*. Champaign, Ill.: Garrard Publishing Co., 1961, 59 pp. For beginners.

Kettlekamp, Larry. *Shadows*. New York: Morrow, 1957, 64 pp. Experiments and information about shadows on the earth, eclipses, and other related phenomena.

Parker, Bertha M. *Light*. New York: Harper & Row, 1959, 36 pp. Discussion of the various aspects of the phenomenon of light, including reflection, refraction, and the various uses.

Pine, Tillie S., and Joseph Levine. *Light All Around*. New York: Whittlesey, 1961, 48 pp. Easy reading material about light and its nature. Helpfully illustrated.

Ruchlis, Hy. *The Wonder of Light: A Picture Story of How and Why We See*. New York: Harper & Row, 1960, 148 pp. Light and its various phenomena explained, including more than a hundred diagrams and exciting photographs.

Schwartz, Julius. *Now I Know*. New York: Whittlesey, 1955, 32 pp. Simple explanations of children's experiences with reflections, shadows, lightning, darkness.

———. *Through the Magnifying Glass*. New York: Whittlesey, 1954, 142 pp. Understanding and using a magnifying glass to see common things.

Tannenbaum, Beulah, and Myra Stillman. *Understanding Light: The Science of Visible and Invisible Rays*. New York: Whittlesey, 1960, 138 pp. The story of light—artificial, natural, the eye, uses of light energy—with experiments.

For Teachers

Asher, Harry. *Experiments in Seeing*. New York: Basic Books, 1961, 271 pp. Eye structure and how it works.

Lemon, Harvey B. *From Galileo to Cosmic Rays*. Chicago: University of Chicago Press, 1934, 450 pp.

Let's See. Cornell Science Leaflet, Vol. 39, No. 3. Ithaca, N.Y.: Cornell University Press, Winter 1945–1946. 32 pp. How eyes differ; light; what and how we see; color, optical illusions, eye safety, and interpretation of things seen.

FLIGHT AND SPACE

For Children

Adler, Irving. *Man-Made Moons*. New York: John Day, 1957, 128 pp. Earth's satellites, their nature and use.

Asimov, Isaac. *Satellites in Outer Space*. New York: Random House, 1960, 80 pp. Well-illustrated.

Beeler, Nelson, and Franklyn Branley. *Experiments with Airplane Instruments*. New York: Crowell, 1953, 111 pp. Descriptions of airplane instruments and simple experiments that show their principles of operation.

Bendick, Jeanne. *The First Book of Airplanes*. New York: F. Watts, 1958, 69 pp. Introductory information for young children; well-illustrated.

―――. *The First Book of Space Travel*. Rev. ed. New York: F. Watts, 1963, 90 pp. About space, space travel, and rocket ships.

Blough, Glenn O. *Masters of the Air*. Washington, D.C.: The Smithsonian Institution, 1954, 31 pp. Illustrated history of aviation.

Branley, Franklyn M. *A Book of Moon Rockets for You*. New York: Crowell, 1959, 64 pp. Easy. Drawings and explanations of space travel.

―――. *Experiments in the Principles of Space Travel*. New York: Crowell, 1955, 119 pp. The facts about space travel with experiments to help in understanding.

―――. *Exploring by Astronaut: The Story of Project Mercury*. New York: Crowell, 1961, 108 pp. The why and how of space travel.

―――. *Exploring by Satellite: The Story of Project Vanguard*. New York: Crowell, 1957, 42 pp. Exceptionally well-illustrated.

Coombs, Charles. *Lift-off: The Story of Rocket Power*. New York: Morrow, 1963, 93 pp. Beginners' book with very good illustrations.

―――. *Project Mercury*. New York: Morrow, 1960, 64 pp. Beginners' book with helpful diagrams.

―――. *Rockets, Missiles, and Moons*. New York: Morrow, 1957, 256 pp. Illustrated survey interestingly treated.

―――. *Survival in the Sky*. New York: Morrow, 1956, 247 pp. Information about pilots and how they survive at great speeds and altitudes.

Gottlieb, William P. *Aircraft and How They Work*. New York: Garden City, 1960, 50 pp. Photographs, drawings, and practical experiments on flight.

―――. *Jets and Rockets and How They Work*. New York: Doubleday, 1959, 56 pp. Principles on which jets and rockets operate.

Holsaert, Eunice, and Ronnie Solbert. *Outer Space: A Book to Begin On*. New York: Holt, Rinehart and Winston, 1959, unpaged. Easy reading with excellent drawings.

Hyde, Margaret O. *Flight Today and Tomorrow*. New York: Whittlesey, 1962, 139 pp. Principles of flight and their applications with discussion of future possibilities.

―――. *Off into Space! Science for Young Space Travelers*. New York: Whittlesey, 1959, 64 pp. An exciting book of information about future space travel.

Kay, Terence. *Space Volunteers*. New York: Harper & Row, 1960, 136 pp. Man's conquest of space interestingly told.

Kinney, William A. *Medical Science and Space Travel*. New York: F. Watts, 1959, 147 pp. Medical research and techniques related to the hazzards and demands of space travel.

Lawrence, Mortimer W. *The Rockets' Red Glare: The Challenge of Outer Space*. New York: Coward-McCann, 1960, 113 pp. Exciting, interesting details of space travel, with excellent photographs.

Lent, Henry B. *The Helicopter Book*. New York: Macmillan, 1956, 143 pp. Up-to-date information.

Lewellen, John. *Birds and Planes*. New York: Crowell, 1953, 130 pp. Principles of flight.

―――. *Helicopters: How They Work*. New York: Crowell, 1954, 136 pp. Kinds of helicopters and their uses.

―――. *Jet Transports*. New York: Crowell, 1955, 151 pp. How jets fly, how they are controlled, and their future.

Lewellen, John. *Tommy Learns to Fly*. New York: Crowell, 1956, unpaged. Information for beginners about flight and airplanes.

Marshack, Alexander. *The World in Space: The Story of the International Geophysical Year*. Nelson, 1958, 174 pp. The story of the International Geophysical Year with excellent photographs.

Nephew, William, and Michael Chester. *Moon Base*. New York: Putnam, 1959, 72 pp. An exciting account of the details of moon travels. Easy.

Newell, Homer E., Jr. *Express to the Stars: Rockets in Action*. New York: McGraw-Hill, 1961, 311 pp.

———. *Guide to Rockets and Missiles and Satellites*. New York: Whittlesey, 1958, 53 pp. Detailed descriptions of each of the space vehicles and weapons with excellent photographs.

———. *Space Book for Young People*. New York: Whittlesey, 1960, 128 pp. Facts about space, space travel, rockets, and satellites told by a scientist.

Parker, Bertha M. *Rockets and Missiles. Satellites and Space Travel*. New York: Harper & Row, 1963, 36 pp. A comprehensive treatment.

Poole, Lynn. *Ballooning in the Space Age*. New York: Whittlesey, 1958, 159 pp. Free ballooning during the first 175 years, with emphasis on its usefulness and relationship to the space age.

Posin, Dan Q. *Life beyond Our Planet: A Scientific Look at Other Worlds in Space*. New York: Whittlesey, 1962, 128 pp.

Rush, Hanniford. *Man to the Moon*. Chicago: Rand McNally, 1962, 96 pp. Why, how, when of moon travel and a good description of what happens after the landing.

Schneider, Leo. *Space in Your Future*. New York: Harcourt, 1961, 255 pp. Astronomy, the tools of the astronomer, and space travel.

Schussler, Eileen, and Raymond Schussler. *Starbound: The Story of Rocketry*. New York: Putnam, 1960, 158 pp. Development and present-day information.

Schwartz, Julius. *The Earth is Your Spaceship*. New York: McGraw-Hill, 1963, 32 pp. Easy reading about the movements of the earth through space and their effects.

Solomon, Louis. *Telstar: Communication Break-through by Satellite*. New York: McGraw-Hill, 1962, 62 pp. The essential information illustrated by excellent photographs.

For Teachers

Adams, Carsbie C. *Space Flight*. New York: McGraw-Hill, 1958, 364 pp. A comprehensive background to the understanding of space travel including the history of astronautics.

Bergaust, Erik. *Satellites and Space Probes*. New York: Putnam, 1959, 47 pp.

Bizony, M. T. (ed.). *The Space Encyclopedia*. New York: Dutton, 1958, 287 pp. Alphabetically arranged information about astronomy and space travel.

Costa, Arthur. *Space Science*. Darien, Conn.: Teachers Publishing Corporation, 1964, 96 pp. One in the series produced with the National Science Teachers Association. Information and activities.

Hynek, J. Allen, and Norman D. Anderson. *Challenge of the Universe*. New York: McGraw-Hill, 1962, 143 pp.

Newell, Homer E. *Express to the Stars: Rockets in Action*. New York: McGraw-Hill, 1961, 311 pp. Excellent background information.

INDEX

Italic page numbers refer to methods and activities (Part I chapters, B chapters); roman page numbers refer to science subject matter (A chapters).

absorption of heat, *452–453*

AC, *see* current, alternating

acceleration, man in space and, 602

accidents, *see* safety

ACTIVITY

  animal, keeping a pet, *238–239*

  animal life, observation of, *291–296*

  aquarium, making an, *251–252*

  bird-feeding station, making a, *270*

  blueprints, making, *581*

  body functions, study of, *323–324*

  camera, examination of a, *581*

  compass, making and using a, *530–531*

  conservation education, *386, 393*

  conservation map, *389–390*

  day and night, change in, *134–135*

  dinosaur model, making a, *357–358*

  electric motor, study of an, *540*

  electrical questionnaire, making an, *538–539*

  electricity and magnetism, *528*

  elements collection, making an, *406–407*

  eyes, study of the, *582*

  fire prevention, *423–429*

  fire station visit, *429*

  fires, keeping track of, *428*

  flight and space travel, *609*

  fossil study, *354, 355*

  frogs' eggs, raising of, *356–357*

  fuel exhibit, *427–428*

  garden, planting a, *244–245*

  heat, finding sources of, *449*

  light, *577*

ACTIVITY (*cont.*)

  living things, study of, *234*

  magnetism and electricity, *528*

  microscope, using the, *253*

  mountain formation, *105*

  periscope, making a, *579*

  planets, looking at, *132*

  plants, raising indoor, *246–247*

  rainfall measuring gauge, making a, *199–200*

  rock collecting, *103–104*

  sand examination, *104*

  silkworms, raising, *248–249*

  soil examination, *103, 385*

  solar system, model of the, *132*

  solar system, stories of the, *140*

  sound, *561*

  "star box," making a, *158*

  studying pictures, *104*

  tadpoles, raising, *249–250*

  telegraph set, making a, *539–540*

  terrarium, making a, *252–253*

  thermometer, study of a, *449–450*

  weather map, study of a, *206*

  weather station, setting up a, *207*

  weather study, *197*

  see also EXPERIMENT; OBSERVATION

adenoids, 307

adhesion, 491

adrenal glands, 314

advection fogs, 176

agriculture, radioisotopes in, 470–471

air, composition of, 164

  conservation of, 378

  distribution of, 161

  effect of heat on, *452*

  heat convection and, 437

air (*cont.*)

  observation of, *611*

  pollution of, 378–379

  resistance of, 585

  respiration and, 307

  source material for, *56*

  weather and, 165–166

  see also air mass

air conditioning, 442–443

air currents, airplanes and, *611–612*

air front analysis, 183

air mass, 181–183

  highs and lows, 183–184

air pressure, experiment in, 203

  heat and, 436–437

air sacs, 307

  see also respiration, human

air and weather, teaching of, *196–208*

airplane, atomic powered, 593

  controls of the, 588–590

  dynamics of the, 586–588

  jet, 593–594

  "kite" and "vacuum" effects in the, 586–588

  navigation of the, 591–592

  piloting of the, 590–591

  propeller, 588

  rocket, 595

  stability of the, 590

  weather study and the, *614*

  see also aviation

airport, field trip to an, *613*

alcohol, 434

alcohol thermometer, 434

algae, 214, 336

alimentary canal, 304–305

Alnico, 508

alpha particles, 461, 463

alternating generator, 520

americum, 474

ampere, 516

amphibians, 220

anatomy, human, *see* human body

Andromeda constellation, 146

anemometer, 207

641